# STATISTICS 121 LECTURE NOTES

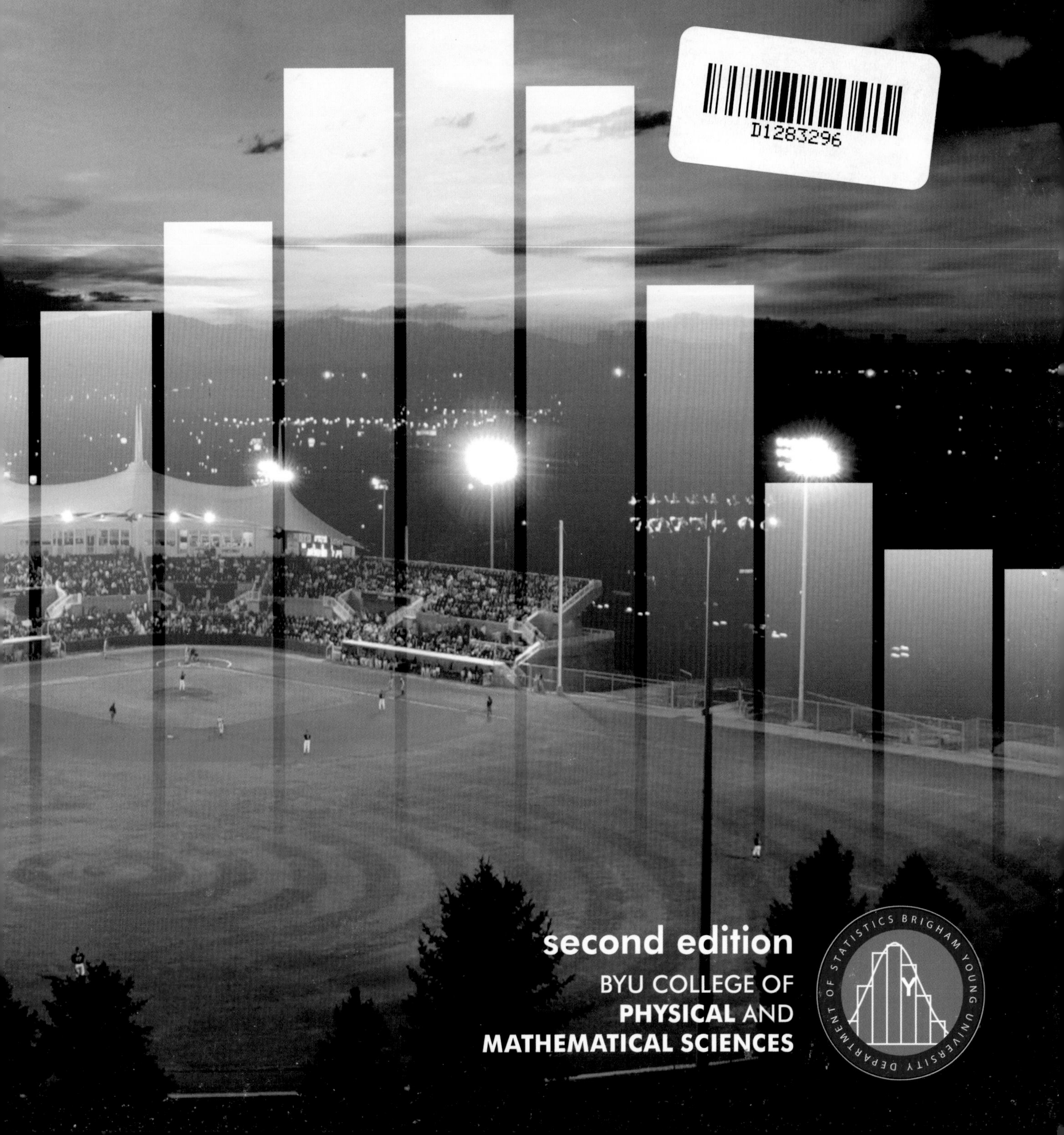

second edition

BYU COLLEGE OF **PHYSICAL** AND **MATHEMATICAL SCIENCES**

# CONTENTS

1-1

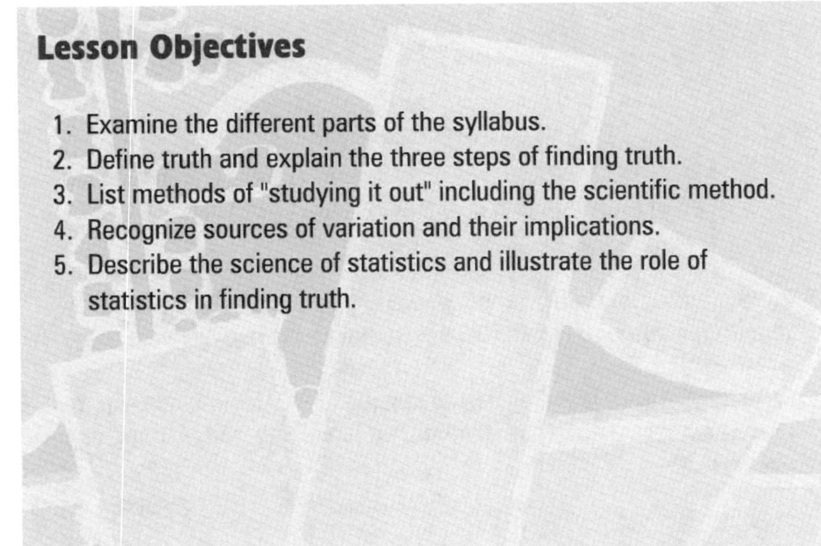


1-2

## Lesson Objectives

1. Examine the different parts of the syllabus.
2. Define truth and explain the three steps of finding truth.
3. List methods of "studying it out" including the scientific method.
4. Recognize sources of variation and their implications.
5. Describe the science of statistics and illustrate the role of statistics in finding truth.

1-3

Syllabus

## Statistics 221 Syllabus

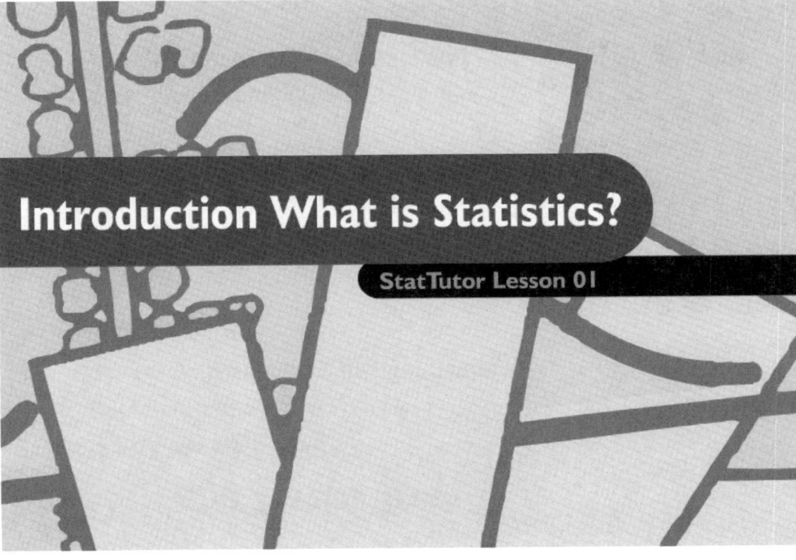


1-4

What is Truth?

## What is Science?

Science is the objective, systematic pursuit of truth.

## What is Truth?

1-5



## What is Science?

Science is the objective, systematic pursuit of truth.

## What is Truth?

"Truth is knowledge of things as they are, and as they were, and as they are to come;"

Doctrine and Covenants 93:24

1-6



## How do We Find Truth?

"I say unto you, that you must study it out in your mind; then you must ask me if it be right, and if it is right I will cause that your bosom shall burn within you; therefore, you shall feel that it is right. But if it be not right you shall have no such feelings."

Doctrine and Covenants 9:7-9

1-7



## Three Steps for Finding Truth

1. **Study it out in your mind**
   - Gather information
   - Make conclusions based on information
2. **Ask if it be right**
   - Pray
   - Ask explicitly about your conclusion
3. **Receive and recognize revelation**
   - Feel burning in the bosom--that it is right

     or
   - Feel "stupor of thought" if it is not right

     (Doctrine and Covenants 9:9)

1-8



## Key Points

- The "study it out" step must be thorough and done well if we hope to develop a theory that contains even a kernel of truth.
- Next, a wisely chosen hypothesis is formulated from the information and knowledge gained by "studying it out." This is presented in prayer for confirmation.
- Finally, we must be in tune spiritually in order for truth to be confirmed in answer to prayer.

1-9

Studying It Out

## Familiar Methods of "Studying It Out"

**1. Observe and collect facts**

Consult research literature and library sources
Consult authorities

**2. Develop a theory to explain what is observed.**

Use rational argument and logic
Use personal experience and evaluation

**3. Confirm theory through experimentation and study.**

Follow protocol

**4. Have others verify theory.**

**Apply the Scientific Method**

1-10

Studying It Out

## Steps of the Scientific Method ("Studying It Out")

1. Observe some phenomenon in the universe.
2. Formulate a research question (hypothesis) about the phenomenon.
3. Test the hypothesis with experiments (i.e., collect data).
4. Summarize data and draw a conclusion about the validity of the hypothesis.
5. Modify the hypothesis in the light of the results.
6. Test the new hypothesis with new experiments and continue the search for truth.

**At what point would you pray and seek for confirmation?**

1-11

Studying It Out

## Reproducibility in the Scientific Method

Reproducibility is essential for establishing a valid scientific theory. (Someone else should be able to follow your protocol and get the same or similar results.)

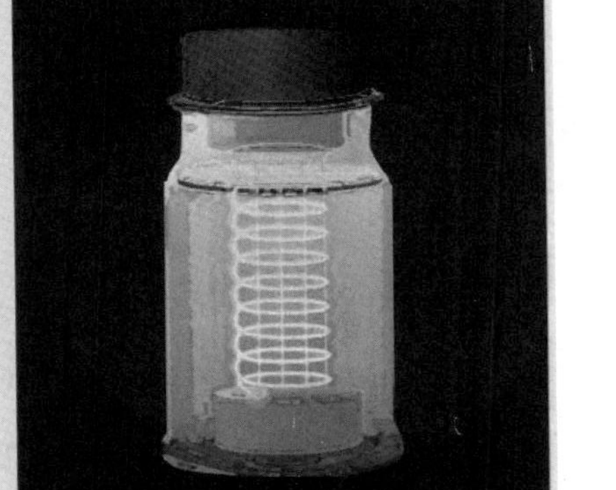

**Example:**

Two professors at a prominent state university, Pons and Fleishman, announced that they could produce cold fusion. All attempts to reproduce their study failed. Their claim was held to be invalid.

1-12

Studying It Out

## Shortcomings of the Scientific Method

**1. Problems with hypotheses:**

- Some hypotheses, like religious beliefs, cannot be tested scientifically.
  **Example**: There is life after death.
- Some hypotheses pose ethical dilemmas.
  **Example**: Smoking causes cancer.
  Experiments require assigning some persons to smoke, but human subjects refuse such edicts.
- Some hypotheses cannot be verified because the experimental conditions cannot be reproduced.
  **Example**: A collision between an asteroid and a planet will alter the orbit of the planet.
  Conditions are forever changed.

1-13

Studying It Out

## Shortcomings of the Scientific Method (Cont.)

**2. The Scientific Method will never generate certainty because of variation.**

"No theory can have the status of absolute certainty. No matter how many confirming data exist, the possibility always remains that new data will come along which contradicts the theory."

David Snoke, Dept. of Physics and Astronomy, University of Pittsburgh

**3. Variation is omnipresent.**

Variation occurs when an experiment is reproduced, when repeated measurements are taken, when different subjects are used, etc.

1-14

Variation

## Sources of Variation

**Variation from Experiment to Experiment**

Variation in results when an experiment is reproduced using the same protocol. (No one can reproduce an experiment and control all conditions exactly.)

**Measurement Variation**

Variation from repeated measurements on the same object.

**Natural Variation**

Variation from object to object in a population.

**What are some reasons for variation?**

1-15

Variation

## Consider Natural Variation in Peppers

A population of peppers varies in:

| | |
|---|---|
| Color | Weight |
| Shape | "Hotness" |
| Size | Length |
| Genetic Makeup | Etc. |

1-16

Variation

## Consider Natural Variation in Peppers

A population of peppers varies in:

| | |
|---|---|
| Color | Weight |
| Shape | "Hotness" |
| Size | Length |
| Genetic Makeup | Etc. |

Even within a species, peppers vary in:

| | |
|---|---|
| Color | Weight |
| Shape | "Hotness" |
| Size | Length |
| Genetic Makeup | Etc. |

**Variation in populations is pervasive and ubiquitous.**

1-17



## Consider a Population Without Variation

**What If:**

Everyone looked the same?
Everyone thought the same?
Everyone believed the same?

**How many people would you have to interview to know everything about the population with regard to**

- **looks?**
- **thoughts?**
- **beliefs?**

1-18



## For Populations With Variation:

Everyone looks different.
Everyone thinks different.
Everyone believes different.

**Interviews or observations are required on multiple members of the group for valid conclusions about group characteristics.**

**The science of statistics EXISTS because of variation.**

1-19



## What is the Science of Statistics?

**A systematic and objective methodology for effectively using data to answer research questions and test hypotheses *in the presence of variation* by:**

- collecting data
- summarizing data
- drawing conclusions from data

**We use Statistics in the Scientific Method.**

1-20



## Statistics and Variation

- Statistics aids in finding truth.
- Statistics provides methods for measuring variation, modeling variation and if needed, identifying sources of variation.
- Because of variation, statistical conclusions about hypotheses are made using probability and stated reflecting the uncertainty that variation imposes.
- Conclusions drawn in the presence of uncertainty using statistics can be investigated in a never-ending pursuit of truth.

1-21

Discipline of Statistics

## Florence Nightingale, a Famous Statistician

"With our present amount of sanitary knowledge, it is as criminal to have a mortality or 17, 19, and 20 per 1000 in the Line, Artillery, and Guards in England, when that of Civil life is only 11 per 1000 as it would be to take 1100 men per annum out upon Salisbury Plains and shoot them--no body of men being so much under control, none so dependent upon their employers for health, life, and morality as the Army."

Florence Nightingale

1-22

Discipline of Statistics

## Florence Nightingale, a Famous Statistician

"We had, during the last six months of war a mortality among our sick not much more than among our **healthy** guards at home, and a mortality among our troops in the last five months, two-thirds only of what it is among our troops at home."

Florence Nightingale

1-23

Discipline of Statistics

## Florence Nightingale, a Famous Statistician

"The true foundation of theology is to ascertain the character of God. It is by the aid of Statistics that law in the social sphere can be ascertained and codified, and certain aspects of the character of God thereby revealed. The study of statistics is therefore a religious experience."

Florence Nightingale

1-24

Role of Statistics

## Summary

**What is truth?**

Truth is knowledge of things as they were, as they are and as they are to come.

**How do we find it?**

1. Observe and collect facts.
2. Develop a theory to explain what is observed.
3. Confirm theory through experimentation and study.
4. Have others verify theory.

} **Apply Scientific Method**

**What is the role of statistics in finding truth?**

Statistics provides a systematic and objective methodology for appropriately collecting data, summarizing data and drawing conclusions from data to answer research questions in the presence of variation.

1-25



## Summary

**What is truth?**

Truth is knowledge of things as they were, as they are and as they are to come.

**How do we find it?**

In the gospel, the three steps for finding truth are:

1. Study it out
2. Ask if it be right
3. Receive and recognize revelation

**With respect to the gospel, how will knowledge of statistics help us find truth?**

**What is the role of statistics in finding truth?**

Statistics provides a systematic and objective methodology for appropriately collecting data, summarizing data and drawing conclusions from data to answer research questions in the presence of variation.

1-26

## Vocabulary

**Truth**
**Statistics**
**Measurement Variation**
**Natural Variation**
**Variation from Reproduction of Experiment**

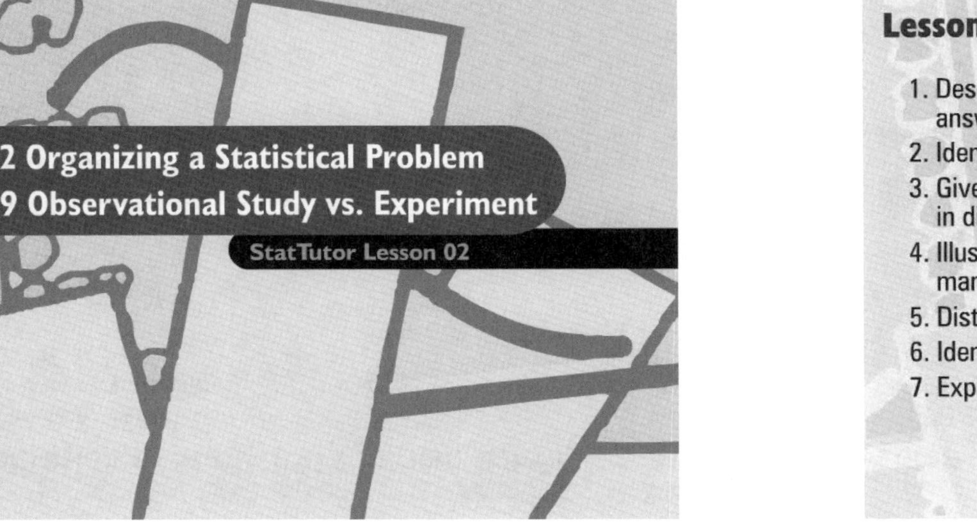




## Lesson Objectives

1. Describe types of questions from our daily lives that can be answered with statistical problem solving.
2. Identify the four components of statistical problem solving.
3. Give several examples of the uses of statistical problem solving in different fields.
4. Illustrate how the steps of statistical problem solving can be manipulated to distort facts.
5. Distinguish between a sample survey and an experiment.
6. Identify whether a study is observational or an experiment.
7. Explain the advantage of experiment over observational study.



## Review: What Is Statistics?

The methodology for appropriately collecting data, summarizing data and drawing conclusions from data to answer research questions *in the presence of variation*.

**Statistics is the science of making decisions in the face of uncertainty.**

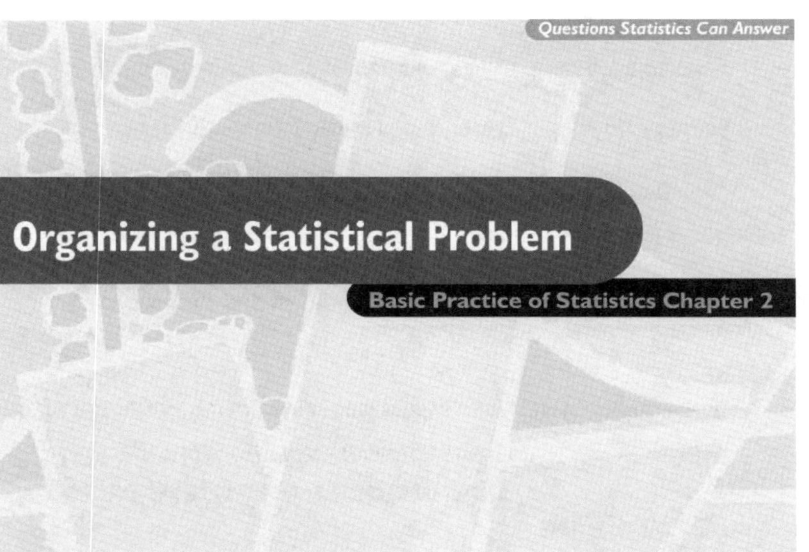

2-5



## Questions from Everyday Life

**Business:** Will a new marketing strategy be profitable?
**Industry:** Will a product's life exceed the warranty period?
**Medicine:** Will a low carbohydrate diet reduce blood pressure?
**Education:** Will technology improve learning?
**Government:** Will a change in interest rates affect inflation?

**Statistical problem solving can help provide answers.**

2-6



## Steps to Statistical Problem Solving

1. **STATE Question:** Articulate research question.
2. **PLAN Solution:** Plan statistical analysis for answering research question.
3. **SOLVE:**
   **Data Production:** Collect defensible and relevant data.
   (Can't do census ⇒ carefully sample population.)

   **Data Summarization:** Graph data and compute numerical summaries.

   **Data Analysis:** Compute values needed for statistical inference.
4. **CONCLUDE:** Draw conclusions about how results apply in broader context.
   (Statistical inference--using sample data to draw conclusions about population.)

2-7



## An Application of Statistical Problem Solving

- **STATE Question:** Is the shower's water temperature comfortable?
- **PLAN Solution:** Decide to hand check water temperature.
- **SOLVE:** Hand check water temperature several times.
- **CONCLUDE:** Decide to get in or to change the water temperature.

**We make decisions every day with data.**

2-8



## Step 1: STATE Question

**Articulate the research question and determine what needs to be measured on each unit.**

**Examples:**

When should I kiss her?

Should we get married?

2-9



## Step 2: PLAN Solution

**Decide what statistical procedure should be used to analyze data and answer research question. Also, specify how to collect data.**

**Decide how to:**

- collect appropriate data
- summarize and graph data
- analyze data for inference

2-10



## Step 3: SOLVE

**DATA COLLECTION**

**Collect relevant data that can be used to answer the research question.**

**Methods:**

1. Scientific surveys:
   - Federal, state, or local government surveys
   - Institutional surveys
   - Private research firms surveys
2. Designed Experiments:
   - Laboratory studies and experiments
   - Clinical trials
   - University-sponsored experiments
   - Hospital studies

2-11



## Step 3: SOLVE

**DATA SUMMARIZATION**

**Obtain graphs and numerical summaries appropriate for data that will aid in answering research question. Interpret these in context.**

**Graphs:**

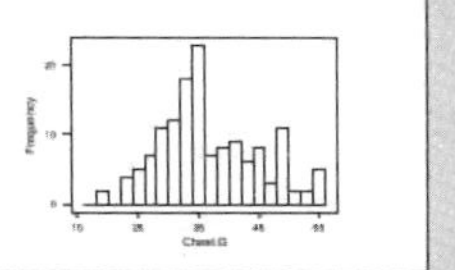

Leaf Unit = 0.010

29 | 3
29 | 9
30 | 4
30 | 69
31 | 1
31 | 79
32 | 023
32 | 567
33 | 1
33 |
34 | 0

Dotplot for Elasticity

**Numerical summaries:**

| | Drug | Placebo |
|---|---|---|
| $\bar{x}$ | 8.48 | 7.93 |
| s | 0.750 | 0.564 |
| n | 10 | 10 |

| Column | n | Mean | Std. Dev. | Median | Min | Max | Q1 | Q3 |
|---|---|---|---|---|---|---|---|---|
| Weight | 143 | 192.2 | 110.6 | 154 | 26 | 514 | 116 | 250 |

2-12



## Step 3: SOLVE

**DATA ANALYSIS for Inference**

**Compute values necessary for statistical inference. (Note: Only do this analysis when inference is performed.)**

**Example:**

A survey of 215 middle and high school students finds that in addition to books and school stuff, 80% of kids carry food and water. These results have a margin of error of 5%.

2-13

Four Steps

## Step 4: CONCLUDE

Draw conclusions in context based on results from the SOLVE step.

Example:

### Try tai chi -- it's gentle exercise

Studies of tai chi, a 2,000-year-old form of exercise, show it reduces blood pressure, episodes of anxiety and depression, and helps give a boost to the immune system.

2-14

Examples

## Statistical Problem Solving in Politics

1996 Presidential Election: Clinton vs. Dole

**Step I: STATE Question**
Before election day: "Who will win the election?"

**Step 2: PLAN Solution**
Gallup planned an exit poll of voters, designed questionnaire, and decided which analysis procedure to use.

**Step 3: SOLVE**
**Data collection:** Gallup conducted an exit poll of 2,370 voters.
**Data summarization:** 52.0% polled said they voted for Clinton.
**Data analysis:** 2% margin of error computed.

**Step 4: CONCLUDE in context**
Gallup organization declared Clinton a winner.

2-15

Examples

## Comparison of Gallup's Results with Actual Winners

View Movie Clip

2-16

Examples

## Comparison of Gallup's Results with Actual Winners

| Year | Gallup Winner | Gallup % | Actual Winner | Actual % for Gallup Winner | Difference | Sample Size |
|---|---|---|---|---|---|---|
| 1936 | Roosevelt | 55.7% | Roosevelt | 62.5% | -6.8% | » 50,000 |
| 1940 | Roosevelt | 52.0% | Roosevelt | 55.0% | -3.0% | » 50,000 |
| 1944 | Roosevelt | 51.5% | Roosevelt | 53.3% | -1.8% | » 50,000 |
| 1948 | Dewey | 49.5% | Truman | 45.1% | 4.4% | » 50,000 |
| 1952 | Eisenhower | 51.0% | Eisenhower | 55.4% | -4.4% | 5385 |
| 1956 | Eisenhower | 59.5% | Eisenhower | 57.8% | +1.7% | 8144 |
| 1960 | Kennedy | 51.0% | Kennedy | 50.1% | +0.9% | 8015 |
| 1964 | Johnson | 64.0% | Johnson | 61.3% | +2.7% | 6625 |
| 1968 | Nixon | 43.0% | Nixon | 43.5% | -0.5% | 4414 |
| 1972 | Nixon | 62.0% | Nixon | 61.8% | +0.2% | 3689 |
| 1976 * | Ford | 49.0% | Carter | 48.0% | 1.0% | 3439 |
| 1980 | Reagan | 47.0% | Reagan | 50.8% | -3.8% | 3500 |
| 1984 | Reagan | 59.0% | Reagan | 59.1% | -0.1% | 3456 |
| 1988 | Bush | 56.0% | Bush | 53.9% | -2.1% | 4089 |
| 1992 ** | Clinton | 49.0% | Clinton | 43.2% | +5.8% | 2019 |
| 1996 | Clinton | 52.0% | Clinton | 50.1% | +1.9% | 2370 |
| **2000 *** | **Bush** | **48.0%** | Bush | **48.0%** | **0.0%** | 2733 |
| **2004 *** | **Kerry** | **46.3%** | Bush | **50.7%** | **6.7%** | 2013 |

* No prediction made by Gallup.
** The Ross Perot candidacy created an additional source of error in estimating the 1992 presidential vote. Gallup's decision to allocate none of the undecided vote to Perot, based on past performance of third party and independent candidates, resulted in this overestimation of Clinton's vote.

2-17

Examples

## Statistical Problem Solving in Education

**Step I: STATE Question**

Faculty in the Brigham Young University Department of Statistics wanted to answer the question, "Is teaching with multi-media more effective than using traditional overheads in introductory statistics?"

**Step 2: PLAN Solution**

- A team of statisticians designed a clinical trials type experiment.
- The team also formulated the method of analysis.

2-18

Examples

## Statistical Problem Solving in Education

**Step 3: SOLVE--Data Production**

**Designed Experiment with eight classes and four professors**

- Each professor was randomly assigned two classes.
- Each professor taught one class with multi-media and the other with overheads; method was randomly assigned to class.
- Instructional material was prepared so that content was the same for both methods .
- All students did the same homework and took the same exams; TA's conducted all labs the same and were monitored, etc.

**What data was collected?**

- Scores on pre- and post-surveys taken by students to assess their math anxiety and learning styles.
- Scores on tests consisting of conceptual essay and multiple choice questions that measured knowledge and understanding.

2-19

Examples

## Statistical Problem Solving in Education

**Step 3: SOLVE (cont.)--Data Summarization**

**Graph**

**Numerical summaries**

**Means from the exams of student learning:**

| | Exam 1 | Exam 2 | Exam 3 | Final |
|---|---|---|---|---|
| multimedia | 85.29 | 83.51 | 78.32 | 78.95 |
| control | 85.59 | 83.50 | 78.71 | 78.92 |

2-20

Examples

## Statistical Problem Solving in Education

**Step 3: SOLVE (cont.)--Data Analysis**

Analysis methods similar to those covered later in this course were used.

**Step 4: CONCLUDE**

No significant difference was found between the average test scores of the two methods.

2-21

2-22

*Manipulating Statistical Information*

## Can People Lie With Statistics?

"There are three kinds of lies:
lies, damned lies, and
statistics."
Mark Twain

**Because the statistical problem solving process can be abused, facts can be distorted.**

2-23

*Manipulating Statistical Information*

## Manipulating Data Production

**Sampling biases:**
One group in a population is over represented compared to another.

**Example:** A newspaper headline read, "New Longitudinal Study Finds that Having a Working Mother Does No Significant Harm to Children"

However, another reporter concluded:

**Uncovering Sources of Bias**

By Sharon Conway Rutberg
Newspaper Staff Writer

"The media brouhaha began with inaccurate reporting that attributed undeserved significance to the Harvey study. . .It provided no information, however, about the economic status or social situation of the families surveyed. . . Rather than note that the sample was not 'representative' of average or higher-income families, it strongly implied that the study might be considered the last-word in the debate over whether having a parent at home benefits young c...

**the sample was not 'representative' of average or higher-income families**

**What other biases might be present?**

2-24

*Manipulating Statistical Information*

## Manipulating Data Production

**Ignoring influential variables:**
Reporting results without considering important variables that affect those results.

**Example:** Differences in pay for men and women

**Media report:**
As of 1994, full-time employed women earned on average only about 76 percent as much as full-time employed men.

Does this difference show that women are discriminated against?
**No, because occupation has been ignored.**

More men have received training for higher paying profession jobs.

Manipulating Statistical Information

## Manipulating Data Summarization

**Graphically misrepresenting data:** with misleading pictures.

A prominent newspaper's graph of the diminishing purchasing power of the dollar

Visually correct representation of the diminishing purchasing power of the dollar

Purchasing Power of the Diminishing Dollar

**What is misleading in this graph?**



Manipulating Statistical Information

## Manipulating Data Summarization

**Graphically misrepresenting data:** with misleading scales.

1990 Daily Universe graph of the growth of the Mormon church over time

Mormon Church Growth (1844-1994)

Members in millions
Missionaries in tens of thousands

0, 2, 4, 6, 8, 10
1844 1947 1963 1971 1982 1989 1991 1994

Visually correct graph of the growth of the Mormon church over time

Mormon Church Growth (1844-1994)

Members in millions
Missionaries in tens of thousands

0, 2, 4, 6, 8, 10
1834 1914 1994

**What is misleading in this graph?**



Manipulating Statistical Information

## Manipulating Data Summarization

**Reporting misleading statistics**

**Example:** The average income of medical doctors

The American Medical Association (AMA) issues annual reports on the average income of doctors in private practice. After 1992, when the average income reached an unsatisfactorily high level, AMA stopped releasing this data. In 1994, AMA announced they would resume releasing average income, this time grouping doctors in private practice with those in training and those who work for the government.

**What is the effect of this grouping?** Average income is lower because those in training and those working for the government were included.



Manipulating Statistical Information

## Manipulating Conclusions from Statistical Inference

**Reporting invalid conclusions and interpretations**

**Example:** Consider this newspaper article:

# New jail decreases crime

By HEATHER BAKER
Universe Staff Writer

Crimes per 1,000 residents
Utah County

| 1995 | 1996 |
|---|---|
| 45.21 | 42.63 |

3% Decrease

source: Bureau of Criminal Identification and Dept. of Public Safety

State Crime Rates

**Did the new jail really "cause" the decrease in crime?**
**Or did the decrease just happen when the new jail opened?**

2-29



## Manipulating the Facts

Steps 3 and 4 of statistical problem solving can be manipulated either innocently or deliberately to influence people's opinions.

| Steps of Statistical Problem Solving | Sources of Distortion |
|---|---|
| Data Collection | Sampling and measurement biases<br>Ignoring influential variables |
| Data Summarization | Graphically misrepresenting data<br>Choosing misleading statistics |
| Drawing Conclusions | Reporting invalid conclusions<br>Giving incorrect interpretations |

2-30



## Statistical Do's:

**Step 2: PLAN Solution**
- Determine what measurements are relevant to research question.

**Step 3: SOLVE--Data collection**
- Appropriately collect data for valid conclusions.
- Select subjects without human subjectivity or bias.

**Step 3: SOLVE--Data summarization**
- Utilize appropriate graphs and numerical summaries.
- Report numerical summaries (and all conclusions) in context; for example, 8.5 is a number without context, but *the baby weighs 8.5 pounds* is a number in context.

**Step 4: CONCLUDE**
- Exercise common sense before believing conclusions.
- Make sure data justify conclusion.
- Report a reliability measure that reflects uncertainty due to variation.

**Develop a healthy skepticism for statistical information you encounter in the media.**

2-31



## Summary

**Statistics: interpretive science consisting of**

1. **Stating a research question.**
2. **Planning a solution.**
3. **Solving for an answer:**
   **Collecting** data to answer research question.
   **Summarizing** data for understanding.
   **Analyzing** data for statistical inference.
4. **Drawing conclusions in context in the presence of variation.**

**Each step must be correctly performed for results to be valid.**

"It is not enough to be able to 'do' the routine (either by hand or on the computer); one must know why one has chosen it, what its application tells one, and what limitations one must place upon its conclusions."

A.E. Kelly, et al. in *Simple Approaches to Assessing Underlying Understanding of Statistical Concepts.*

2-32



## Observation versus Experiment

Basic Practice of Statistics Chapter 9

2-33



## Sample Survey

- **Data Production:**
  Select a sample (a part or subset) from a population.
- **Data Summarization:**
  Describe sample.
- **Statistical Inference:**
  Attribute characteristics of sample to population.

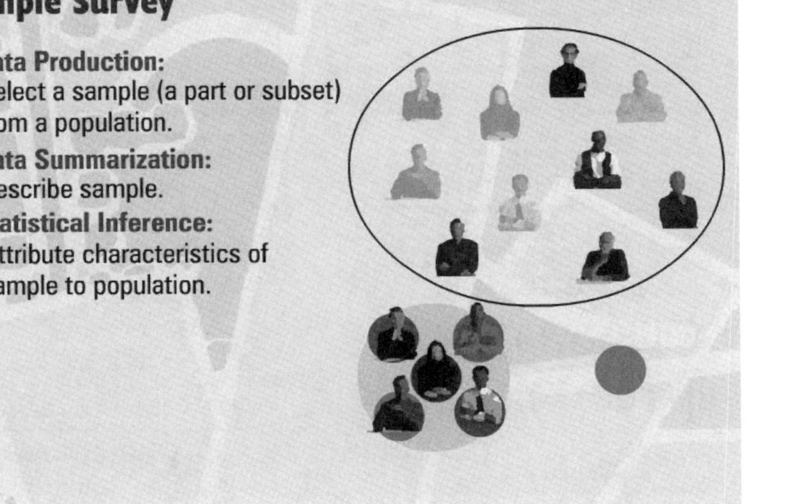

2-34



## Sample Survey

- **Data Production:**
  Select a sample (a part or subset) from a population.
- **Data Summarization:**
  Describe sample.
- **Statistical Inference:**
  Attribute characteristics of sample to population.

**Why sample?**
To obtain information about a population for which a census is impractical.

2-35



## Experiment

- **Data Production:**
  Assign subjects to groups. Impose specific "treatments" on the subjects. (One treatment may be a placebo or no treatment.)
- **Data Summarization:**
  Describe the "treatment" groups.
- **Statistical Inference:**
  Compare responses from both groups to assess effects of "treatments."

**Why experiment?**
To establish that the treatments "cause" changes in the responses.

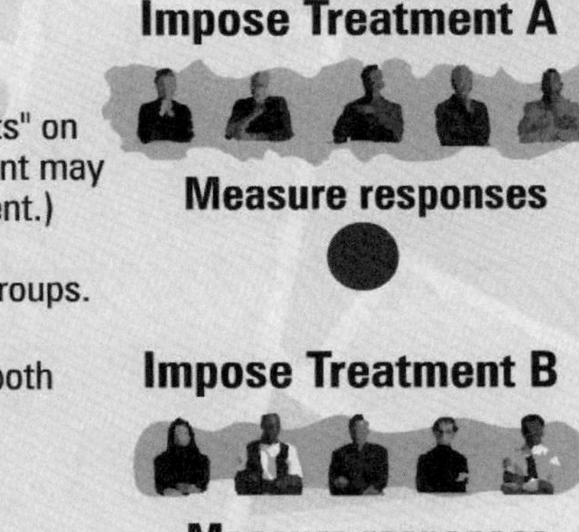


2-36



## Observational Studies versus Experiments

**Observational Study:**
A study where researchers observe individuals and record information about variables of interest. No treatment is imposed.

- Sample surveys are observational studies.

**Experiment:**
A study where researchers deliberately impose treatments on individuals and measure their responses to the treatments.

- Experiments allow researchers to establish "cause and effect" relationships.

2-37

*Observation vs. Experiment*

## Important Terms

**Explanatory variable (X)** A set of treatments imposed on the subjects that may affect the outcome of the study.

**Response variable (Y)** The outcome measured on each subject to reveal the effects of the treatments.

2-38

*Observation vs. Experiment*

## Observational Study or Experiment?

Did researchers assign families to live near power lines or did families self-select to live near power lines? **So, observational study**

**Can you conclude causation? NO!**

Leukemia Risk No Higher Near Power Lines

**Children exposed to electromagnetic fields by living near electrical power lines are not more susceptible to developing leukemia...**

The study asked parents of 638 children with leukemia if their child had lived near power lines; parents of 620 youngsters without cancer were also asked ...

Researchers also checked to see if child's mother had lived near a power line when she was pregnant.

**Leukemia Example**

| | |
|---|---|
| Explanatory variable: | Whether child lived near power lines |
| Response Variable: | Whether child contracted leukemia |

2-39

*Observation vs. Experiment*

## Observational Study or Experiment?

Did researchers assign whether patient received Botox or salt water or did patient self-select which to receive? **So, experiment**

**Can you conclude causation?**
**Yes**

**Heart Disease Example**

| | |
|---|---|
| Explanatory Variable: | Botox injection or salt water injection |
| Response Variable: | Whether patient had decrease in sweating |

**Study: Botox can help excessive sweating**

WASHINGTON — Doctors have found a new use for Botox, the wrinkle-smoothing botulism toxin: It seems to curb excessive sweating.

People with a condition called hyperhidrosis produce four or five times the amount of sweat as is normal. There are various treatments, including powerful antiperspirants, drugs to prevent sweat gland stimulation, even surgery on those glands.

Botox, a weakened form of the food-poisoning toxin botulism, already is widely used to treat wrinkles.

It is being tried to treat excessive sweating because it seems to temporarily paralyze a nerve that stimulates sweat glands.

Researchers gave 322 patients underarm injections of either Botox or salt water.

They received 12 to 14 injections per armpit. Although injection site pain was the main side effect, lead investigator Dr. Dee Anna Glaser of St. Louis University School of Medicine said the needles are so tiny that most patients weren't bothered.

A month later, 75 percent of the Botox users reported a significant decrease in sweating, compared with a quarter of the placebo patients, Glaser said.

2-40

*Observation vs. Experiment*

## Observational Study or Experiment?

Did researchers assign subjects to drink or not drink wine, beer and/or grape juice or did subjects decide? **So, observational study**

**Can you conclude causation? NO**

**Heart Disease Example**

| | |
|---|---|
| Explanatory Variable: | Whether subject drank wine, beer and/or grape juice |
| Response Variable: | Presence/absence of heart disease |

Netscape: CNN - In-Depth Health: Study: Wine, beer, grape juice help pre

Back Forward Reload Home Search Netscape Images Print Security Stop

**Studies show wine, beer and grape juice help prevent heart disease**

March 18, 1997

From Correspondent Al Hinman

(CNN) -- It may not replace the current advice of an aspirin a day, but many heart doctors are thinking of prescribing a drink-a-day for their coronary heart disease patients.

The latest research presented at the American College of Cardiologists' annual conference shows that what you drink can affect your heart.

If people drank alcohol, they were less likely to be hospitalized than if they didn't

"We found that people who drank any type of alcohol seemed to be at lower risk."
- Dr. Klatsky, cardiologist

of the Kaiser Permanente Medical Care Program says his research k down the commonly held belief that it's red wine that you have to the heart.

people who drank any type of alcohol seemed to be at lower risk. In

2-41



## Lurking Variable and Confounding

**Lurking variable** A variable that affects the relationship between the response variable and the explanatory variable but is not included among the variables studied.

**Confounding** A condition where the effects of two different variables on the response variable cannot be distinguished from each other. Typically, these two variables are the explanatory variable and a lurking variable.

2-42

Lurking Variables & Confounding

## Example: Lurking Variable and Confounding

**Breast-fed babies do better in school than bottle-fed babies**

Researchers at the National Institute of Environmental Heath Sciences reported that at age two, children who had been breast-fed more than five months were smarter and more coordinated than children who had been bottle-fed or breast-fed for a short time. These results were based on various tests which measured mental (including verbal and memory skills) and motor skills.

**FACT:** Mother's who breast-feed for more than 5 months likely do not work full time; they are also more likely to have time to spend on their child's development.

**Explanatory Variable:** Whether child is breast-fed.

**Lurking Variable:** Whether mother has time to breast-feed versus whether mother is forced to bottle-feed due to working full time.

**Confounding:** Time spent with child is confounded with whether child is breast-fed.

**A lurking variable is often confounded with the explanatory variable in an observational study.**

2-43

## Vocabulary

**Statistical Problem Solving**
**Question Formulation**
**Data Collection**
**Data Analysis**
**Statistical Inference**
**Confounding**
**Experiment**
**Explanatory Variable**
**Lurking Variable**
**Observational Study**
**Response Variable**

3-1

# Chapter 8
# Producing Data: Sampling

StatTutor Lesson 03

3-2

## Lesson Objectives

1. Distinguish between a population and a sample.
2. Identify and describe four types of non-probability sampling methods.
3. Identify and describe three types of probability sampling methods.
4. Use a random digit table to obtain a simple random sample.
5. Obtain a stratified sample.
6. Obtain a multistage sample.
7. Identify and describe selection bias, non-response bias, and measurement bias.
8. Describe the strengths and weaknesses of non-probability and probability sampling.

3-3

*Sample Surveys*

## Sampling

Basic Practice of Statistics Chapter 8

3-4

*Sample Surveys*

## Sample Survey--Review

- **Data Production:** Select a sample (a part or subset) from a population.
- **Data Summarization:** Describe sample.
- **Statistical Inference:** Attribute characteristics of sample to population.

**Why sample?**
To obtain information about a population for which a census is impractical.

3-5

Sample Surveys

## Sample Survey

View Movie Clip.

3-6

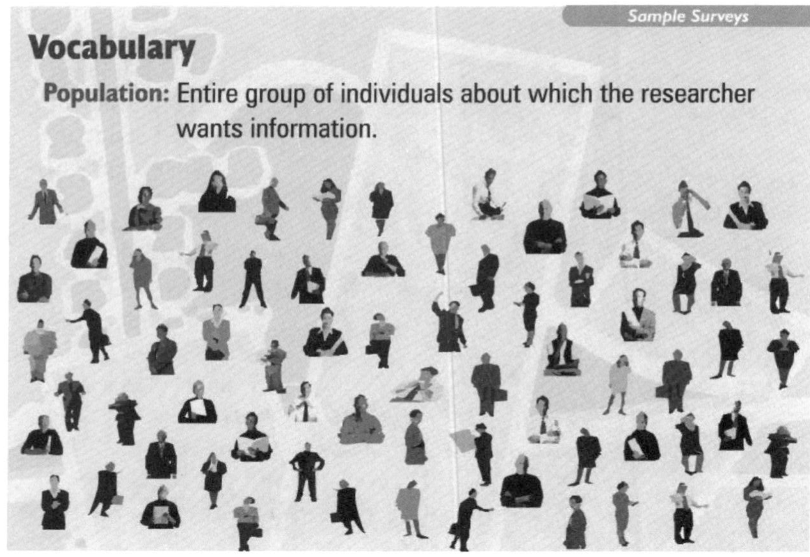


3-7

Sample Surveys

## Vocabulary

**Variable:** A characteristic measured or recorded on individuals in the sample or population. A variable takes on different values for different individuals.

3-8

Sample Surveys

## Vocabulary

**Data Production**

**Sample:** A part of population that is selected and measured.

3-9

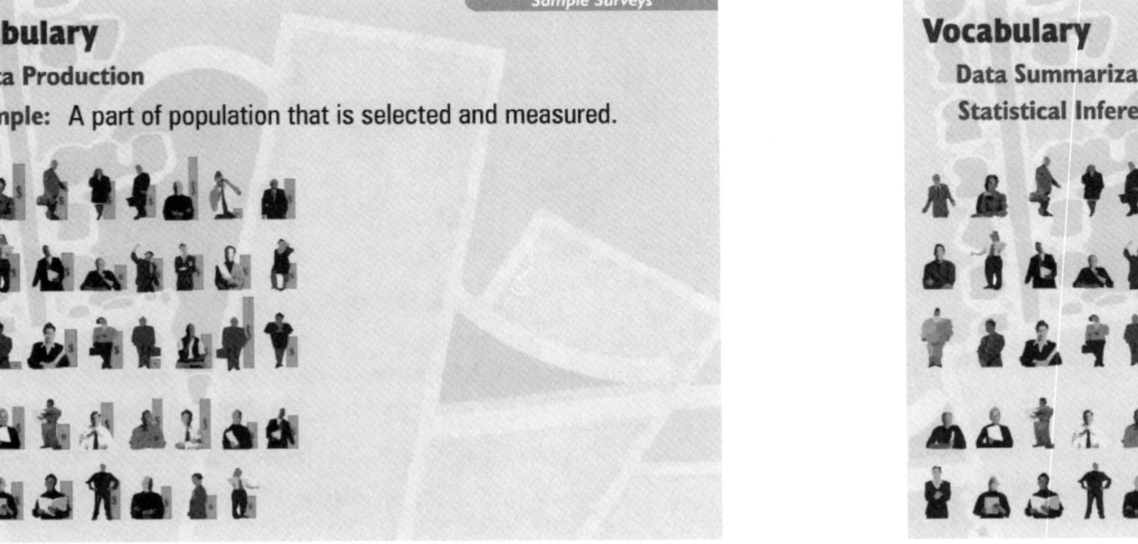


3-10

Sample Surveys

## Vocabulary

**Data Summarization** Data are graphed and mean computed.

**Statistical Inference** Conclusions are made about a population based on sample data.

**The average salary of these CEO's is 2.5 million.**

**The average salary of all CEO's is 2.5 million.**

3-11

Sample Surveys

## Important Pre-Survey Questions

**Question 1** Exactly what population do we want to describe?
Exactly what is meant by "CEO's"?

**Question 2** Exactly what do we want to measure?
Exactly what is meant by "salary of CEO"?

**The average salary of all CEO's is 2.5 million.**

3-12

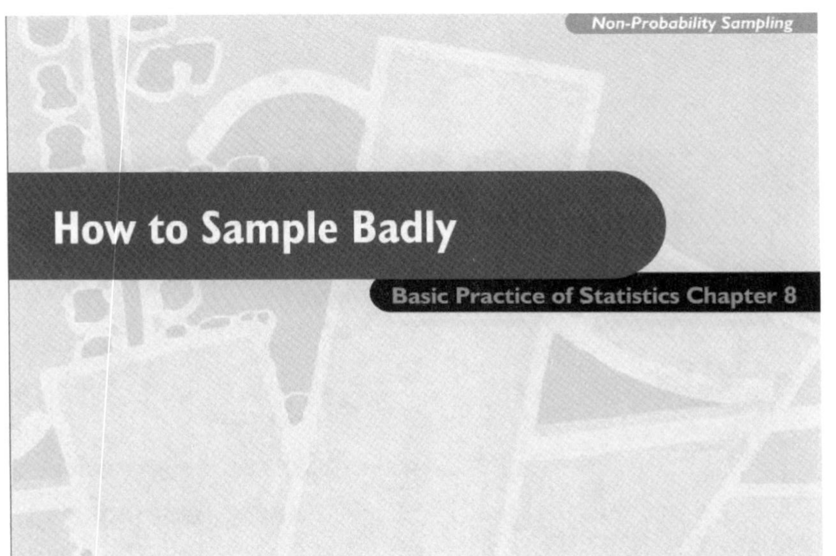

3-13



## How to Sample Badly: Non-Probability Sample

A sample chosen using personal judgment or human subjectivity to determine which individuals are in the sample and which are not. The probability of selecting a specified individual from the population cannot be computed.

**Examples**

- Convenience Sample
- Voluntary Response Sample
- Mall-Intercept Sample
- Quota Sample

3-14



## Convenience Sample

**Sample chosen for ease of selection**

3-15



## Voluntary Response Sample

**Individuals are self-selected (choose themselves)**

**Example:** **A Call-in Opinion Poll**

**Question: Do you favor women working outside the home?**

Dial 1-900-456-1234 if yes Dial 1-900-456-1235 if no

**Who is more likely to respond?**

3-16



## "Mall-Intercept Sample

**Mall shoppers are interviewed.**

- Survey 1:
  Ask questions about shopping habits.
- Survey 2:
  Ask questions about national/state politics.

**For which survey can the responses be generalized?**

3-17



## Quota Sample

**Interviewers select individuals to fill quotas**

**Population Characteristics by Gender/Race**

| | Hispanic | White | Black | Other | % |
|---|---|---|---|---|---|
| **Male** | 5.5% | 36.0% | 6.0% | 2.5% | 50.0% |
| **Female** | 5.5% | 36.0% | 6.0% | 2.5% | 50.0% |
| **%** | 11.0% | 72.0% | 12.0% | 5.0% | 100.0% |

**Quotas to Meet**

| | Hispanic | White | Black | Other | Total |
|---|---|---|---|---|---|
| **Male** | 22 | 144 | 24 | 10 | 200 |
| **Female** | 22 | 144 | 24 | 10 | 200 |
| **Total** | 44 | 288 | 48 | 20 | 400 |

**Why is quota sampling a non-probability sampling method?**
Because the probability of selecting each individual cannot be determined.

3-18



## Why Are These Bad Samples?

**Bias**

A study is biased if it systematically favors certain outcomes.

**Convenience samples** often produce unrepresentative data.

**Voluntary response samples** consist of people with really strong opinions who are more likely to respond.

**Mall samples** overrepresent retired, middle-class and teenagers and underrepresent the poor.

**These types of samples are likely to be biased.**

3-19



## Simple Random Samples

**Basic Practice of Statistics Chapter 8**

3-20



## Simple Random Sample (SRS)

A sample of size *n* chosen from the population in such a way that every set of *n* individuals has an *equal* chance to be the sample actually selected.

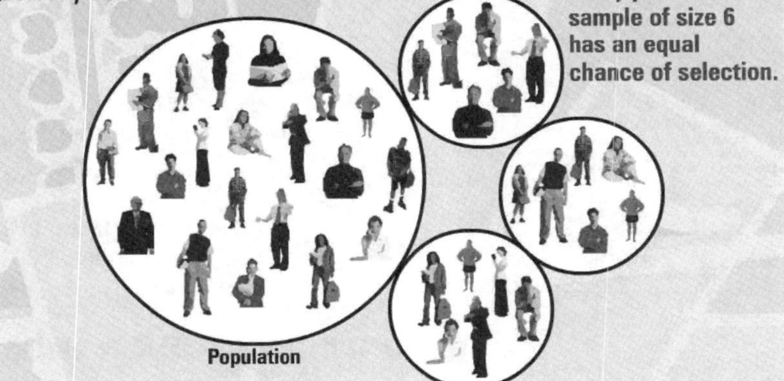

3-21



## How To Select a Simple Random Sample

- Use a random digit table.
- Use a statistical software package.
- Use other acceptable random devices.

3-22



## What is a Random Digit Table?

**Random Digit Table:**

List of digits 0, 1, 2, 3, 4, 5, 6, 7, 8, and 9 with two properties:

**Property 1:**

Each digit in the table is equally likely to be any of the 10 digits 0 through 9.

**Property 2:**

The entries are independent of each other; that is, knowledge of one part of the table gives no information about any other part.

| Line | Random Digits | | | | | | | |
|---|---|---|---|---|---|---|---|---|
| 101 | 19223 | 95034 | 05756 | 28713 | 96409 | 12531 | 42544 | 82853 |
| 102 | 73676 | 47150 | 99400 | 01927 | 27754 | 42648 | 82425 | 36290 |
| 103 | 45467 | 71709 | 77558 | 00095 | 32863 | 29485 | 82226 | 90056 |
| 104 | 52711 | 38889 | 93074 | 60227 | 40011 | 85848 | 48767 | 52573 |
| 105 | 95592 | 94007 | 69971 | 91481 | 60779 | 53791 | 17297 | 59335 |
| 106 | 68417 | 35013 | 15529 | 72765 | 85089 | 57067 | 50211 | 47487 |
| 107 | 82739 | 57890 | 20807 | 47511 | 81676 | 55300 | 94383 | 14893 |
| 108 | 60940 | 72024 | 17868 | 24943 | 61790 | 90656 | 87964 | 18883 |
| 109 | 36009 | 19365 | 15412 | 39638 | 85453 | 46816 | 83485 | 41979 |
| 110 | 38448 | 48789 | 18338 | 24697 | 39364 | 42006 | 76688 | 08708 |
| 111 | 81486 | 69487 | 60513 | 09297 | 00412 | 71238 | 27649 | 39950 |
| 112 | 59636 | 88804 | 04634 | 71197 | 19352 | 73089 | 84898 | 45785 |
| 113 | 62568 | 70206 | 40325 | 03699 | 71080 | 22553 | 11486 | 11776 |
| 114 | 45149 | 32992 | 75730 | 66280 | 03819 | 56202 | 02938 | 70915 |
| 115 | 61041 | 77684 | 94322 | 24709 | 73698 | 14526 | 31893 | 32592 |
| 116 | 14459 | 26056 | 31424 | 80371 | 65103 | 62253 | 50490 | 61181 |
| 117 | 38167 | 98532 | 62183 | 70632 | 23417 | 26185 | 41448 | 75532 |
| 118 | 73190 | 32533 | 04470 | 29669 | 84407 | 90785 | 65956 | 86382 |
| 119 | 95857 | 07118 | 87664 | 92099 | 58806 | 66979 | 98624 | 84826 |
| 120 | 35476 | 55972 | 39421 | 65850 | 04266 | 35435 | 43742 | 11937 |
| 121 | 71487 | 09984 | 29077 | 14863 | 61683 | 47052 | 62224 | 51025 |
| 122 | 13873 | 81598 | 95052 | 90908 | 73592 | 75186 | 87136 | 95761 |
| 123 | 54580 | 81507 | 27102 | 56027 | 55892 | 33063 | 41842 | 81868 |
| 124 | 71035 | 09001 | 43367 | 49497 | 72719 | 96758 | 27611 | 91596 |
| 125 | 96746 | 12149 | 37823 | 71868 | 18442 | 35119 | 62103 | 39244 |

3-23



## Using Random Digit Tables to Select a Simple Random Sample

**View Movie Clip.**

3-24



## Additional Example

A random sample of 25 surgeons belonging to a Health Maintenance Organization (HMO) is to be interviewed about their most recent surgery. There are 105 surgeons on the membership list of the HMO.

3-25



Step 1: Assign each surgeon a three-digit label from 001 to 105

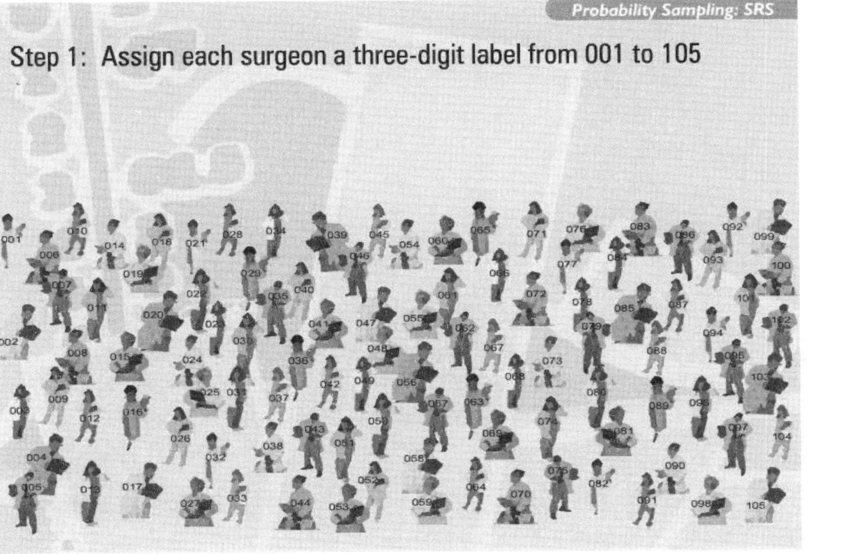

3-26



Step 2: Enter any line in the random digit table and select 25 three digit numbers.

- Ignore all numbers greater than 105.
- Skip any three digit number already selected.

| Line | Random Digits | | | | | | | | | | | | | |
|---|---|---|---|---|---|---|---|---|---|---|---|---|---|---|
| 101 | [illegible] | [illegible] | [illegible] | [illegible] | [illegible] | [illegible] | [illegible] | [illegible] | [illegible] | [illegible] | [illegible] | [illegible] | [illegible] | |
| 102 | [illegible] | [illegible] | [illegible] | [illegible] | [illegible] | [illegible] | [illegible] | [illegible] | [illegible] | [illegible] | [illegible] | [illegible] | [illegible] | |
| 103 | [illegible] | [illegible] | [illegible] | [illegible] | [illegible] | [illegible] | [illegible] | [illegible] | [illegible] | [illegible] | [illegible] | [illegible] | [illegible] | [illegible] |
| 104 | [illegible] | [illegible] | [illegible] | [illegible] | [illegible] | [illegible] | [illegible] | [illegible] | [illegible] | [illegible] | [illegible] | [illegible] | [illegible] | |
| 105 | [illegible] | [illegible] | [illegible] | [illegible] | [illegible] | [illegible] | [illegible] | [illegible] | [illegible] | [illegible] | [illegible] | [illegible] | [illegible] | |
| 106 | 358 | 841 | 735 | 013 | 155 | 297 | 276 | 565 | 089 | 570 | 675 | 021 | 147 | 487 |
| 107 | 827 | 395 | 789 | 020 | 807 | 475 | 118 | 167 | 655 | 300 | 943 | 831 | 489 | |
| 108 | 360 | 940 | 720 | 241 | 785 | 824 | 943 | 617 | 909 | 065 | 687 | 964 | 188 | |
| 109 | 833 | 600 | 919 | 965 | 154 | 123 | 963 | 885 | 453 | 468 | 168 | 348 | 541 | 979 |
| 110 | 384 | 484 | 878 | 918 | 338 | 246 | 973 | 936 | 447 | 006 | 768 | 880 | 870 | |
| 111 | [illegible] | [illegible] | [illegible] | [illegible] | [illegible] | [illegible] | [illegible] | [illegible] | [illegible] | [illegible] | [illegible] | [illegible] | [illegible] | |
| 112 | [illegible] | [illegible] | [illegible] | [illegible] | [illegible] | [illegible] | [illegible] | [illegible] | [illegible] | [illegible] | [illegible] | [illegible] | [illegible] | [illegible] |
| 113 | [illegible] | [illegible] | **020** | [illegible] | [illegible] | **036** | [illegible] | [illegible] | **022** | [illegible] | [illegible] | [illegible] | [illegible] | |
| 114 | [illegible] | [illegible] | [illegible] | [illegible] | [illegible] | **066** | [illegible] | **038** | [illegible] | [illegible] | [illegible] | [illegible] | [illegible] | |
| 115 | [illegible] | **104** | [illegible] | [illegible] | [illegible] | [illegible] | [illegible] | [illegible] | [illegible] | [illegible] | [illegible] | [illegible] | [illegible] | [illegible] |
| 116 | 144 | 592 | 605 | 631 | 424 | 803 | 716 | 510 | 362 | 253 | 504 | 906 | 118 | |
| 117 | 138 | 167 | 885 | 326 | 218 | 370 | 632 | **034** | 172 | 618 | 541 | 446 | 755 | |
| 118 | 327 | 319 | **032** | 533 | **044** | 702 | 966 | 984 | 407 | **007** | 856 | 595 | 685 | 332 |
| 119 | 908 | 970 | 711 | 887 | 654 | 920 | 965 | 880 | 656 | 979 | 986 | 248 | 482 | |
| 120 | 635 | 478 | **059** | 723 | 942 | 165 | 850 | **042** | 653 | 843 | 543 | 742 | 119 | |
| 121 | [illegible] | [illegible] | [illegible] | [illegible] | [illegible] | **071** | [illegible] | [illegible] | [illegible] | [illegible] | [illegible] | [illegible] | **051** | **025** |
| 122 | [illegible] | [illegible] | [illegible] | [illegible] | **052** | [illegible] | **087** | [illegible] | [illegible] | [illegible] | [illegible] | **069** | [illegible] | |
| 123 | [illegible] | **080** | [illegible] | **072** | [illegible] | [illegible] | **027** | [illegible] | [illegible] | [illegible] | [illegible] | [illegible] | [illegible] | |
| 124 | [illegible] | **103** | [illegible] | **001** | [illegible] | [illegible] | [illegible] | [illegible] | **019** | [illegible] | [illegible] | [illegible] | [illegible] | [illegible] |
| 125 | [illegible] | [illegible] | [illegible] | [illegible] | [illegible] | [illegible] | [illegible] | [illegible] | [illegible] | [illegible] | [illegible] | **033** | [illegible] | [illegible] |

3-27



Step 3: Interview the 25 doctors with label numbers corresponding to the numbers selected from the random digit table.

020, 022, 036, 066, 038, 104, 032, 034, 044, 007, 059, 042, 071, 051, 052, 025, 087, 069, 080, 072, 027, 103, 001, 019, 033

3-28



# Other Sampling Designs

Basic Practice of Statistics Chapter 8

3-29



## Probability Sample

A sample chosen by chance where:

- Some type of random device is used--not human subjectivity.
- Each individual in the population has a chance of being selected.
- We know what samples are possible.
- We can compute chance (probability) of getting each possible sample.

**Examples of Probability Samples:**

Simple Random Sample (SRS)
Stratified Sample
Multistage Sample

3-30



## Simple Random Sample--a Probability Sample

A sample of size $n$ chosen from the population in such a way that every set of $n$ individuals has an *equal* chance to be the sample actually selected.

**Every possible sample of size 6 has an equal chance of selection.**

**Population**

3-31



## Stratified Sample

**A sample chosen as follows:**

1. Classify the individuals of a population into groups (strata) according to some characteristic known prior to the survey.
2. Choose a probability sample within each stratum.
3. Combine the samples from all strata to form complete sample.

3-32



## Stratified Sample

**Example: Choose a sample of university students so that all majors are represented.**

Population: University students

**Step 1:** Classify university students into strata by major.

**Step 2:** Choose probability sample within each major.

**Step 3:** Combine resulting samples from each stratum to form a complete sample of students representing all majors.

**Engineering** **Mathematics**

**History** **Humanities**

3-33



## Multistage Sample

**A sample done in stages.**

**For three stage sampling:** first a probability sample of groups is selected; second, a probability sample of sub-groups is taken from each selected group; finally, units are sampled from within each selected sub-group.

**For four stage sampling:** first groups are randomly selected using a probability method; second sub-groups are randomly sampled from the selected groups using a probability method; third a probability sample of sub-sub-groups is taken from the selected sub-groups; finally, individuals are randomly sampled from within selected sub-sub-groups.

**Etc.**

3-34



## Multistage Sample

**Example: Select a multistage sample of farms from the United States.**

Stage 1: Choose a probability sample of six states.

3-35



## Multistage Sample

**Example: Select a multistage sample of farms from the United States.**

Stage 2: Choose a probability sample of two counties within each selected state.

3-36



## Multistage Sample

**Example: Select a multistage sample of farms from the United States.**

Stage 3: Choose a probability sample of two farms within each selected county. **Total sample size n = 24 farms**

3-37

## Summary of Probability Samples

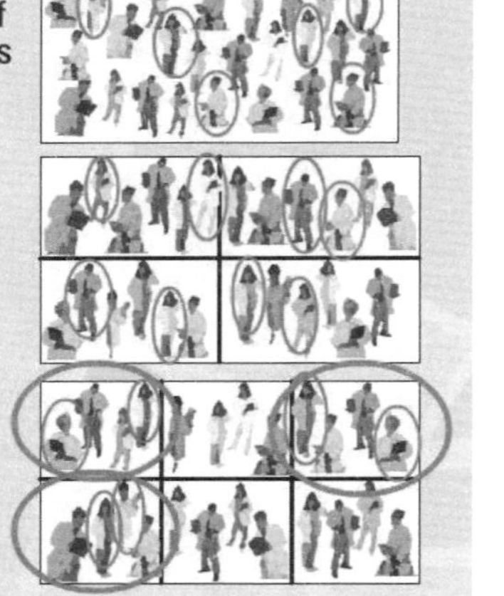

**Simple Random:** Population is composed of individuals that are not grouped; the sample is taken from the entire population.

**Stratified:** Individuals of the population are classified into strata according to some characteristic known prior to sampling; sampling of individuals is done within every stratum.

**Two-stage:** Individuals of the population are classified in groups according to some characteristic. First, groups are randomly selected; then, individuals are randomly sampled from only the selected groups.

3-38

Bias in Surveys

## Cautions about Sample Surveys

Basic Practice of Statistics Chapter 8

3-39

Bias in Surveys

## Potential Sources of Bias in Surveys

**Bias** Tendency to systematically favor certain outcomes over others.

**Sources for bias**

- Under-coverage
- Non-response
- Response
- Question Wording

**Bias can occur in both probability and non-probability samples.**

3-40

Bias in Surveys

## Bias Due to Under-coverage

Occurs because some groups in a population are left out when the sample is chosen.

**Example:** A survey of households excludes:
Homeless who can't be found.
People who have extremely busy lives.
Subjects who are in hospitals, nursing homes, motels, etc.

3-41



## Bias Due to Non-Response

Occurs when an individual chosen in the sample refuses to provide answers or can't be contacted.

**Example:** According to the U.S. Bureau of Census:

In the 2000 census 28% of the households that received census forms did not mail them back. Even with follow-up interviews, the estimated undercount is 1.15% of the nation.

In the 1990 census, the estimated undercount was 1.8%.

In New York City alone, 47% of households that were mailed forms did not mail them back. Of those 47%, 20% were still not contacted even after six tries.

3-42



## Bias Due to Response

**Respondent Bias**

Occurs when the respondent (person being surveyed) gives responses that influence the results in a systematic way.

**Example I:**

In a telephone survey conducted by student newspaper reporters, students sampled at a large university were asked whether they had cheated on exams.

**Example 2:**

A sample of college students were asked whether their teeth had been cleaned in the last six months.

3-43



## Bias Due to Response

**Interviewer Bias**

Occurs when an interviewer (because of social position, poor training, etc.) influences the response in a systematic way.

**Example:**

A sample of black residents living in Detroit was asked: "Do you personally feel that you can trust most white people, some white people, or none at all?"

-- Schuman and Converse (1971)

Of those interviewed by a white person, 35% responded "Most white people." Of those interviewed by a black person, 7% responded "Most white people."

3-44



## Bias Due to Question Wording

Occurs when questions have leading phrases, loaded words, or ambiguities that influence the response.

**Example:**

"Does it seem possible or does it seem impossible to you that Nazi extermination of the Jews never happened?"

**22%** responded that it seemed possible.

**Note the presence of two negatives.**

**Example:**

"The term Holocaust usually refers to the killing of millions of Jews in Nazi death camps during World War II. In your opinion did the Holocaust: definitely happen, probably happen, probably not happen, definitely did not happen?"

**4%** responded that it may not have happened either probably or definitely.

3-45



## What type of bias is possible in each example?

**Select from:**

- Under-coverage
- Non-response
- Response
  - Respondent Bias
  - Interviewer Bias
  - Question Wording Bias

**Example 1**

Telephone Surveys

Types of Bias? **Under-coverage / Non-response / Response**

3-46



## What type of bias is possible in each example?

**Select from:**

- Under-coverage
- Non-response
- Response
  - Respondent Bias
  - Interviewer Bias
  - Question Wording Bias

**Example 2**

Mail-in Survey

Types of Bias? **Under-coverage / Non-response / Response**

3-47



## What type of bias is possible in each example?

**Select from:**

- Under-coverage
- Non-response
- Response
  - Respondent Bias
  - Interviewer Bias
  - Question Wording Bias

**Example 3**

Convenience Sample

Types of Bias? **Under-coverage**

3-48



# Inference about the Population

Basic Practice of Statistics Chapter 8

3-49



## Comparing Probability and Non-Probability Samples

| PROBABILITY SAMPLES | NON-PROBABILITY SAMPLES |
|---|---|
| **Ease and Convenience** | |
| Comparatively more complex and difficult | Designed for ease and convenience |
| **Under-Coverage Bias** | |
| Can occur, but less likely | Usually present, but often ignored or over-looked |
| **Non-Response and Response Bias** | |
| Can occur | Can occur |
| **Validity of Statistical Inference** | |
| Have sound theoretical and methodical base for using chance to make inferences. Size of error due to sampling is measurable. | Have no comparable theoretical base for making inferences. Principles of chance don't apply. Size of error is unmeasurable. |

3-50



## Important Characteristics of Probability Samples

- "It is unlikely that the results from a sample are exactly the same as for the entire population."
- "If we select two samples at random from the same population, we will draw different individuals. So the sample results will almost certainly differ somewhat."
- "Properly designed samples avoid systematic bias, but their results are rarely exactly correct and they vary from sample to sample."
- "Larger samples give more accurate results than smaller samples."

-- David S. Moore, *The Basic Practice of Statistics, 4th Edition,* 2006

3-51

## Vocabulary

**Population**
**Sample**
**Response Variable**
**Statistical Inference**
**Random Digit Table**
**Non-Probability Sample**
**Convenience Sample**
**Voluntary Response Sample**
**Mall-Intercept Sample**
**Quota Sampling**
**Probability Sample**
**Simple Random Sample**
**Stratified Sample**
**Multistage Sample**
**Bias**
**Under-coverage bias**
**Non-response bias**
**Response bias**
**Respondent bias**
**Interviewer bias**
**Question wording bias**

4-1

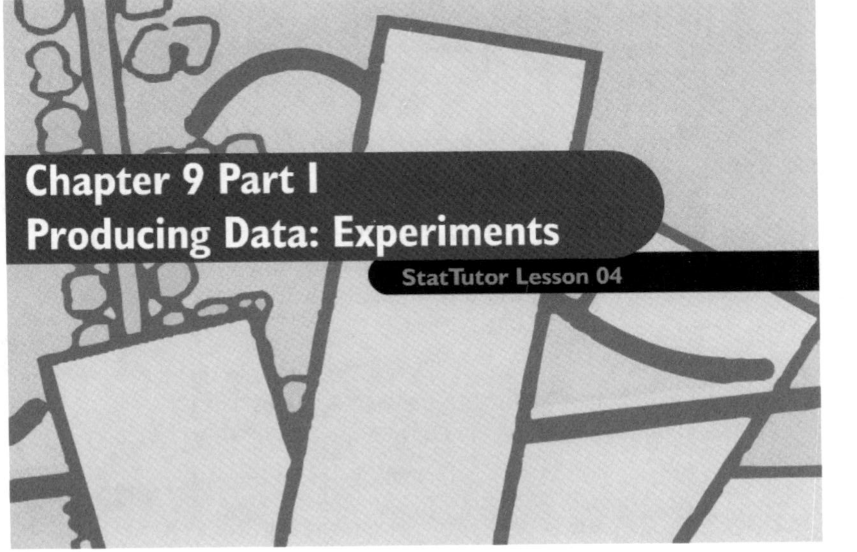


4-2

## Objectives

1. Identify the response and explanatory variables, the experimental units, and the treatments in an experiment.
2. Identify lurking variables and confounding in a study or experiment.
3. List the three principles of good experimental design.
4. Define statistical significance.

4-3

*Experiments*

## Chapter 9 Introduction

Basic Practice of Statistics Chapter 9

4-4

*Experiments*

## Producing Data with Experiments

**Experiment:** A study where the researcher deliberately imposes treatments on selected individuals and observes the response.

- **Data Production:** Impose specific "treatments" on subjects and record responses.
- **Data Summarization:** Describe the "treatment" groups.
- **Statistical Inference:** Compare responses from both groups to assess effects of "treatments."

**Impose Treatment A**

**Impose Treatment B**

Note: Just as probability sampling should be used to select individuals for a sample, randomization should be used to assign individuals to treatment groups.

4-5



# Experiments

Basic Practice of Statistics Chapter 9

4-6



## Definitions

**Subject** Individual, particularly a person, upon which an experiment is performed.

**Treatment** A specific experimental condition imposed on the subjects. (Sometimes this refers only to the treatment with the active ingredient.)

**Explanatory variable (X)** (also called **Factor**) A set of treatments imposed on the subjects that may affect the outcome of the study.

**Response variable (Y)** The outcome measured on the subjects to reveal the effects of the treatments.

4-7



## Definitions

**Control** A treatment without the active ingredient (either no treatment or a placebo treatment) that is imposed on the subjects.

**Placebo** A dummy treatment that outwardly resembles the active treatment; e.g. sugar pill without an active ingredient, an injection with glucose rather than the vaccine, etc.

4-8



## Application of Definitions

**Example** To compare 3 new test fertilizers, a farmer applies them to several corn fields. Each field is divided into 3 plots and the 3 fertilizers are randomly assigned, one to each plot within each field. Harvested corn yield is compared for the 3 fertilizers.

Individual: **Each corn plot**

Treatments: **Three test fertilizers**

Explanatory Variable: **Fertilizer type**

Response Variable: **Corn yield**

Control: **None**

Placebo: **None**

4-9

Experiments

## The Salk Vaccine Experiment

View Movie Clip.

4-10

Experiments

## The Salk Vaccine Experiment

What is the:

- Subject? A student in grades 1, 2 or 3
- Explanatory variable? Content of injection (saline or vaccine)
- Response variable? Whether student contracts polio
- Control group? Students receiving saline injections
- Placebo? Saline injection

4-11

Experiments

## The Salk Vaccine Experiment

Subjects: Approximately 402,000 children in grades 1,2, and 3

Explanatory Variable (X):
Injection of saline solution (placebo) $X = 0$
Injection of polio vaccine $X = 1$

Response Variable (Y):
Individual did not contract polio $Y = 0$
Individual did contract polio $Y = 1$

| Treatments | # of Subjects | Incidences of Polio | Incidence Rate (%) |
|---|---|---|---|
| Placebo | 201,229 | 142 | 0.071 |
| Vaccine | 200,745 | 57 | 0.028 |

4-12

Lurking Variables and Confounding

## Lurking Variables, Confounding and Interaction

**Lurking variable** A variable that affects the relationship between the response variable and the explanatory variable but is not included among the variables studied.

**Confounding** A condition where the effects of two different variables on the response variable cannot be distinguished from each other.

**Interaction** A condition where the effect of one variable on the response variable changes depending on the level of another variable.

4-13



## Example: Lurking Variable

### Nicotine Patches

In 1994 at Rochester, Minnesota 240 smokers were randomly assigned to receive either nicotine patches or placebo patches. After eight weeks, 46% of the nicotine patch group had quit while only 20% of the placebo group had quit.

**Lurking Variable:** Presence or absence of other smokers in the home

- If there were other smokers in the home, only 31% had quit smoking after eight weeks of nicotine patch therapy.
- If there were no other smokers in the home, 58% had quit smoking after eight weeks of nicotine patch therapy.
- In the placebo group, 20% quit smoking whether there were other smokers in the home or not.

**The presence or absence of other smokers in the home affected the association between treatments and whether smokers quit.**

4-14



## Example 1: Confounding

Jane wants to determine whether the cheaper store brand cleans her clothes as effectively as the more expensive name brand.

**Which of these proposed studies has confounding?**

**Proposal A:**

| | Name Brand | Store Brand |
|---|---|---|
| Hot water | 3 batches | 3 batches |
| Cold water | 3 batches | 3 batches |

**Proposal B:**

| | Name Brand Hot water | Store Brand Cold water |
|---|---|---|
| | 6 batches | 6 batches |

In proposal "B", brand of detergent is confounded with water temperature; their effects on cleanliness index cannot be separated.

In proposal "A", we can investigate interaction between brand of detergent and water temperature to determine which combination is best.

4-15



## Example 2: Confounding

A researcher in education wants to determine which method of teaching (multi-media or overheads) will result in higher test scores.

**Which of these proposed studies has confounding?**

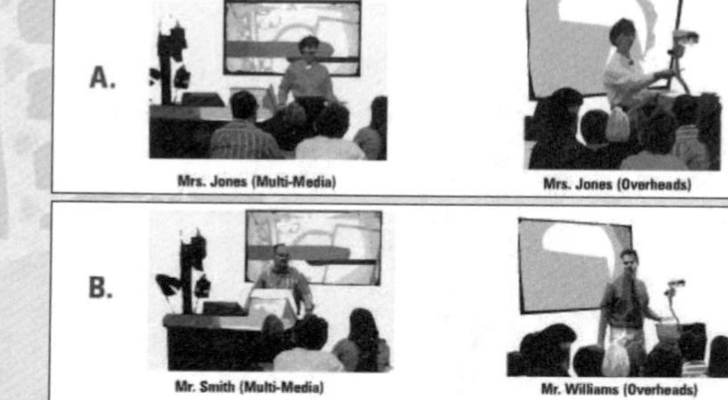


In proposal "B", teaching method is confounded with instructor; their effects on test scores cannot be separated.

To avoid confounding, each instructor should teach with both methods.

4-16



## How to Experiment Badly

Basic Practice of Statistics Chapter 9

4-17



## Facts about Experiments

- Preferred for examining the effect of explanatory variable on the response variable.
- Guidelines for conducting are based on statistical principles.
- Can be poorly performed just like sampling.

4-18



## Example of Badly Conducted Experiment

A study conducted by the Agriculture Department supports findings that calcium helps women deal with the stress and anxiety of premenstrual syndrome (PMS).

- Ten women participated.
- Each was instructed to consume 1,300 milligrams of calcium daily.
- After 5½ months, nine told nutritional experts they were in a better mood before and during their menstrual periods while on the diet.

**Problems**

- No control group--don't know if better mood resulted from calcium or from some other factor.
- Subjects self-reported--don't know whether better mood was due to calcium or to the fact that subjects were in a study.

**Results may be worthless due to confounding with lurking variables.**

4-19



## Design of Experiment

**Calcium Study**

Increased calcium ⟶ Observe mood

**In general**

Treatment ⟶ Observe response

**This simple design can yield worthless results because of confounding with lurking variables.**

--David S. Moore

**Improved Design**

PMS subjects ↗ Calcium Treatment ⟶ Observe mood

PMS subjects ↘ Placebo Treatment ⟶ Observe mood

4-20



# Randomized Comparative Experiments

Basic Practice of Statistics Chapter 9

4-21



## How Do You Experiment Well?

**Conduct a randomized comparative experiment!**

**Randomized Comparative Experiment**

An experiment that uses both comparison of two or more treatments and chance assignment of subjects to treatments.

**Two Randomized Comparative Designs:**

- Completely Randomized Design
- Randomized Block Design

4-22



## Principle 1: Control or Comparison

**Determine a treatment's effect by comparing:**

**1. Treatment vs. Control (No Treatment)**

Exercise Program — Ordinary Lifestyle

**2. Treatment vs. Control (Placebo)**

Vaccine — Glucose/Placebo

**3. Treatment 1 vs. Treatment 2 (Comparison)**

Teaching Method #1 — Teaching Method #2

4-23



## Principle 2: Randomization

**Subjects are allocated at random to two treatments.**

Treatment 1 ⟵ Comparative Experiment ⟶ Treatment 2

Randomization

## Principle 3: Replication

**Each treatment is assigned to 15 rats.**

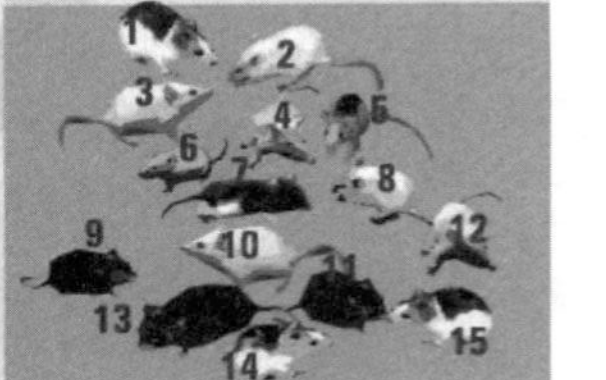
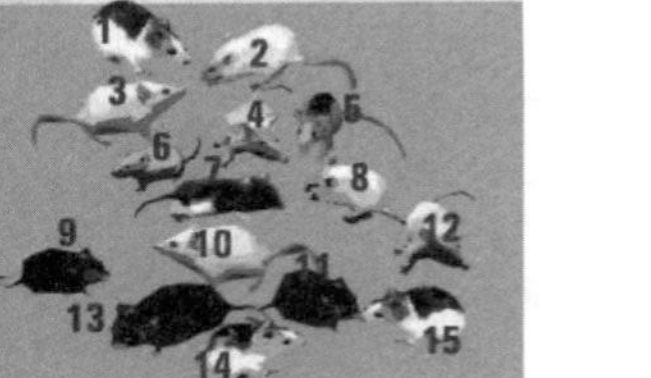

4-24



## Randomized Comparative Experiments

**Control or Comparison:** Comparing active treatment with control treatment ***or*** comparing two or more treatments.

**Randomization:** Using random device to assign subjects to treatments.

**Replication:** Applying each treatment to more than one subject in each treatment group.

**Benefits of incorporating all three principles:**

- Bias is reduced and unwanted confounding is eliminated.
- Laws of probability can be applied to assess whether treatment effects are larger than expected due to chance variation.
- **A well-designed experiment provides evidence of a cause and effect relationship.**

4-25



## Observational Studies

Studies where treatments are not assigned to subjects--researchers observe individuals and record information about variables of interest.

**Control or comparison:** Generally, active treatment compared with control ***or*** two or more treatments compared.

**Randomization:** No assignment of subjects to treatments; subjects usually self-select treatments.

**Replication:** Enough subjects to measure chance variation.

**Possible Consequences of no randomization:**

- Bias and confounding of explanatory variable with lurking variable.
- Cannot correctly apply the laws of probability to assess whether treatment effects are larger than expected due to chance variation.
- Cannot conclude cause and effect relationship between the explanatory variable and the response variable.

4-26



## Experiments versus Observational Studies

| | Well-Designed Experiment | Observational Study |
|---|---|---|
| Control or comparison | Yes | Usually |
| Randomization | Yes | No |
| Replication | Yes | Yes |
| Establish cause and effect | Yes | No |

The media often makes observational studies look like experiments.

4-27



## Completely Randomized Design (CRD)

A randomized comparative experiment where all subjects are allocated at random among all the treatments.

**Example**

**Experimental Unit**
Newly weaned male rats

**Response Variable**
Weight gain

**Explanatory Variable**
Type of diet:

Treatment 1: Standard diet
Treatment 2: New diet

4-28



## Completely Randomized Design (CRD) Example

4-29

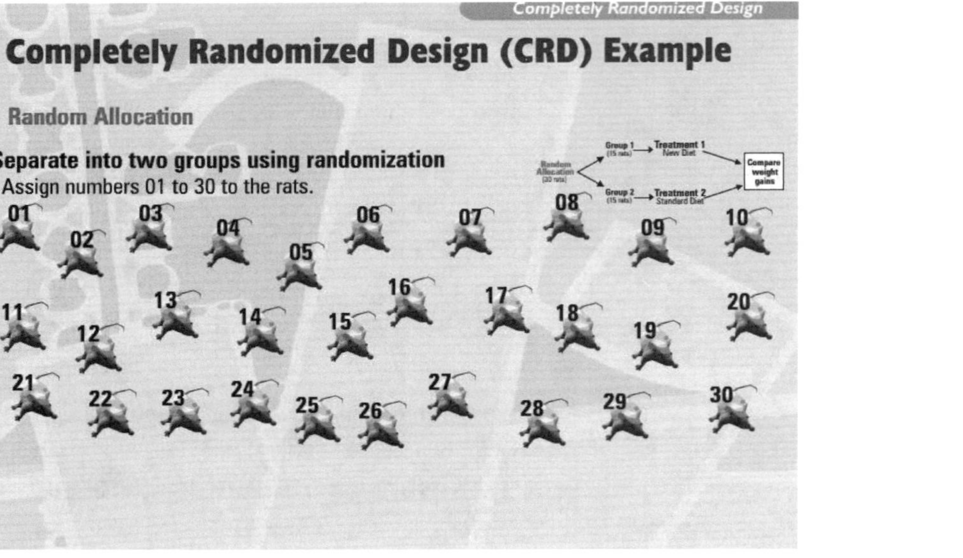


4-30

Completely Randomized Design

## Completely Randomized Design (CRD) Example

### Random Allocation

**Separate into two groups using randomization**
Select an SRS of 15 rats.

Compare weight gains

01 02 03 04 05 06 07 08 09 10
11 12 13 14 15 16 17 18 19 20
21 22 23 24 25 26 27 28 29 30

Random Digit Table: Choose 15 numbers to identify rats for group 1 (See Table B: Lines 130 to 134)

05 16 17 20 19 04 25 29 18 07 13 02 23 27 21

4-31

Completely Randomized Design

## Completely Randomized Design (CRD) Example

### Random Allocation

**Separate into two groups using randomization**

Compare weight gains

**Group 1:**

02 04 05 07 13
16 17 18 19 20
21 23 25 27 29

**Group 2:**

01 03 06 08 09
10 11 12 14 15
22 24 26 28 30

4-32

Completely Randomized Design

## Completely Randomized Design (CRD) Example

### Application of Treatments

Compare weight gains

**Administer a treatment to each group**

**Group 1:** New Diet

02 04 05 07 13
16 17 18 19 20
21 23 25 27 29

**Group 2:** Standard Diet

01 03 06 08 09
10 11 12 14 15
22 24 26 28 30

4-33

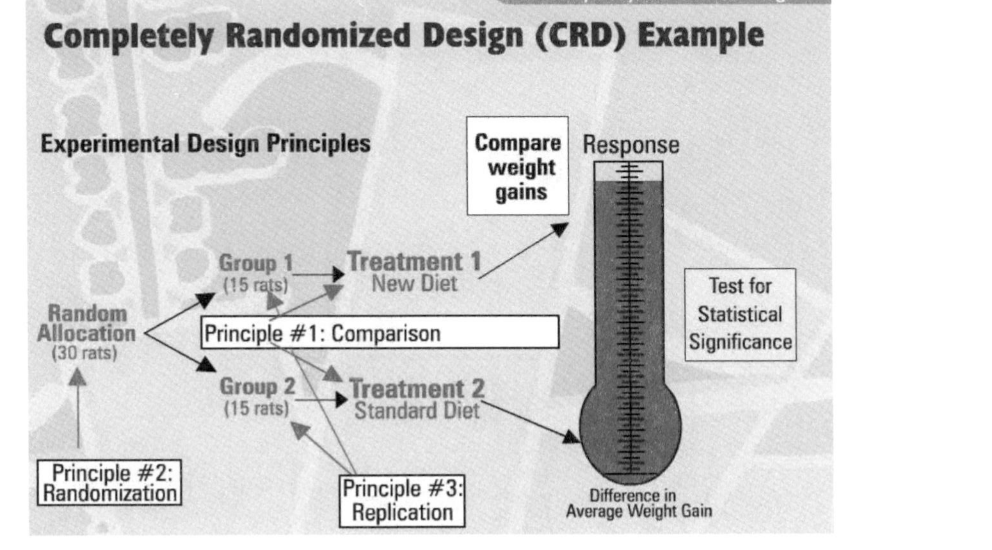


4-34

## Vocabulary

- Completely Randomized Design
- Confounding
- Control or Comparison
- Experiment
- Explanatory variable
- Lurking variable
- Observational Study
- Observed effect
- Placebo
- Randomization
- Randomized Comparative Experiment
- Replication
- Response variable
- Statistical significance
- Subject
- Treatment

5-1

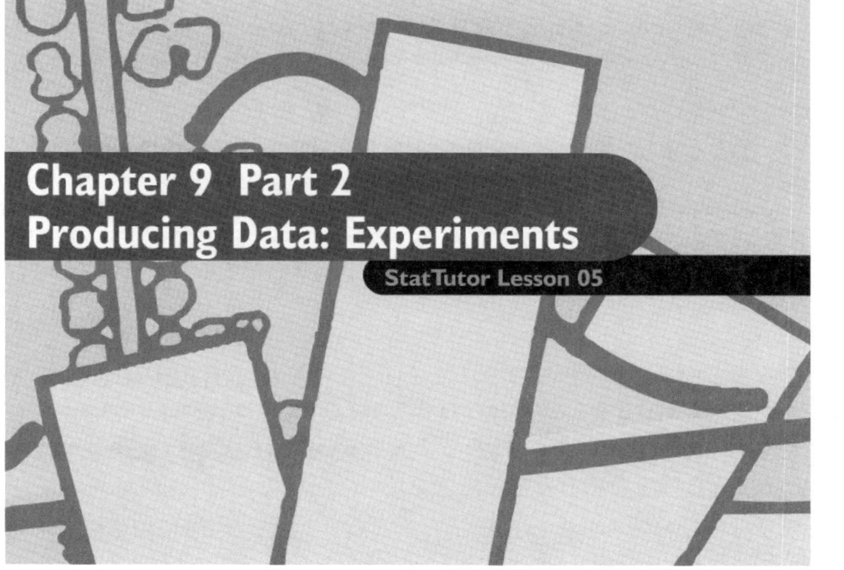


5-2

## Lesson Objectives

1. Explain when an observed effect is statistically significant.
2. List and give examples of three common problems of experiments.
3. Describe a randomized block design (RBD).
4. Identify matched pairs design.
5. Compare the benefits of RBD over CRD with regard to the principles of good experimental design.

5-3

*Randomized Comparative Experiments*

## The Logic of Randomized Comparative Experiments

Basic Practice of Statistics Chapter 9

5-4

*Randomized Comparative Experiments*

## The Logic:

Randomly assign subjects into groups that should be similar in all respects before treatments are applied.

**Result:**

Influences other than treatments operate equally on all groups.

**Consequence:**

Differences in average response must be due either to the treatments or to the play of chance.

5-5

Randomized Comparative Experiments

## Principles of Good Experimental Design

**Control or Comparison**

**What:** Comparing active treatment with control treatment ***or*** compare two or more treatments.

**Why:** To neutralize the effect of lurking variables and measure treatment differences.

**Randomization**

**What:** Using random device to assign subjects to treatments.

**Why:** To eliminate bias and invoke assumptions for statistical inference.

**Replication**

**What:** Applying each treatment to more than one subject in each treatment group.

**Why:** To measure and reduce chance variation in the results by increasing the number of subjects in each group.

5-6

Randomized Comparative Experiments

## Statistical Significance

**Purpose of Experiment:** To determine whether the treatments affect the response.

**Control or comparison:** Insures influences from lurking variables operate equally on all groups.

**Randomization:** Forms treatment groups that are similar in all respects before treatments are applied.

**Replication:** Allows us to measure chance variation so we can compare treatments.

**Observed Effect:** The difference between what we see in the data and what we ***expect*** to see in the data.

**Statistically Significant:** An observed effect that is too large to attribute plausibly to chance variation.

**If the difference between the responses for two treatments is statistically significant, then the treatments affect the response.**

5-7

Randomized Comparative Experiments

## Statistical Significance

An observed effect that is too large to attribute plausibly to chance variation.

**Example:**

The polio rate of those receiving the vaccine was 0.028% compared to 0.071% for those receiving the placebo.

Is the difference between the polio rates small enough to be chance variation or large enough to attribute to the vaccine?
i.e., is the observed difference in rates statistically significant? **YES**

**Since the difference between the percentages for two treatments is statistically significant, we conclude that the vaccine affected the polio rate of the vaccinated group.**

5-8

Problems in Experiments

## Cautions about Experimentation

**Basic Practice of Statistics Chapter 9**

5-9

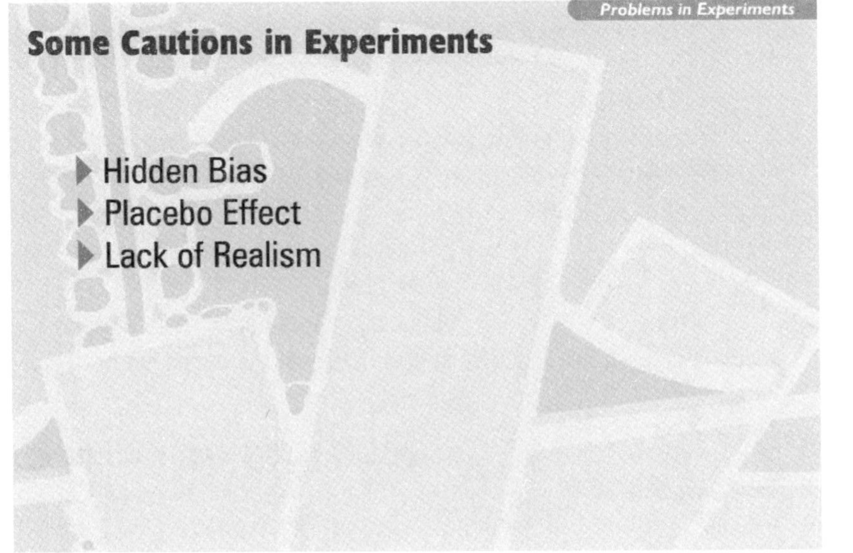

Problems in Experiments

## Some Cautions in Experiments

- Hidden Bias
- Placebo Effect
- Lack of Realism

5-10

Hidden Bias Problems

## Hidden Bias

**Bias that is introduced by not treating all individuals identically after treatments are applied.**

- A herd of cows was randomly divided into two groups.
- One group wore ear tags with insecticide while the other group wore ear tags without insecticide (placebo).
- The group with the insecticide ear tags was confined to a fenced-in pen. The other group roamed free.

**What is the hidden bias?** Fenced-in cows attract flies more than cows that roam free. This biases the effectiveness of insecticide ear tags.

5-11

Hidden Bias Problems

## Solution: Treat All Individuals the Same

**How?**

One solution: Keep both groups of cows in two different fenced-in areas that are as similar as possible.

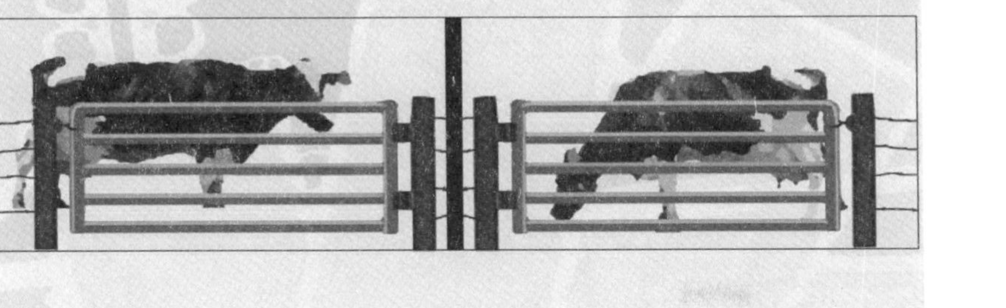

5-12

Placebo Bias Problems

## Placebo Effect

**Positive response for subjects taking a placebo due to confidence in doctor and hope in medication.**

Consequence: Placebo alleviates symptoms.

Solution: Use control group that gets a placebo to determine whether active treatment is effective or whether improvement is due to the placebo effect.

**Another issue: Suppose the doctor knows who received the active treatment and who received the placebo.**

Consequence: Medical advice could be different; evaluation of benefit of the active treatment could be influenced by this knowledge.

**Result: Hidden Bias**

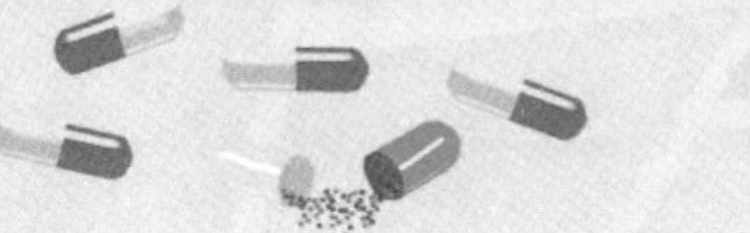

5-13



## Solution: Use a Double Blind Experiment

**Neither the subject nor the doctor/diagnostician knows who receives the placebo or who receives the active treatment.**

- Study of the effect of zinc gluconate on the duration of the common cold
- Treatment: zinc gluconate lozenge or placebo lozenge
- Subjects visited nurse daily
- Nurse: no knowledge of which treatment subjects received
- Subjects: no knowledge of which treatment they receive
- **Double-blind study**

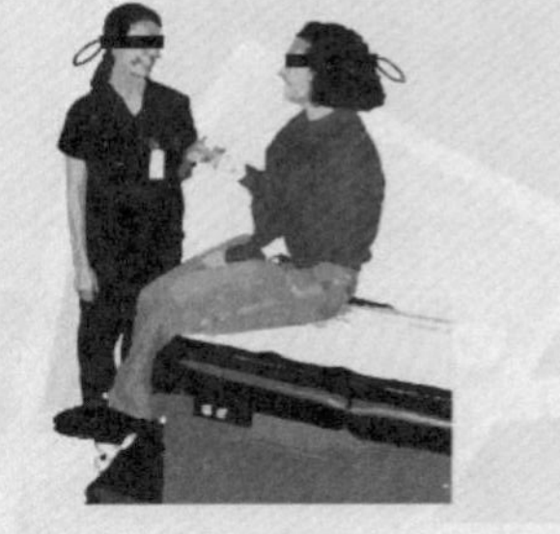

5-14



## Lack of Realism

**Subjects, treatment, or setting does not realistically duplicate the conditions we want to study.**

Example: Experiment to compare effectiveness of commercials

- Subjects: Undergraduates of a university
- Treatments: 6 combinations of length and # of times shown

| Length of Commercials | # of Times Shown in 60 Minute Program: Once | 3 times | 5 times |
|---|---|---|---|
| 30 Seconds | treatment 1 | treatment 2 | treatment 3 |
| 90 seconds | treatment 4 | treatment 5 | treatment 6 |

Problems:
- Students knew they were in an experiment.
- "Student viewers" are different from "typical viewers."

**Consequence: Bias in the results.**

5-15



## Solution: Use Good Judgment

- Apply sound statistical principles as much as possible.
- Report study limitations honestly.

**Realism may not be possible (e.g., may have to substitute rats for pregnant women in experiment on smoking vs. non-smoking).**

5-16



# Matched Pairs and Block Designs

Basic Practice of Statistics Chapter 9

5-17

Randomized Block Design

## Randomized Block Design (RBD)

**What is a block?**

A group of individuals that are:

- similar with respect to some characteristic known before the experiment begins and that characteristic is expected to affect the response to the treatments.
- often equal in number to the number of treatments.

**What is a randomized block design?**

An experimental design where the random assignment of individuals to treatments is carried out separately within each block.

Note: Blocks are another form of control--they control the effects of the variable that defines the blocks.

5-18

Randomized Block Design

## Randomized Block Design

**View Movie Clip.**

5-19

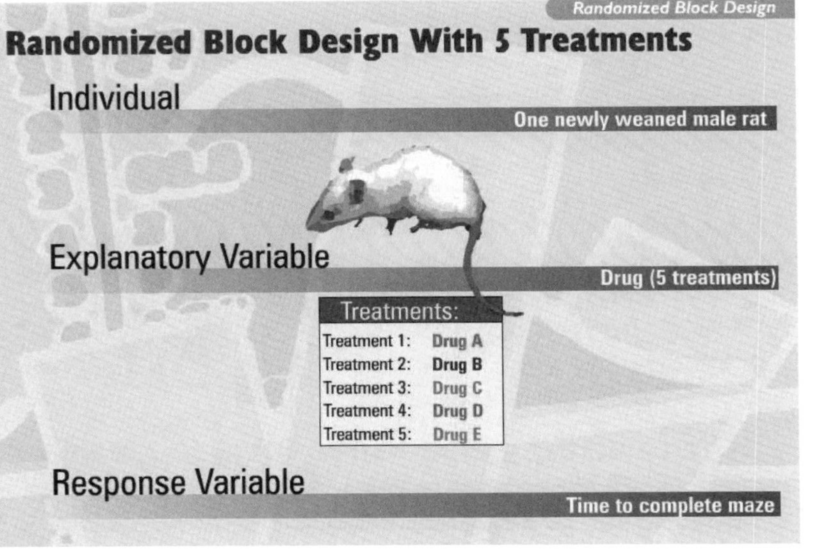


5-20

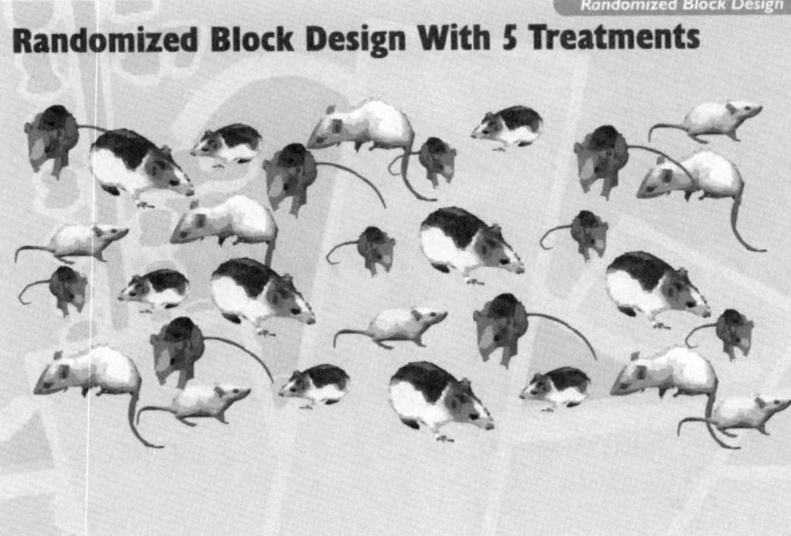

5-21

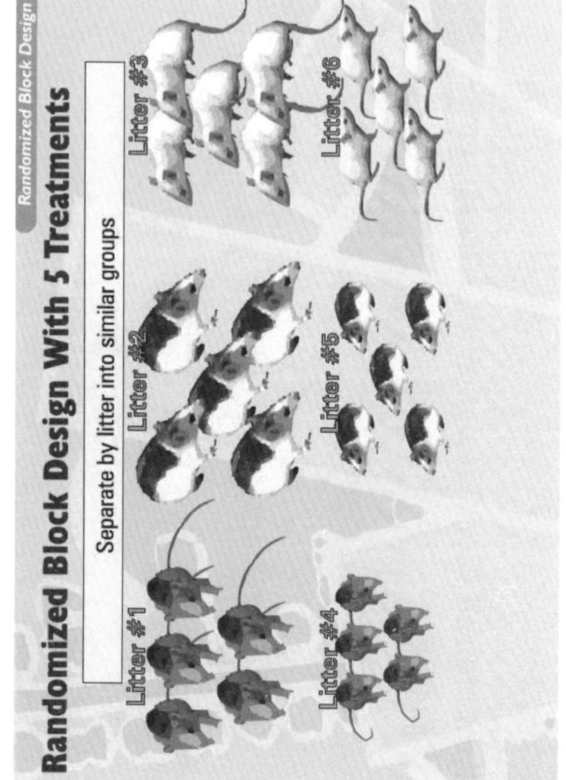

Randomized Block Design
Randomized Block Design With 5 Treatments
Separate by litter into similar groups
Litter #1
Litter #2
Litter #3
Litter #4
Litter #5
Litter #6

5-22

Randomized Block Design
Randomized Block Design With 5 Treatments
Randomly assign treatments (drugs) within each block (litter)
Litter #1
Litter #2
Litter #3
Litter #4
Litter #5
Litter #6

5-23

Randomized Block Design
Randomized Block Design With 5 Treatments
Comparing five drugs fulfills principle # 1 (Comparison)
Litter #1
Litter #2
Litter #3
Litter #4
Litter #5
Litter #6

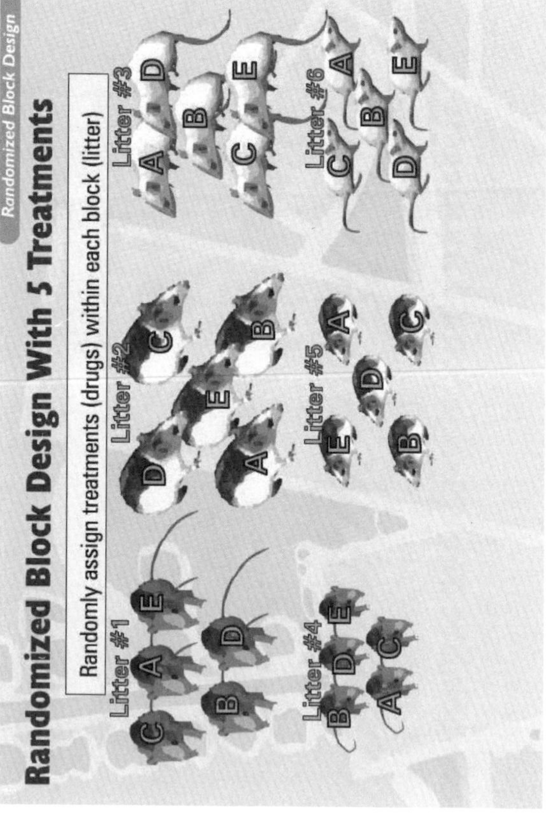

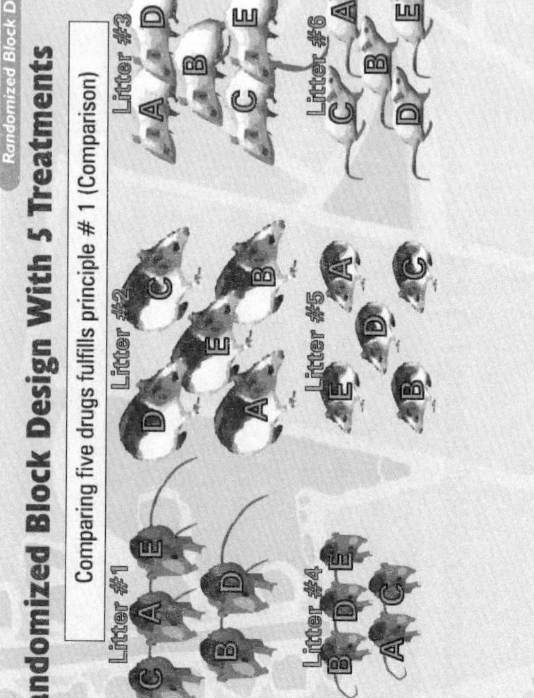

5-24

Randomized Block Design
Randomized Block Design With 5 Treatments
Randomly assigning drugs fulfills principle # 2 (Randomization)
Litter #1
Litter #2
Litter #3
Litter #4
Litter #5
Litter #6

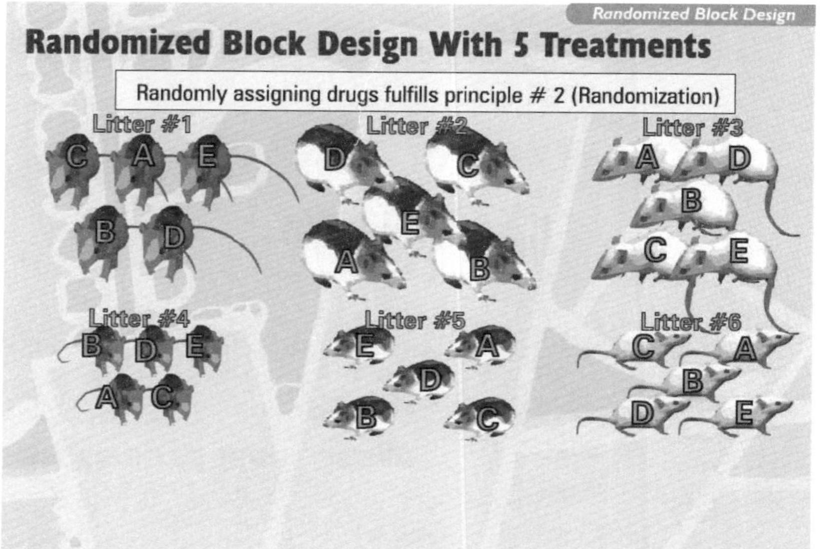

5-25

*Randomized Block Design*

## Randomized Block Design With 5 Treatments

Using six blocks or litters fulfills principle # 3 (Replication)

Litter #1: C A E B D

Litter #2: D C E A B

Litter #3: A D B C E

Litter #4: B D E A C

Litter #5: E A D B C

Litter #6: C A B D E

5-26

*Randomized Block Design*

## Outline of Randomized Block Design: 5 Treatments

**RBD follows the principles of a good experimental design**

| Replication | Randomization | Comparison |
|---|---|---|
| Litter 1 | Rat 2, Rat 4, Rat 1, Rat 5, Rat 3 | Drug A, Drug B, Drug C, Drug D, Drug E |
| Litter 2 | Rat 4, Rat 3, Rat 5, Rat 1, Rat 2 | Drug A, Drug B, Drug C, Drug D, Drug E |
| Litter 3 | Rat 1, Rat 4, Rat 2, Rat 3, Rat 5 | Drug A, Drug B, Drug C, Drug D, Drug E |
| Litter 4 | Rat 2, Rat 4, Rat 5, Rat 1, Rat 3 | Drug A, Drug B, Drug C, Drug D, Drug E |
| Litter 5 | Rat 5, Rat 1, Rat 4, Rat 2, Rat 3 | Drug A, Drug B, Drug C, Drug D, Drug E |
| Litter 6 | Rat 3, Rat 1, Rat 4, Rat 2, Rat 5 | Drug A, Drug B, Drug C, Drug D, Drug E |

Rats

**Compare Responses**

Test for Statistical Significance

5-27

*Randomized Block Design*

## Matched Pairs

- Special case of randomized block designs
- Block: Pair of individuals or pair of measurements
- Explanatory variable: two treatments
- Examples
  - Twins: each receiving a treatment
  - Two treatments on each individual
  - Measurements before and after treatment on each individual

**Three Principles of Experiments:**

1. **Randomly** assign the two treatments to the two individuals within each pair (block) ***OR*** **randomize** the order of applying the treatments to each individual.
2. **Replication** equals the number of pairs.
3. **Compare** the two treatments. Each pair serves as its own **control**.

5-28

*Randomized Block Design*

## Dieting Example--Paired Individuals

**Dieting with exercise and dieting without exercise is compared using twenty sets of identical twins.**

- Explanatory Variable: Whether dieting includes exercise
- Response Variable: Cholesterol level
- Block: A pair of identical twins
- **Comparison**: two treatments
- **Randomization**: randomly select one twin to diet with exercise; the other to diet without.
- **Replication**: 20 pairs of identical twins

5-29

Randomized Block Design

## Pepsi Challenge Example--Paired Measurements

**The Pepsi Cola Company wanted to demonstrate that people prefer Pepsi to Coca-Cola in a side-by-side experiment.**

- Explanatory Variable: Type of cola
- Response Variable: Whether cola is "*preferred*" or "*not preferred*"
- Block: The pair of ratings for the two colas by each subject
- **Comparison**: Two types of cola
- **Randomization**: Randomize the cola tasting order for each subject. (Subjects assumed to be randomly selected.)
- **Replication**: Forty subjects

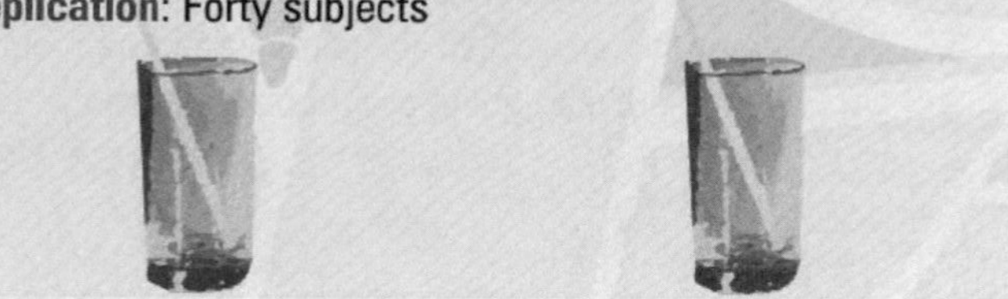

5-30

Randomized Block Design

## Pepsi Challenge Example--Paired Measurements

**Conclusions:**

- Pepsi concluded that the difference in the number of subjects preferring Pepsi compared to those preferring Coca-Cola was large enough to be **statistically significant**.
- Each glass with Pepsi was marked with a letter 'M'; each glass with Coca-Cola was marked with a letter 'Q'. Coca-Cola concluded that there was a preference for the letter 'M' over the letter 'Q' and that taste was not a factor. Preference of soda was **confounded** with letter preference.

M Q

5-31

RBD vs. CRD

## Benefits of RBD Compared to CRD

**Individuals: 20 young rats (4 litters, 5 rats per litter)**

- Treatments: Five different diets.
- Response Variable: Weight gain after 2 weeks.
- Lurking Variable: Size/genetics of the rat (potentially correlated with weight gain)

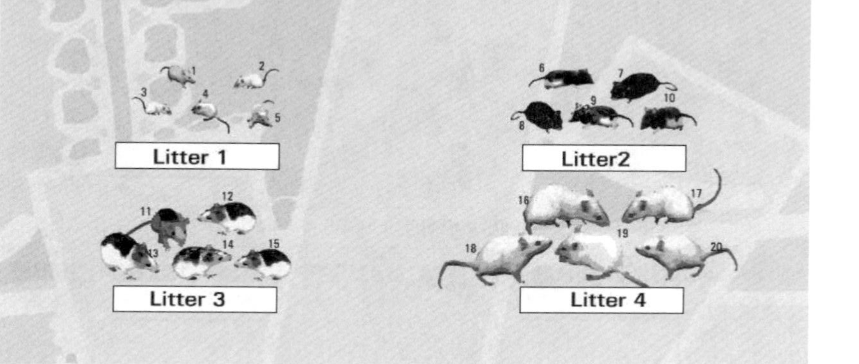


5-32

RBD vs. CRD

## Benefits of RBD Compared to CRD

**Individuals: 20 young rats (4 litters, 5 rats per litter)**

- Treatments: Five different diets.
- Response Variable: Weight gain after 2 weeks.
- Lurking Variable: Size/genetics of the rat (potentially correlated with weight gain)

**Completely Randomized Design**

One possible randomization

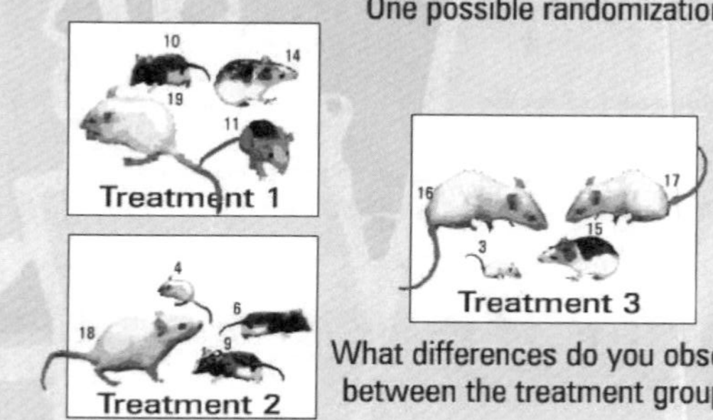


What differences do you observe between the treatment groups?

5-33

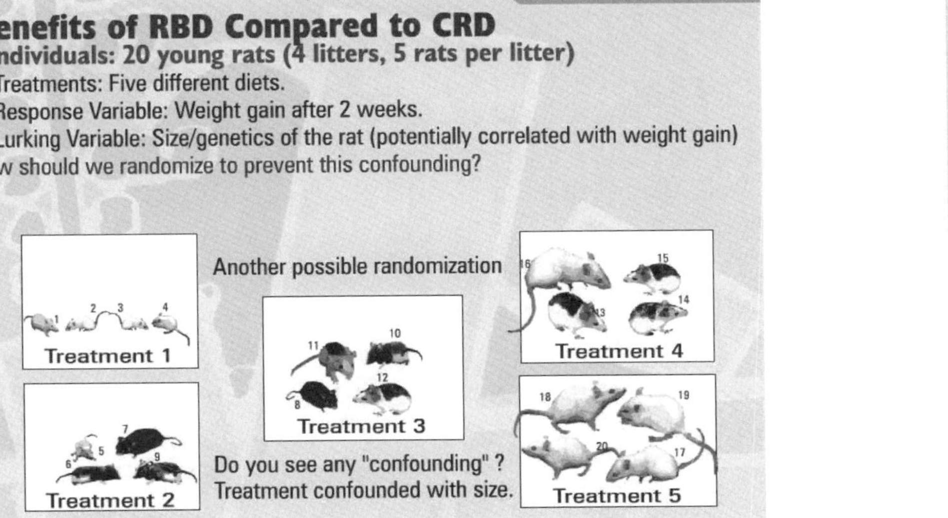


5-34

RBD vs. CRD

## Benefits of RBD Compared to CRD

**Individuals: 20 young rats (4 litters, 5 rats per litter)**

- Treatments: Five different diets.
- Response Variable: Weight gain after 2 weeks.
- Lurking Variable: Size/genetics of the rat (potentially correlated with weight gain)

How should we randomize to prevent this confounding? Randomly assign one rat from each litter to each treatment.

What design does this randomization? **Randomized Block Design**

Treatment 1 · Treatment 2 · Treatment 3 · Treatment 4 · Treatment 5

5-35

RBD vs. CRD

## Benefits of RBD Compared to CRD

**When is a completely randomized design ok?**

When the individuals are similar.

**These rats are similar with respect to size/genetics.**

**When is a randomized block design recommended?**

When the individuals are similar within a block, but very different from block to block.

Litter 1 · Litter2 · Litter 3 · Litter 4

**Rat size is similar within litters, but different between litters.**

5-36

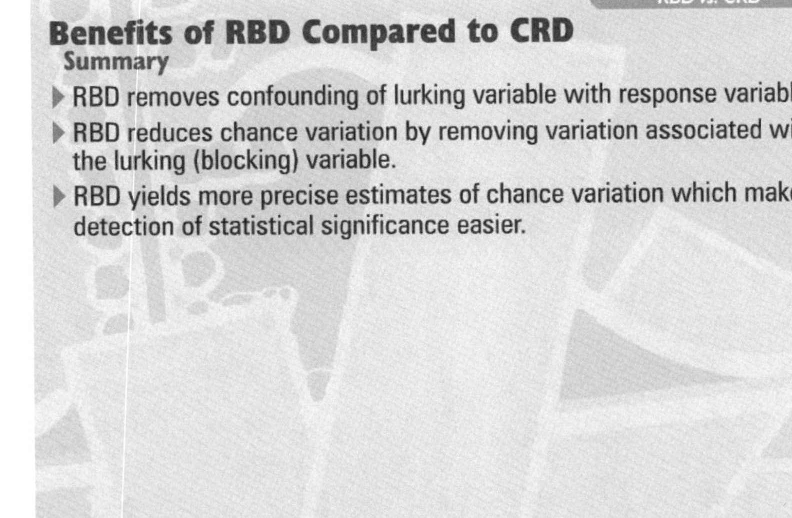

5-37

## Vocabulary

Block
Control or Comparison
Randomization
Replication
Completely Randomized Design
Randomized Block Design
Matched Pairs
Double Blind Technique
Observational Study
Placebo Effect

6-1

6-2

## Lesson Objectives

1. Explain why we organize and summarize data.
2. Discuss how the type of data (categorical or quantitative) determines how we organize and summarize data.
3. Display categorical data with a table, a bar graph or pie chart.
4. Display quantitative data with a dotplot and a histogram.
5. Describe shape, center and spread as it relates to a histogram.
6. Contrast bar charts and histograms.
7. Display quantitative data with a stemplot.

6-3

Why Organize and Summarize Data

## Introduction to Chapter 1

Basic Practice of Statistics Chapter 1

6-4

Why Organize and Summarize Data

**These data were collected to predict graduating GPA's of incoming freshmen at a large university.**

**What do the data tell us about:** the distribution of ACT scores? their relationship with high school GPA? with graduating GPA?

**Can't determine without organizing, summarizing and graphing data.**

47 College Graduates

| STDNT NO. | College GPA | HS GPA | ACT ENG | ACT MATH | ACT SS | ACT NS | ACT TOTAL | AGE | MARITAL STATUS | SEX |
|---|---|---|---|---|---|---|---|---|---|---|
| 1 | 3.13 | 3.19 | 19 | 33 | 21 | 30 | 26 | 24 | 2 | 1 |
| 2 | 3.05 | 3.68 | 27 | 25 | 28 | 24 | 26 | 24 | 1 | 0 |
| 3 | 2.73 | 3.05 | 19 | 21 | 10 | 25 | 19 | 22 | 1 | 0 |
| 4 | 3.55 | 3.33 | 24 | 31 | 28 | 31 | 29 | 26 | 1 | 0 |
| 5 | 2.79 | 3.72 | 23 | 30 | 30 | 28 | 28 | 25 | 2 | 0 |
| 6 | 3.76 | 3.65 | 22 | 25 | 28 | 30 | 26 | 23 | 1 | 1 |
| 7 | 3.22 | 3.75 | 28 | 28 | 30 | 28 | 29 | 21 | 2 | 0 |
| 8 | 3.76 | 3.74 | 24 | 27 | 27 | 30 | 27 | 31 | 2 | 1 |
| 9 | 3.89 | 4.00 | 30 | 31 | 26 | 31 | 30 | 22 | 2 | 0 |
| 10 | 2.95 | 3.02 | 19 | 21 | 10 | 20 | 18 | 25 | 2 | 1 |
| ...... | ...... | ...... | ...... | ...... | ...... | ...... | ...... | ...... | ...... | ...... |
| ...... | ...... | ...... | ...... | ...... | ...... | ...... | ...... | ...... | ...... | ...... |
| ...... | ...... | ...... | ...... | ...... | ...... | ...... | ...... | ...... | ...... | ...... |
| 44 | 2.91 | 2.30 | 21 | 26 | 24 | 29 | 25 | 26 | 1 | 1 |
| 45 | 3.16 | 3.31 | 26 | 28 | 19 | 31 | 26 | 22 | 1 | 0 |
| 46 | 2.93 | 2.67 | 17 | 22 | 12 | 25 | 19 | 24 | 1 | 1 |
| 47 | 3.90 | 3.51 | 21 | 26 | 24 | 33 | 26 | 24 | 1 | 1 |

6-5

Terms and Definitions

# Individuals and Variables

Basic Practice of Statistics Chapter 1

6-6

Terms and Definitions

## Definitions

**Individual** An object about which data are collected.

**Examples** A person (often called a subject), an animal, a classroom, a plot of ground, etc.

**Variable** A characteristic of an individual that is of interest to the researcher. Takes on different values for different individuals.

**Examples** Height, weight, race, gender, etc.

6-7

Terms and Definitions

## Definitions

**Quantitative Variable** A variable with numeric values that have meaning and for which arithmetic operations such as adding and averaging make sense.

**Examples** Height, weight, income, heart rate, etc.

**Categorical Variable (or Qualitative Variable)** A variable with word descriptors that reflect the classifications or categories to which an individual belongs.

**Examples** Race, gender, marital status, occupation, etc.

6-8

Terms and Definitions

## Definitions

**Measurement** The value of a variable obtained and recorded on an individual.

**Examples** 145 recorded as a person's weight; 65 recorded as the height of a tree; dark blue recorded as the color of a computer monitor screen saver.

**Data** A set of measurements made on a group of individuals.

**Examples** Blood pressures of 20 hospital patients; ages for 45 retirees at a senior citizens center; race of 16 immigrants applying for citizenship.

6-9

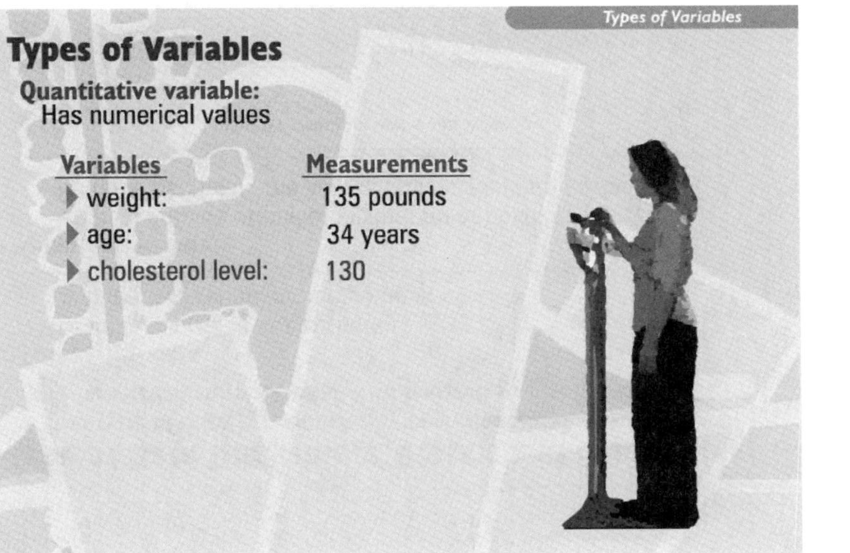


6-10

*Types of Variables*

## Types of Variables

**Categorical / Qualitative variable:**
Has words describing categories.

| Variables | Measurements |
|---|---|
| ▸ gender: | male |
| ▸ race: | Caucasian |
| ▸ opinion on question: | agree |

Do you agree or disagree with the current health plans?

6-11

*Relevant Questions*

## Questions to Ask about Data Sets

1. **Who?** What individuals do the data describe? **How many** individuals are described?
2. **What?** What variables are recorded on the individuals? How are these variables defined? In what unit of measure is each variable recorded?
3. **Why?** What question are these data supposed to answer? Do these data answer that question? Do we want to draw conclusions about individuals other than these on which the data were collected?

6-12

*Relevant Questions*

## Questions to Ask about Data Sets

1. **Who?** These data were collected on 47 college graduates.
2. **What?** High school GPA, ACT scores, marital status, gender, and graduating GPA were recorded.
3. **Why?** These data were collected to determine whether high school GPA and or ACT scores could be used to predict graduating GPA.

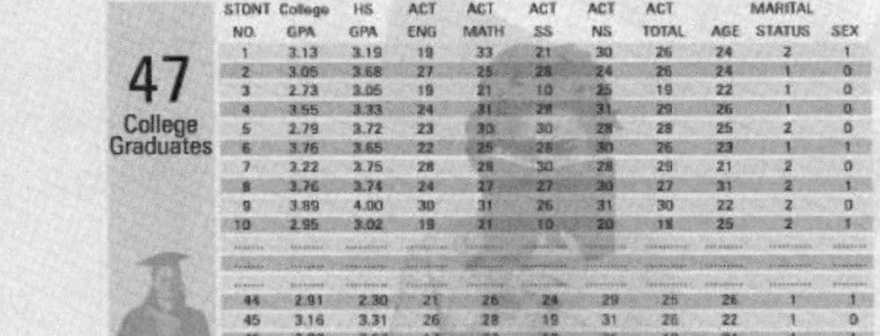


| STDNT NO. | College GPA | HS GPA | ACT ENG | ACT MATH | ACT SS | ACT NS | ACT TOTAL | AGE | MARITAL STATUS | SEX |
|---|---|---|---|---|---|---|---|---|---|---|
| 1 | 3.13 | 3.19 | 19 | 33 | 21 | 30 | 26 | 24 | 2 | 1 |
| 2 | 3.05 | 3.68 | 27 | 25 | 28 | 24 | 26 | 24 | 1 | 0 |
| 3 | 2.73 | 3.05 | 19 | 21 | 10 | 25 | 19 | 22 | 1 | 0 |
| 4 | 3.55 | 3.33 | 24 | 31 | 28 | 31 | 29 | 26 | 1 | 0 |
| 5 | 2.79 | 3.72 | 23 | 30 | 30 | 28 | 28 | 25 | 2 | 0 |
| 6 | 3.76 | 3.65 | 22 | 25 | 28 | 30 | 26 | 23 | 1 | 1 |
| 7 | 3.22 | 3.75 | 28 | 28 | 30 | 28 | 29 | 21 | 2 | 0 |
| 8 | 3.76 | 3.74 | 24 | 27 | 27 | 30 | 27 | 31 | 2 | 1 |
| 9 | 3.89 | 4.00 | 30 | 31 | 26 | 31 | 30 | 22 | 2 | 0 |
| 10 | 2.95 | 3.02 | 19 | 21 | 10 | 20 | 18 | 25 | 2 | 1 |
| 44 | 2.91 | 2.30 | 21 | 26 | 24 | 29 | 25 | 26 | 1 | 1 |
| 45 | 3.16 | 3.31 | 26 | 28 | 19 | 31 | 26 | 22 | 1 | 0 |
| 46 | 2.93 | 2.67 | 17 | 22 | 12 | 25 | 19 | 24 | 1 | 1 |
| 47 | 3.90 | 3.51 | 21 | 26 | 24 | 33 | 26 | 24 | 1 | 1 |

6-13

*Categorical and Quantitative Data*

## Type of Data Determines Graphs and Summaries

Note: All graphs and summaries will be described later.

**Categorical data**
Graphs: bar graph or pie chart
Summaries: counts or percentages

**Quantitative data**
Graphs: dotplot, stemplot, histogram or boxplot
Summaries: mean, median, quartiles, standard deviation, etc.

6-14

*Categorical and Quantitative Data*

## Type of Data Determines Graphs and Summaries

**What type of data is produced by each question? What graphs and numerical summaries should be used to display the data?**

**Categorical data**
Graphs: bar graph or pie chart
Summaries: counts or percentages

**Quantitative data**
Graphs: dotplot, stemplot, histogram or boxplot
Summaries: mean, median, quartiles, standard deviation, etc.

1. Have you ever been told you have diabetes (or sugar diabetes)?
a. yes
b. no

6-15

*Categorical and Quantitative Data*

## Type of Data Determines Graphs and Summaries

**What type of data is produced by each question? What graphs and numerical summaries should be used to display the data?**

**Categorical data**
Graphs: bar graph or pie chart
Summaries: counts or percentages

**Quantitative data**
Graphs: dotplot, stemplot, histogram or boxplot
Summaries: mean, median, quartiles, standard deviation, etc.

2. What was your mother's age when you were born?
________

6-16

*Categorical and Quantitative Data*

## Type of Data Determines Graphs and Summaries

**What type of data is produced by each question? What graphs and numerical summaries should be used to display the data?**

**Categorical data**
Graphs: bar graph or pie chart
Summaries: counts or percentages

**Quantitative data**
Graphs: dotplot, stemplot, histogram or boxplot
Summaries: mean, median, quartiles, standard deviation, etc.

3. Are you now taking medicine for high blood pressure?
a. yes
b. no

6-17

*Categorical and Quantitative Data*

## Type of Data Determines Graphs and Summaries

**What type of data is produced by each question? What graphs and numerical summaries should be used to display the data?**

**Categorical data**
Graphs: bar graph or pie chart
Summaries: counts or percentages

**Quantitative data**
Graphs: dotplot, stemplot, histogram or boxplot
Summaries: mean, median, quartiles, standard deviation, etc.

4. What is your resting pulse rate?

_________ beats per minute

6-18

*Categorical and Quantitative Data*

## Type of Data Determines Graphs and Summaries

**What type of data is produced by each question? What graphs and numerical summaries should be used to display the data?**

**Categorical data**
Graphs: bar graph or pie chart
Summaries: counts or percentages

**Quantitative data**
Graphs: dotplot, stemplot, histogram or boxplot
Summaries: mean, median, quartiles, standard deviation, etc.

5. Did either of your natural parents die of a heart attack before age 60? (If your parents are younger than 60, mark no.)
a. yes, one of them
b. yes, both of them
c. no
d. not sure

6-19

*Displaying Categorical Data*

## Categorical Variables: Pie Charts and Bar Graphs

Basic Practice of Statistics Chapter 1

5. Did either of your natural parents die of a heart attack before age 60? (If your parents are younger than 60, mark no.)
a. yes, one of them
b. yes, both of them
c. no
d. not sure

6-20

*Displaying Categorical Data*

## Exploratory Data Analysis

1. Determine type of each variable.
2. For each variable, graph data and interpret graph.
3. For each variable, add numerical summaries.
4. Examine relationships among variables.

5. Did either of your natural parents die of a heart attack before age 60? (If your parents are younger than 60, mark no.)
a. yes, one of them
b. yes, both of them
c. no
d. not sure

6-21

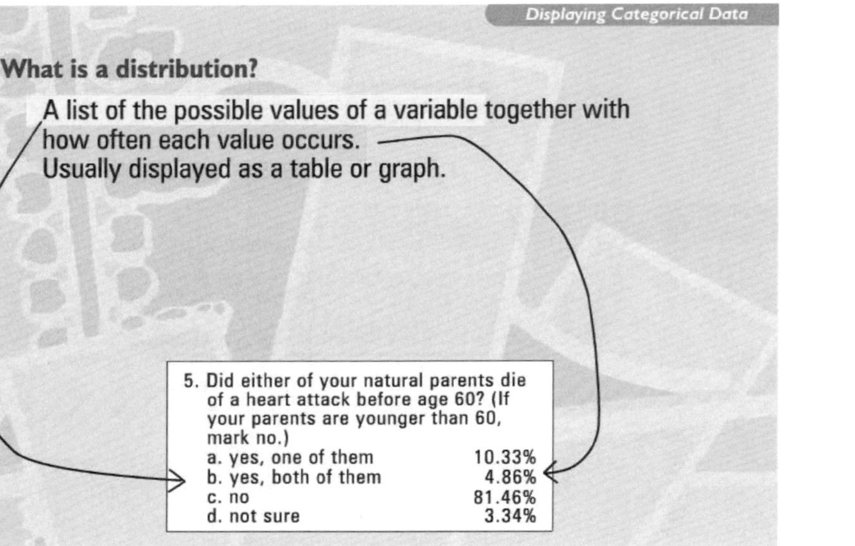


6-22

Displaying Categorical Data

## How can we display categorical data? In a table

5. Did either of your natural parents die of a heart attack before age 60? (If your parents are younger than 60, mark no.)
   a. yes, one of them 10.33%
   b. yes, both of them 4.86%
   c. no 81.46%
   d. not sure 3.34%

| Category | Count | Percentage (%) |
|---|---|---|
| **a. yes, one of them** | **34** | **10.33%** |
| **b. yes, both of them** | **16** | **4.86%** |
| **c. no** | **268** | **81.46%** |
| **d. not sure** | **11** | **3.34%** |
| Total | 329 | 99.99 |

Note 1: Usually only counts or percentages are given--both are not necessary.
Note 2: Percentages don't sum to 100% due to round-off error.

6-23

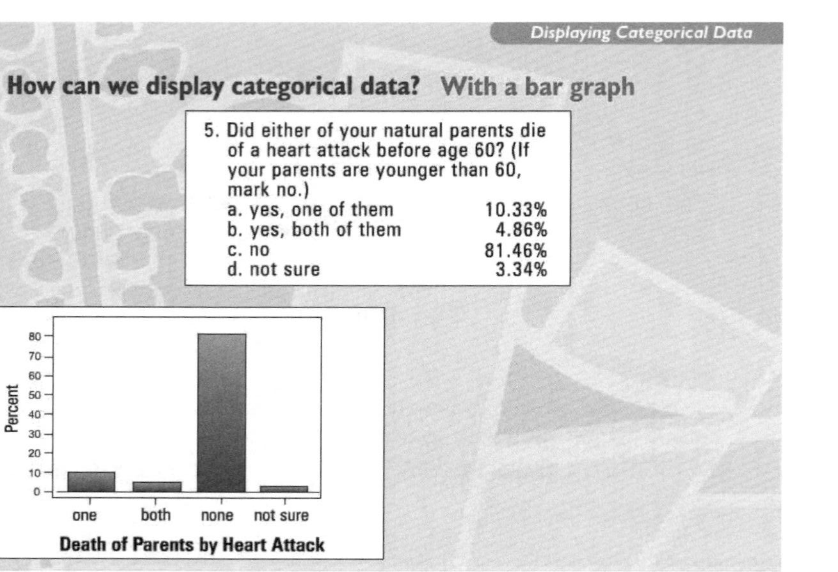


6-24

Displaying Categorical Data

## How can we display categorical data? With a pie chart

5. Did either of your natural parents die of a heart attack before age 60? (If your parents are younger than 60, mark no.)
   a. yes, one of them 10.33%
   b. yes, both of them 4.86%
   c. no 81.46%
   d. not sure 3.34%

Key
One
Both
None
Not Sure

6-25



## Which is better--Bar Graphs or Pie Charts?

A bar graph is nearly always better than a pie chart.

- Comparing bars in a bar chart is easier than comparing wedges in a pie chart.
- Pie charts display only distributions whereas bar graphs can be used for other types of categorical data.

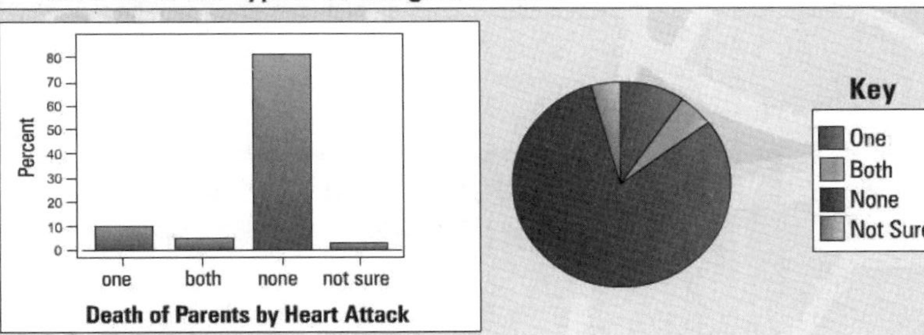


6-26



# Quantitative Variables: Histograms

Basic Practice of Statistics Chapter 1

6-27



**How can we display quantitative data?** With a dotplot

Transform data into dots on the real number line.

Stack repeated points.

4. What is your resting pulse rate?

_______ beats per minute

**Resting pulse rate from a simple random sample of 92 persons**

| | | | | | | | | | |
|---|---|---|---|---|---|---|---|---|---|
| 64 | 58 | 62 | 66 | 64 | 74 | 84 | 68 | 62 | 76 |
| 90 | 80 | 92 | 68 | 60 | 62 | 66 | 70 | 68 | 72 |
| 70 | 74 | 66 | 70 | 96 | 62 | 78 | 82 | 100 | 68 |
| 96 | 78 | 88 | 62 | 80 | 62 | 60 | 72 | 62 | 76 |
| 68 | 54 | 74 | 74 | 68 | 72 | 68 | 82 | 64 | 58 |
| 54 | 70 | 62 | 48 | 76 | 88 | 70 | 90 | 78 | 70 |
| 90 | 92 | 60 | 72 | 68 | 84 | 74 | 68 | 84 | 61 |
| 64 | 94 | 60 | 72 | 58 | 88 | 66 | 84 | 62 | 66 |
| 80 | 78 | 68 | 72 | 82 | 76 | 87 | 90 | 78 | 68 |
| 86 | 76 | | | | | | | | |

50 60 70 80 90 100

6-28



**How can we display quantitative data?** With a histogram

**General Rules:**

1. Choose classes of equal width so each individual falls in exactly one class.
2. Count number of individuals in each class.
3. Display number of individuals in each class with a vertical bar.

6-29

*Quantitative Data: Histograms*

## How can we display quantitative data? With a histogram

**Example:**

1. Choose a class width of 5.0 and starting point for first class of 45.
2. Count number of individuals in each class.
3. Display number of individuals in each class with a vertical bar.

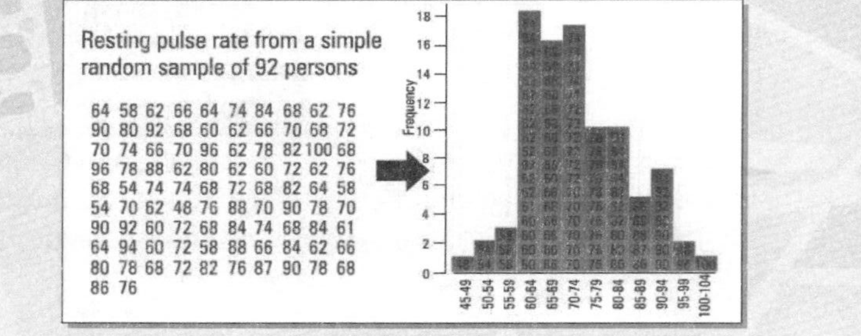


6-30

*Quantitative Data: Histograms*

## How can we display quantitative data? With a histogram

**Another version:**

1. Choose class width of 10 and starting point of 40.
2. Count number of individuals in each class.
3. Display number of individuals in each class with a vertical bar.

Resting pulse rate from a simple random sample of 92 persons

64 58 62 66 64 74 84 68 62 76
90 80 92 68 60 62 66 70 68 72
70 74 66 70 96 62 78 82 100 68
96 78 88 62 80 62 60 72 62 76
68 54 74 74 68 72 68 82 64 58
54 70 62 48 76 88 70 90 78 70
90 92 60 72 68 84 74 68 84 61
64 94 60 72 58 88 66 84 62 66
80 78 68 72 82 76 87 90 78 68
86 76

**Horizontal Axis**
Scaled according to measurements.

**Vertical Axis**
Frequency or Percent (not both)

Frequency: 35, 30, 25, 20, 15, 10, 5, 0
Bars: 1, 5, 34, 27, 15, 9, 1
Beats/Min: 40, 50, 60, 70, 80, 90, 100, 110

6-31

*Histogram Applet*

## Effect of Interval Size on Histogram

Histogram of Exam Scores: Varying Interval Width

Number of Students: 40, 30, 20, 10, 0
Exam Scores in Percents: 0, 20, 40, 60, 80, 100
Set Interval Size: 4
1, 10, 20

Move the green circle on the bottom bar to see how the appearance of the histogram is affected by the interval width.

6-32

Never use bar chart for quantitative data

*Compare Bar charts and Histograms*

## Distinctions Between Bar Charts & Histograms

| Bar Chart | Histogram |
|---|---|
| 5. Did either of your natural parents die of a heart attack before age 60? (If your parents are younger than 60, mark no.)<br>a. yes, one of them 10.33%<br>b. yes, both of them 4.86%<br>c. no 81.46%<br>d. not sure 3.34% | 3. What is your resting pulse rate? ______ beats per minute4 |
| Percent; one, both, none, not sure<br>Death of Parents by Heart Attack | Percent; 30 40 50 60 70 80 90 100 110 120<br>Pulse Rate |

- Horizontal axis is categorical.
- Shape, center, and spread have no meaning in a bar chart.
- Bars are separated by spaces.

- Horizontal axis is quantitative.
- Histograms are described by shape, center, and spread.
- Bars are usually adjacent.

6-33

Shape / Center / Spread / Outliers

# Interpreting Histograms

Basic Practice of Statistics Chapter 1

6-34

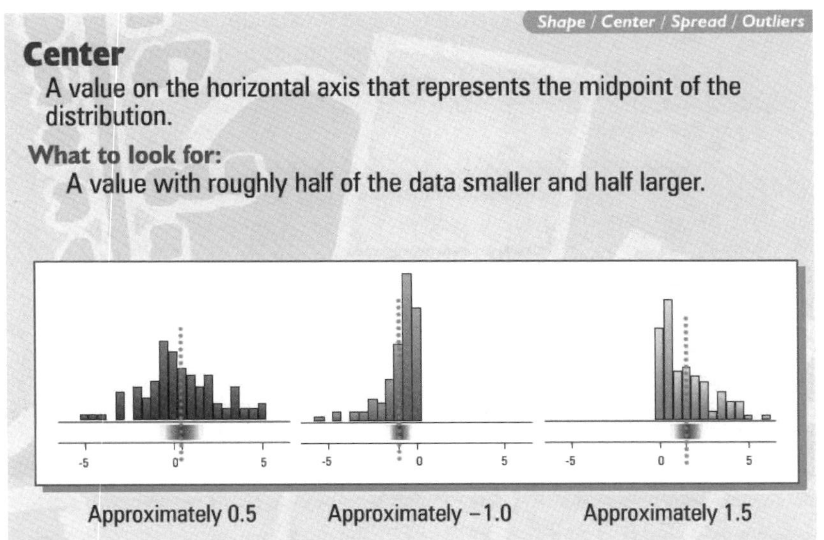


6-35

| Name of shape | Description | Example |
|---|---|---|
| Bell-shaped | Quite symmetric<br>Central peak | |
| Right Skewed | Long tail on right<br>Peak toward left | |
| Left Skewed | Long tail on left<br>Peak toward right | |
| Bimodal | Somewhat symmetric<br>Two peaks | |
| Flat or uniform | Quite symmetric<br>No obvious peaks or valleys | |

6-36

Shape / Center / Spread / Outliers

## Center

A value on the horizontal axis that represents the midpoint of the distribution.

**What to look for:**

A value with roughly half of the data smaller and half larger.

| Approximately 0.5 | Approximately −1.0 | Approximately 1.5 |
|---|---|---|

6-37



## Spread

The variability of data in a distribution; describes how tightly grouped or widely dispersed the data are around the center. Most useful for comparing two distributions.

**What to look for:**

The minimum (Min) and maximum (Max) values.

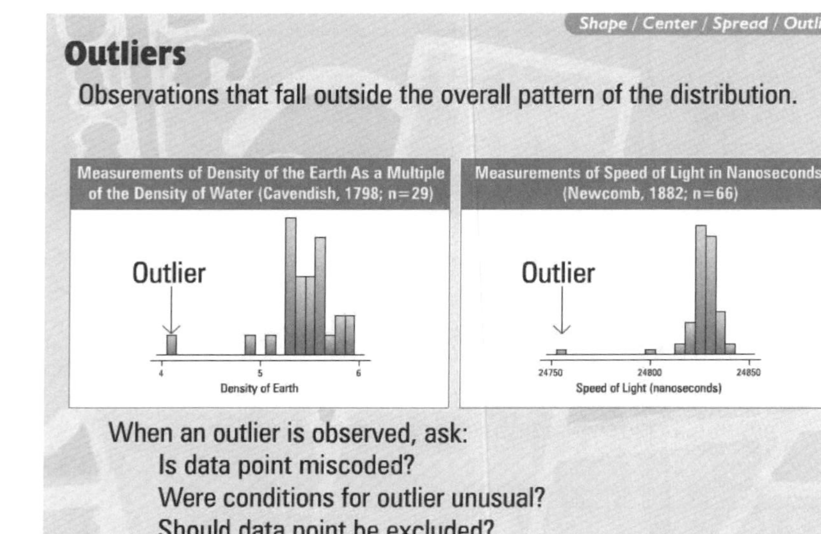


6-38



## Outliers

Observations that fall outside the overall pattern of the distribution.

Measurements of Density of the Earth As a Multiple of the Density of Water (Cavendish, 1798; n=29)

Outlier

Density of Earth

Measurements of Speed of Light in Nanoseconds (Newcomb, 1882; n=66)

Outlier

Speed of Light (nanoseconds)

When an outlier is observed, ask:

- Is data point miscoded?
- Were conditions for outlier unusual?
- Should data point be excluded?

6-39



## Identify Shape, Estimate Center and Spread, Check for Outliers for the Following Distribution

**Hours spent watching TV in a week for 120 individuals (ages 12 -95)**

| | | | | | |
|---|---|---|---|---|---|
| Shape: | Bell-shaped | Left skewed | (Right skewed) | Uniform | |
| Center: | 10 | (20) | 30 | 40 | 50 |
| Spread: | 0 to 20 | 20 to 57 | 10 to 50 | (0 to 57) | |
| Outliers: | yes | (no) | | | |

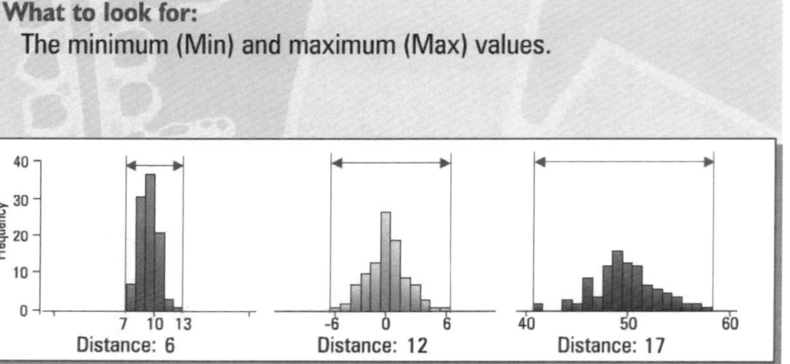


6-40



## Identify Shape, Estimate Center and Spread, Check for Outliers for the Following Distribution

**Quiz scores for 445 students in an introductory statistics class**

| | | | | | |
|---|---|---|---|---|---|
| Shape: | Bell-shaped | (Left skewed) | Right skewed | Uniform | |
| Center: | 5 | 7 | 9 | (11) | 13 |
| Spread: | 2 to 5 | 5 to 10 | 7 to 15 | (2 to 15) | |
| Outliers: | A yes | B (no) | | | |

Quiz Score

6-41

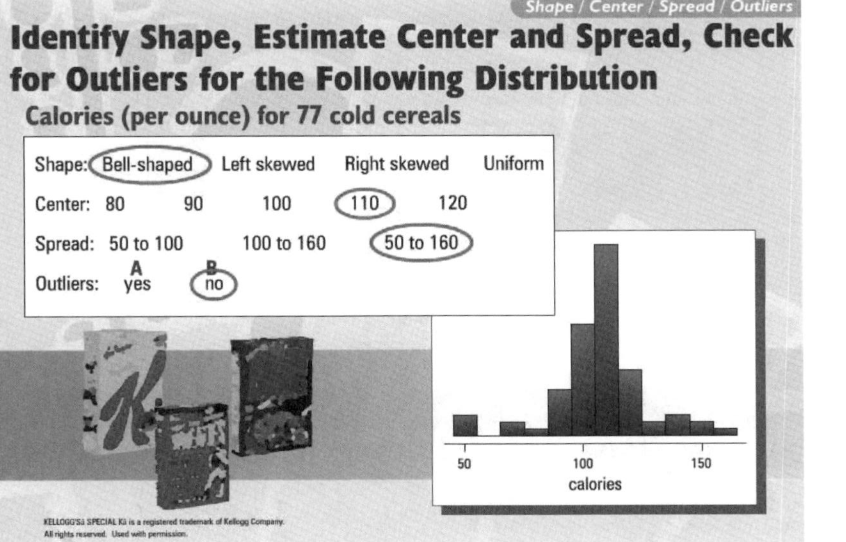


6-42

*Displaying Quantitative Data: Stemplo*

# Quantitative Variables: Stemplots

**Basic Practice of Statistics Chapter 1**

6-43

*Displaying Quantitative Data: Stemplo*

**How can we display quantitative data?** **With a stemplot**
First determine stems and leaves.

## Stems and leaves

Each number in the data set consists of two pieces:
1. A stem (the tens place)
2. A leaf (the ones place)

| Pulse Rate | Stem | Leaves |
|---|---|---|
| 62<br>64<br>68 | 6 | 2 4 8 |

6-44

*Displaying Quantitative Data: Stemplo*

**How can we display quantitative data?**
First determine stems and leaves.
Then, arrange stems on the left and leaves on the right.

**Resting pulse rate from a simple random sample of 92 persons**

| | | | | | | | | | | | | | | | | | | |
|---|---|---|---|---|---|---|---|---|---|---|---|---|---|---|---|---|---|---|
| 64 | 58 | 62 | 66 | 64 | 74 | 84 | 68 | 62 | 76 | 90 | 80 | 92 | 68 | 60 | 62 | 66 | 70 | 68 |
| 72 | 70 | 74 | 66 | 70 | 96 | 62 | 78 | 82 | 100 | 68 | 96 | 78 | 88 | 62 | 80 | 62 | 60 | 72 |
| 62 | 76 | 68 | 54 | 74 | 74 | 68 | 72 | 68 | 82 | 64 | 58 | 54 | 70 | 62 | 48 | 76 | 88 | 70 |
| 90 | 78 | 70 | 90 | 92 | 60 | 72 | 68 | 84 | 74 | 68 | 84 | 61 | 64 | 94 | 60 | 72 | 58 | 88 |
| 66 | 84 | 62 | 66 | 80 | 78 | 68 | 72 | 82 | 76 | 87 | 90 | 78 | 68 | 86 | 76 | | | |

whole numbers    partial numbers

**Stemplot (leaf unit = 1.0)**

```
 4 | 8
 5 | 44888
 6 | 00001222222222244444666668888888888
 7 | 0000002222222444446666668888
 8 | 000222444467888
 9 | 000022466
10 | 0
```

tells every number

6-45

*Displaying Quantitative Data: Stemplo*

**How can we display quantitative data?**
First determine stems and leaves.
Then, arrange stems on the left and leaves on the right.

| Resting pulse rate from a simple random sample of 92 persons | | | | | | | | | | | | | | | | | | |
|---|---|---|---|---|---|---|---|---|---|---|---|---|---|---|---|---|---|---|
| 64 | 58 | 62 | 66 | 64 | 74 | 84 | 68 | 62 | 76 | 90 | 80 | 92 | 68 | 60 | 62 | 66 | 70 | 68 |
| 72 | 70 | 74 | 66 | 70 | 96 | 62 | 78 | 82 | 100 | 68 | 96 | 78 | 88 | 62 | 80 | 62 | 60 | 72 |
| 62 | 76 | 68 | 54 | 74 | 74 | 68 | 72 | 68 | 82 | 64 | 58 | 54 | 70 | 62 | 48 | 76 | 88 | 70 |
| 90 | 78 | 70 | 90 | 92 | 60 | 72 | 68 | 84 | 74 | 68 | 84 | 61 | 64 | 94 | 60 | 72 | 58 | 88 |
| 66 | 84 | 62 | 66 | 80 | 78 | 68 | 72 | 82 | 76 | 87 | 90 | 78 | 68 | 86 | 76 | | | |

**Another variation:**

Stemplot (leaf unit = 1.0)

```
 4|8
 5|44
 5|888
 6|0000122222222244444
 6|6666688888888888
 7|00000022222244444
 7|6666688888
 8|0002224444
 8|67888
 9|0000224
 9|66
10|0
```

6-46

*Displaying Quantitative Data: Stemplo*

**How can we display quantitative data?**
First determine stems and leaves.
Then, arrange stems on the left and leaves on the right.

**Another example:** Weights of 143 bears in pounds
74, 142, 196, 80, 128, 344, 371, 416, 29, 476, 248, . . .

```
Leaf Unit = 10

   0|223444
   0|666666777778889999
   1|00111111111222222222233333444444444444444
   1|55555555555566666677888888999
   2|00000111222334
   2|5677899
   3|00112233444
   3|556667899
   4|011334
   4|77
   5|1
```

6-47

*Compare Graphs - Quantitative*

## Comparing Dotplots, Stemplots and Histograms

Quantative

**Dotplots and Stemplots:**

```
 1    4 | 8
 3    5 | 44
 6    5 | 888
24    6 | 000012222222224444
40    6 | 6666688888888888
(17)  7 | 00000022222244444
35    7 | 6666688888
25    8 | 0002224444
15    8 | 67888
10    9 | 00002224
 3    9 | 66
 1   10 | 0          leaf unit = 1.0
```

- Work well for small data sets.
- Can easily be done by hand.

**Histograms:**

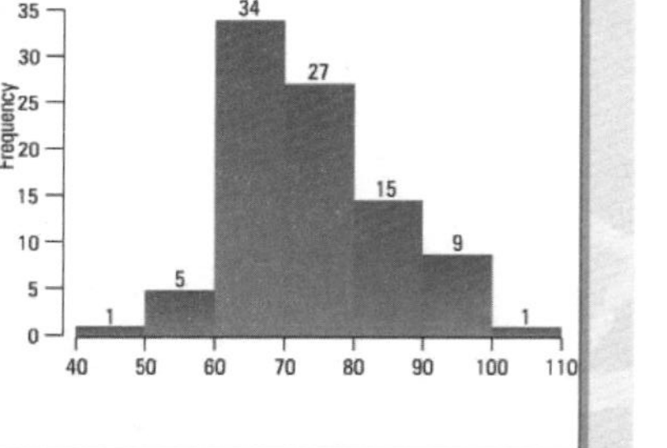


- Work well for large data sets.
- Usually require a computer.

6-48

# Vocabulary

Bar Graph
Categorical (Qualitative)Variable
Data
Distribution
Dotplot
Histogram
Individual
Measurement
Quantitative Variable
Pie Chart
Stemplot
Table
Variable
Shape
Center
Spread (Variability)
Outlier

7-1

# Chapter 2 Part I Describing Distributions with Numbers

StatTutor Lesson 07

7-2

## Lesson Objectives:

1. Give symbols for measures of center and location as well as mathematical notation.
2. Describe how to compute mean and median, both characteristics of center.
3. Connect mean to balancing point and median to point that divides area of histogram in half.
4. Determine whether the mean or the median should be selected as the measure of center.
5. Compute five-number summary and convert it to a boxplot.
6. Demonstrate relationship between a histogram and a boxplot.
7. Contrast shape, center, and spread of several different data sets using boxplots.

7-3

## Introduction to Chapter 2

Basic Practice of Statistics Chapter 2

7-4

## Numerical Summaries

Kickoff Question

**How could the center and spread of this distribution be represented numerically?**

60 70 80 90 100 110

7-5



## Numerical Summaries

**Center:** The location of data on the number line.
**Measures of Center:** Mean, Median

**Spread:** The dispersion of data around the center.
**Measures of Spread:** Range, Interquartile Range, Standard Deviation

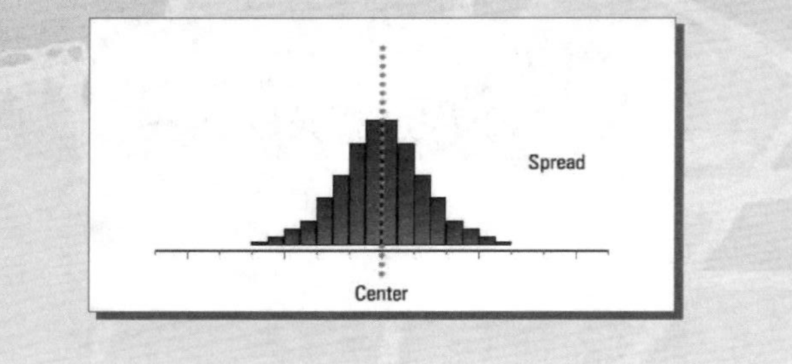


7-6



## Measuring Center: the Mean

Basic Practice of Statistics Chapter 2

7-7



## Background Information: Mathematical Notation

| Symbol | Description |
|---|---|
| $\Sigma$ | The summation sign used to represent a sum of numbers (upper case Greek letter sigma). |
| $x_1$ | The first value in a data set |
| $x_i$ | The $i^{th}$ value in a data set |
| $n$ | The number of values in a data set |
| $\sum_{i=1}^{n} x_i$ | The sum of all n values in a data set |

7-8



## Computing the Mean

**Mean: the arithmetic average**

Yearly Deaths of Occupants in Auto Accidents in the U.S.

| Year | Deaths | Year | Deaths |
|---|---|---|---|
| 1975 | 25,715 | 1988 | 25,825 |
| 1976 | 26,163 | 1989 | 25,269 |
| 1977 | 26,698 | 1990 | 24,413 |
| 1978 | 27,898 | 1991 | 22,738 |
| 1979 | 27,518 | 1992 | 21,824 |
| 1980 | 27,282 | 1993 | 22,117 |
| 1981 | 26,406 | 1994 | 22,622 |
| 1982 | 23,144 | 1995 | 23,122 |
| 1983 | 22,801 | 1996 | 23,341 |
| 1984 | 23,482 | | 541,449 |
| 1985 | 23,076 | | ÷ 22 |
| 1986 | 24,880 | | |
| 1987 | 25,115 | | = 24,611 |

$$\bar{x} = \frac{1}{n}\sum_{i=1}^{n} x_i$$

$$= \frac{541,449}{22}$$

$$= 24,611$$ Mean Deaths / Year

7-9

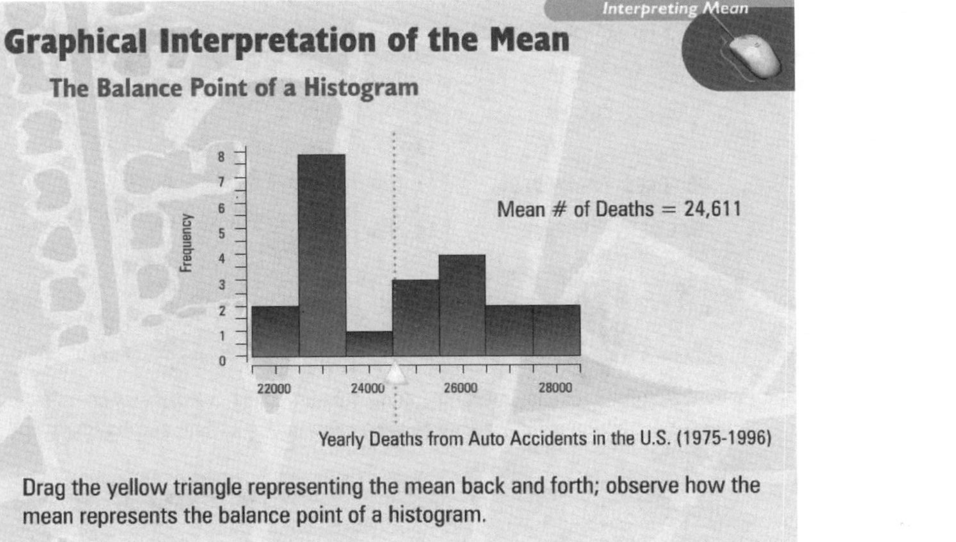


7-10

*Computing Mean, Median*

# Measuring Center: the Median

**Basic Practice of Statistics Chapter 2**

7-11

*Computing Mean, Median*

## Computing the Median (n Odd)

1. Order the data.
2. If the number of observations is odd, median equals the middle observation.

**# of Computers / 1000 Persons** (Ordered : Small to Large)

| | | |
|---|---|---|
| 201.6 | Switzerland | Five Observations |
| 214.8 | Netherlands | |
| 216.5 | United Kingdom | |
| 224.8 | New Zealand | |
| 244.1 | Sweden | |
| ⇨ 245.5 | Finland | Median |
| 252.5 | Denmark | Five Observations |
| 254.8 | Canada | |
| 259.5 | Norway | |
| 264.3 | Australia | |
| 364.7 | United States | |

$n = 11$

Source: Computer Industry Almanac, Inc.

**Median : M = 245.5**

7-12

*Computing Mean, Median*

## Computing the Median (n Even)

1. Order the data.
2. If the number of observations is even, median equals the average (mean) of two middle observations.

$n = 12$

**Batting Averages of 12 American League Teams (1998)** (Ordered : Large to Small)

| | | |
|---|---|---|
| 0.289 | Texas | Six Observations |
| 0.288 | New York | |
| 0.280 | Boston | |
| 0.276 | Seattle | |
| 0.273 | Baltimore | |
| 0.272 | Cleveland | |
| 0.271 | Chicago | Six Observations |
| 0.266 | Minnesota | |
| 0.266 | Toronto | |
| 0.264 | Detroit | |
| 0.263 | Kansas City | |
| 0.257 | Oakland | |

$$\text{Median} = \frac{(0.272 + 0.271)}{2} = 0.2715$$

7-13



## A Graphical Interpretation of The Median

Area of histogram to left of median approximately equals area to right
(The number of observations below the median equals the number above.)

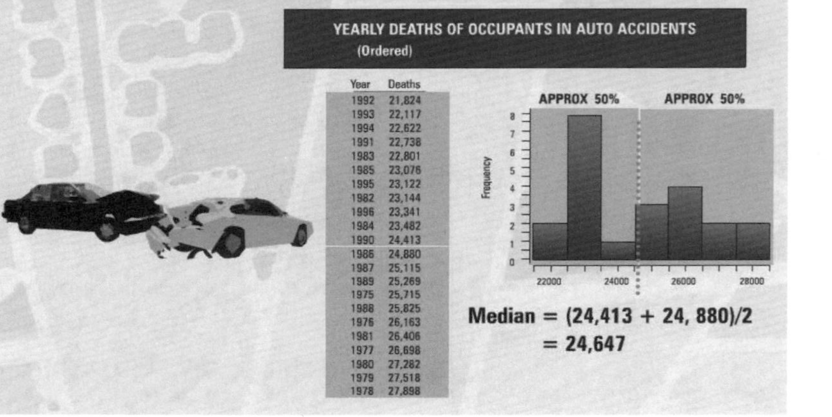


| Year | Deaths |
|---|---|
| 1992 | 21,824 |
| 1993 | 22,117 |
| 1994 | 22,622 |
| 1991 | 22,738 |
| 1983 | 22,801 |
| 1985 | 23,076 |
| 1995 | 23,122 |
| 1982 | 23,144 |
| 1996 | 23,341 |
| 1984 | 23,482 |
| 1990 | 24,413 |
| 1986 | 24,880 |
| 1987 | 25,115 |
| 1989 | 25,269 |
| 1975 | 25,715 |
| 1988 | 25,825 |
| 1976 | 26,163 |
| 1981 | 26,406 |
| 1977 | 26,698 |
| 1980 | 27,282 |
| 1979 | 27,518 |
| 1978 | 27,898 |

**Median = (24,413 + 24, 880)/2 = 24,647**

7-14



## Comparing Mean and Median

Basic Practice of Statistics Chapter 2

- either one might be called average in media
- roughly equal if histogram is roughly symmetric.
- median resistent to outliers and long tails
- mean has desirable properties for inference

1. construct histogram
2.

7-15



## Mean or Median?

? Kickoff Question

In 1993, Forbes Magazine published a list of the best small firms in terms of return on investment. Below are the firms' CEO's annual salaries (in thousands):

| | | | |
|---|---|---|---|
| 145 | 621 | 262 | 208 |
| 362 | 424 | 339 | 736 |
| 291 | 581 | 498 | 643 |
| 390 | 332 | 750 | 368 |
| 659 | 234 | 396 | 300 |
| 343 | 536 | 543 | 217 |
| 298 | 1103 | 406 | 254 |
| 862 | 204 | 206 | 250 |
| 213 | 298 | 350 | 800 |
| 726 | 370 | 536 | 291 |
| 808 | 543 | 149 | 350 |
| 242 | 198 | 213 | 296 |
| 317 | 482 | 155 | 802 |
| 200 | 282 | 573 | 388 |
| 250 | 396 | 572 | |

**Mean= $404,170**

**Median= $350,000**

**Which is a better measure of center for the CEO's annual salaries?**

7-16



## Mean vs. Median: Effect of Outliers

**Drag the blue box to see how its value affects the mean and median.**

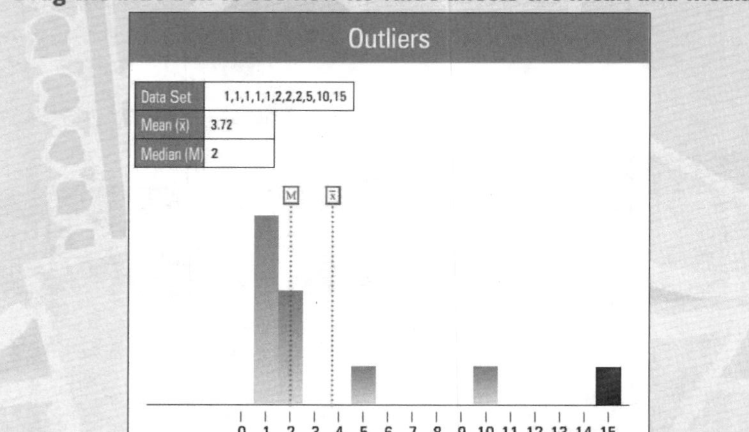

7-17



## Choosing Whether to Use the Mean or Median

**Skewed distributions:**
Median is the best measure of center; mean is affected by outliers and skewness.

**Symmetric distributions:**
Both mean and median can be used as measure of center, but the mean is preferred because of its additional mathematical properties.

7-18



**Which is a better measure of center for the CEO's annual salaries?**
**Mean or median**

| | | | |
|---|---|---|---|
| 145 | 621 | 262 | 208 |
| 362 | 424 | 339 | 736 |
| 291 | 581 | 498 | 643 |
| 390 | 332 | 750 | 368 |
| 659 | 234 | 396 | 300 |
| 343 | 536 | 543 | 217 |
| 298 | 1103 | 406 | 254 |
| 862 | 204 | 206 | 250 |
| 213 | 298 | 350 | 800 |
| 726 | 370 | 536 | 291 |
| 808 | 543 | 149 | 350 |
| 242 | 198 | 213 | 296 |
| 317 | 482 | 155 | 802 |
| 200 | 282 | 573 | 388 |
| 250 | 396 | 572 | |

7-19



**Which is a better measure of center for the CEO's annual salaries?**
**Mean or median**

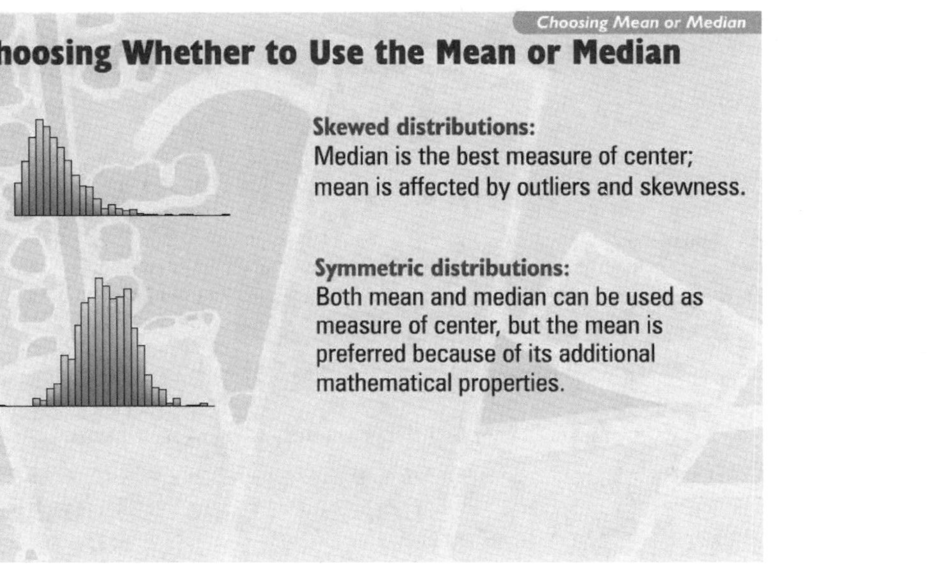


**Because of the skewness of this histogram, the median is the preferred measure of center.**

7-20



## Measuring Spread: the Quartiles

Basic Practice of Statistics Chapter 2

Should respond to 2 aspects of spread
- overall spread
- degree of clustering near the center

Range = maximum − minimum
- measures overall spread
- but only overall spread
- highly affected by outliers.

7-21



## Quartiles

**$Q_1$: The First Quartile** Value that has approximately 25% of the observations in the ordered data set below it and 75% above. "Median" of observations below the median.

**$Q_2$: The Second Quartile** The median (M).

50% of values ≤ $Q_2$,
50% of values ≥ $Q_2$

**$Q_3$: The Third Quartile** Value that has approximately 75% of the observations in the ordered data set below it and 25% above. "Median" of observations above the median.

Interquartile Range = r occupied by middle 50% of data
= 3rd quartile − 1st quartile
- if small relative to range, highly clustered
- if large relative to range, less clustered
- resistant to outliers

7-22



## Computing $Q_1$ and $Q_3$ (n odd)

1. Order the data and find the median. **Median = 245.5**
2. If the number of observations is odd, leave the overall median out of the computation of the quartiles.
3. $Q_1$ = median of lower half of data; $Q_3$ = median of upper half.

**# of Computers / 1000 Persons** (Ordered : Small to Large)

$Q_1 = 216.5$ $Q_3 = 259.5$

| | | | |
|---|---|---|---|
| | 201.6 | Switzerland | |
| | 214.8 | Netherlands | Lower half = |
| ⇨ | 216.5 | United Kingdom | Five |
| | 224.8 | New Zealand | Observations |
| | 244.1 | Sweden | |
| | 245.5 | Finland | Leave out median |
| | 252.5 | Denmark | |
| | 254.8 | Canada | Upper half = |
| ⇨ | 259.5 | Norway | Five |
| | 264.3 | Australia | Observations |
| | 364.7 | United States | |

n = 11

Source: Computer Industry Almanac, Inc.

7-23



## Computing $Q_1$ and $Q_3$ (n even)

1. Order the data and find the median. **Median =** $\frac{(0.272 + 0.271)}{2} = 0.2715$
2. If the number of observations is even, use all observations in calculating the quartiles.
3. $Q_1$ = median of lower half of data; $Q_3$ = median of upper half.

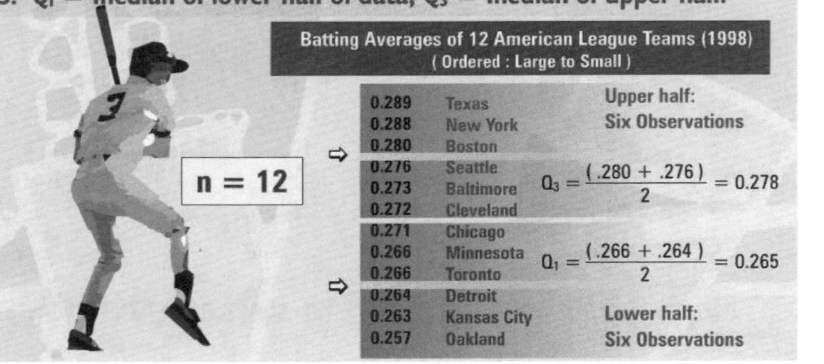

n = 12

**Batting Averages of 12 American League Teams (1998)** (Ordered : Large to Small)

| | | | |
|---|---|---|---|
| | 0.289 | Texas | Upper half: |
| | 0.288 | New York | Six Observations |
| ⇨ | 0.280 | Boston | |
| | 0.276 | Seattle | |
| | 0.273 | Baltimore | $Q_3 = \frac{(.280 + .276)}{2} = 0.278$ |
| | 0.272 | Cleveland | |
| | 0.271 | Chicago | |
| | 0.266 | Minnesota | $Q_1 = \frac{(.266 + .264)}{2} = 0.265$ |
| ⇨ | 0.266 | Toronto | |
| | 0.264 | Detroit | |
| | 0.263 | Kansas City | Lower half: |
| | 0.257 | Oakland | Six Observations |

7-24



## The Five-Number Summary and Boxplots

Basic Practice of Statistics Chapter 2

Jan 24

7-25

Five Number Summary

## The Five-Number Summary and the Boxplot

**The five-number summary:**

- Min (minimum)
- $Q_1$ (1st quartile)
- $Q_2$ (median)
- $Q_3$ (3rd quartile)
- Max (maximum)

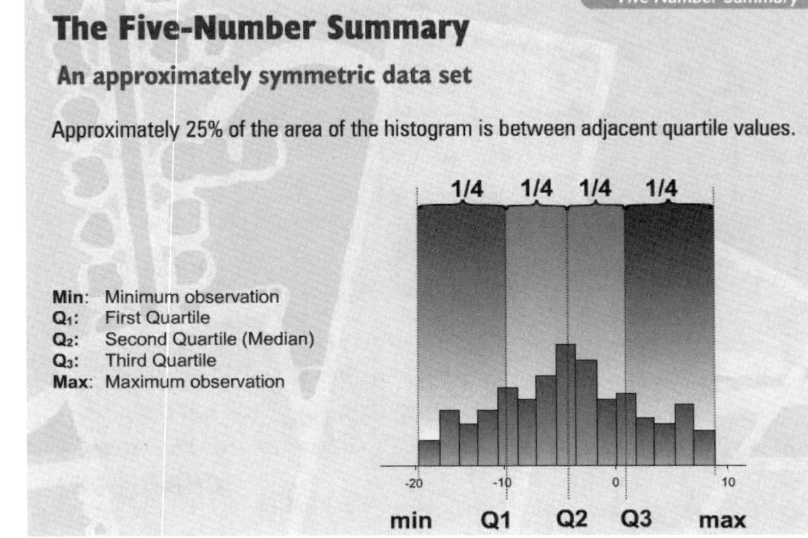


7-26

Five Number Summary

## The Five-Number Summary

**An approximately symmetric data set**

Approximately 25% of the area of the histogram is between adjacent quartile values.

**Min**: Minimum observation
**$Q_1$**: First Quartile
**$Q_2$**: Second Quartile (Median)
**$Q_3$**: Third Quartile
**Max**: Maximum observation

1/4 1/4 1/4 1/4

-20 -10 0 10

min Q1 Q2 Q3 max

7-27

Five Number Summary

## The Five-Number Summary

**A right-skewed data set**

Approximately 25% of the area of the histogram is between adjacent quartile values.

**Min**: Minimum observation
**$Q_1$**: First Quartile
**$Q_2$**: Second Quartile (Median)
**$Q_3$**: Third Quartile
**Max**: Maximum observation

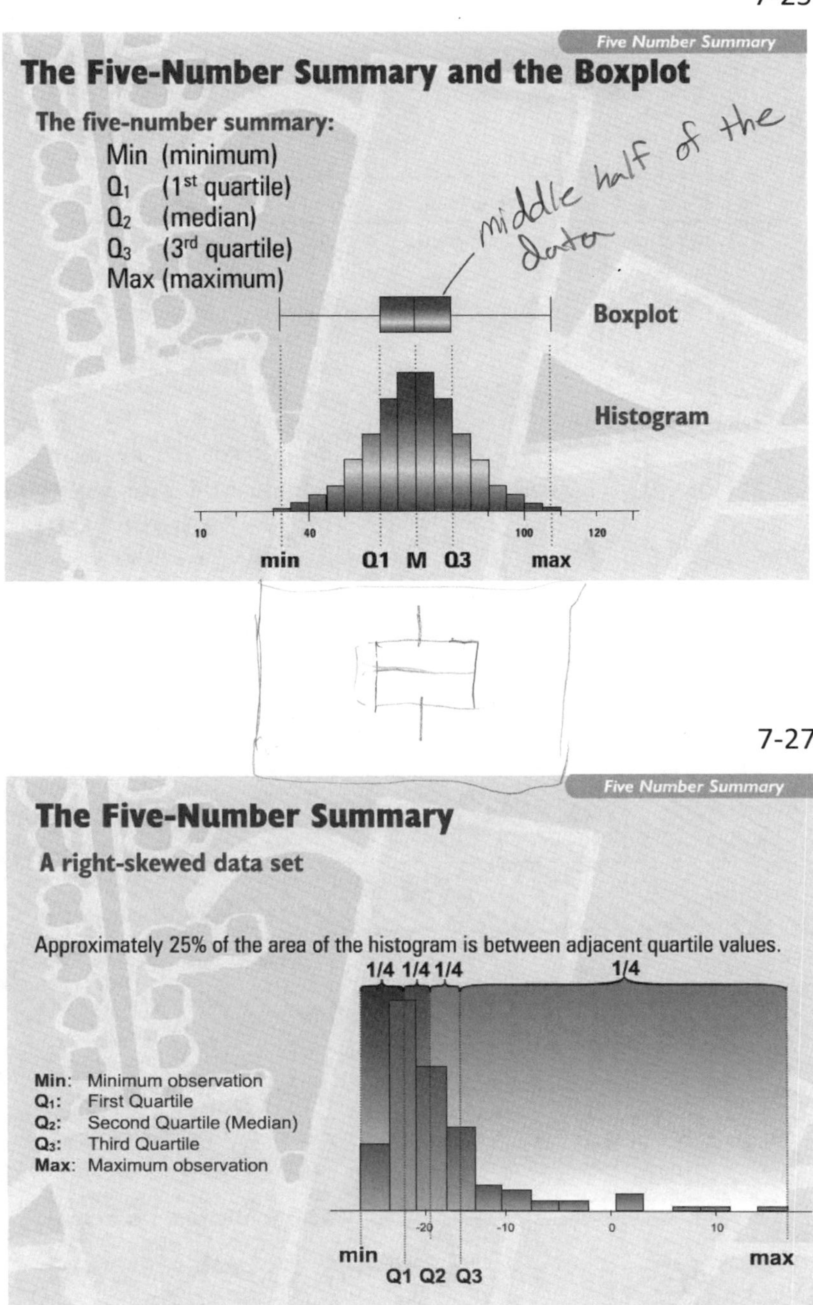


7-28

Five Number Summary

## The Five-Number Summary

**A left-skewed data set**

Approximately 25% of the area of the histogram is between adjacent quartile values.

**Min**: Minimum observation
**$Q_1$**: First Quartile
**$Q_2$**: Second Quartile (Median)
**$Q_3$**: Third Quartile
**Max**: Maximum observation

7-29

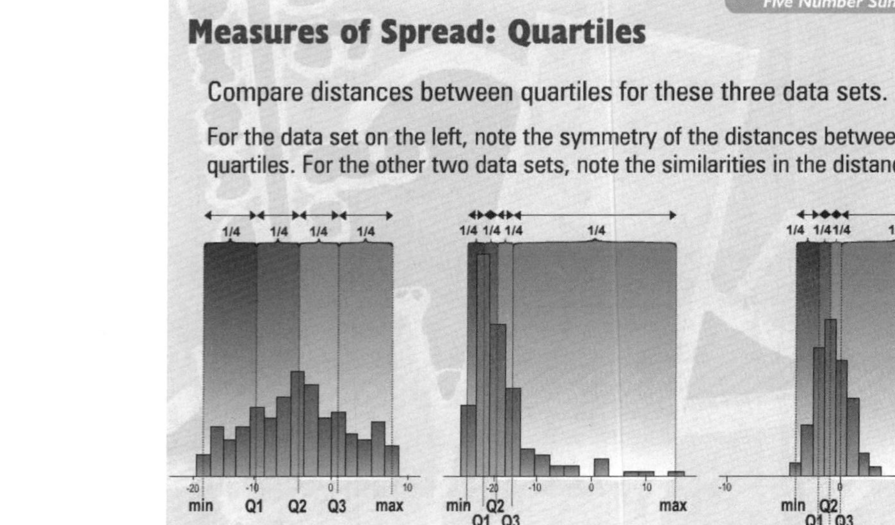


7-30

Five Number Summary

## Measures of Spread: Quartiles

Compare distances between quartiles for these three data sets.

For the data set on the left, note the symmetry of the distances between the quartiles. For the other two data sets, note the similarities in the distances.

1/4 1/4 1/4 1/4

1/4 1/4 1/4 1/4

1/4 1/41/4 1/4

-20 -10 0 10

min Q1 Q2 Q3 max

-20 -10 0 10

min Q2 max

Q1 Q3

-10 0 10

min Q2 max

Q1 Q3

7-31

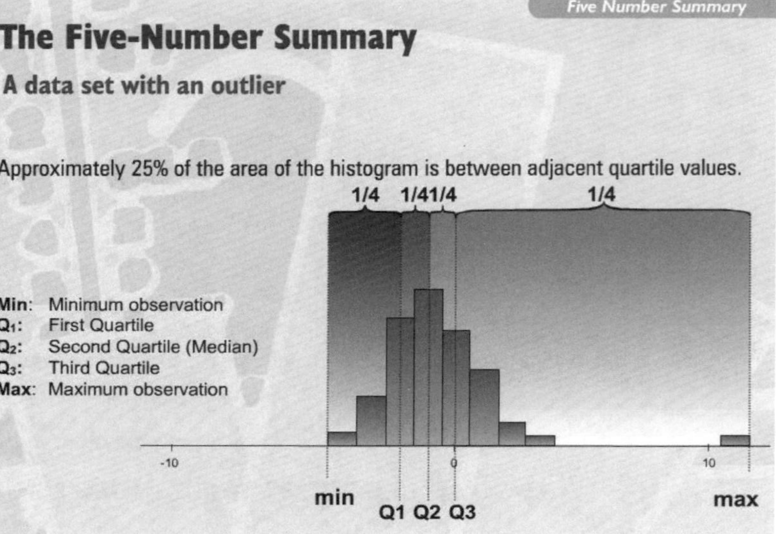


7-32

Boxplot

## The Boxplot

**A graphical representation of the five-number summary**

- A central box spans the quartiles.
- A line in the box marks the median.

Quiz scores

50% 50%

0 5 10 15 20 25 30 35 40

8 Obs. 8 Obs. 8 Obs. 8 Obs.

| Min | Q1 | M | Q3 | Max |
|---|---|---|---|---|
| 6 | 23 | 28.5 | 33.5 | 37 |

7-33

Boxplot

## The Boxplot

**A graphical representation of the five-number summary**

- A central box spans the quartiles.
- A line in the box marks the median.
- Lines extend from the box to the smallest and largest observations.

Quiz scores for 32 students and the five number summary:

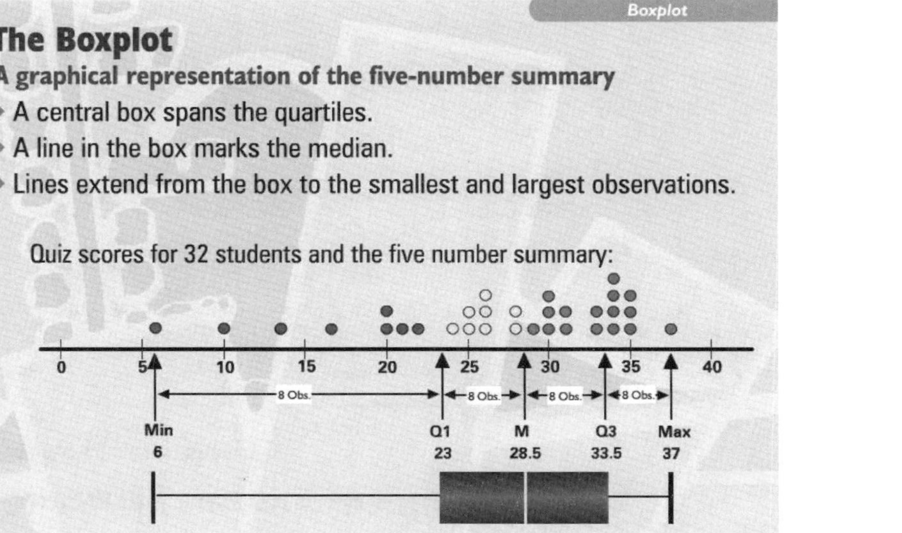


7-34

Boxplot

## Application: The Five-Number Summary & Boxplots

View Video Clip

7-35

Boxplot

## Finding the Five-Number Summary for a Data Set

**GNP of 26 European Countries (ordered small to large)**

- Find the Minimum and Maximum
- Find the Median (M = Q2)
- Find Q1 ("median" of lower half)
- Find Q3 ("median" of upper half)

| 26 EUROPEAN COUNTRIES | GNP (BILS) | |
|---|---|---|
| Malta | 2.60 | min=2.60 |
| Cyprus | 7.50 | |
| Slovakia | 10.10 | |
| Slovenia | 12.50 | |
| Luxembourg | 14.20 | |
| Romania | 25.40 | |
| Czech Repub. | 28.20 | Q1=28.20 |
| Hungary | 34.30 | |
| Ireland | 44.90 | |
| Greece | 76.70 | |
| Portugal | 77.70 | |
| Poland | 87.30 | |
| Finland | 96.20 | M = 97.90 |
| Ukraine | 99.60 | |
| Norway | 113.50 | |
| Denmark | 137.60 | |
| Austria | 183.50 | |
| Belgium | 213.40 | |
| Sweden | 216.30 | |
| Switzerland | 254.00 | Q3=254.00 |
| Netherlands | 316.40 | |
| Russia | 343.40 | |
| Spain | 533.90 | |
| Italy | 1134.90 | |
| France | 1,289.20 | |
| Germany | 2,004.80 | max=2004.80 |

Data from: www.mightymall.com

7-36

Boxplot

## Histogram, Five-Number Summary, and Boxplot

GNP OF
26 EUROPEAN COUNTRIES
(1996 – Billions of $)

Frequency: 0, 5, 10

0 min, M, Q1, Q3, 1000, 2000 max

GNP (in billions $)

| 26 EUROPEAN COUNTRIES | GNP (BILS) | |
|---|---|---|
| Malta | 2.60 | min=2.60 |
| Cyprus | 7.50 | |
| Slovakia | 10.10 | |
| Slovenia | 12.50 | |
| Luxembourg | 14.20 | |
| Romania | 25.40 | |
| Czech Repub. | 28.20 | Q1=28.20 |
| Hungary | 34.30 | |
| Ireland | 44.90 | |
| Greece | 76.70 | |
| Portugal | 77.70 | |
| Poland | 87.30 | |
| Finland | 96.20 | M = 97.90 |
| Ukraine | 99.60 | |
| Norway | 113.50 | |
| Denmark | 137.60 | |
| Austria | 183.50 | |
| Belgium | 213.40 | |
| Sweden | 216.30 | |
| Switzerland | 254.00 | Q3=254.00 |
| Netherlands | 316.40 | |
| Russia | 343.40 | |
| Spain | 533.90 | |
| Italy | 1134.90 | |
| France | 1,289.20 | |
| Germany | 2,004.80 | max=2004.80 |

Data from: www.mightymall.com

7-37

*Boxplot*

## Histogram, Five-Number Summary, and Boxplot

GNP OF
26 EUROPEAN COUNTRIES
(1996 – Billions of $)

0 1000 2000

| 26 EUROPEAN COUNTRIES | GNP (BILS) | |
|---|---|---|
| Malta | 2.60 | min=2.60 |
| Cyprus | 7.50 | |
| Slovakia | 10.10 | |
| Slovenia | 12.50 | |
| Luxembourg | 14.20 | |
| Romania | 25.40 | |
| Czech Repub. | 28.20 | Q1=28.20 |
| Hungary | 34.30 | |
| Ireland | 44.90 | |
| Greece | 76.70 | |
| Portugal | 77.70 | |
| Poland | 87.30 | |
| Finland | 96.20 | M = 97.90 |
| Ukraine | 99.60 | |
| Norway | 113.50 | |
| Denmark | 137.60 | |
| Austria | 183.50 | |
| Belgium | 213.40 | |
| Sweden | 216.30 | |
| Switzerland | 254.00 | Q3=254.00 |
| Netherlands | 316.40 | |
| Russia | 343.40 | |
| Spain | 533.90 | |
| Italy | 1134.90 | |
| France | 1,289.20 | |
| Germany | 2,004.80 | max=2004.80 |

Data from: www.mightymall.com

7-38

*Histogram and Boxplot*

## Comparing Boxplots with Histograms

Each boxplot displays center and shape in the same manner as its corresponding histogram.

min Q1 M Q3 max

Note symmetry of box and whiskers.

min Q1 M Q3 max

Note long whisker on the right.

min Q1 M Q3 max

Note long whisker on the right.

7-39

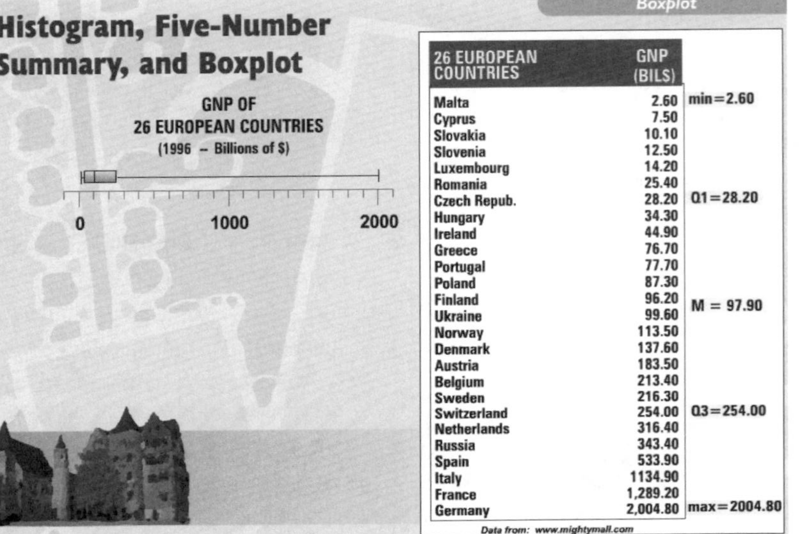


7-40

*Comparing Boxplots*

## Side-by-Side Box Plots

**A comparative experiment**

10 men received calcium supplements for six weeks
11 men received placebo for six weeks

Response Variable:
Difference between post- and pre-blood pressures = change in blood pressure

Blood Pressure Experiment

Systolic Blood Pressure Change

Calcium Placebo

**Does increasing calcium in the diet reduce blood pressure?**
**Yes, the boxplot for the calcium group is lower.**

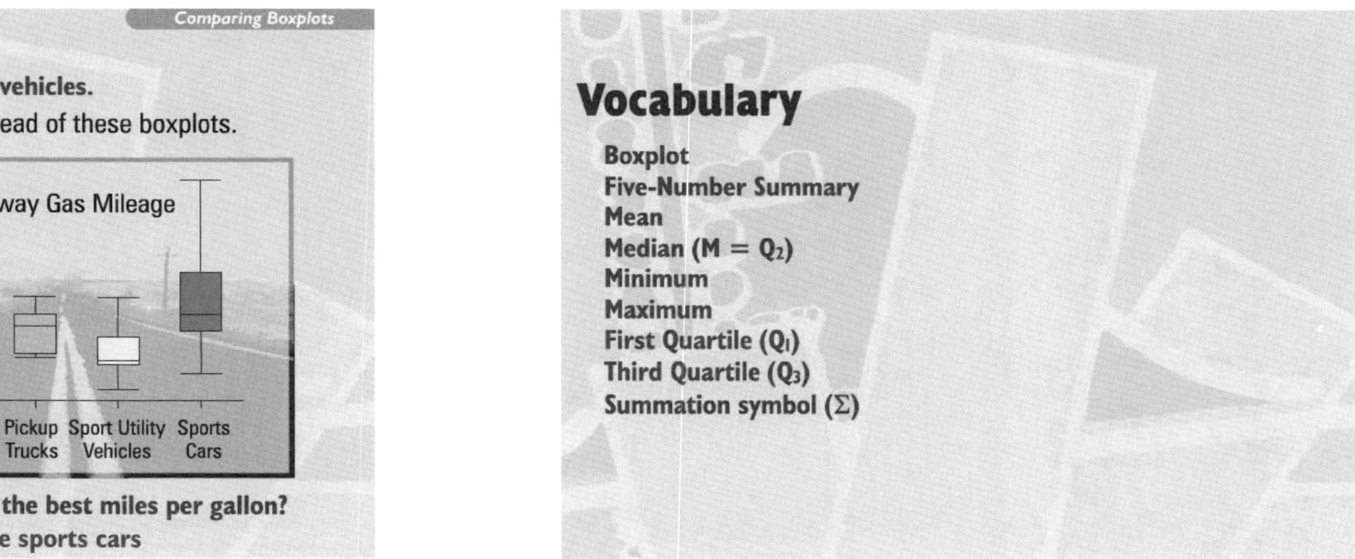
Comparing Boxplots
Side-by-Side Box Plots
Highway gas mileage of four types of vehicles.
Compare the shape, center and spread of these boxplots.
Highway Gas Mileage
Miles Per Gallon
40
30
20
Midsize Cars
Pickup Trucks
Sport Utility Vehicles
Sports Cars
Which type of vehicle gets the best miles per gallon?
Midsize cars and some sports cars



Vocabulary
Boxplot
Five-Number Summary
Mean
Median (M = Q2)
Minimum
Maximum
First Quartile (Q1)
Third Quartile (Q3)
Summation symbol (Σ)

8-1

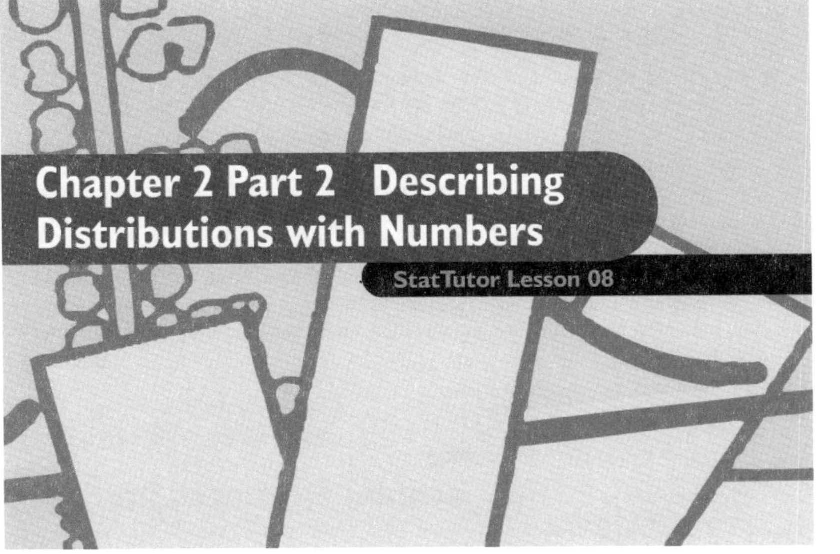


8-2

## Objectives

1. Contrast measures of center and measures of spread.
2. Compute range (R) and interquartile range (IQR) as measures of spread.
3. Compute sample standard deviation as a measure of spread.
4. Identify advantages and disadvantages of using standard deviation as a measure of spread.
5. Estimate the standard deviation for data summarized in a histogram.
6. Compare data sets and draw conclusions using mean and standard deviation.

8-3

Range & IQR

## Spotting Suspected Outliers

Basic Practice of Statistics Chapter 2

8-4

Range & IQR

## Range and Interquartile Range (IQR)

Range = Max minus Min

Interquartile Range (IQR) = $Q_3$ minus $Q_1$

Review: Five Number Summary

**Min:** Minimum observation
$Q_1$: The First Quartile
$Q_2$: The Second Quartile = Median (M)
$Q_3$: The Third Quartile
**Max:** Maximum observation

Boxplot
Range
min Q1 M Q3 max

8-5

Range & IQR

## Example: Computing Range and IQR

Range = Max – Min

Interquartile range (IQR) = $Q_3 - Q_1$

Sodium Content in Hot Dogs (mg/ hot dog)

Sodium (mg / hot dog): 700, 600, 500, 400, 300, 200, 100, 0

Beef Meat Poultry

Note: Meat hotdogs are mostly pork and beef, but up to 15% poultry meat.

| Type | Min | $Q_1$ | M | $Q_3$ | Max |
|---|---|---|---|---|---|
| Beef | 253.0 | 319.8 | 380.5 | 478.5 | 645.0 |
| Meat | 144.0 | 379.0 | 405.0 | 501.0 | 545.0 |
| Poultry | 357.0 | 379.0 | 430.0 | 535.0 | 588.0 |

| Type | Range | IQR |
|---|---|---|
| Beef | 645.0-253.0=392.0 | 478.5-319.8=158.7 |
| Meat | 545.0-144.0=401.0 | 501.0-379.0=122.0 |
| Poultry | 588.0-357.0=231.0 | 535.0-379.0=156.0 |

8-6

Advantages & Disadvantages

## Advantages & Disadvantages of Range and IQR

**Advantages**
- Both simple to compute.
- IQR not sensitive to outliers.

**Disadvantages**
- Neither involve all actual data values
- Neither commonly used.
- Both have complex theoretical properties.
- Range is sensitive to outliers.

IQR
Range
10 40 100 120
Min Q1 M Q3 Max

**Needed: A measure of spread that uses all data values and has nice theoretical properties.**

8-7

Advantages & Disadvantages

## Using IQR to Identify Outliers

**Call an observation an outlier if:**

Observation < Q1 – (1.5 x IQR)
or
Observation > Q3 + (1.5 x IQR)

**Example:**

Doctors used X-rays to measure the angle (in degrees) of big toe deformity in 38 patients under the age of 21 who came to a medical center for corrective surgery. Here are the data with their histogram and numerical summaries:

| | | | | | | | | | | | | | |
|---|---|---|---|---|---|---|---|---|---|---|---|---|---|
| 28 | 32 | 25 | 34 | 38 | 26 | 25 | 18 | 30 | 26 | 28 | 13 | 20 | 21 |
| 17 | 16 | 21 | 23 | 14 | 32 | 25 | 21 | 22 | 20 | 18 | 26 | 16 | 30 |
| 30 | 20 | 50 | 25 | 26 | 28 | 31 | 38 | 32 | 21 | | | | |

| Variable | n | Mean | Median | StDev | Minimum | Maximum | Q1 | Q3 |
|---|---|---|---|---|---|---|---|---|
| Angle | 38 | 25.42 | 25.00 | 7.47 | 13.00 | 50.00 | 20.00 | 30.00 |

Frequency; Angle

Is 50 an outlier? **yes**

IQR = Q3 – Q1 = 30 - 20 = 10

Q3 + (1.5 x IQR) = 30 + (1.5 x 10) = 45

Since 50 > 45, we declare 50 an outlier.

8-8

Center vs. Spread

## Measuring Spread: the Standard Deviation

Basic Practice of Statistics Chapter 2

Jan 24

8-9

Center vs. Spread

## Question 1

A warm, stable climate can greatly affect some individuals' health. Atlanta and San Diego have about equal average temperatures (62° vs. 64°). If a person's health requires a stable climate, in which city would you recommend they live?

Average monthly temperature (1964 - 1993)

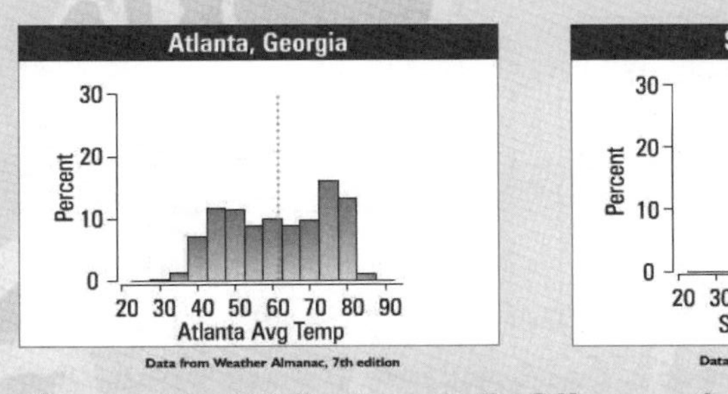


Data from Weather Almanac, 7th edition

San Diego, CA

Percent: 0, 10, 20, 30

20 30 40 50 60 70 80 90

San Diego Avg Temp

Data from Weather Almanac, 7th edition

**How are the distributions similar? How are they different?**

8-10

Center vs. Spread

Kickoff Question

## Question 2

Suppose your grandfather passed away and left $100,000 to support your grandmother. You can invest the money in one of two mutual funds with similar yearly average returns (9.8% vs. 9.9%). Which mutual fund should you choose?

Percent return on investment

Schwab Short-Term Bond Market Index, 6/96 - 6/99

Percent: 0, 10, 20, 30

9.5 10.0 10.5

SWBDX Percent Return

Schwab Total Bond Market Index, 6/96 - 6/99

Percent: 0, 10, 20, 30

9.5 10.0 10.5

SWLBX Percent Return

**How are the distributions similar? How are they different?**

8-11

Standard Deviation

## A Measure of Spread Using All of the Data

1. Choose a measure of center as a reference point.
2. Compute all deviations (distances) from data points to reference point.
3. Select a representative deviation.

8-12

Standard Deviation

**I. Choose a reference point.**

The mean and median are logical choices—the mean is most commonly used.

**Sodium Content in Beef Hotdogs** (mg / hotdogs)

$\bar{x}$

240 320 400 480 560 640

| Sodium (mg / hot dog) | |
|---|---|
| 645 | 375 |
| 587 | 370 |
| 495 | 330 |
| 482 | 322 |
| 479 | 322 |
| 477 | 319 |
| 440 | 317 |
| 425 | 300 |
| 401 | 298 |
| 386 | 253 |

$\Sigma x = 8023$

$n = 20$

$\bar{x} = 401.2$

8-13

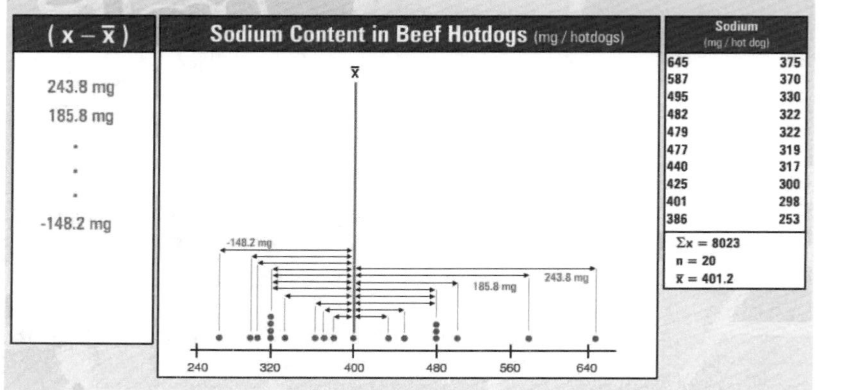


8-14

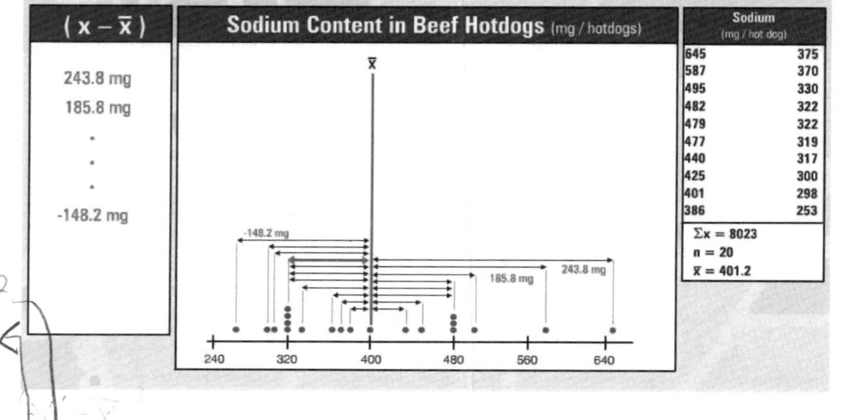


8-15

Standard Deviation

**A formula for computing a representative deviation: sample variance and sample standard deviation**

**SAMPLE VARIANCE:** The average squared deviation from the mean

$$s^2 = \frac{\sum (x_i - \bar{x})^2}{n - 1}$$

**SAMPLE STANDARD DEVIATION:** The square root of the variance

$$s = \sqrt{\frac{\sum (x_i - \bar{x})^2}{n - 1}}$$

| $X_i$ | $X_i - \bar{X}$ | $(X_i - \bar{X})^2$ |
|---|---|---|
| 69" | −1.4 | 2.04 |
| 71" | +0.6 | .33 |
| 66" | −4.4 | 19.6 |
| 73" | +2.6 | 6.6 |
| 72" | +1.6 | 2.50 |
| 72" | +1.6 | 2.50 |
| 70" | −0.4 | .18 |
| | | 33.7 |

$\bar{X} = 70.4$

Variance $= \frac{33.7}{6} = 5.619$   Std. dev. $= \sqrt[6]{\text{variance}} = 2.37$

Why $n-1$? Because 7th piece of info is known.

8-16

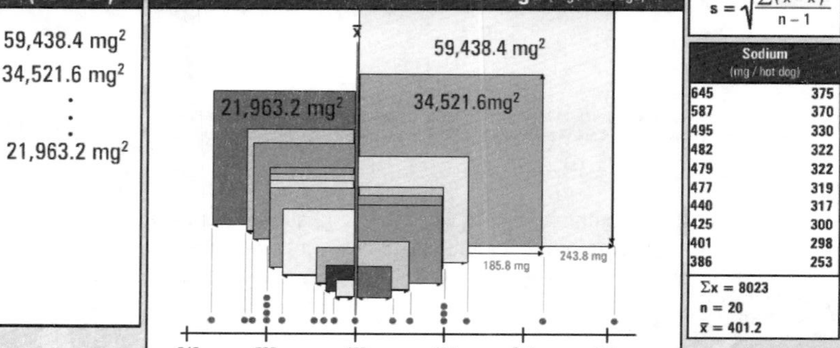


Standard deviation is highly influenced by outliers

8-17

Standard Deviation

**Computing Variance and Standard Deviation**

**Add all of the squared deviations**

Sum of squared deviations

| $(x - \bar{x})^2$ |
|---|
| 59,438.4 mg² |
| 34,521.6 mg² |
| ⋮ |
| 21,963.2 mg² |
| 199,365 mg² |

**Sodium Content in Beef Hotdogs** (mg / hotdogs)

$\bar{x}$

-148.2 mg  185.8 mg  243.8 mg

240 320 400 480 560 640

$s = \sqrt{\frac{\Sigma(x-\bar{x})^2}{n-1}}$

| Sodium (mg / hot dog) | |
|---|---|
| 645 | 375 |
| 587 | 370 |
| 495 | 330 |
| 482 | 322 |
| 479 | 322 |
| 477 | 319 |
| 440 | 317 |
| 425 | 300 |
| 401 | 298 |
| 386 | 253 |

Σx = 8023
n = 20
$\bar{x}$ = 401.2

8-18

Standard Deviation

**Computing Variance and Standard Deviation**

**Find the average squared deviation**

[Note: divide by n – 1, not n]

The area of this average square = variance

| $(x - \bar{x})^2$ |
|---|
| 59,438.4 mg² |
| 34,521.6 mg² |
| ⋮ |
| 21,963.2 mg² |
| 199,365 mg² |
| ÷ 19 |
| **10,493 mg²** |
| = **Variance** |

**Sodium Content in Beef Hotdogs** (mg / hotdogs)

$\bar{x}$

**Variance = 10,493 mg²**

-148.2 mg  185.8 mg  243.8 mg

240 320 400 480 560 640

$s = \sqrt{\frac{\Sigma(x-\bar{x})^2}{n-1}}$

| Sodium (mg / hot dog) | |
|---|---|
| 645 | 375 |
| 587 | 370 |
| 495 | 330 |
| 482 | 322 |
| 479 | 322 |
| 477 | 319 |
| 440 | 317 |
| 425 | 300 |
| 401 | 298 |
| 386 | 253 |

Σx = 8023
n = 20
$\bar{x}$ = 401.2

8-19

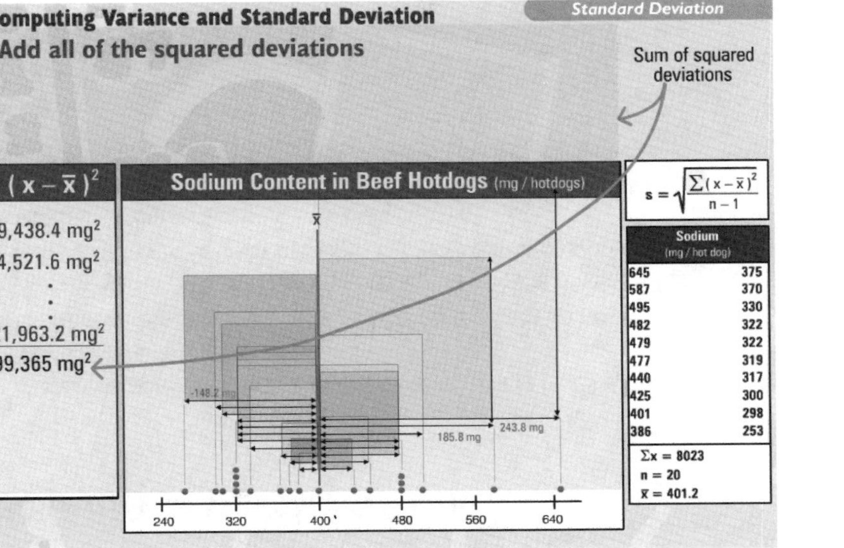


8-20

Standard Deviation

**Computing Variance and Standard Deviation**

**Computing standard deviation is one way of finding a typical deviation.**

| $(x - \bar{x})^2$ |
|---|
| 59,438.4 mg² |
| 34,521.6 mg² |
| ⋮ |
| 21,963.2 mg² |
| 199,365 mg² |
| ÷ 19 |
| $\sqrt{10{,}493\ mg^2}$ |
| **= 102.43 mg** |
| **= SD** |

**Sodium Content in Beef Hotdogs** (mg / hotdogs)

$\bar{x}$

SD = 102.43 mg

-148.2 mg  185.8 mg  243.8 mg

240 320 400 480 560 640

s = 102.43 mg

| Sodium (mg / hot dog) | |
|---|---|
| 645 | 375 |
| 587 | 370 |
| 495 | 330 |
| 482 | 322 |
| 479 | 322 |
| 477 | 319 |
| 440 | 317 |
| 425 | 300 |
| 401 | 298 |
| 386 | 253 |

Σx = 8023
n = 20
$\bar{x}$ = 401.2

8-21



## Computing a Standard Deviation by Hand

1. Calculate the mean $\bar{x}$
2. Calculate the deviations $(x-\bar{x})$
3. Square the deviations $(x-\bar{x})^2$
4. Sum the squared deviations $\sum(x-\bar{x})^2$
5. Divide by $n-1$
   Variance: $s^2 = \frac{\sum(x-\bar{x})^2}{n-1}$
6. Take the square root
   Standard Deviation: $s = \sqrt{\frac{\sum(x-\bar{x})^2}{n-1}}$

**Home Runs by Mark McGwire (1987 - 1998)**

| Year | x | $(x-\bar{x})$ | $(x-\bar{x})^2$ |
|---|---|---|---|
| 1987 | 49 | 11.167 | 124.70 |
| 1988 | 32 | -5.833 | 34.02 |
| 1989 | 33 | -4.833 | 23.36 |
| 1990 | 39 | 1.167 | 1.36 |
| 1991 | 22 | -15.833 | 250.68 |
| 1992 | 42 | 4.167 | 17.36 |
| 1993 | 9 | -28.833 | 831.34 |
| 1994 | 9 | -28.833 | 831.34 |
| 1995 | 39 | 1.167 | 1.36 |
| 1996 | 52 | 14.167 | 200.70 |
| 1997 | 58 | 20.167 | 406.71 |
| 1998 | 70 | 32.167 | 1034.72 |
| Sum | 454 | 0 | 3757.7 |
| Divide | ÷ 12 | | ÷ 11 |
| $\bar{x}$ | 37.83 | $s^2$ | 341.61 |
| | | | $\sqrt{341.61}$ |
| | | s | 18.43 |

8-22



## Standard Deviation Applet

Investigate how standard deviation is related to the distance of data points from the mean with this applet.

**View Applet**

8-23



## Properties of Standard Deviation

- Measures spread of data about the mean. (Only use *s* when the mean is an appropriate measure of center.)
- Is either zero or positive. (If s = 0, then the data do not vary.)
- Has the same unit of measurement as the original observations. (e.g., If data are heights measured in inches, then report *s* in inches.)
- Inflated by outliers.

8-24



## Calculating Standard Deviation: Population vs. Sample

Use N as the divisor for population data.

Use *n* – *1* as the divisor for sample data.

Most calculators provide options for either divisor.

Population

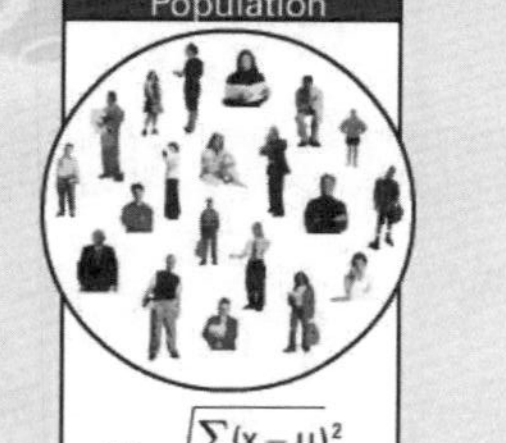

$\sigma = \sqrt{\frac{\sum(x-\mu)^2}{N}}$

Sample

$s = \sqrt{\frac{\sum(x-\bar{x})^2}{n-1}}$

8-25

Standard Deviation

## Why divide by $n-1$?

- To establish important theoretical properties for statistical inference.
- To make the sample variance ($s^2$) an unbiased estimate of the population variance ($\sigma^2$).

Population

$$\sigma = \sqrt{\frac{\sum(x-\mu)^2}{N}}$$

Sample

$$s = \sqrt{\frac{\sum(x-\bar{x})^2}{n-1}}$$

8-26

Advantages & Disadvantages

## Advantages & Disadvantages of Standard Deviation

**Advantages**

- Commonly used.
- Uses deviations from every data point unlike range and IQR which use only two numbers from the five-number summary.
- Has well-established theoretical properties.

Sodium Content in Beef Hotdogs (mg / hotdogs)

$\bar{x}$ s = 102.43

240 320 400 480 560 640

**Disadvantage**

- Inflated by outliers and/or strong skewness.

8-27

Estimating Standard Deviation

**The mean chest size for 5,378 Scottish militiamen is 39.831 inches. Estimate standard deviation by inspecting histogram.**

Look at the possible deviation sizes.

- Smallest deviations are less than half an inch.
- Largest deviations are 5-7 inches.
- Majority of deviations are between half an inch and 3 inches.

Choose a representative deviation: about 2 inches

Chest size for Scottish Militiamen (n=5378)

Percent: 0, 10, 20

Chest Size (in): 33, 38, 43, 48

Actual Value: s = 2.048 (in)

≈34 if bell-shaped ≈47

$sd \approx \frac{range}{6} = \frac{13}{6} = 2.15$

8-28

Estimating Standard Deviation

**The mean chest size for 5,378 Scottish militiamen is 39.831 inches. Estimate standard deviation by inspecting histogram.**

Guidelines:

- Standard deviation is usually less than one fourth of the range.
- For large bell-shaped symmetric data sets, estimate s with range / 6.
- For large skewed data sets, estimate s with range / 5.

Chest size for Scottish Militiamen (n=5378)

Percent: 0, 10, 20

Chest Size (in): 33, 38, 43, 48

Actual Value: s = 2.048 (in)

8-29

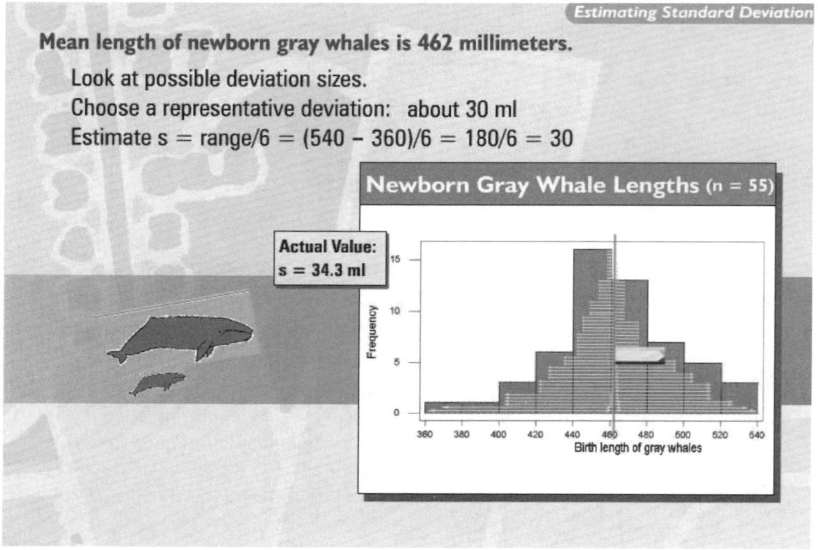

Estimating Standard Deviation

**Mean length of newborn gray whales is 462 millimeters.**

Look at possible deviation sizes.
Choose a representative deviation: about 30 ml
Estimate s = range/6 = (540 – 360)/6 = 180/6 = 30

Newborn Gray Whale Lengths (n = 55)

Actual Value:
s = 34.3 ml

Frequency
Birth length of gray whales
360 380 400 420 440 460 480 500 520 540

8-30

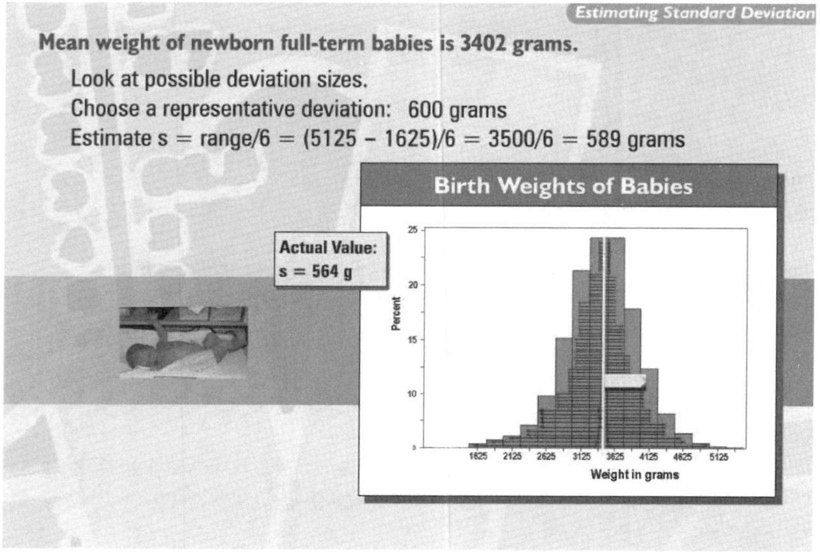

Estimating Standard Deviation

**Mean weight of newborn full-term babies is 3402 grams.**

Look at possible deviation sizes.
Choose a representative deviation: 600 grams
Estimate s = range/6 = (5125 – 1625)/6 = 3500/6 = 589 grams

Birth Weights of Babies

Actual Value:
s = 564 g

Percent
Weight in grams
1625 2125 2625 3125 3625 4125 4625 5125

8-31

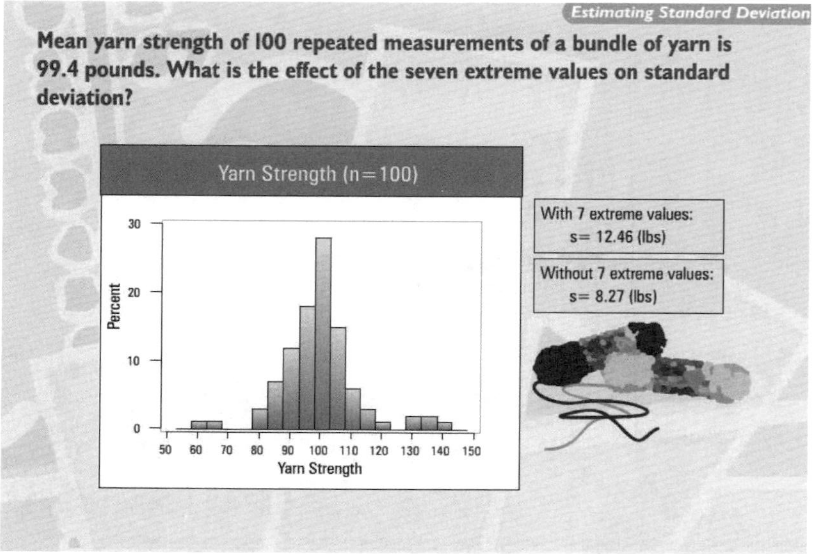

Estimating Standard Deviation

**Mean yarn strength of 100 repeated measurements of a bundle of yarn is 99.4 pounds. What is the effect of the seven extreme values on standard deviation?**

Yarn Strength (n=100)

Percent
Yarn Strength
50 60 70 80 90 100 110 120 130 140 150

With 7 extreme values:
s= 12.46 (lbs)

Without 7 extreme values:
s= 8.27 (lbs)

8-32

Estimating Standard Deviation

**Mean yarn strength of 100 repeated measurements of a bundle of yarn is 99.4 pounds. What is the effect of the seven extreme values on standard deviation?**

Yarn Strength (n=100)

Percent

With 7 extreme values:
s= 12.46 (lbs)

Without 7 extreme values:
s= 8.27 (lbs)

Measurement error may have occurred in the seven extreme values.

**Warning: Outliers inflate standard deviation!**

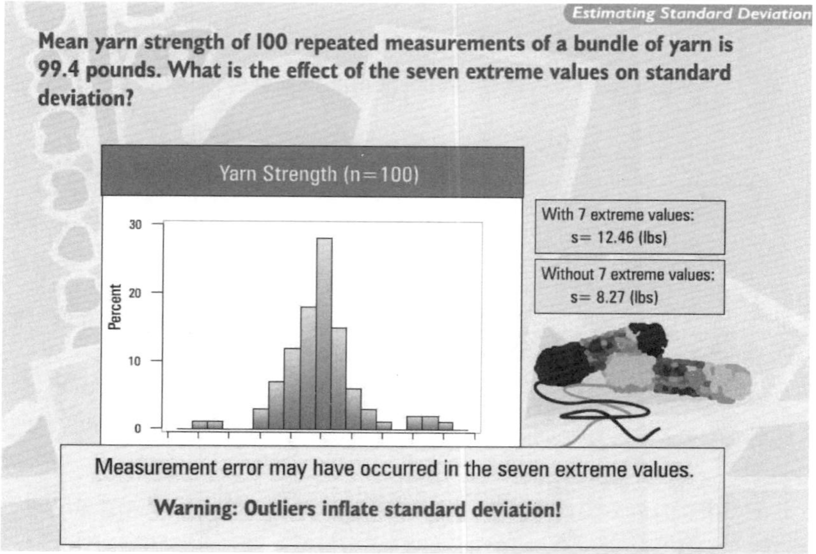

8-33



## Answering the kickoff questions

A warm, stable climate can greatly affect some individuals' health. Atlanta and San Diego have about equal average temperatures (62° vs. 64°). If a person's health requires a stable climate, in which city would you recommend they live?

Average monthly temperature (1964 - 1993)

**Atlanta, Georgia**

| Mean | Std. Dev. |
|---|---|
| 61.5 | 13.5 |

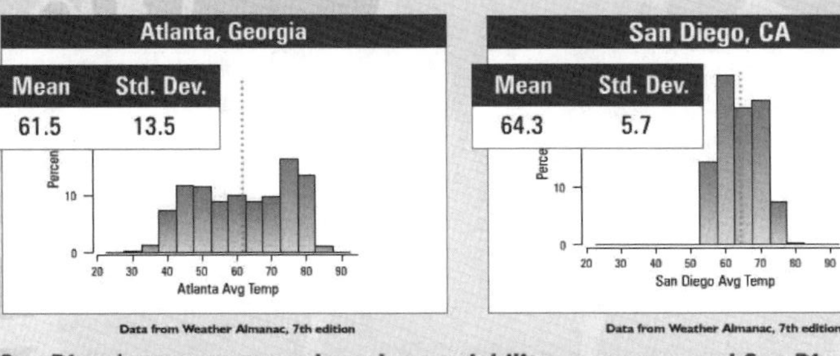


**San Diego, CA**

| Mean | Std. Dev. |
|---|---|
| 64.3 | 5.7 |

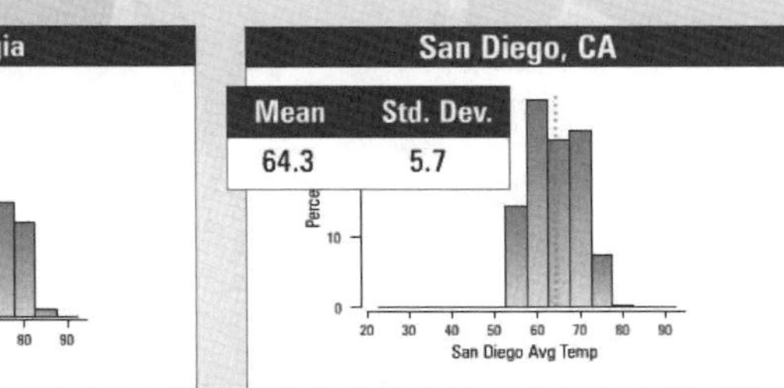


Data from Weather Almanac, 7th edition

Data from Weather Almanac, 7th edition

**San Diego's temperatures have less variability so recommend San Diego.**

8-34



## Answering the kickoff questions

Suppose your grandfather passed away and left \$100,000 to support your grandmother. You can invest the money in one of two mutual funds with similar yearly average returns (9.8% vs. 9.9%). Which mutual fund should you choose?

Percent return on investment:

**Schwab Short-Term Bond Market Index, 6/96 - 6/99**

| Mean | Std. Dev. |
|---|---|
| 9.80% | 0.09% |

SWBDX Percent Return

**Schwab Total Bond Market Index, 6/96 - 6/99**

| Mean | Std. Dev. |
|---|---|
| 9.88% | 0.25% |

SWLBX Percent Return

**The short term bonds have less variability and hence, will provide your grandmother greater security.**

8-35



# Choosing Measures of Center and Spread

Basic Practice of Statistics Chapter 2

8-36



## Five Number Summary versus $\bar{x}$ and s

**For skewed distributions or distributions with outliers, use five number summary.**

**For symmetric distributions without outliers, use mean ($\bar{x}$) and standard deviation (s).**

**Market Value / Replacement Cost (50 Firms)**

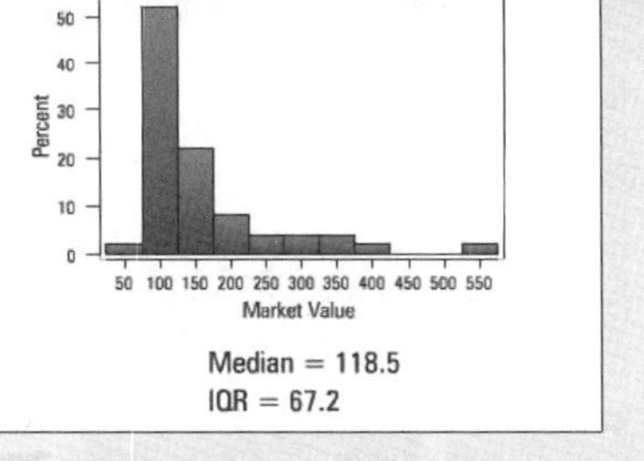


Median = 118.5
IQR = 67.2

**Chest size for Scottish Militiamen (n=5378)**

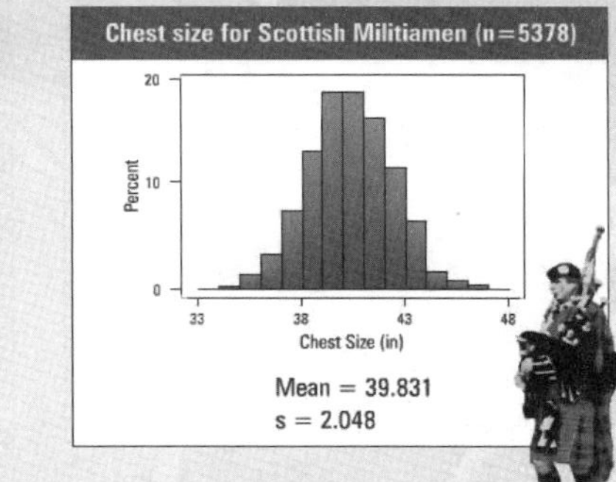


Mean = 39.831
s = 2.048

8-37

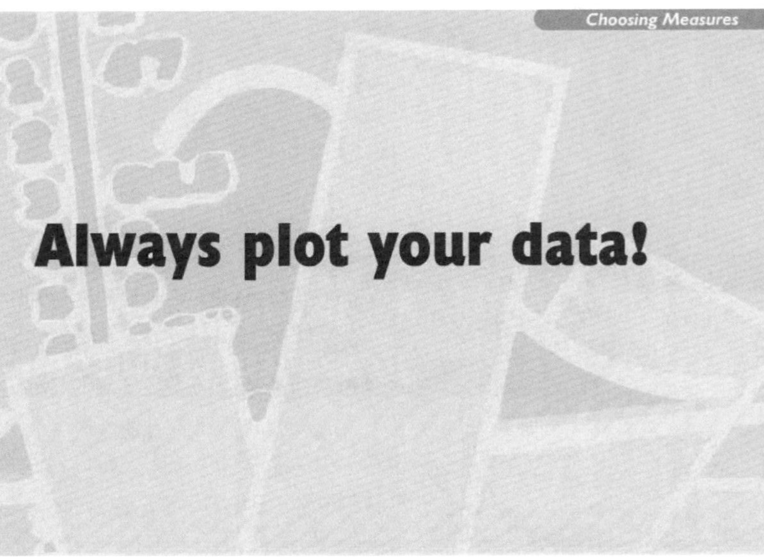
Choosing Measures
Always plot your data!

8-38

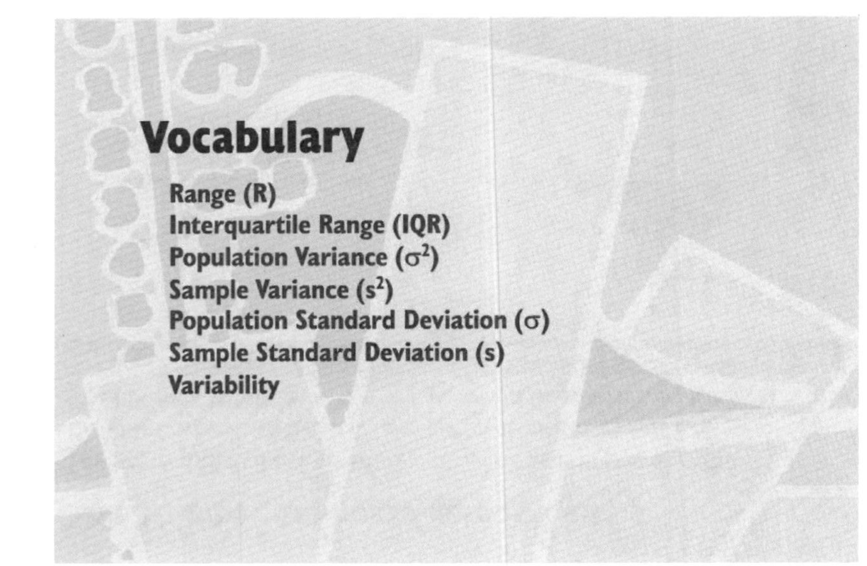
Vocabulary
Range (R)
Interquartile Range (IQR)
Population Variance ($\sigma^2$)
Sample Variance ($s^2$)
Population Standard Deviation ($\sigma$)
Sample Standard Deviation (s)
Variability

9-1

# Chapter 3 Part I
# The Normal Distribution

StatTutor Lesson 09

9-2

Jan 27

## Objectives

1. Describe the relationship between a density curve and a histogram.
2. List the properties of a density curve.
3. Compare the mean and median of right-skewed, left-skewed, and symmetric density curves.
4. Describe the Normal density curve.
5. List the properties of the Normal density curve.
6. Apply the 68-95-99.7 rule to a Normal density curve.
7. Identify the properties of the standard Normal distribution.
8. Standardize a value from a given Normal distribution.
9. Associate table entries from the standard Normal probability table with areas under the standard Normal curve.

9-3

Modeling Data

## Steps for Exploring Data

1. Start with a plot of the data, usually a histogram or stemplot.
2. Look for overall pattern and obvious deviations from the pattern such as outliers.
3. Give numerical summaries for center and spread.

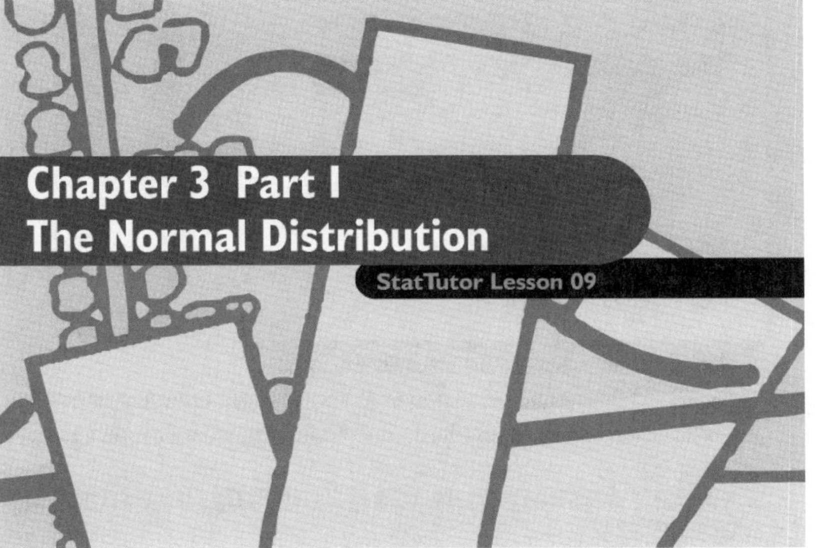


Duration of Old Faithful Eruption

9-4

Models: Scaffolding, not perfect truth

Modeling Data

## Steps for Modeling Data

4. For large samples, if the overall pattern is regular, model the data with a smooth curve called a density curve.

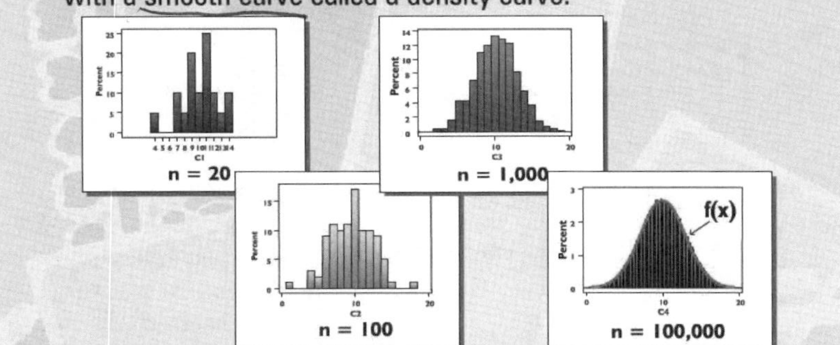


**Density curve: a mathematical function that describes the overall pattern of the data and the underlying population.**

smooth curve

9-5

Density Curves

# Density Curves

Basic Practice of Statistics Chapter 3

9-6

Density Curves

## Density Curves

A smooth curve that describes the overall pattern of a distribution.

**Properties of density curves**

1. Always on or above the x-axis
2. Total area under curve equals one (or 100%)
3. Area under curve between two values =
   Proportion of population expected in that interval

Area = 0.31

(31% of the values are in the interval from 2 to 4)

Area = 0.31

0 2 4 6 8 10

9-7

Modeling Data

## Reasons for Modeling Data with Density Curves

1. Easier to investigate population properties.
2. Can estimate probabilities of various outcomes.

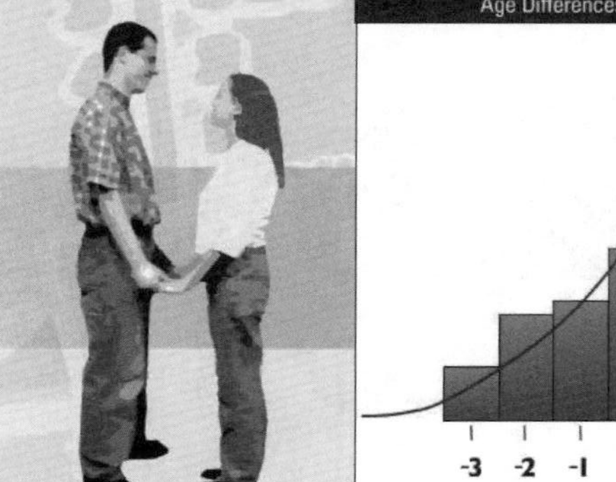

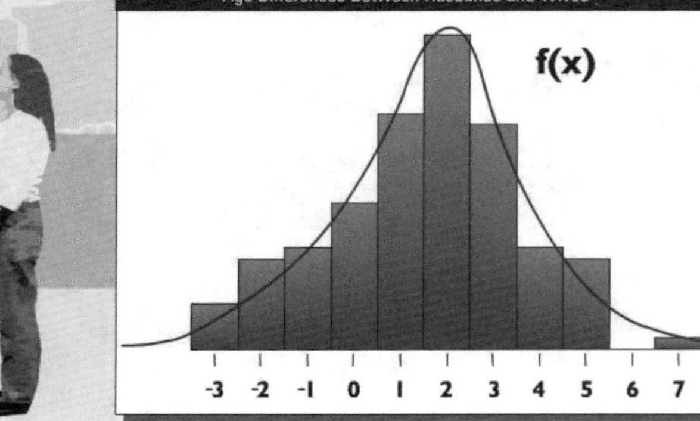


9-8

Modeling Data

## Common Shapes (Models) for Density Curves

Right Skewed

Hours spent watching TV for 120 individuals

Right Skewed

GNP of 26 European Countries

Left Skewed

Quiz score totals for 445 students in an introductory statistics course

Bell-shaped/Symmetric

Chest size of 5378 Scottish militiamen

9-9

Mean/Median

# Describing Density Curves

Basic Practice of Statistics Chapter 3

9-10

Mean/Median

## Comparing Mean and Median

**Mean and median are used to describe center of a density curve.**

9-11

Mean/Median

## Comparing Mean and Median

**Mean:** Point at which curve would balance if made of solid material.

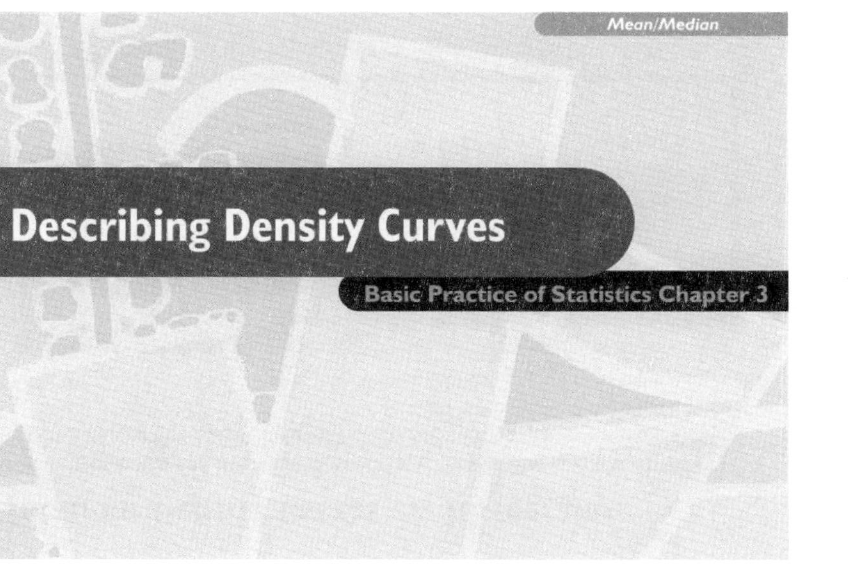


Drag the "balancing" triangle to see how the mean represents the balance point of a density curve.

9-12

Mean/Median

## Comparing Mean and Median

**Median:** Point at which the area of the density curve is cut in half.

Illustration of median

Area =0.5

Area = 0.5

0 2 4 6 8 10

9-13

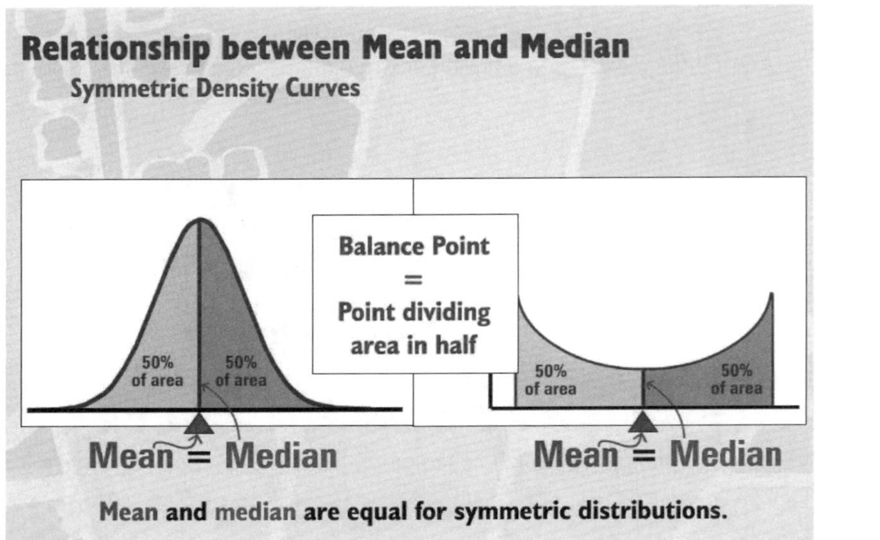


9-14

Mean/Median

## Relationship between Mean and Median

### Skewed Density Curves

Right-skewed

50% 50%

Median < Mean

**Mean is right of median.**

Left-skewed

50% 50%

Mean < Median

**Mean is left of median.**

Mean and median are not equal when distribution is skewed.

9-15

## Notation: Density Curves vs. Histograms

The notation for mean and standard deviation is different for density curves (populations) than for histograms (samples).

| Characteristic | Name | Density Curve (Population) Notation | Histogram (Sample) Notation |
|---|---|---|---|
| Center | Mean | $\mu$ (mu) | $\bar{x}$ |
| Spread | Standard Deviation | $\sigma$ (sigma) | s |

9-16

Normal Distribution

# Normal Distributions

Basic Practice of Statistics Chapter 3

9-17

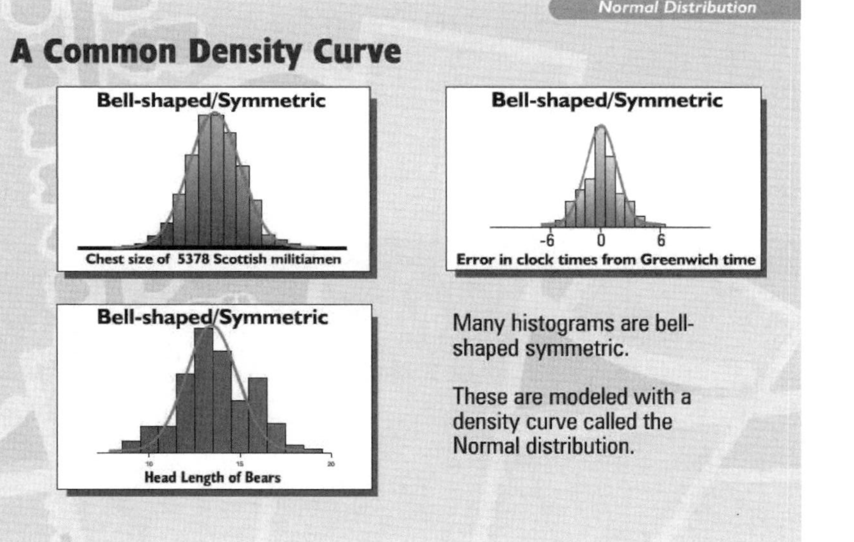


9-18

Normal Distribution

## Characteristics of a Normal Distribution

- Symmetric
- Bell-shaped
- One peak
- Mean = Median

50% 50%

birth weight of full-term babies

9-19

Normal Distribution

## Characteristics of a Normal Distribution

$\mu$ = mean
= point of symmetry in a Normal distribution

$\sigma$ = standard deviation
= distance from the mean to the point where curve begins to fall less steeply

Accelerating (Falling more steeply)

Decelerating (falling less steeply)

$\mu-3\sigma$ $\mu-2\sigma$ $\mu-\sigma$ $\mu$ $\mu+\sigma$ $\mu+2\sigma$ $\mu+3\sigma$

sigma sigma

9-20

Normal Distribution

## Characteristics of a Normal Distribution

Standard deviation ($\sigma$) is the distance from the mean ($\mu$) to where the skier begins to decelerate.

Accelerating (Falling more steeply)

Decelerating (falling less steeply)

$\mu-3\sigma$ $\mu-2\sigma$ $\mu-\sigma$ $\mu$ $\mu+\sigma$ $\mu+2\sigma$ $\mu+3\sigma$

9-21



## Characteristics of a Normal Distribution

**Observe the effect of changing mean and standard deviation on the Normal curve.**

**View Applet**

9-22



## Importance of Normal Distribution

- Describes many distributions of real data and "chance" outcomes.
- Models many roughly symmetric distributions for statistical inference.

9-23

## The 68-95-99.7% Rule

Basic Practice of Statistics Chapter 3

burned onto cerebrum

9-24



## Normal Distribution Areas

**About 68% of the area lies within one standard deviation of the mean.**

9-25

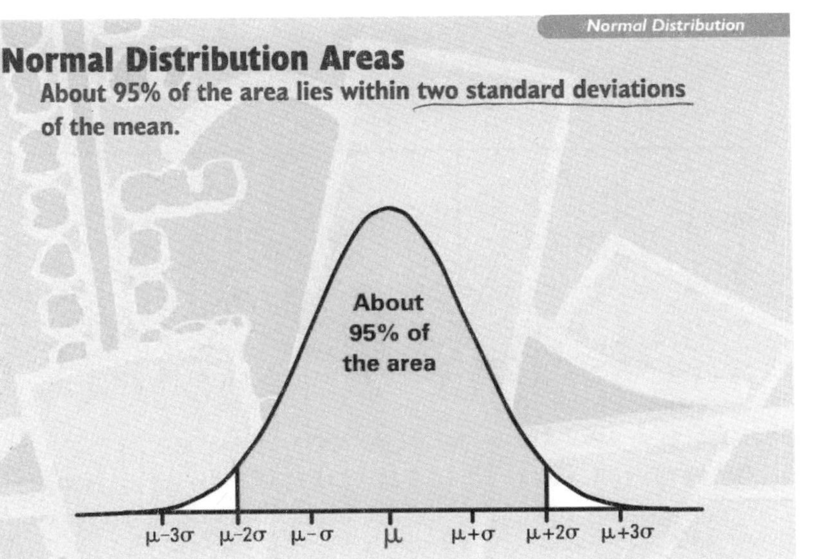


9-26

Normal Distribution

## Normal Distribution Areas

About 99.7% of the area lies within three standard deviations of the mean.

About 99.7% of the area

μ−3σ μ−2σ μ−σ μ μ+σ μ+2σ μ+3σ

9-27

68-95-99.7 Rule

## Percentage of Area within Intervals

95% − 68% = 27%

99.7% − 95% = 4.7%

100.0% − 99.7% = 0.3%

0.15% 2.35% 13.5% 34% 34% 13.5% 2.35% 0.15%

μ−3σ μ−2σ μ−σ μ μ+σ μ+2σ μ+3σ

9-28

68-95-99.7 Rule

## Cumulative Percentages

**Cumulative percentage:** Area to the left of a value.

0.15% 2.5% 16% 50% 84% 97.5% 99.85% 100%

μ−3σ μ−2σ μ−σ μ μ+σ μ+2σ μ+3σ

9-29

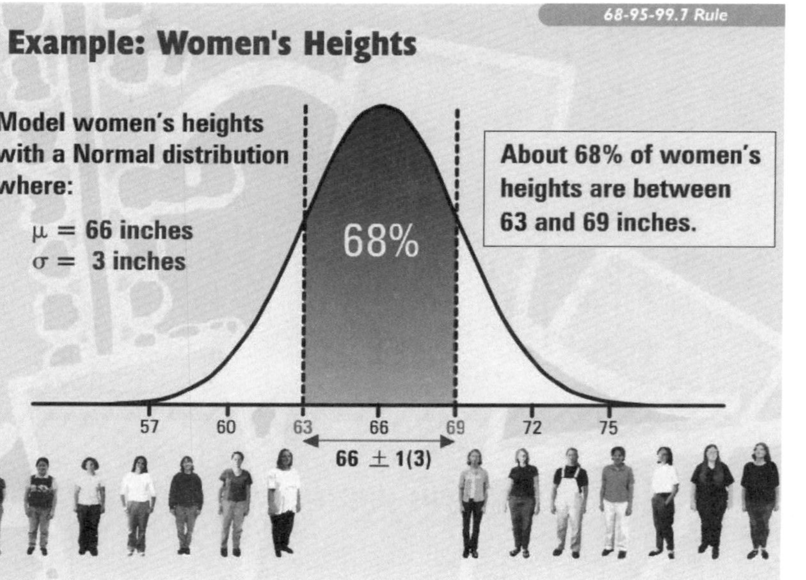


9-30

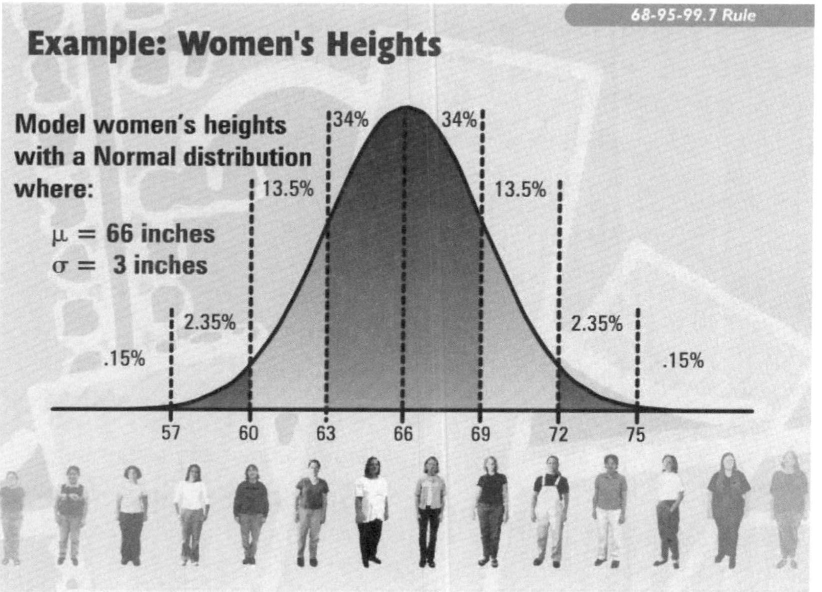


95/2

9-31

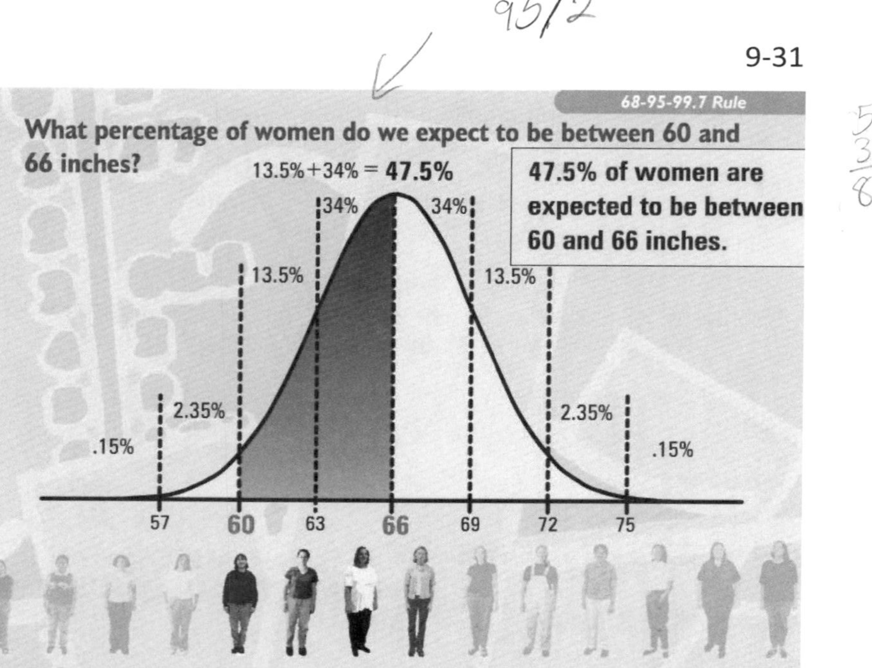


50
34
84

9-32

## The Standard Normal Distribution

Basic Practice of Statistics Chapter 3

9-33

## Review--Normal Distributions

- Bell shaped
- Characterized by μ and σ
- Symmetric around μ
- Values are denoted by x's
- Total area equals 1 (or 100%)
- 68-95-99.7% rule:

**All Normal curves are the same if we measure in units of size σ from μ.**

- Example: line is half a standard deviation (σ) above the mean, μ.
- Changing to these units is called *standardizing*.

9-34

Standardization

**Standardization:** The process of converting an x-value from a normal distribution into a z-score (units of length σ from the center, μ.)

z-score formula: $z = \dfrac{x - \mu}{\sigma}$

**A z-score reports how many standard deviations an x-value lies from the mean and in which direction.**

Standard Normal Curve — **N(0,1)**

-3 -2 -1 0 1 2 3

Normal Curve — **N(μ, σ)**

μ−3σ μ−2σ μ−σ μ μ+σ μ+2σ μ+3σ

9-35

Standardization

## Example

The Iowa Test vocabulary scores for 947 seventh-grade students from Gary, Indiana are displayed in the histogram.

These scores have a mean of 6.84 and a standard deviation of 1.55.

A Normal curve with μ = 6.84 and σ = 1.55 models these data.

Percent: 10, 5

μ = 6.84
σ = 1.55

2.2 6.84 11.5

**Iowa Test Vocabulary Scores**

9-36

Standardization

## Example

Susan scored 8.7 on the vocabulary portion of the Iowa Test.
What is her standardized score?

**View Applet**

$$x = 8.7$$

$$z = \frac{x - \mu}{\sigma} = \frac{8.7 - 6.84}{1.55} = 1.20$$

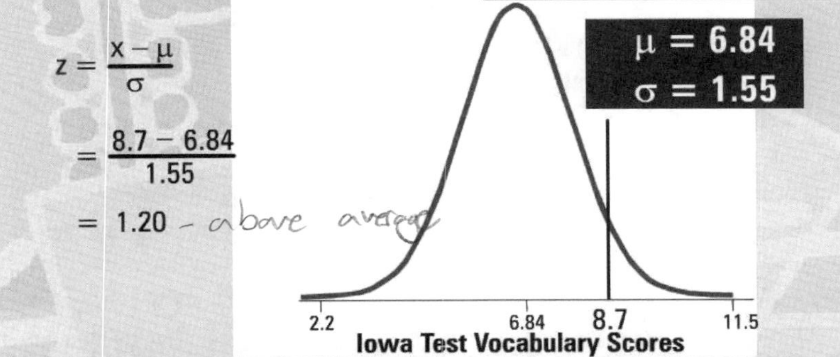


**Interpretation: Susan's score is 1.2 standard deviations above the mean.**

9-37



**Standard Normal Distribution:** A special Normal distribution.

**Properties**
- Bell shaped
- Symmetric around 0 (i.e., $\mu = 0$)
- Has standard deviation equal to 1 (i.e., $\sigma = 1$)
- Total area is 1 (or 100%)
- Values are denoted by z's or z-scores
- Has a table which gives areas under the curve to the left of a z-score

**Purpose**: use table to find areas under any Normal curve

Table A Standard Normal Probabilities

−3 −2 −1 0 1 2 3

**Remember: Area under curve = Proportion (probability) of observations in interval**

9-38



## Comparing a Normal Curve and the Standard Normal Curve

**If a variable x has a Normal distribution with mean $\mu$ and standard deviation $\sigma$,**

Standard Normal | Normal

−3 0 1.2 3 | 2.2 6.84 8.7 11.5

$$z = \frac{x - \mu}{\sigma}$$

**then the standardized variable: $z = \frac{x - \mu}{\sigma}$ has the standard Normal distribution with mean 0 and standard deviation 1.**

9-39



## Compare Areas for Any Normal Curve with the Standard Normal Curve

**View Applet**

9-40

## Vocabulary

**Mean**
**Median**
**Density Curve**
**Normal Distribution**
**Standard Deviation**
**$\mu$ (mu)**
**$\sigma$ (sigma)**

10-1

## Chapter 3 Part 2
## The Normal Distribution

StatTutor Lesson 10

10-2

## Lesson Objectives

Using the standard normal table:

1. Find the area under the curve below a z-score, above a z-score, and between two z-scores.
2. Find z-scores for the corresponding area under the curve to the left, to the right, and in the middle (symmetric around 0).
3. Find area under a normal curve given an x-value.
4. Find an x-value given an area under a normal curve.

10-3

## Finding Normal Proportions

Basic Practice of Statistics Chapter 3

10-4

## Review--Normal Distributions

- Values are denoted by x's
- 68-95-99.7% rule gives areas within 1, 2 and 3 standard deviations:

≈68% ≈95% ≈99.7%

**How do we find other areas?**
**In particular, how do we find the yellow area?**

To find areas under any normal curve:

- Use statistical software
- Or use the standard Normal table

?

$\mu-3\sigma$ $\mu-2\sigma$ $\mu-\sigma$ $\mu$ $\mu+\sigma$ $\mu+2\sigma$ $\mu+3\sigma$

10-5



## Finding Areas for Normal Distributions

**Cumulative proportion for a value, x:**

The proportion of observations in a distribution that lie at or below x.

Yellow area = proportion less than or equal to "a"
= cumulative proportion for "a"

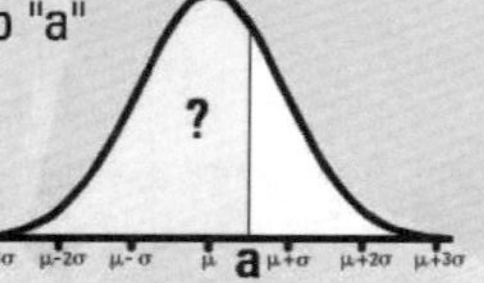


**Keys to finding Normal proportions:**

1. Match area you want with cumulative proportion area(s).
2. Get cumulative area(s) using software or standard Normal table.

**Note: Cumulative proportion called "cumulative distribution" or "cumulative probability" in software.**

10-6



## Three Types of "Find Areas" Problems

**1. Area to the left of "a"** = cumulative proportion for "a"

a

**2. Area to the right of "b"** = 1.0 – cumulative proportion for "b"

b = 100% – b

**3. Area between "c" and "d"** = cumulative proportion for "d"
– cumulative proportion for "c"

c d = d – c

10-7



## Finding Cumulative Proportions

Scores on the vocabulary portion of the Iowa Test for seventh-grade students from Gary, Indiana are approximately normally distributed with a mean of 6.84 and a standard deviation of 1.55. What proportion of the students score less than 8.7?

**Using statistical software:**

Enter the value for the mean, $\mu$=6.84, and the value for the standard deviation, $\sigma$= 1.55.

Ask for the cumulative proportion for 8.7.

**Using Standard Normal table:**

Compute z-score for 8.7: $z = \frac{x - \mu}{\sigma} = \frac{8.7 - 6.84}{1.55} = 1.20$

Look up z = 1.20 on the Standard Normal table to find the cumulative proportion.

10-8

## Using the Standard Normal Table

Basic Practice of Statistics Chapter 3

10-9

## Finding Area for Normal Distributions

**Cumulative proportion for a value x = a:**
Proportion of observations in distribution that are less than or equal to "a"

$\mu-3\sigma$ $\mu-2\sigma$ $\mu-\sigma$ $\mu$ **a** $\mu+\sigma$ $\mu+2\sigma$ $\mu+3\sigma$

**To find areas under any normal curve:**

1. Match area you want with areas of cumulative proportions.
2. Use statistical software or standard normal table to get cumulative proportions.

10-10

Standard Normal Table

## How to Read the Standard Normal table

Table Entry

z

| z | .00 | .01 |
|---|---|---|
| -3.4 | .0003 | .0003 |
| -3.3 | .0005 | .0005 |
| -3.2 | .0007 | .0007 |
| -3.1 | .0010 | .0009 |
| -3.0 | .0013 | .0013 |
| -2.9 | .0019 | .0018 |

NOTE: Table entry for z is the cumulative proportion for z (i.e., area under the standard normal curve left of z)

10-11

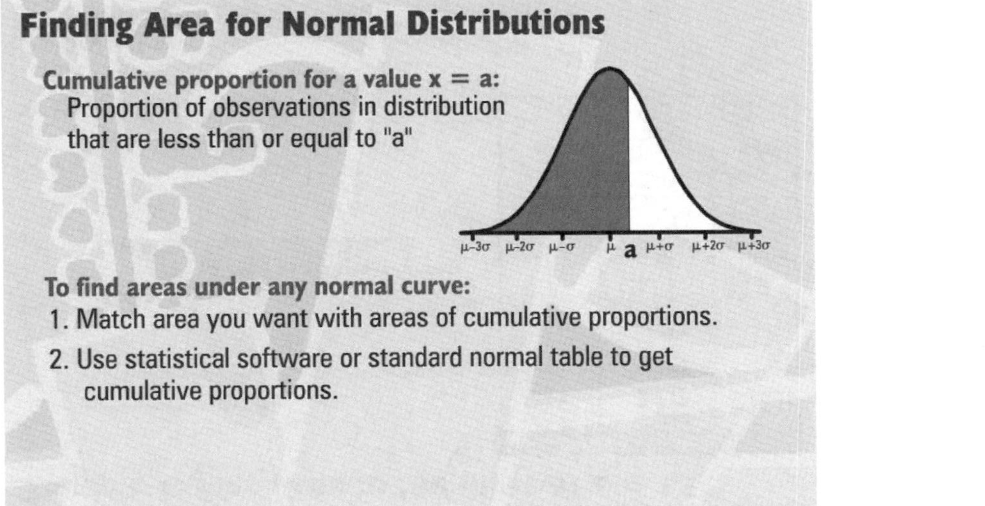


10-12

Standard Normal Table

## Two Ways to Use Standard Normal Table

**Use I: Given z ⟶ Find cumulative proportion**

-3 -2 -1 0 1 2 3
z

**Use 2: Given cumulative proportion ⟶ Find z**

-3 -2 -1 0 1 2 3

10-13



## Reminder: Three Types of "Find Area" Problems

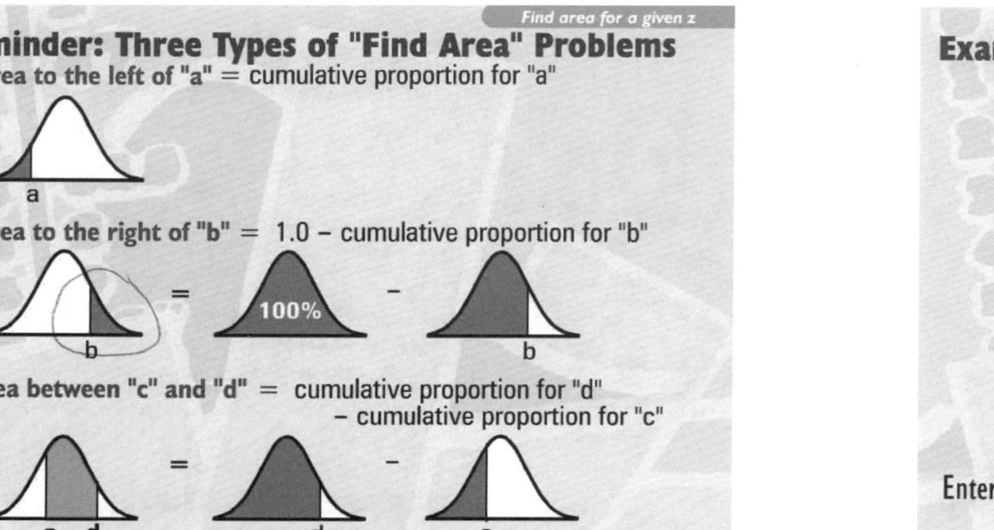


10-14



## Example 1: Find Area to the Left of z = –1.64

Table A Standard Normal Probabilities

| z | .04 | .05 |
|---|---|---|
| -1.8 | .0329 | .0322 |
| -1.7 | .0409 | .0401 |
| -1.6 | .0505 | .0495 |
| -1.5 | .0618 | .0606 |
| -1.4 | .0749 | .0735 |
| -1.3 | .0901 | .0885 |

-1.64

Enter table for z= –1.64 to find area to the left .0505

10-15



## Example 2: Find Area to the Right of z = 1.56

Table A Standard Normal Probabilities

| z | .05 | .06 |
|---|---|---|
| 1.2 | .8944 | .8962 |
| 1.3 | .9115 | .9131 |
| 1.4 | .9265 | .9279 |
| 1.5 | .9394 | .9406 |
| 1.6 | .9505 | .9515 |
| 1.7 | .9599 | .9608 |
| 1.8 | .9678 | .9686 |

.9406 .0594

z = 1.56

1. Enter table for z=1.56 to find cumulative area. **.9406**
2. Subtract from one.

**1.0000 – .9406 = .0594**

10-16



## Example 3: Find area between z=-0.50 and z=2.25

Standard Normal Probabilities

| z | .00 | .01 |
|---|---|---|
| -0.5 | .3085 | .3050 |
| -0.4 | .3446 | .3409 |
| -0.3 | .3821 | .3783 |
| -0.2 | .4207 | .4168 |
| -0.1 | .4602 | .4562 |
| -0.0 | .5000 | .4960 |

.6793

$z = -0.50$ $z_2 = 2.25$

Step 1: Find cumulative proportion for larger z-score (2.25) .9878
Step 2: Find cumulative proportion for smaller z-score (-0.50) –.3085
Step 3: Subtract smaller area from larger area: .6793

10-17

**Given x, find area**

## x-value to Area

**Given an x-value from a Normal distribution, find desired area.**

1. Draw Normal curve and shade desired area
2. Standardize x to get z

$$z = \frac{x - \mu}{\sigma}$$

3. Find cumulative proportion using Standard Normal Table; use cumulative proportion to get desired area.

Table Entry

Table A Standard Normal Probabilities

**Locate z in margins; read area inside table.**

10-18

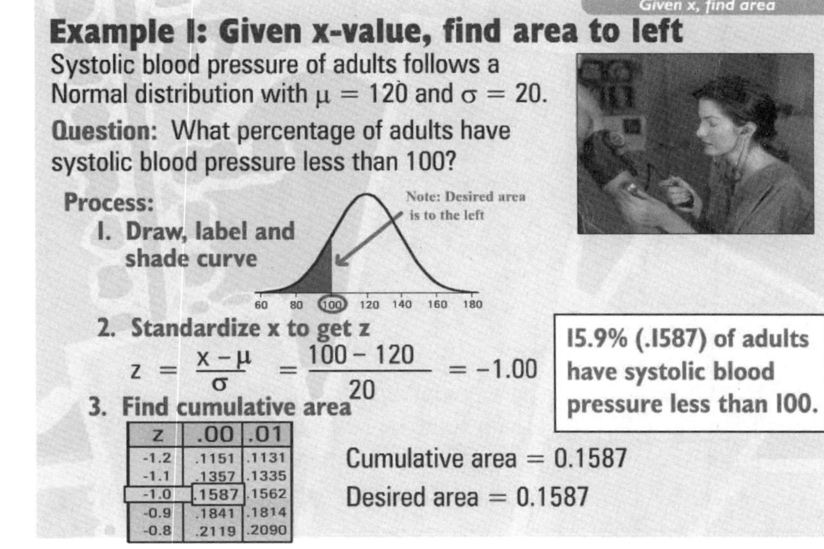

**Given x, find area**

## Example 1: Given x-value, find area to left

Systolic blood pressure of adults follows a Normal distribution with $\mu = 120$ and $\sigma = 20$.

**Question:** What percentage of adults have systolic blood pressure less than 100?

**Process:**

1. **Draw, label and shade curve**

Note: Desired area is to the left

2. **Standardize x to get z**

$$z = \frac{x - \mu}{\sigma} = \frac{100 - 120}{20} = -1.00$$

3. **Find cumulative area**

| z | .00 | .01 |
|---|---|---|
| -1.2 | .1151 | .1131 |
| -1.1 | .1357 | .1335 |
| -1.0 | .1587 | .1562 |
| -0.9 | .1841 | .1814 |
| -0.8 | .2119 | .2090 |

Cumulative area = 0.1587

Desired area = 0.1587

**15.9% (.1587) of adults have systolic blood pressure less than 100.**

10-19

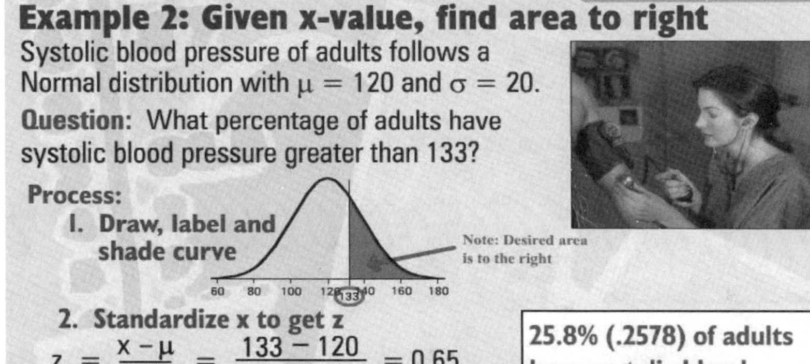

**Given x, find area**

## Example 2: Given x-value, find area to right

Systolic blood pressure of adults follows a Normal distribution with $\mu = 120$ and $\sigma = 20$.

**Question:** What percentage of adults have systolic blood pressure greater than 133?

**Process:**

1. **Draw, label and shade curve**

Note: Desired area is to the right

2. **Standardize x to get z**

$$z = \frac{x - \mu}{\sigma} = \frac{133 - 120}{20} = 0.65$$

3. **Find cumulative area**

| z | .04 | .05 |
|---|---|---|
| 0.4 | .6700 | .6736 |
| 0.5 | .7054 | .7088 |
| 0.6 | .7389 | .7422 |
| 0.7 | .7704 | .7734 |
| 0.8 | .7995 | .8023 |

Cumulative area = 0.7422

Desired area = 1 – 0.7422 = 0.2578

**25.8% (.2578) of adults have systolic blood pressure greater than 133.**

10-20

**Given x, find area**

## Example 3: Given two x-values, find area between

Systolic blood pressure of adults follows a Normal distribution with $\mu = 120$ and $\sigma = 20$.

**Question:** What percentage of adults have systolic blood pressure between 100 and 133?

**Process:**

1. **Draw, label and shade curve**

Note: Desired area is in between

2. **Standardize x's to get z's**

$$z_1 = \frac{x_1 - \mu}{\sigma} = \frac{100 - 120}{20} = -1.00 \quad z_2 = \frac{x_2 - \mu}{\sigma} = \frac{133 - 120}{20} = 0.65$$

3. **Find cumulative area**

| z | .00 | .01 |
|---|---|---|
| -1.2 | .1151 | .1131 |
| -1.1 | .1357 | .1335 |
| -1.0 | .1587 | .1562 |
| -0.9 | .1841 | .1814 |
| -0.8 | .2119 | .2090 |

| z | .04 | .05 |
|---|---|---|
| 0.4 | .6700 | .6736 |
| 0.5 | .7054 | .7088 |
| 0.6 | .7389 | .7422 |
| 0.7 | .7704 | .7734 |
| 0.8 | .7995 | .8023 |

Cumulative area of smaller z = 0.1587

Cumulative area of larger z = 0.7422

Desired area = 0.7422 – 0.1587
= 0.5835

10-21

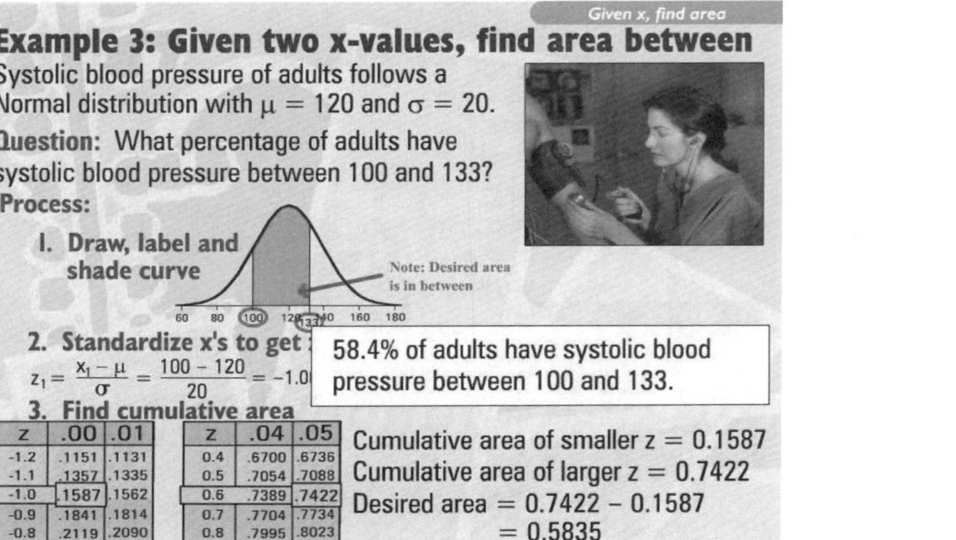


10-22

Standard Normal Table

# Finding a Value Given a Proportion

Basic Practice of Statistics Chapter 3

10-23

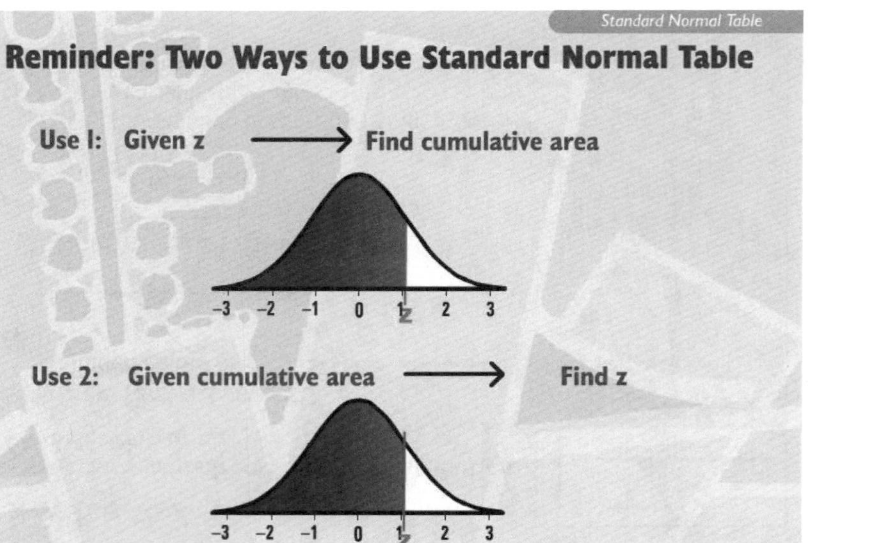


10-24

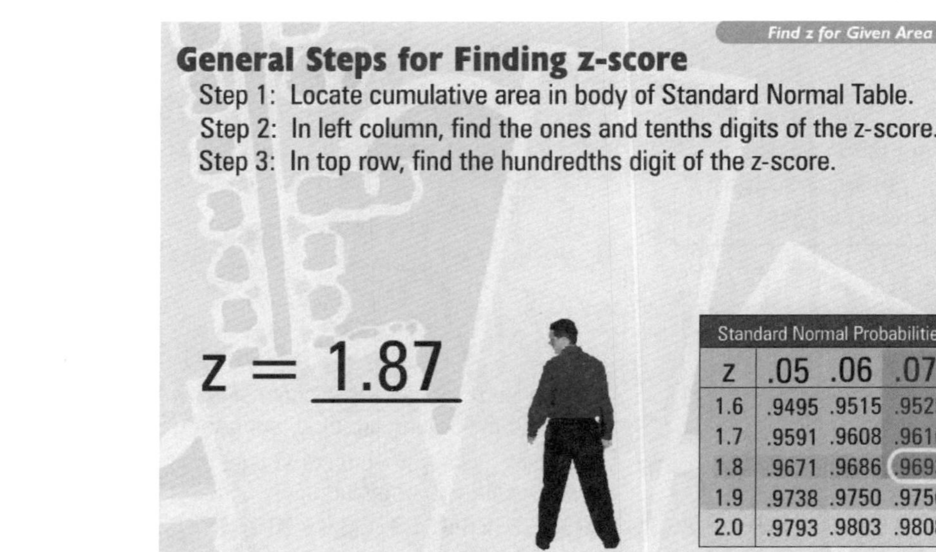

10-25

Find z for Given Area

## General Steps for Finding z-score

Step 1: Locate cumulative area in body of Standard Normal Table.
Step 2: In left column, find the ones and tenths digits of the z-score.
Step 3: In top row, find the hundredths digit of the z-score.

Remember: Table A always gives the cumulative area for a z-score. Be sure to convert given area to a cumulative area before using Table A.

Standard Normal Probabilities

| z | .05 | .06 | .07 |
|---|---|---|---|
| 1.6 | .9495 | .9515 | .9525 |
| 1.7 | .9591 | .9608 | .9616 |
| 1.8 | .9671 | .9686 | .9693 |
| 1.9 | .9738 | .9750 | .9756 |
| 2.0 | .9793 | .9803 | .9808 |

10-26

Finding z for Given Area

## Example I: Find the z-score that has area 0.9750 to the left.

.9750

-3 -2 -1 0 1 2 3

z = 1.96

Standard Normal Probabilities

| z | .05 | .06 | .07 |
|---|---|---|---|
| 1.6 | .9495 | .9515 | .9525 |
| 1.7 | .9591 | .9608 | .9616 |
| 1.8 | .9671 | .9686 | .9693 |
| 1.9 | .9738 | .9750 | .9756 |
| 2.0 | .9793 | .9803 | .9808 |

Find area inside table; read z-score in margins. z = 1.96

10-27

Finding z for Given Area

## Example 2: Find the z-score that has 88.1% of the area to its right.

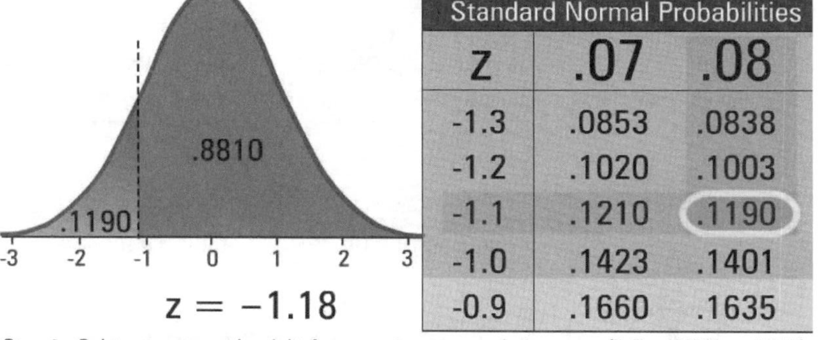


z = −1.18

Standard Normal Probabilities

| z | .07 | .08 |
|---|---|---|
| -1.3 | .0853 | .0838 |
| -1.2 | .1020 | .1003 |
| -1.1 | .1210 | .1190 |
| -1.0 | .1423 | .1401 |
| -0.9 | .1660 | .1635 |

Step 1: Subtract area on the right from one to get cumulative area. (1.0 – .8810 = .1190)

Step 2: Locate area on left = .1190 inside the table and find z-score in the margins.
z = −1.18

10-28

Finding z for Given Area

## Example 3: Find the two z-scores enclosing middle area of 50% symmetric about μ = 0

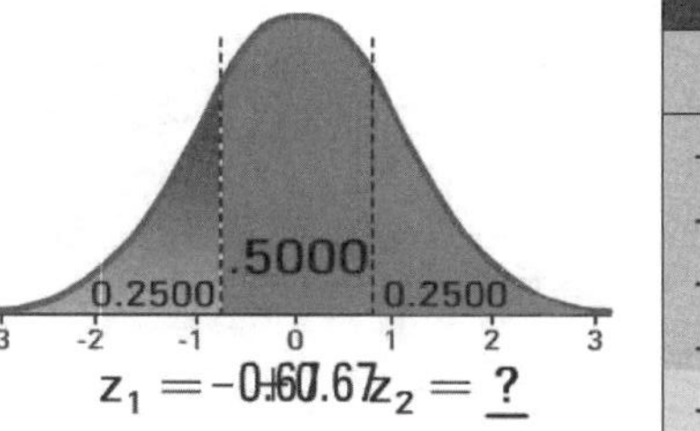


$z_1 = -0.67$ $z_2 = 0.67$ ?

Standard Normal Probabilities

| z | .07 | .08 | .09 |
|---|---|---|---|
| -0.8 | .1922 | .1894 | .1867 |
| -0.7 | .2206 | .2177 | .2148 |
| -0.6 | .2514 | .2483 | .2451 |
| -0.5 | .2843 | .2810 | .2776 |
| -0.4 | .3192 | .3156 | .3121 |

1. Subtract the given area from one and divide by two (since curve is symmetric) to find the areas of the tails.
   1.0 – 0.5 = 0.5 → 0.5 / 2 = 0.25
2. Locate area closest to .2500 inside the table; find z-score in the margin.
   Because of symmetry, $z_1 = -0.67$ → $z_2 = 0.67$

10-29

*Given Area Find x*

## Area to x-value

**Given an area under a normal curve, find the corresponding x-value.**

**Process:** Given area → z → x

1. Draw curve; shade in given area; determine cumulative area.

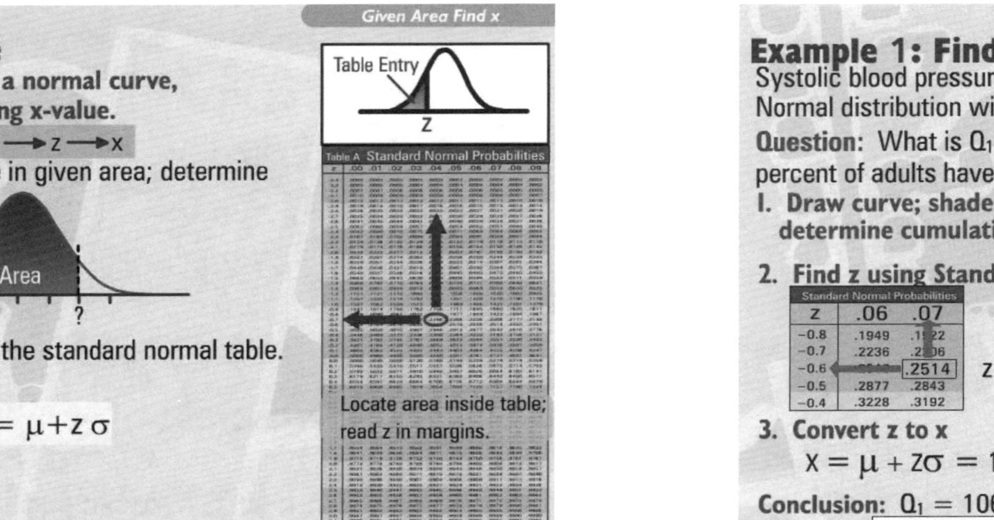


2. Find z-score using the standard normal table.

3. Convert z to x: $x = \mu + z\sigma$

10-30

*Given Area Find x*

## Example 1: Find x-value given area to left

Systolic blood pressure of adults follows a Normal distribution with $\mu = 120$ and $\sigma = 20$.

**Question:** What is $Q_1$ for systolic blood pressure? (i.e., twenty-five percent of adults have systolic blood pressure below what level?)

**1. Draw curve; shade given area; determine cumulative area.**

Note: Given area is to the left.

.25

60 80 100 120 140 160 180

? x

**2. Find z using Standard Normal Table**

| z | .06 | .07 |
|---|---|---|
| −0.8 | .1949 | .1922 |
| −0.7 | .2236 | .2206 |
| −0.6 | | .2514 |
| −0.5 | .2877 | .2843 |
| −0.4 | .3228 | .3192 |

$z = -0.67$

**3. Convert z to x**

$x = \mu + z\sigma = 120 + (-0.67)(20) = 106.6$

**Conclusion:** $Q_1 = 106.6$

25% of adults have systolic blood pressure below 106.6.

10-31

*Given Area Find x*

## Example 2: Find x-value given area to right

Systolic blood pressure of adults follows a Normal distribution with $\mu = 120$ and $\sigma = 20$.

**Question:** Ten percent of all adults have systolic blood pressure above what level?

**1. Draw curve; shade given area; determine cumulative area.**

Cumulative area = 1.00 − 0.10 = 0.90

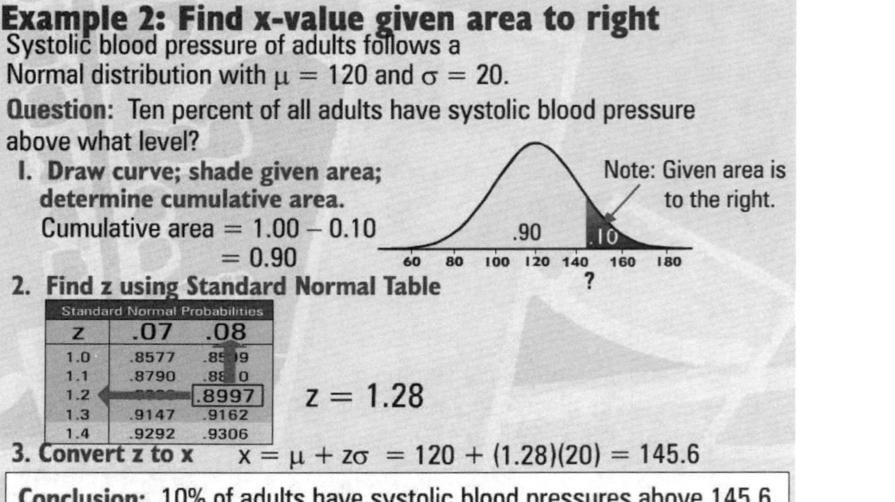


**2. Find z using Standard Normal Table**

| z | .07 | .08 |
|---|---|---|
| 1.0 | .8577 | .8599 |
| 1.1 | .8790 | .8810 |
| 1.2 | | .8997 |
| 1.3 | .9147 | .9162 |
| 1.4 | .9292 | .9306 |

$z = 1.28$

**3. Convert z to x** $x = \mu + z\sigma = 120 + (1.28)(20) = 145.6$

**Conclusion:** 10% of adults have systolic blood pressures above 145.6.

10-32

*Given Area Find x*

## Example 3: Find two x-values given area in middle

Systolic blood pressure of adults follows a Normal distribution with $\mu = 120$ and $\sigma = 20$.

**Question:** Fifty percent of all adults have systolic blood pressures between what two levels symmetric about the mean of $\mu = 120$?

**1. Draw picture; shade given area; determine area to left.**

1.0 − 0.5 = 0.5 = area in tails

.50

60 80 100 120 140 160 180

? ?

**2. Find z's using Standard Normal Table**

| z | .06 | .07 |
|---|---|---|
| −0.8 | .1949 | .1922 |
| −0.7 | .2236 | .2206 |
| −0.6 | | .2514 |
| −0.5 | .2877 | .2843 |
| −0.4 | .3228 | .3192 |

$z_1 = -0.67$

**3. Convert z's to x's**

$x_1 = \mu + z_1\sigma = 120 + (-0.67)(20) = 106.6$

$x_2 = \mu + z_2\sigma = 120 + (0.67)(20) = 133.4$

**Conclusion:** 50% of adults have systolic blood pressure between 106.6 and 133.4.

# Vocabulary

- Normal Distribution
- Standard Normal Distribution
- Standard Normal Table
- Standardized Value
- z-score

11-1

# Chapter 4 Part I
# Scatterplots and Correlation

StatTutor Lesson 11

several goals
• characterize

11-2

Jan 31

## Lesson Objectives

1. Define and give examples of bivariate data; identify explanatory and response variables.
2. List steps for analyzing bivariate quantitative data.
3. Construct a scatterplot for bivariate quantitative data.
4. Describe direction, form and strength for the relationship between the two variables in a scatterplot.
5. Add categorical variable to scatterplot.

11-3

Bivariate Data

# Explanatory and Response Variables

Basic Practice of Statistics Chapter 4

11-4

Bivariate Data

## Bivariate Data

Two measurements (two variables) on each individual in a study.

- We study the relationship between these two variables.

**Response Variable:** measures outcome on each individual; denoted by Y.

**Explanatory Variable:** may explain or influences changes in the response variable; denoted by X.

- Sometimes explanatory and response variables cannot be designated.
- Variables can be: both quantitative
  both categorical
  one of each

Example: Pollution of Cities

City Population Size (X)
vs.
City Nitrogen Oxide (NOx) Pollution Level (Y)

| Individual | X | Y | Types of Data | |
|---|---|---|---|---|
| city | population size | NOx level | quantitative | quantitative |
| person | height | income | quantitative | quantitative |
| customer | gender | music preference | categorical | categorical |
| hot dog | type | calorie content | categorical | quantitative |
| professor | gender | rank | categorical | categorical |

11-5



## Examining Relationships

**Study of bivariate data focuses on whether a relationship exists between the explanatory and response variables.**

**Identify explanatory and response variables:**

Is there a relationship between your **ACT math score** and your **college algebra grade?**

X= ACT math score Y = college algebra grade

Can we use a male's **height at age 4** to predict his **height as an adult?**

X = height at age 4 Y = height as an adult

Is there an association between **gender** and **whether a person exercises?**

X = gender Y = whether person exercises

**For which example are both variables categorical?**

11-6



## Analyzing Quantitative Bivariate Data

**Outline**

1. Plot data with a scatterplot; look for overall pattern of relationship and deviations from that pattern, especially outliers.
2. Compute a summary number called correlation coefficient as a measure of strength of linear relationship.
3. Model linear relationship with a straight line equation called the regression equation.

Scatterplot

Response Variable

Explanatory Variable

11-7



# Displaying Relationships: Scatterplots

Basic Practice of Statistics Chapter 4

• direction
• form
• strength
• presence of outliers

11-8



## Graphing Bivariate Data

1. Scale X (Lean Body Mass) horizontally from 0 - 70
2. Scale Y (Metabolic Rate) vertically from 0 - 2000
3. Plot each (X, Y) pair

| Subject # | Mass (kg) | Metabolic Rate (calories / 24 hrs) |
|---|---|---|
| 1 | 62.0 | 1792 |
| 2 | 62.9 | 1666 |
| 3 | 36.1 | 995 |
| 4 | 54.6 | 1425 |
| 5 | 48.5 | 1396 |
| 6 | 42.0 | 1418 |
| 7 | 47.4 | 1362 |
| 8 | 50.6 | 1502 |
| 9 | 42.0 | 1256 |
| 10 | 48.7 | 1614 |
| 11 | 40.3 | 1189 |
| 12 | 33.1 | 913 |
| 13 | 51.9 | 1460 |
| 14 | 42.4 | 1124 |
| 15 | 34.5 | 1052 |
| 16 | 51.1 | 1347 |
| 17 | 41.2 | 1204 |
| 18 | 51.9 | 1867 |
| 19 | 46.9 | 1439 |

Metabolic Rate vs. Lean Body Mass

Metabolic Rate

Mass

11-9

*Making Scatterplots*

## Graphing Bivariate Data

**Statisticians usually construct scatterplots using a statistical software package.**

11-10

*Interpreting Scatterplots*

# Interpreting Scatterplots

Basic Practice of Statistics Chapter 4

11-11

*Interpreting Scatterplots*

## Examine Scatterplot for Relationship

**If relationship exists, describe its**

- Direction positive or negative
- Form linear or curved
- Strength strong or weak

**Assessment of these characteristics is somewhat subjective and will improve with practice.**

11-12

*Interpreting Scatterplots*

## Examine Scatterplot for Relationship

- **Direction**

**Positively sloped:** as X increases, Y increases
**Negatively sloped:** as X increases, Y decreases

11-13

*Interpreting Scatterplots*

## Examine Scatterplot for Relationship

- **Form**

**Linear:** Shape suggests a straight line
**Nonlinear:** Shape suggests curvature (Quadratic, Cubic, Exponential, etc.)

**Linear (Straight Line)** | **Non-linear (Quadratic)** | **Non-linear (Exponential)**

11-14

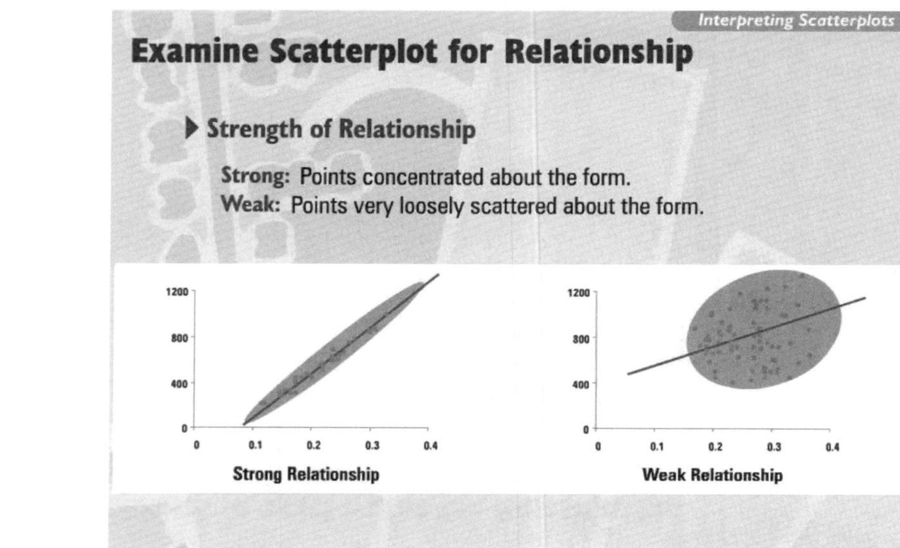


11-15

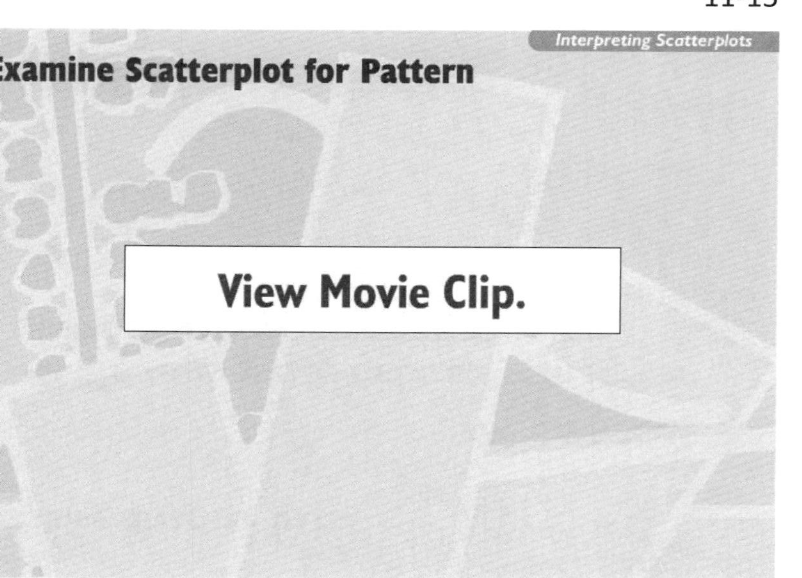


11-16

*Interpreting Scatterplots*

## Examine Scatterplot for Pattern

**Is there a relationship between number of manatee deaths and number of powerboat registrations? Yes**

| Direction | Positive or Negative |
|---|---|
| Form | Linear or Curved |
| Strength | Strong or Weak |

| Year | Powerboat Registrations (in thousands) | Manatees Killed |
|---|---|---|
| 1977 | 447 | 13 |
| 1978 | 460 | 21 |
| 1979 | 481 | 24 |
| 1980 | 498 | 16 |
| 1981 | 513 | 24 |
| 1982 | 512 | 20 |
| 1983 | 526 | 15 |
| 1984 | 559 | 34 |
| 1985 | 585 | 33 |
| 1986 | 614 | 33 |
| 1987 | 645 | 39 |
| 1988 | 675 | 43 |
| 1989 | 711 | 50 |
| 1990 | 719 | 47 |

**Manatees Killed vs. Powerboat Registration in Florida (1977-90)**

Manatees Killed | Powerboat Registrations (1000)

**Will registering more powerboats result in more manatees killed?**

11-17

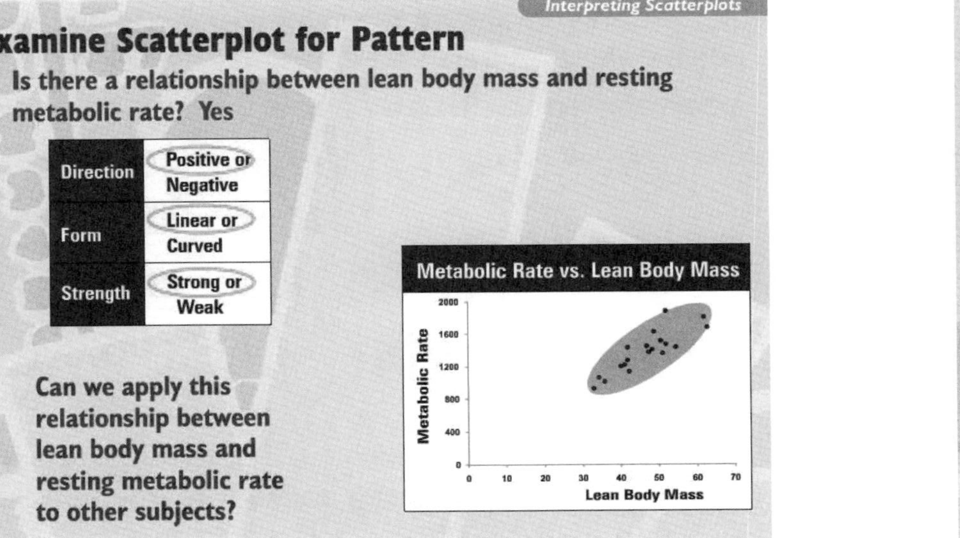


11-18

Interpreting Scatterplots

## Examine Scatterplot for Pattern

Is there a relationship between lung capacity and time to run 1.5 miles for runners? Yes

| Direction | Positive or Negative |
|---|---|
| Form | Linear or Curved |
| Strength | Strong or Weak |

Runners' Lung Capacity vs. Run Time

Time (min) to run 1.5 miles

Lung Capacity ($VO_2$)

Can we apply the relationship between lung capacity and time required to run 1.5 miles to other runners?

11-19

Interpreting Scatterplots

## Examine Scatterplot for Pattern

Is there a relationship between score on a statistics exam and time spent taking the exam? No

| Direction | |
|---|---|
| Form | |
| Strength | |

Exam Score vs. Time Spent Taking Exam

score

time (in minutes)

11-20

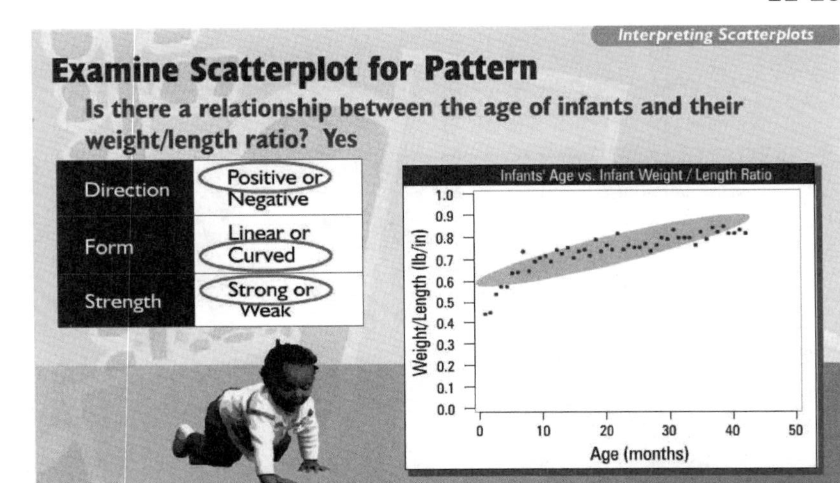

11-21



## Examine Scatterplot for Pattern

Is there a relationship between duration of eruption and time until the next eruption for Old Faithful? Yes or No

| Direction | Positive or Negative |
|---|---|
| Form | Linear or Curved |
| Strength | Moderately Strong or Weak |

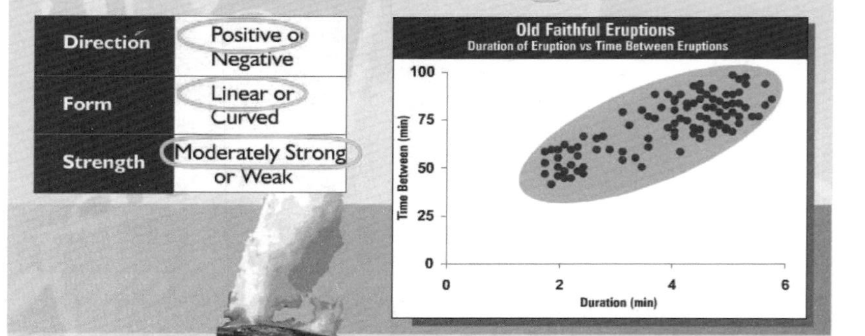


Can we use duration of the previous eruption to predict time until the next eruption of Old Faithful?

11-22



## Examine Scatterplot for Pattern

Is there a relationship between blood alcohol content and sobriety test scores? Yes or No

| Direction | Positive or Negative |
|---|---|
| Form | Linear or Curved |
| Strength | Moderately Strong or Weak |

Blood Alcohol Content vs. Sobriety Score

Blood Alcohol Content

Outlier

Sobriety Test Score

Can we use a person's sobriety test score to determine his/her blood alcohol content?

11-23



## Examine Scatterplot for Pattern

Is there a relationship between diamond size and its price? Yes or No

| Direction | Positive or Negative |
|---|---|
| Form | Linear or Curved |
| Strength | Strong or Weak |

Diamonds

Carats vs Price

Price ($)

Carats

Can we use the relationship between size and price of diamonds to predict price of a .25 carat diamond? a 2.0 carat diamond?

11-24



## Examine Scatterplot for Pattern

Is there a relationship between date of birth and draft number? No But the numerical measure of strength indicates a negative association. Note clusters in upper left and lower right.

| Direction | Positive or Negative |
|---|---|
| Form | Linear or Curved ??? |
| Strength | Strong or Very Weak |

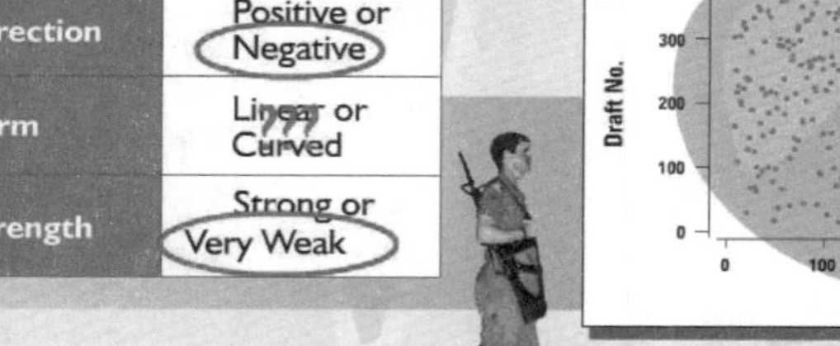


Detecting this negative association requires a measure of strength.

Can these results be applied to other birth dates and draft numbers?

11-25

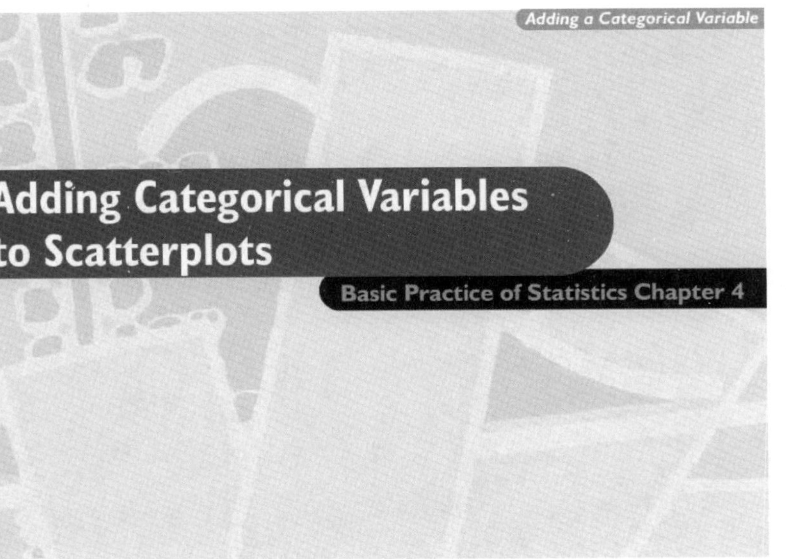


11-26

Adding a Categorical Variable

## Two Quantitative and One Categorical Variables

The scatterplot of calories vs. sodium in hot dogs:
Add a third categorical variable (hot dog type).
Conclusion?

| Obs. | Cal | Sodium | Type |
|---|---|---|---|
| 1 | 186 | 495 | Beef |
| 2 | 181 | 477 | Beef |
| 3 | 176 | 425 | Beef |
| 4 | 149 | 322 | Beef |
| . | . | . | . |
| 20 | 132 | 253 | Beef |
| 21 | 173 | 458 | Meat |
| 22 | 191 | 506 | Meat |
| 23 | 182 | 473 | Meat |
| . | . | . | . |
| 37 | 138 | 339 | Meat |
| 38 | 129 | 430 | Poultry |
| 39 | 132 | 375 | Poultry |
| 40 | 102 | 396 | Poultry |
| . | . | . | . |
| 54 | 144 | 545 | Poultry |

Hot Dogs

Sodium (mg / hot dog)

Calories (cal / hot dog)

Beef
o Meat
x Poultry

11-27

## Vocabulary

Bivariate Data
Direction of Relationship
Explanatory Variable (X)
Form of Relationship
Response Variable (Y)
Scatterplot
Strength of Relationship

12-1

# Chapter 4 Part 2
# Scatterplots and Correlation

StatTutor Lesson 12

Youtube: Hans Roslings 200 countries 4 years

12-2

Jan 31

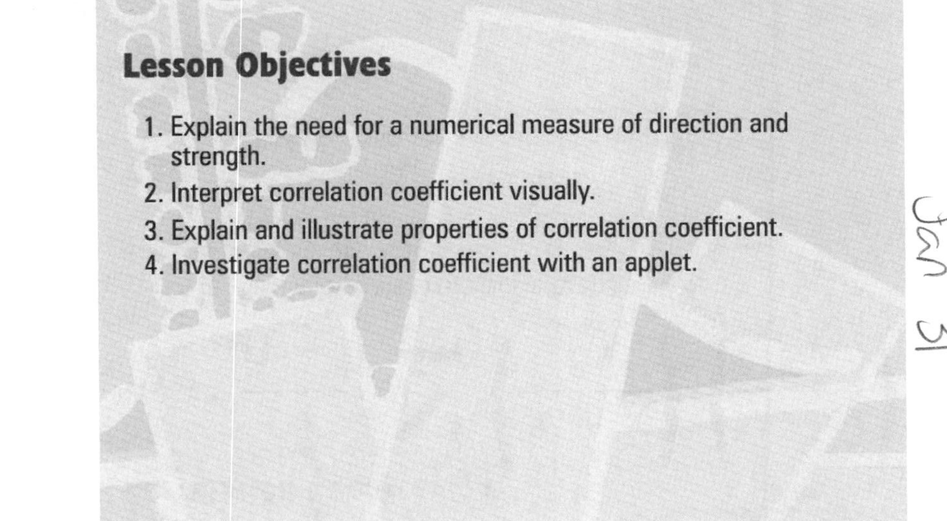


12-3

Need for r

## Measuring Linear Association: Correlation

Basic Practice of Statistics Chapter 4

12-4

Need for r

## Measuring Strength of Relationship

How can we compare the strength of linear relationships more precisely than using words like strong or weak?

12-5

Need for r

## Measuring Strength of Relationship

**Which scatterplot has the strongest relationship between X and Y?**

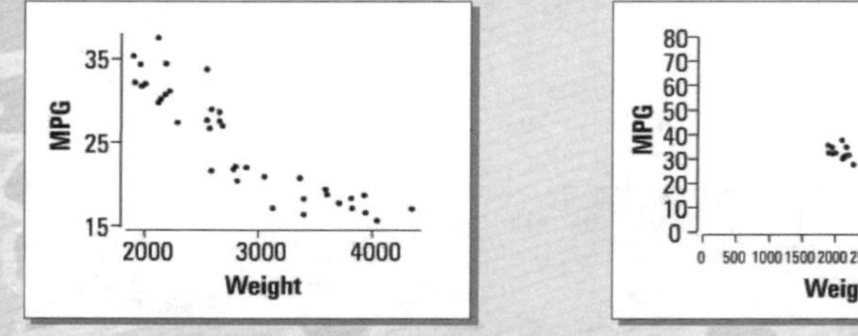


MPG 0 10 20 30 40 50 60 70 80
0 500 1000 1500 2000 2500 3000 3500 4000 4500
Weight

Both scatterplots display the same data but using different scales.

**Needed: A numerical measure because graph can be visually misleading.**

12-6

Need for r

## Measuring Strength of Relationship

**Which scatterplot has the strongest relationship between X and Y?**

Both scatterplots illustrate no relationship between X and Y.

**Needed: A numerical measure of strength.**

12-7

Visualizing r

## Correlation Coefficent, r

**A number that gives a measure of the direction and strength of the linear relationship between two quantitative variables, X and Y.**

$$r = \frac{1}{n-1} \sum \left(\frac{x_i - \bar{x}}{s_x}\right) \cdot \left(\frac{y_i - \bar{y}}{s_y}\right)$$

where

**$\bar{x}$ = mean of $x_i$'s**

**$\bar{y}$ = mean of $y_i$'s**

**$s_x$ = standard deviation of $x_i$'s**

**$s_y$ = standard deviation of $y_i$'s**

12-8

Visualizing r

## Correlation Coefficent, r

$$r = \frac{1}{n-1} \sum \left(\frac{x_i - \bar{x}}{s_x}\right) \cdot \left(\frac{y_i - \bar{y}}{s_y}\right)$$

1. Plot the data and check for nonlinearity and outliers.
2. Create products of z-scores:
   Compute the deviations, $x_i - \bar{x}$; divide by $s_x$
   Compute the deviations, $y_i - \bar{y}$; divide by $s_y$
   Multiply the z-scores; i.e. compute: $\left(\frac{x_i - \bar{x}}{s_x}\right) \cdot \left(\frac{y_i - \bar{y}}{s_y}\right)$
3. Add the products.
4. Divide by n – 1.

12-9



## Example: Correlation Coefficient

- Trends in major league baseball:
  - home runs
  - runs scored
- Quality pitching gives advantage.
- Earned Run Average (ERA) is the number of earned runs allowed per 9 innings.
- ERA measures pitching strength.
  - Low ERA → Strong pitching
  - High ERA → Poor pitching
- Compare ERA vs. winning percentage for teams.

**Objective: to measure the strength and direction of association between a team's pitching ERA (X) and the team's winning percentage (Y).**

12-10

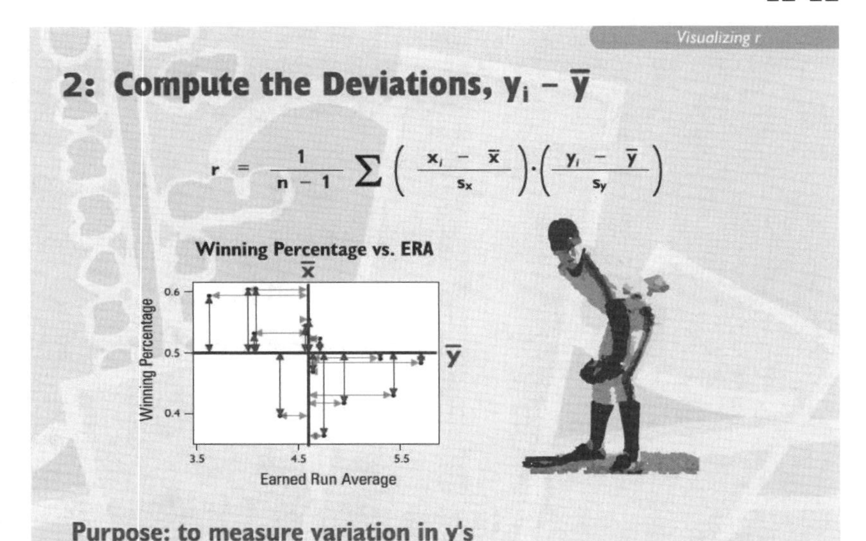


| Team | ERA | Winning Percentage |
|---|---|---|
| Houston | 3.62 | 0.594 |
| Arizona | 3.99 | 0.606 |
| Cincinnati | 4.05 | 0.532 |
| Atlanta | 4.06 | 0.606 |
| San Diego | 4.29 | 0.397 |
| New York | 4.53 | 0.545 |
| Pittsburgh | 4.53 | 0.531 |
| Philadelphia | 4.55 | 0.531 |
| San Francisco | 4.55 | 0.552 |
| Los Angeles | 4.60 | 0.469 |
| Chicago | 4.65 | 0.524 |
| Florida | 4.70 | 0.364 |
| Montreal | 4.90 | 0.419 |
| St Louis | 5.26 | 0.492 |
| Milwaukee | 5.39 | 0.431 |
| Colorado | 5.67 | 0.484 |

12-11

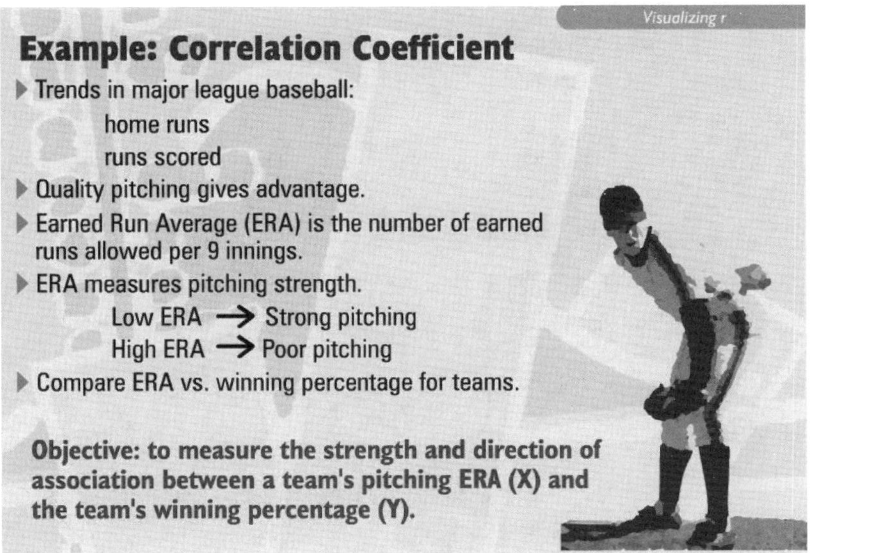


12-12



## 2: Compute the Deviations, $y_i - \bar{y}$

$$r = \frac{1}{n-1} \sum \left( \frac{x_i - \bar{x}}{s_x} \right) \cdot \left( \frac{y_i - \bar{y}}{s_y} \right)$$

Winning Percentage vs. ERA

**Purpose: to measure variation in y's**

12-13

*Visualizing r*

## 2: Divide: x Deviations by $s_x$, y Deviations by $s_y$

$$r = \frac{1}{n-1}\sum\left(\frac{x_i - \bar{x}}{s_x}\right)\cdot\left(\frac{y_i - \bar{y}}{s_y}\right)$$

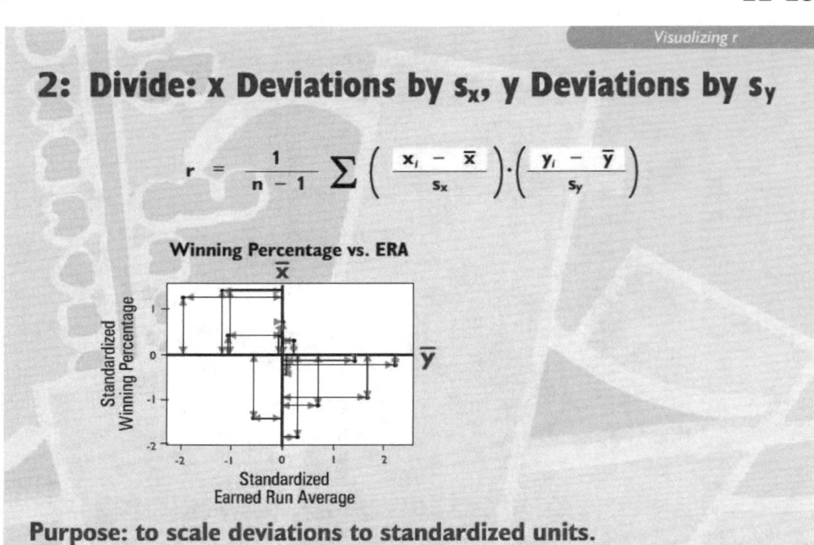


**Purpose: to scale deviations to standardized units.**

12-14

*Visualizing r*

## 2: Multiply z-scores: $\frac{(x_i - \bar{x})}{s_x}$ by $\frac{(y_i - \bar{y})}{s_y}$

$$r = \frac{1}{n-1}\sum\left(\frac{x_i - \bar{x}}{s_x}\right)\cdot\left(\frac{y_i - \bar{y}}{s_y}\right)$$

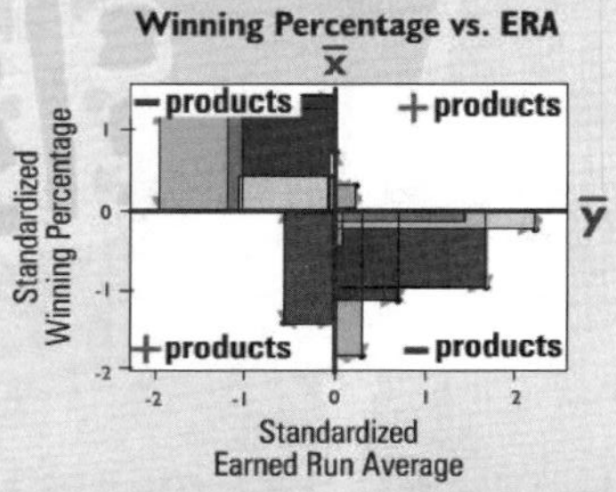

Winning Percentage vs. ERA

− products + products + products − products

Standardized Winning Percentage

Standardized Earned Run Average

**Purpose: to measure size of joint variation in x and y for each point . (Each product gives "area" of rectangle).**

12-15

*Visualizing r*

## 3: Sum the Products (Areas)

$$r = \frac{1}{n-1}\sum\left(\frac{x_i - \bar{x}}{s_x}\right)\cdot\left(\frac{y_i - \bar{y}}{s_y}\right)$$

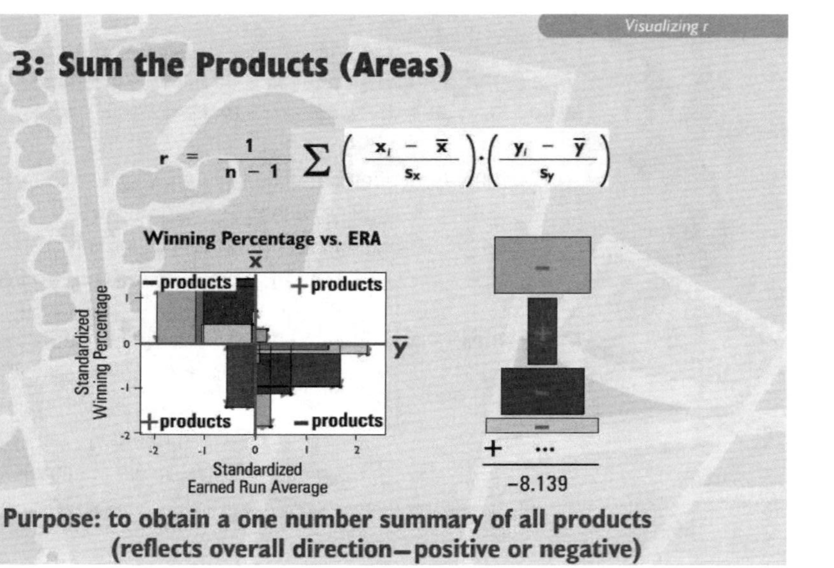


**Purpose: to obtain a one number summary of all products (reflects overall direction—positive or negative)**

12-16

*Visualizing r*

## 4: Divide by n − 1

$$r = \frac{1}{n-1}\sum\left(\frac{x_i - \bar{x}}{s_x}\right)\cdot\left(\frac{y_i - \bar{y}}{s_y}\right)$$

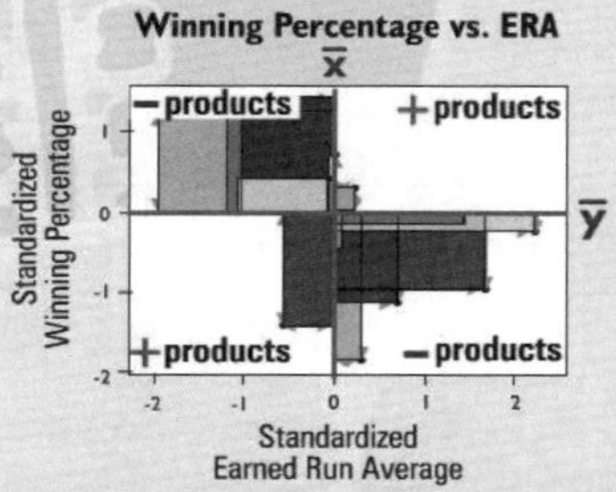

Winning Percentage vs. ERA

− products + products + products − products

Standardized Winning Percentage

Standardized Earned Run Average

−0.54

Average

$-8.139 / (16 - 1) = -0.54$

**Purpose: to find a representative product (rectangle) accounting for positive and negatives.**

12-17

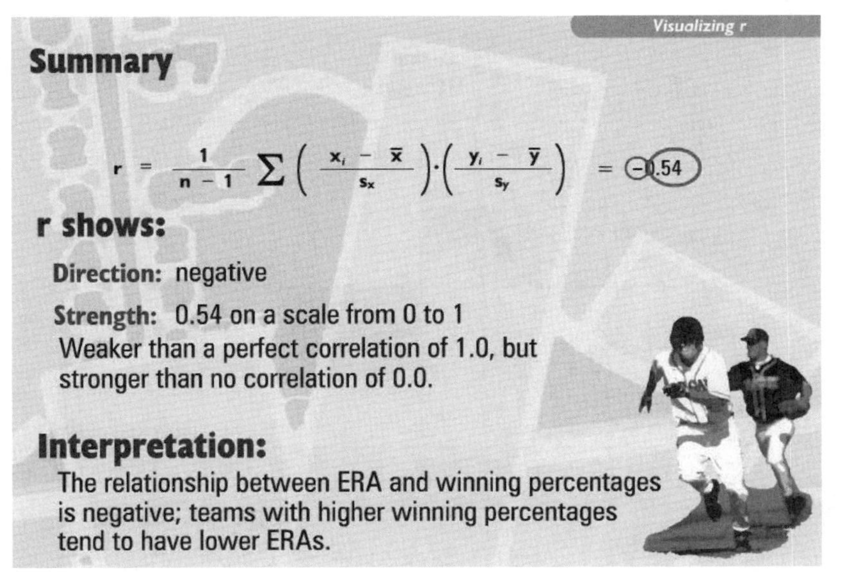


12-18

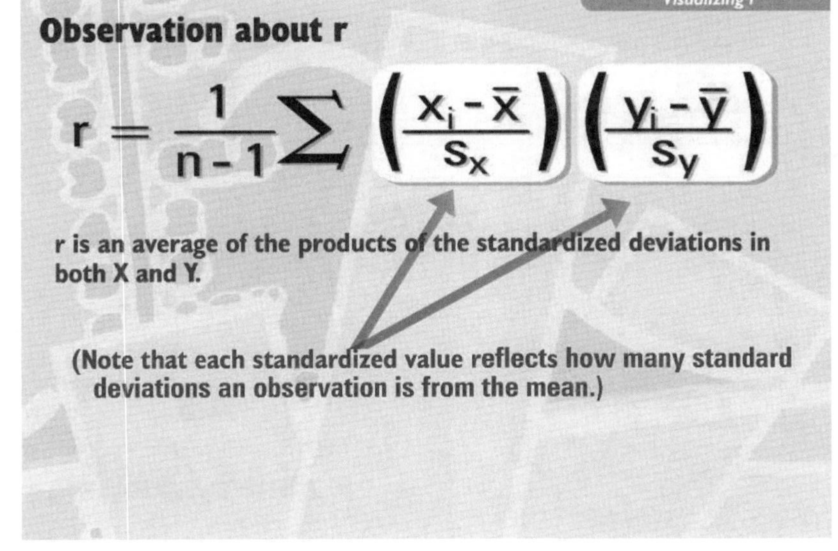


12-19

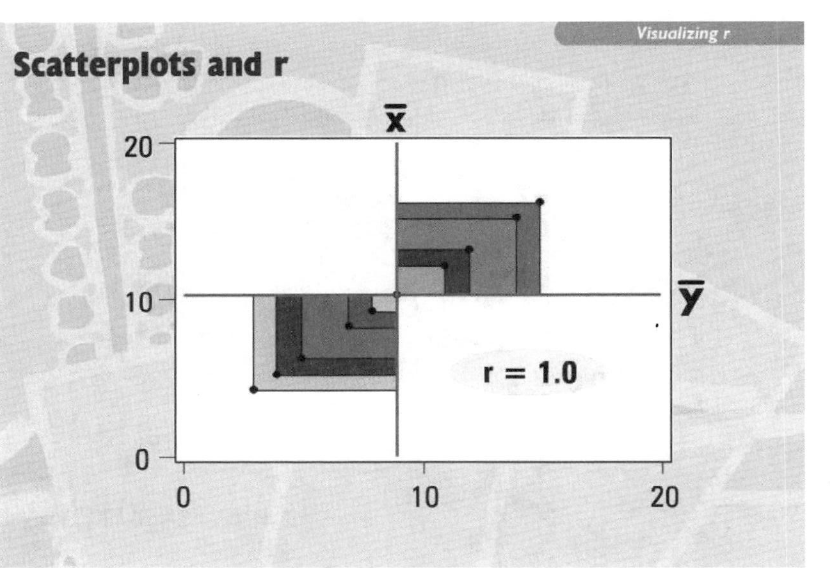


12-20

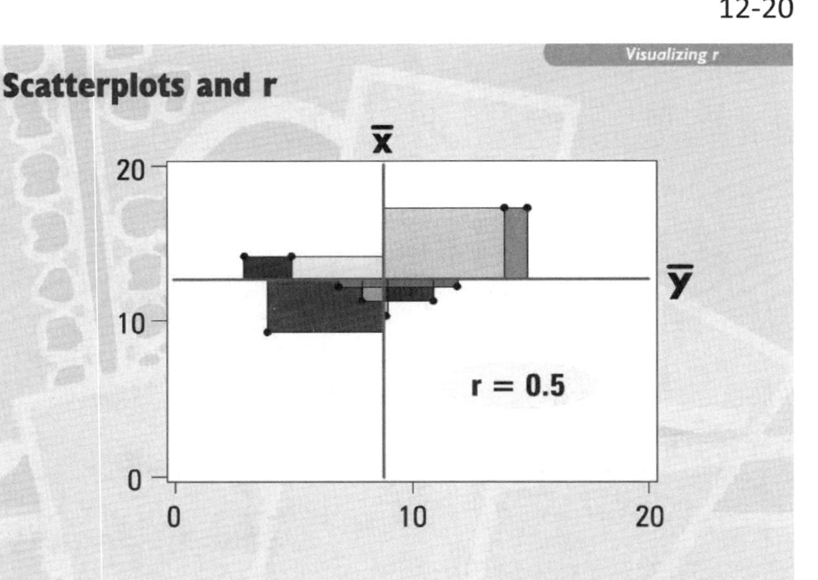

12-21

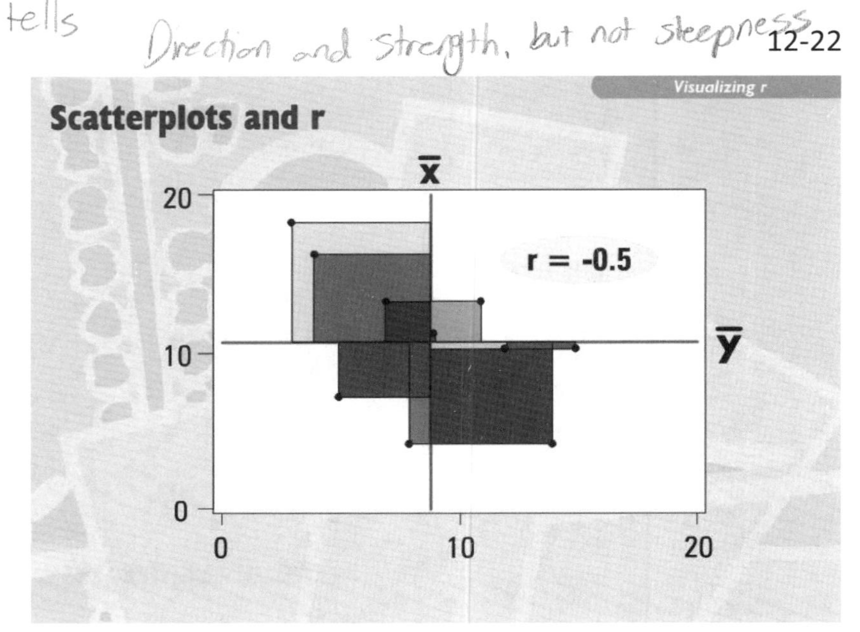


r tells Direction and strength, but not steepness

12-22

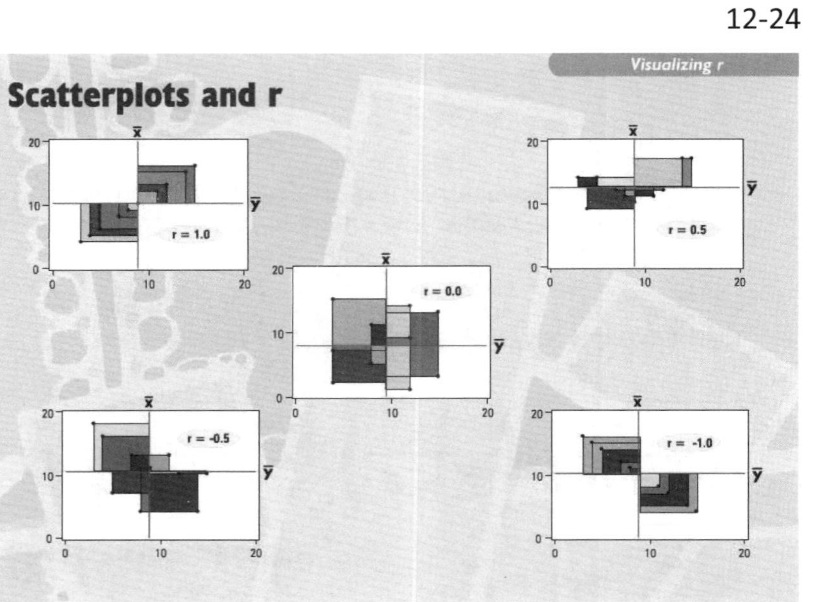


12-23

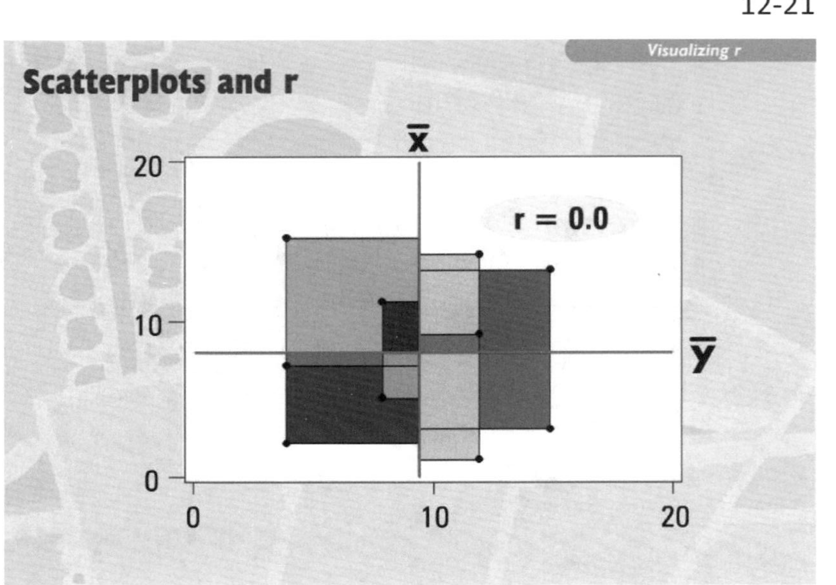


12-24

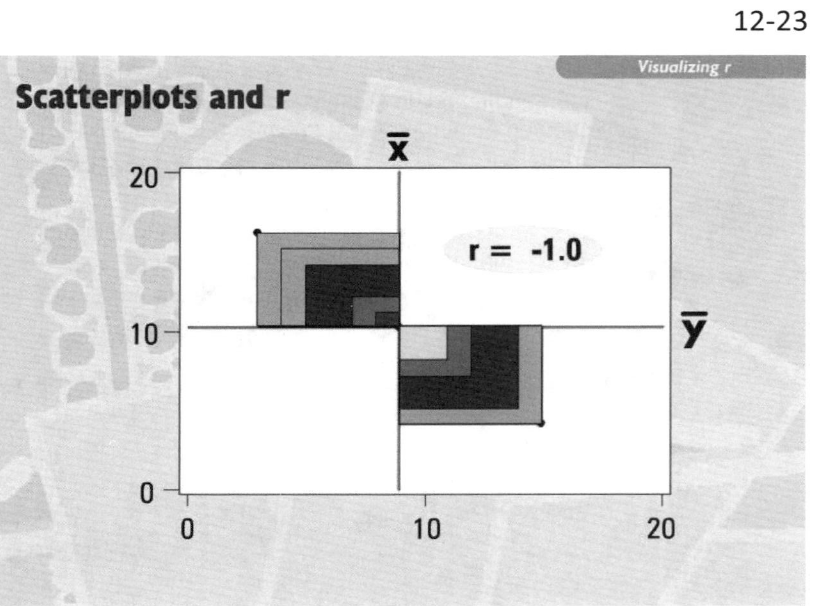

12-25

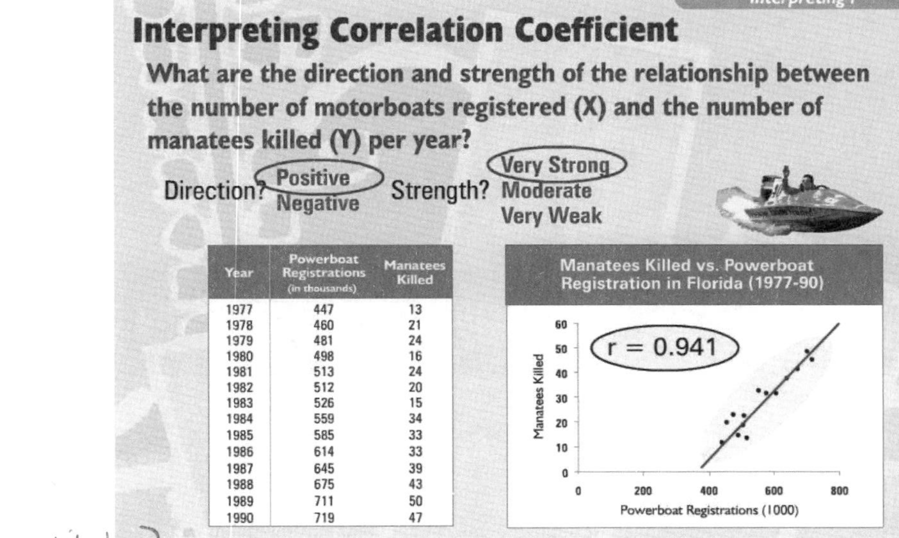


flat - r=0 r only works for numbers (quantitative)
does not make a distinction between explanatory and response variables
r does not change if units of x or y change
r is affected by outliers

12-26

*Interpreting r*

## Interpreting Correlation Coefficient

**What are the direction and strength of the relationship between the number of motorboats registered (X) and the number of manatees killed (Y) per year?**

Direction? Positive / Negative     Strength? Very Strong / Moderate / Very Weak

| Year | Powerboat Registrations (in thousands) | Manatees Killed |
|---|---|---|
| 1977 | 447 | 13 |
| 1978 | 460 | 21 |
| 1979 | 481 | 24 |
| 1980 | 498 | 16 |
| 1981 | 513 | 24 |
| 1982 | 512 | 20 |
| 1983 | 526 | 15 |
| 1984 | 559 | 34 |
| 1985 | 585 | 33 |
| 1986 | 614 | 33 |
| 1987 | 645 | 39 |
| 1988 | 675 | 43 |
| 1989 | 711 | 50 |
| 1990 | 719 | 47 |

Manatees Killed vs. Powerboat Registration in Florida (1977-90)

r = 0.941

Manatees Killed; Powerboat Registrations (1000)

12-27

*Interpreting r*

## Interpreting Correlation Coefficient

**What are the direction and strength of the relationship between the engine displacement (X) and city gas mileage (Y) for sportscars?**

Direction? Positive / Negative     Strength? Very strong / Moderate / Very weak

| Vehicle | MPG (City) | ENG DISP |
|---|---|---|
| Acura NSX | 23 | 3.0 |
| Alpha Romero Spider | 30 | 2.0 |
| Chevrolet Corvette | 25 | 5.7 |
| Dodge Viper | 22 | 8.0 |
| Ferrari 348TB/TS/Spider | 18 | 3.4 |
| Honda Civic Del Sol | 36 | 1.5 |
| Honda Civic Del Sol | 41 | 1.5 |
| Honda Civic Del Sol | 33 | 1.6 |
| Jaguar XJS Convertible | 35 | 1.6 |
| Honda Civic Del Sol | 21 | 4.0 |
| Lotus Esprit Turbo | 27 | 2.2 |
| Mazda MX 5 Miata | 28 | 1.8 |
| Mazda MX 5 Miata | 27 | 1.8 |
| Mazda RX 7 | 24 | 1.3 |
| Mercedes Benz SL320 | 24 | 3.2 |
| Nissan 300ZX | 23 | 3.0 |
| Porsche 911 Carrers 4/2 | 23 | 3.6 |
| Porsche 968 | 25 | 3.0 |
| Toyota MR2 | 27 | 2.0 |

MPG vs Engine Displacement (n=19)

r = −0.553

MPG (City); ENGDispl (liters)

**Warning: Curvilinear**

12-28

*Interpreting r*

## Interpreting Correlation Coefficient

**What are the direction and strength of the relationship between X = date of birth and Y = draft number in the 1970 Draft?**

Direction? Positive / Negative     Strength? Very strong / Moderate / Very weak

1970 US Draft Lottery
Day of Year vs. Draft Number

Draft No.; Day of year

r = -0.226

12-29

12-31

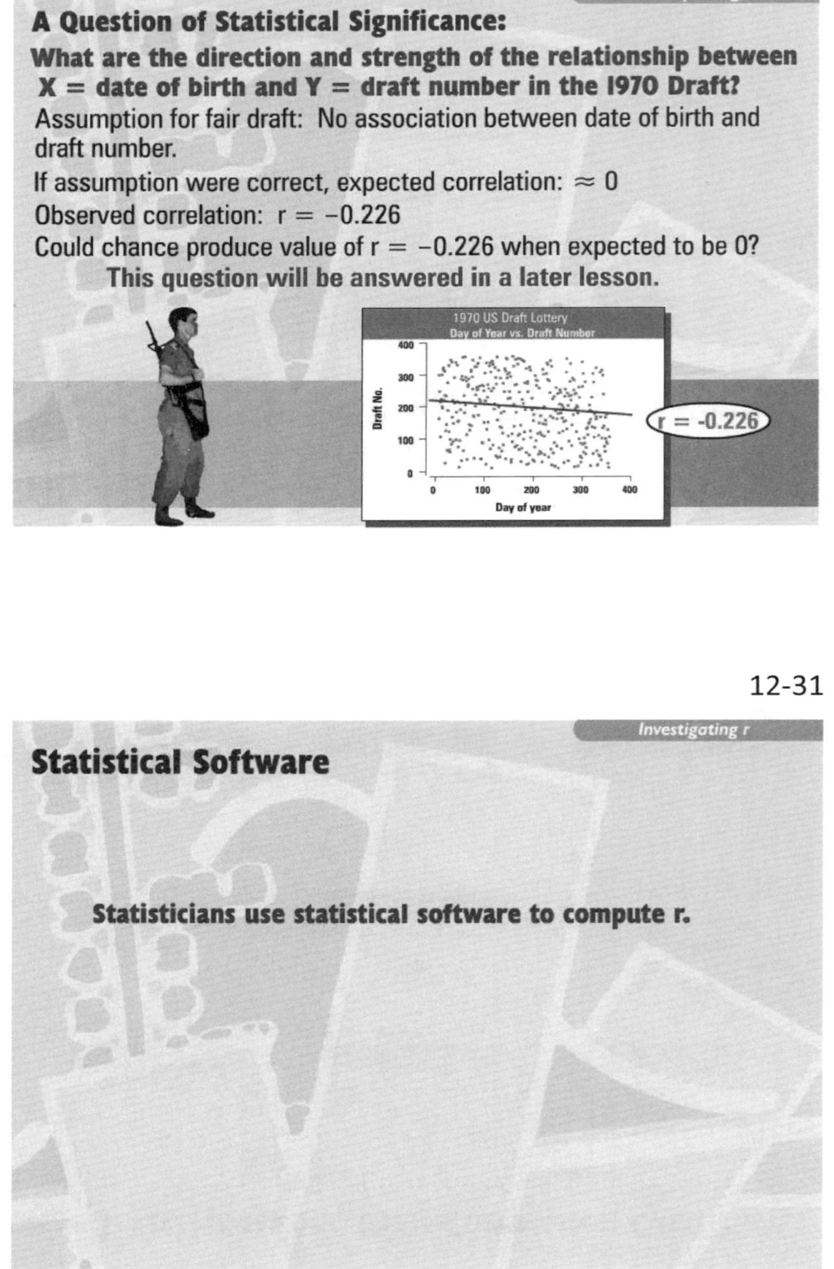


12-30

12-32

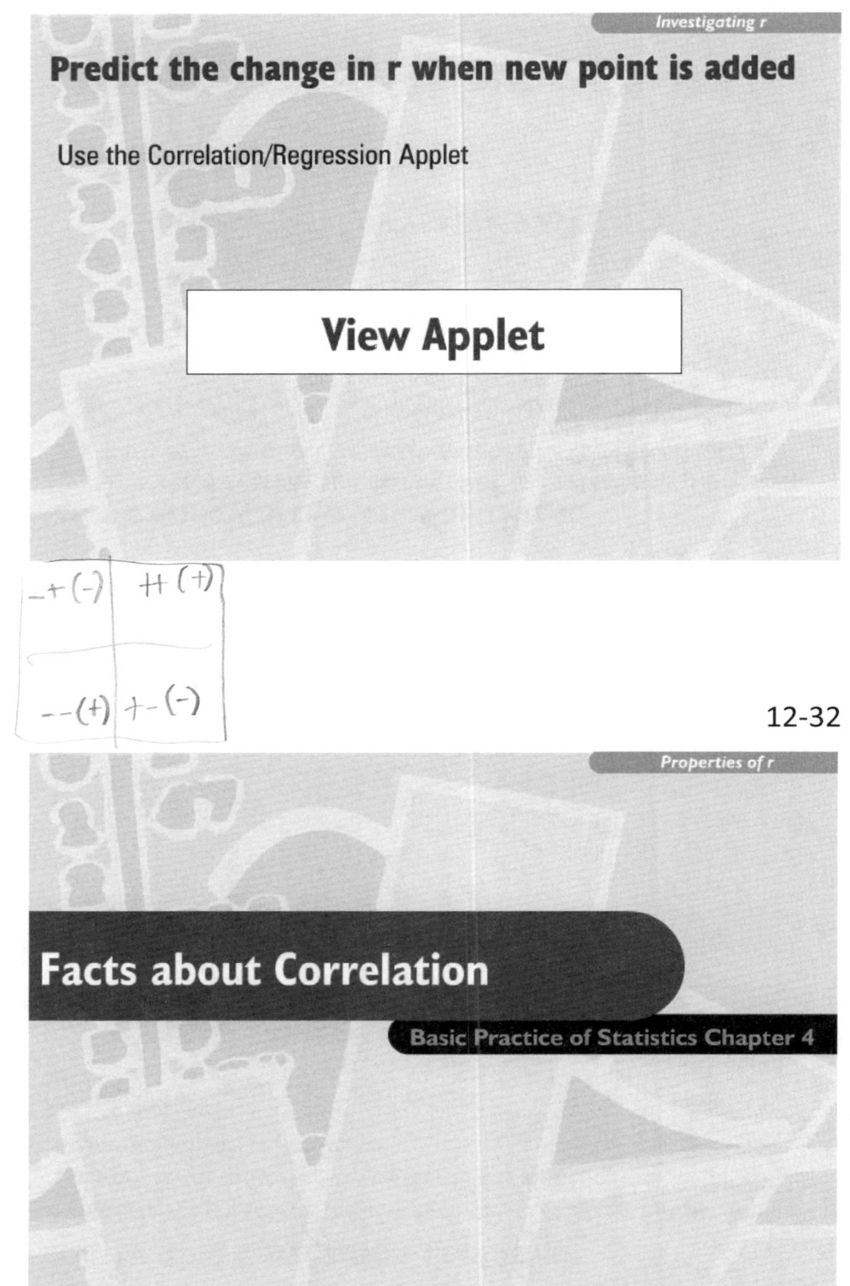

Lesson 12

12-33

Properties of r

## Properties of the formula for correlation

$$r = \frac{1}{n-1}\sum\left(\frac{x_i - \bar{x}}{s_x}\right)\left(\frac{y_i - \bar{y}}{s_y}\right)$$

- No distinction made between explanatory and response variables.
- Both variables must be quantitative.

.65 = football shape cloud

1. plot data - check linear form
2. compute means st devs of x's and y's
3. Standardize x's and y's
4. Compute products
5.

12-34

Feb 3

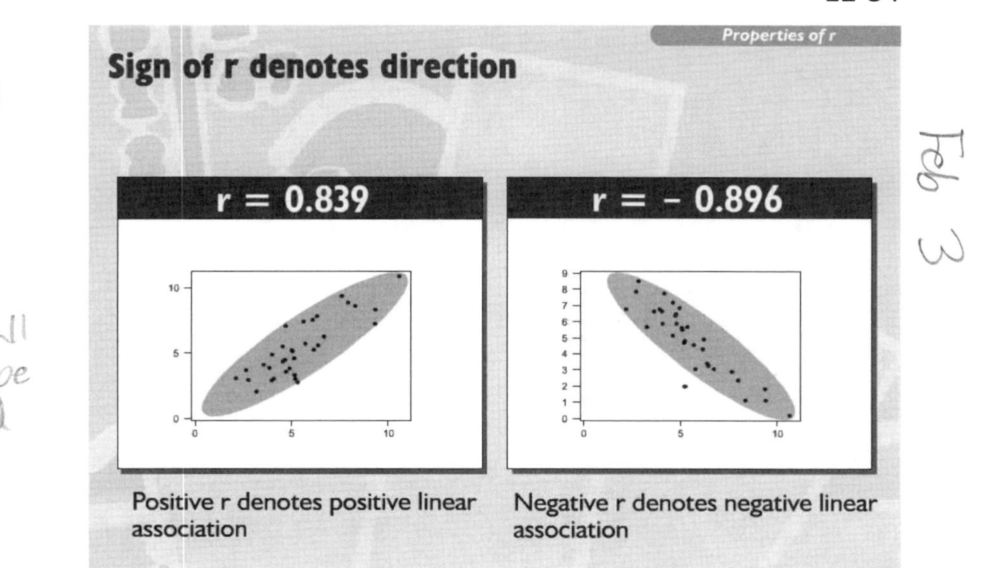


12-35

Properties of r

## r is bounded between –1 and +1

| r = –1.000 | r = 0.026 | r = 1.000 |
|---|---|---|
| Points on a straight line with negative slope. | No linear association. Points appear randomly without linear pattern. | Points on a straight line with positive slope. |

12-36

Properties of r

## r has no unit of measure; changing units for X or Y does not change r

$$r = \frac{1}{n-1}\sum\left(\frac{in - in}{in}\right)\left(\frac{ft^3 - ft^3}{ft^3}\right)$$

x = Diameter (in) y = Volume (ft³)

Trees (Volume vs. Diameter)

Volume (cubic ft)

Diameter (in)

r = 0.967

Has no unit of measure

-- not inches

-- not cubic feet

12-37

Properties of r

## r has no unit of measure; changing units for X or Y does not change r

$$r = \frac{1}{n-1}\sum\left(\frac{cm - cm}{cm}\right)\left(\frac{m^3 - m^3}{m^3}\right)$$

x = Diameter (cm)  y = Volume (m³)

r = 0.967

Has no unit of measure

-- not centimeters

-- not cubic meters

Trees (Volume vs. Diameter)

Note: Changing units of measure did not change r.

12-38

Properties of r

## r measures strength of linear relationship

Warning: r measures the linear component of the curved relationship.

r = 0.884

r = -0.089

r measures scatter of points about a straight line.

r is not appropriate for curvilinear relationships.

0 means no relationship

12-39

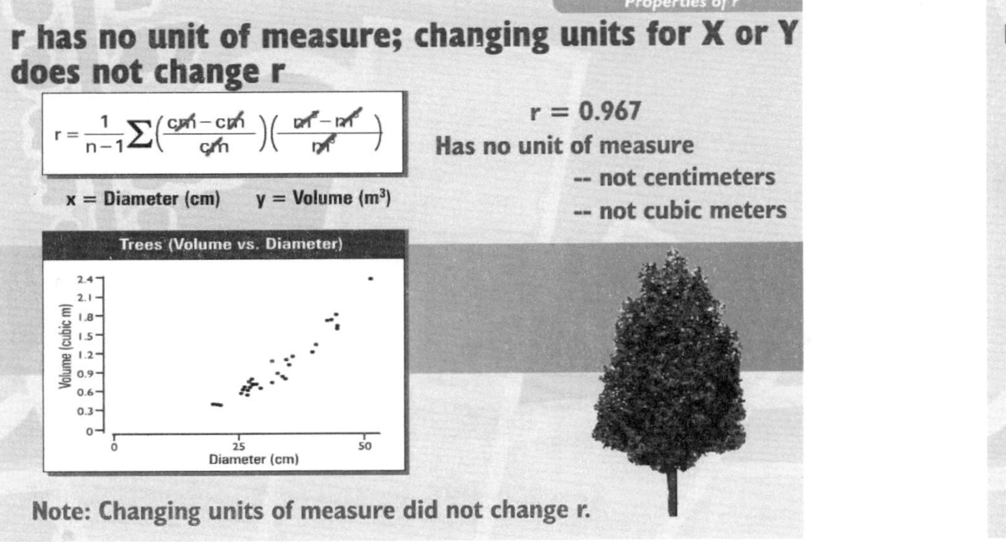


12-40

Properties of r

## r is affected by outliers

Without Outlier

r = 0.90

With Outlier

r = 0.97

12-41



## Summary of Properties of r

1. Makes no distinction between explanatory and response variables.
2. Requires both variables to be quantitative.
3. Denotes positive linear association with positive sign and negative linear association with negative sign.
4. Bounded by −1 and +1; i.e., $-1 \leq r \leq +1$.
5. Has no unit of measure; doesn't change when units of measure for X and Y are changed.
6. Measures strength of the linear relationship. (Misleading for curvilinear relationships.)
7. Affected by outliers.

Correlation

one-number summary of strength and direction of linear relationship

does not indicate location or steepness of linear relationship

12-42

## Vocabulary

**Bivariate Data**
**Correlation coefficient**
**Deviation from the mean**
**Direction of Relationship**
**Explanatory Variable (X)**
**Form of Relationship**
**Response Variable (Y)**
**Strength of Relationship**
**Standardized value**
**z-score product**

# Chapter 5 Part I Regression

StatTutor Lesson 13

Regression - summarizes linear pattern of scatterplot using 'best fitting' straight line



Check i-clicker

Feb 5

## Lesson Objectives

1. Express the relationship between a response variable and an explanatory variable using a statistical model.
2. Predict the value of a response variable for a given value of an explanatory variable using a regression equation.
3. Identify the least-squares regression line as the one that minimizes the sum of squared residuals.
4. Calculate the least-squares regression line and interpret its slope and y-intercept.



Modeling Data

## Introduction to Regression

Basic Practice of Statistics Chapter 5



Modeling Data

## Statistical Modeling

**Statistical Model:** An equation that fits the pattern between a response variable and possible explanatory variables, accounting for deviations from the model. (Simplest case: one quantitative response variable and one quantitative explanatory variable)

**Response Variable (Y):** The quantitative outcome of a study

**Explanatory Variable (X):** A quantitative variable that may explain or predict the response variable

**What is the best model for:** predicting weight (Y) from height (X)?

. . . predicting blood pressure (Y) from age (X)?

Regression - calculate mean of Y given X

13-5

*Modeling Data*

## Modeling Bivariate Data with Straight-Line

- Response Variable (Y)
- Explanatory Variable (X)
- Plot the Data
- Model data with straight line
- Observe deviations about line

straight line

deviations about line

Response Variable

Explanatory Variable

13-6

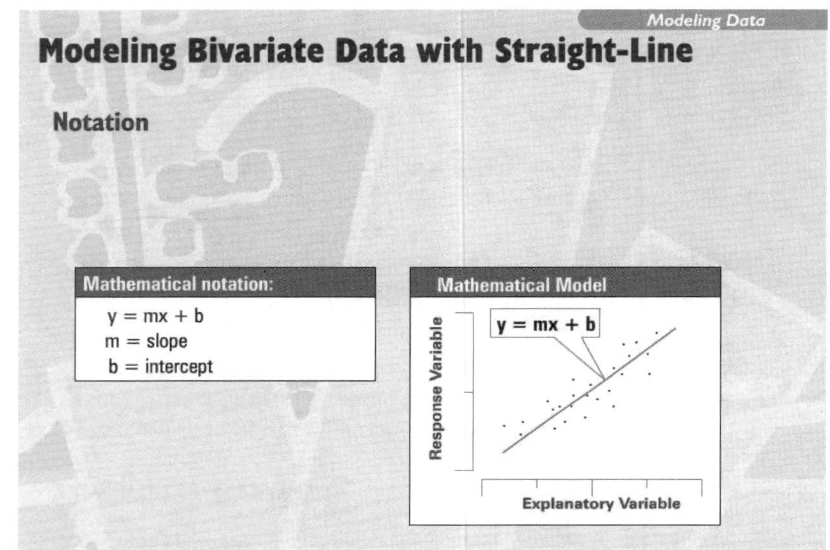


13-7

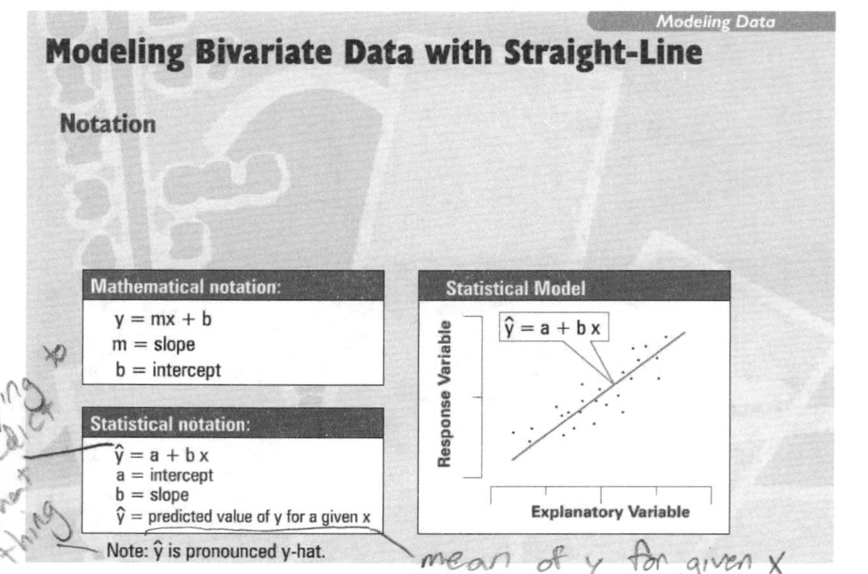


13-8

*Modeling Data*

## Review: Plotting Lines

**Line Equation:** $y = a + b\,x$

a = y-intercept

b = slope = $\frac{\text{rise}}{\text{run}}$

As x increases by 1 unit, y increases by $\frac{\text{rise}}{\text{run}}$ units.

**Plot** $y = 3 + \frac{1}{2}x$

a = 3

rise = 1, run = 2

$b = \frac{1}{2} = \frac{\text{rise}}{\text{run}}$

As x increases by 1 unit, y increases by 1/2 units.

**Plot:** $y = -2 - x$

a = −2

run = 1, rise = −1

$b = \frac{-1}{1} = \frac{\text{rise}}{\text{run}}$

As x increases by 1 unit, y decreases by 1 unit.

13-9



# Regression Lines

Basic Practice of Statistics Chapter 5

Regression line is to scatterplot as mean is to histogram

13-10

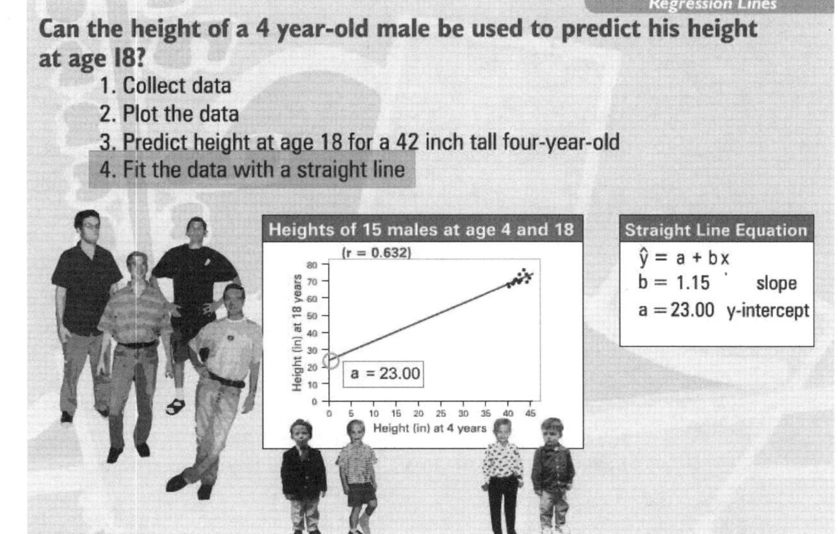


13-11



**Can the height of a 4 year-old male be used to predict his height at age 18?**

1. Collect data
2. Plot the data
3. Predict height at age 18 for a 42 inch tall four-year-old
4. Fit the data with a straight line

Interpretation of slope: $\frac{\text{rise}}{\text{run}}$

For every one inch increase in height at age 4, height increases by 1.15 inches on average at age 18.

Interpretation of y-intercept:

Males who are zero inches tall at age 4 will be 23 inches tall at age 18. ***This interpretation is meaningless because no four-year-olds are zero inches tall.***

**Straight Line Equation**

$\hat{y} = 23.00 + 1.15x$

**Note:** How to obtain this equation will be described later.

13-12



**Can the height of a 4 year-old male be used to predict his height at age 18?**

1. Collect data
2. Plot the data
3. Predict height at age 18 for a 42 inch tall four-year-old
4. Fit the data with a straight line
5. Evaluate the equation for x = 42 inches

Heights of 15 males at age 4 and 18

(r = 0.632)

71.30

42

Height (in) at 4 years

**Straight Line Equation**

$\hat{y} = 23.00 + 1.15(42)$

$\hat{y} = 71.30$ inches

**Prediction:**

Males 42 inches tall at age 4 will have a mean height of approximately 71.30 inches at age 18.

13-13



**Can the height of a 4 year-old male be used to predict his height at age 18?**

1. Collect data
2. Plot the data
3. Predict height at age 18 for a 42 inch tall four-year-old
4. Fit the data with a straight line
5. Evaluate the equation for x = 42 inches

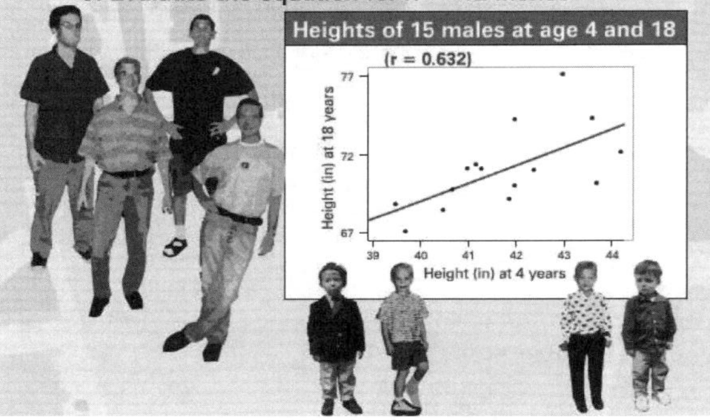

Would another line "fit" the data better?

13-14



# Least-squares regression line

Basic Practice of Statistics Chapter 5

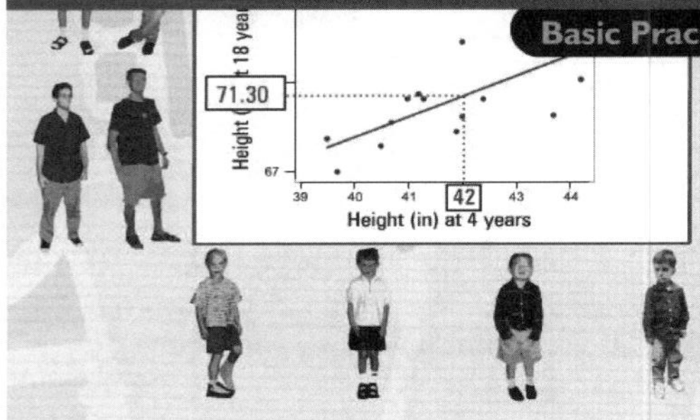

Make vertical distances as small as possible.

13-15



**A good statistical model (regression line) has small prediction errors (called residuals).**

prediction error (residual) = (observed y) − (predicted y) = $y - \hat{y}$

= 74.2 - 71.3

= 2.9

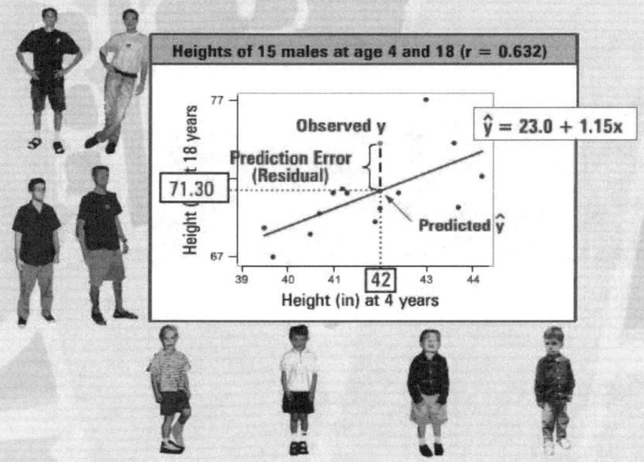

13-16



**A good statistical model (regression line) has small prediction errors (called residuals).**

prediction error (residual) = (observed y) − (predicted y) = $y - \hat{y}$

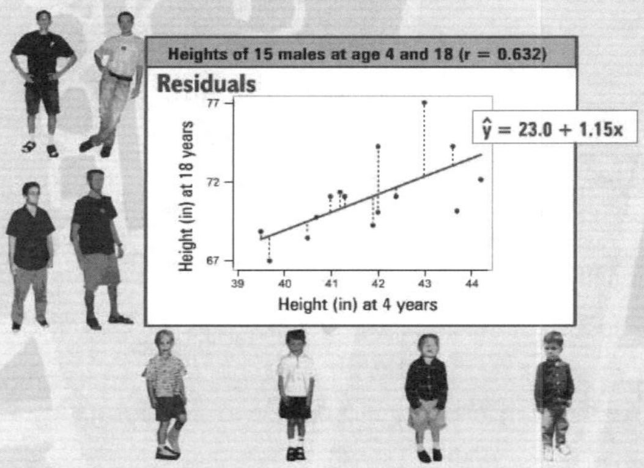

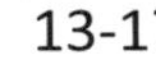

13-17

Least-Squares Regression Line

Squared Error = $(\text{residual})^2 = (y - \hat{y})^2$

Heights of 15 males at age 4 and 18 (r = 0.632)

Squared Residuals

$\hat{y} = 23.0 + 1.15x$

13-18

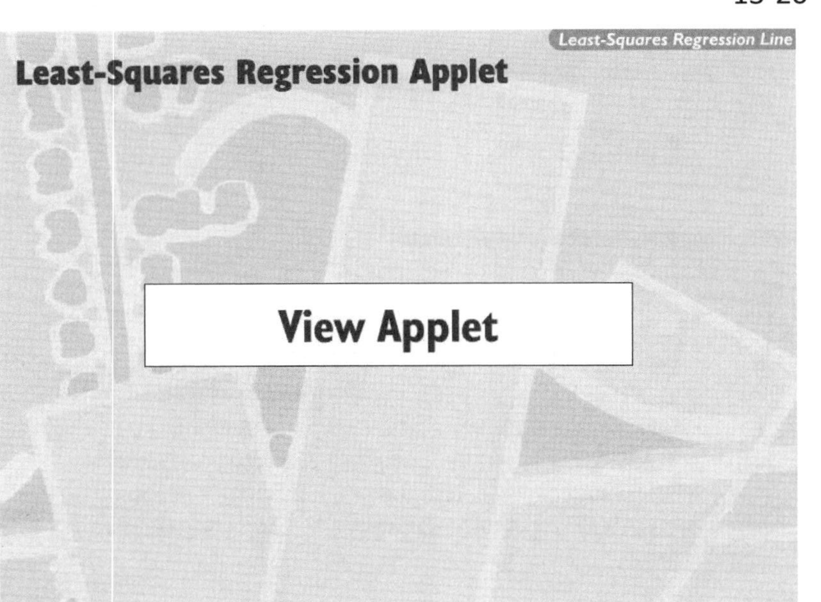


13-19

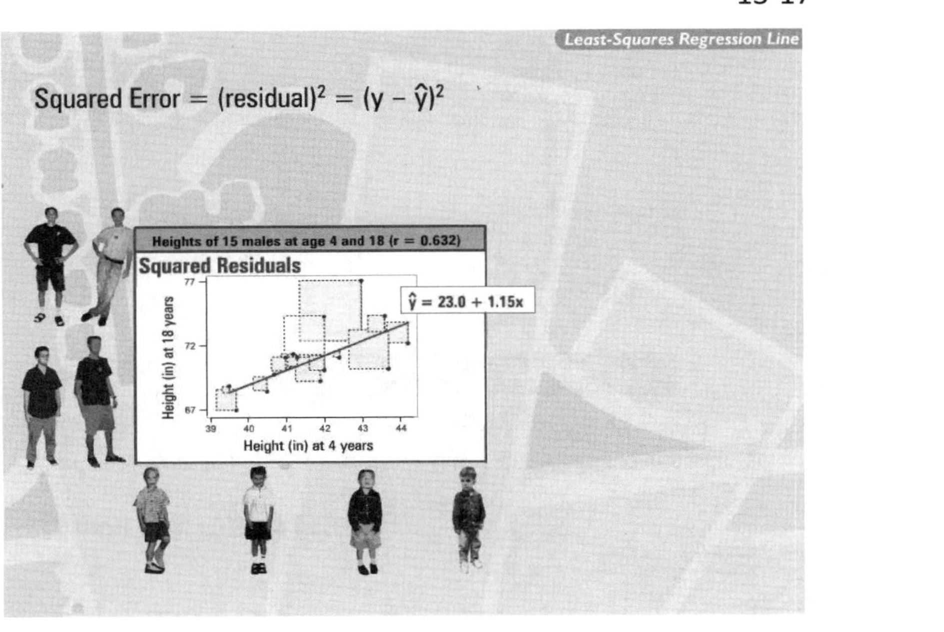


| Regression Equation | SSE |
|---|---|
| $\hat{y} = 19.0 + 2.18x$ | 101.70 |
| $\hat{y} = 23.0 + 1.15x$ | 55.78 |
| $\hat{y} = 58.7 + 0.28x$ | 70.73 |
| $\hat{y} = 42.9 + 0.69x$ | 84.97 |
| $\hat{y} = 100 - 0.71x$ | 160.74 |

13-20

Least-Squares Regression Line

## Least-Squares Regression Applet

View Applet

13-21

Least-Squares Regression Line

## Least-Squares Equations for Slope and Intercept

$$\hat{y} = a + bx$$

**Formula for a**

$$a = \bar{y} - b\bar{x}$$

**Formula for b**

$$b = r\frac{s_y}{s_x}$$

x = Father's heights and mean of
y = sons " " " "
r = correlation

s = standard deviation

13-22

Least-Squares Regression Line

## Calculation of the Least-Squares Regression Line

X = composite ACT score on admissions application
Y = cumulative GPA upon graduation from the university
Data on 47 students who have graduated from a major university.

ACT Score vs. Graduating GPA

| | |
|---|---|
| $\bar{x}$ = 24.213 | $\bar{y}$ = 3.269 |
| $s_x$ = 4.648 | $s_y$ = 0.340 |
| r = 0.695 | |

$\hat{y} = a + bx = 2.034 + 0.051x$

$b = r\frac{s_y}{s_x} = (0.695)\frac{0.340}{4.648} = 0.051$

$a = \bar{y} - b\bar{x} = 3.269 - (0.051)(24.213) = 2.034$

13-23

Least-Squares Regression Line

## Interpretation: b (slope)

One point increase in ACT score ⟶ 0.051 unit increase in predicted graduating GPA on average.

ACT Score vs. Graduating GPA

13-24

Least-Squares Regression Line

## Interpretation: a (y-intercept)

For ACT of 0 ⟶ graduating GPA is predicted to be 2.034.
Is this y-intercept a meaningful number?

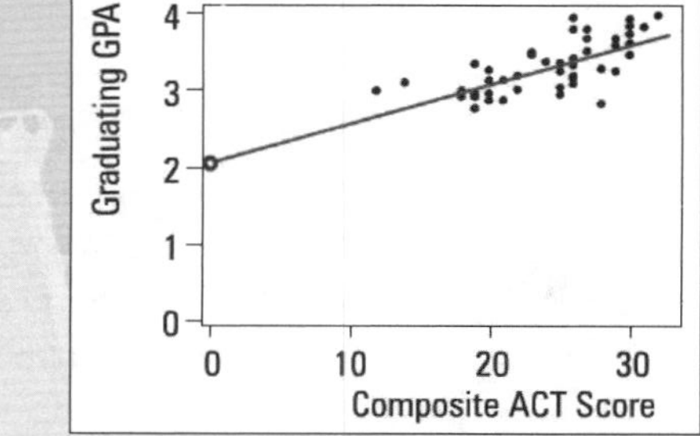

## Vocabulary

**Correlation coefficient**
**Residual (Prediction Error)**
**Sum of Squared Errors (SSE)**
**Least-Squares Regression Line**
**Slope, b**
**Y-intercept, a**

$\hat{bf} = 14.59 + .74 tri$

$b = .74$

For 1 unit increase in $\underline{x}$ you expect the mean of $\underline{y}$ to increase by $\underline{b}$.

$b = r \frac{s_y}{s_x}$

Correalation
measure of direction,
strength of linear relationship
designation of response and explanetory variables irrelevent

Regression
model for mean x

(Slide 3 of lesson 14)

Slope On average, if x increased by 1 unit, we would expect y to change by slope

Y-int
When x=0 we would expect on average for y=yint

$R^2$
$R^2 \times 100\%$ of variation in y can be explained by x.

14-1

# Chapter 5 Part 2 Regression

StatTutor Lesson 14

14-2

## Lesson Objectives

1. Give facts about least-squares regression.
2. Describe the strength of fit of a least-squares regression line using $r^2$.
3. Interpret $r^2$ in context.
4. Use residual plots to validate assumptions for the least-squares regression line.

14-3

Least-Squares Regression Facts

# Facts about least-squares regression

Basic Practice of Statistics Chapter 5

14-4

Least-Squares Regression Facts

## Roles of Correlation and Regression

**Correlation:** Measures direction and strength of linear association between X and Y.

**Regression:** Models the linear relationship between X and Y and can be used to predict a value for the response variable for a specific value of the explanatory variable.

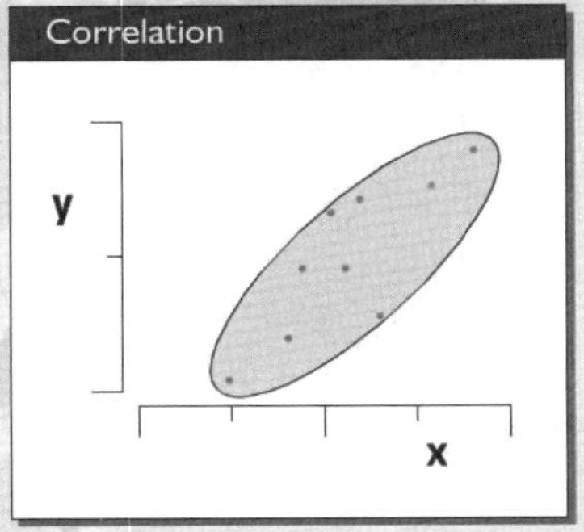

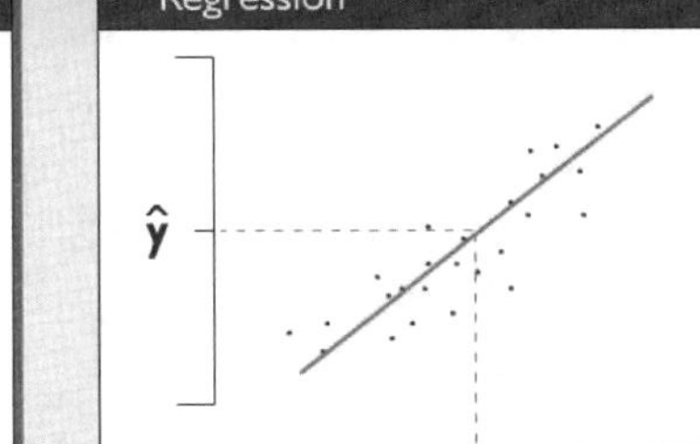

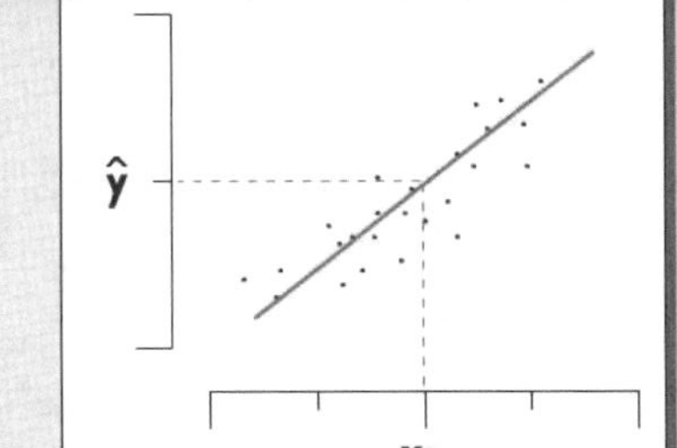

14-5

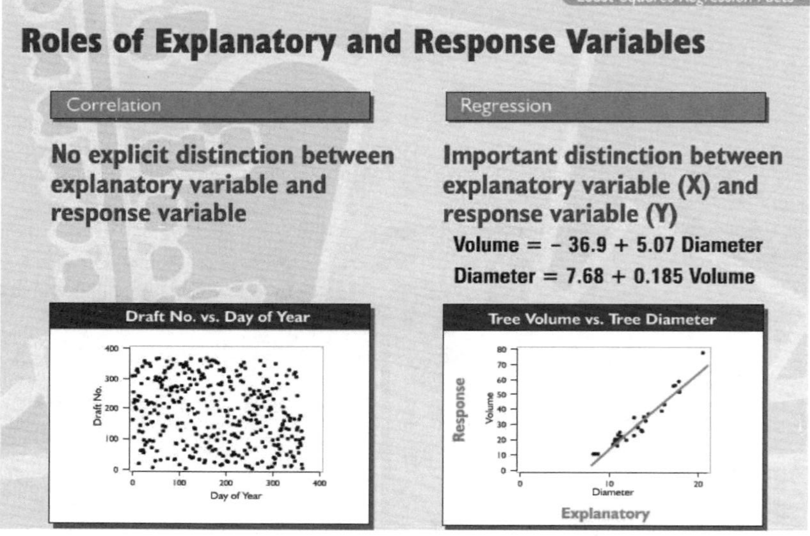


The correlation and regression should be used together

14-6

*Least-Squares Regression Facts*

## Relationship between correlation and slope

$$b = r\frac{s_y}{s_x}$$

correlation — standard deviation

- A change of one standard deviation in x corresponds to a change of r standard deviations in y.
- Slope and r have the same sign.

r > 0; b > 0 | r < 0; b < 0 | r = 0; b = 0

if x and y are standardized, b=r (ie. r is slope of regression line for standardized variables)

14-7

*Least-Squares Regression Facts*

## Connections to $(\bar{x}, \bar{y})$

Correlation products are based on deviations from $\bar{x}$ and $\bar{y}$.

Regression line passes through the $(\bar{x}, \bar{y})$ point.

Correlation — Height at Age 18 (in) vs. Height at Age 4 (in)

Regression — Height at Age 18 (in) vs. Height at Age 4 (in)

14-8

*Least-Squares Regression*

## How Well Does Composite ACT Predict Graduating GPA?

? Kickoff Question

Would another variable predict graduating GPA more accurately?

Would high school GPA be a better predictor than composite ACT?

Does the correlation coefficient give an interpretable measure of fit when comparing the two?

ACT Score vs. Graduating GPA — Graduating GPA vs. Composite ACT Score, r = 0.695

H.S. GPA vs. Graduating GPA — Graduating GPA vs. High School GPA, r = 0.391

14-9



## Quantifying the Strength of Fit

What does a scatterplot look like where 100% of the variation in Y is explained?

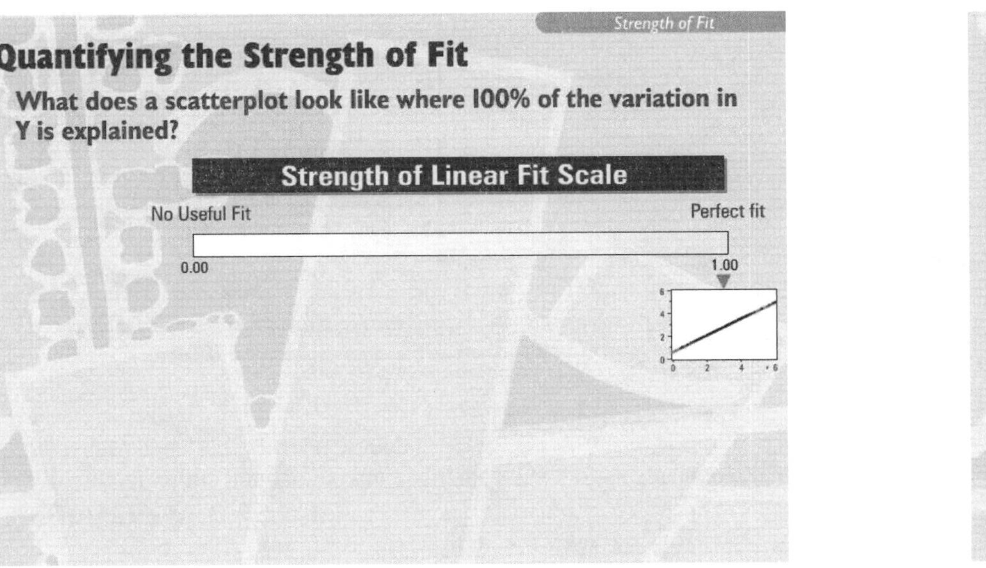


14-10



## Quantifying the Strength of Fit

What is $r^2$ for the data in each of these scatterplots?

**Strength of Linear Fit Scale**

No Useful Fit — Perfect fit

0.00 | 0.25 | 0.50 | 0.75 | 1.00

| | | | | | |
|---|---|---|---|---|---|
| $r$ | 0.00 | 0.50 | 0.71 | 0.87 | 1.00 |
| $r^2$ | 0.00 | 0.25 | 0.50 | 0.75 | 1.00 |

Note: $r^2$ is easier to assess visually than r.

Conclusion: $r^2$ tells us the percentage of variation in Y that is explained by the least-squares regression line.

19.2

more commonly used as companion to regression line to indicate usefulness for prediction.

14-11



## Definition of $r^2$ – what % of variability of y can be predicted by x

The fraction of the variation in the observed values of y explained by the least-squares regression of y on x.

Data on 10 hamburgers sold at fast food restaurants

y = number of calories in a hamburger

x = grams of fat in a hamburger

93% of the variation in the calories is explained by the least-squares regression of calories on grams of fat.

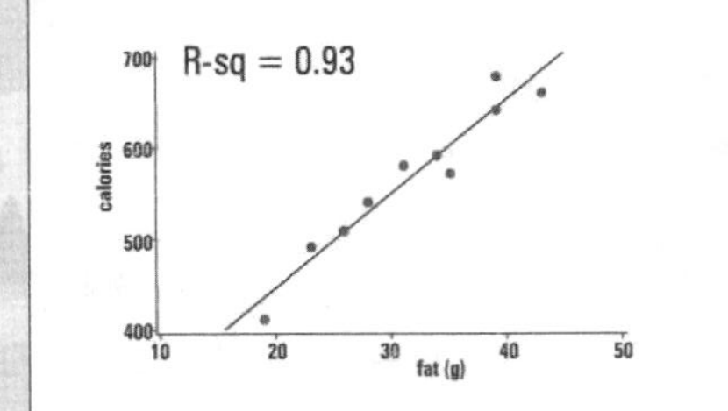


**$r^2$ is a measure of how successfully the regression explains the response, y.**

percent of the variation of y explained by x

14-12



## Definition of $r^2$

The fraction of the variation in the observed values of y explained by the least-squares regression of y on x.

The dashed lines represent deviations of observed y's about $\bar{y}$.

The sum of the squared deviations represent:

the ***total variation*** in the observed values of y.

R-sq = 0.93

$\bar{y}$ line

14-13

## Definition of $r^2$

The fraction of the variation in the observed values of y explained by the least-squares regression of y on x.

**Recall:** Residual = vertical distance from the observed y to the line.

The sum of squared residuals represents:

what is *unexplained* by the regression line.

This plot shows very little *unexplained* by the regression line.

**Squared Residuals**

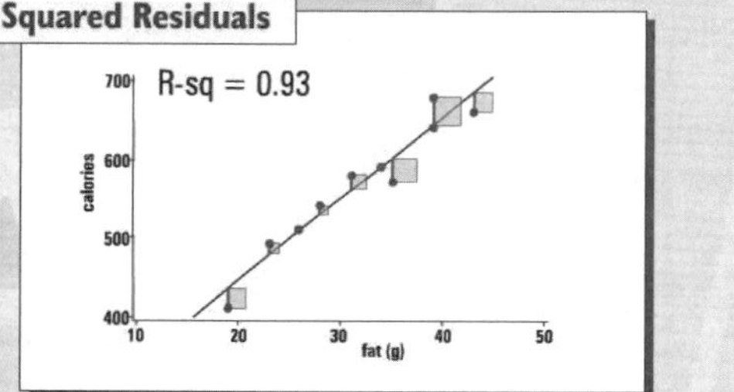


14-14

## Definition of $r^2$

The fraction of the variation in the observed values of y explained by the least-squares regression of y on x.

$$r^2 = \frac{\text{variation in } \hat{y} \text{ as x pulls it along the line}}{\text{total variation in observed values of y}}$$

As x increases, it pulls y with it along the line.

The scatter of data points about the line is **NOT** explained by the regression.

R-sq = 0.93

**$r^2$ tells us how well x pulls y along with it.**

14-15

## Definition of $r^2$

The fraction of the variation in the observed values of y explained by the least-squares regression of y on x.

$$r^2 = \frac{\text{variation in } \hat{y} \text{ as x pulls it along the line}}{\text{total variation in observed values of y}}$$

**Total variation = Unexplained variation + Explained variation**

Points to mean — Points to line — Line to mean

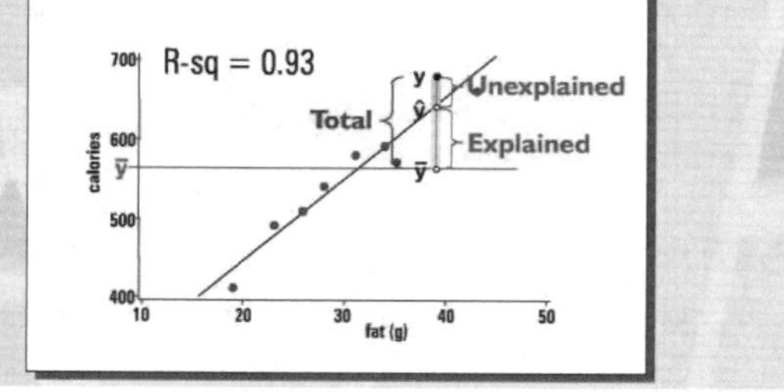


14-16

## Definition of $r^2$

The fraction of the variation in the observed values of y explained by the least-squares regression of y on x.

$$r^2 = \frac{\text{variation in } \hat{y} \text{ as x pulls it along the line}}{\text{total variation in observed values of y}}$$

**Total variation = Unexplained variation + Explained variation**

**For the mathematically curious:**

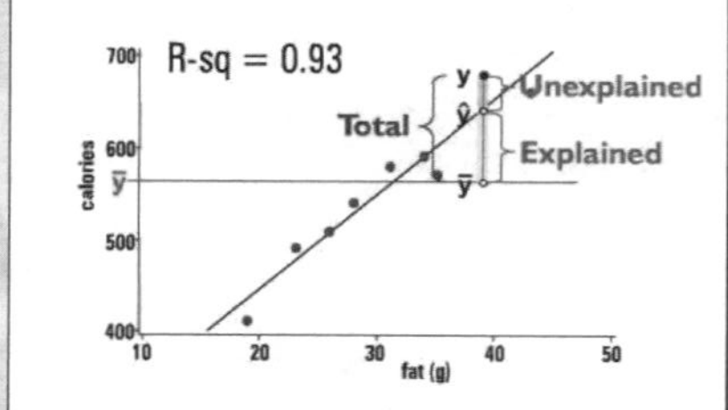


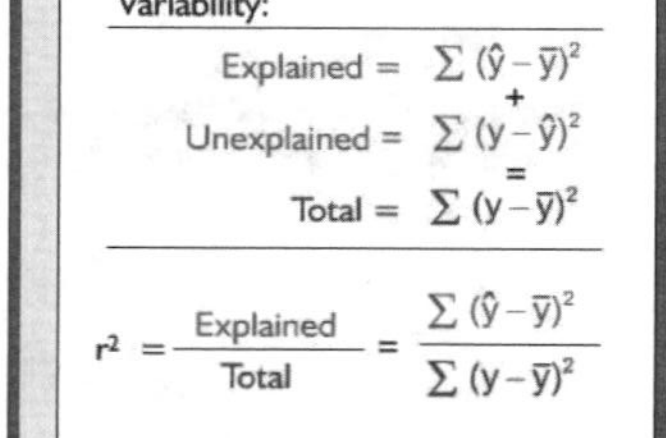

Variability:

$$\text{Explained} = \sum (\hat{y} - \bar{y})^2$$
$$+$$
$$\text{Unexplained} = \sum (y - \hat{y})^2$$
$$=$$
$$\text{Total} = \sum (y - \bar{y})^2$$

$$r^2 = \frac{\text{Explained}}{\text{Total}} = \frac{\sum (\hat{y} - \bar{y})^2}{\sum (y - \bar{y})^2}$$

14-17

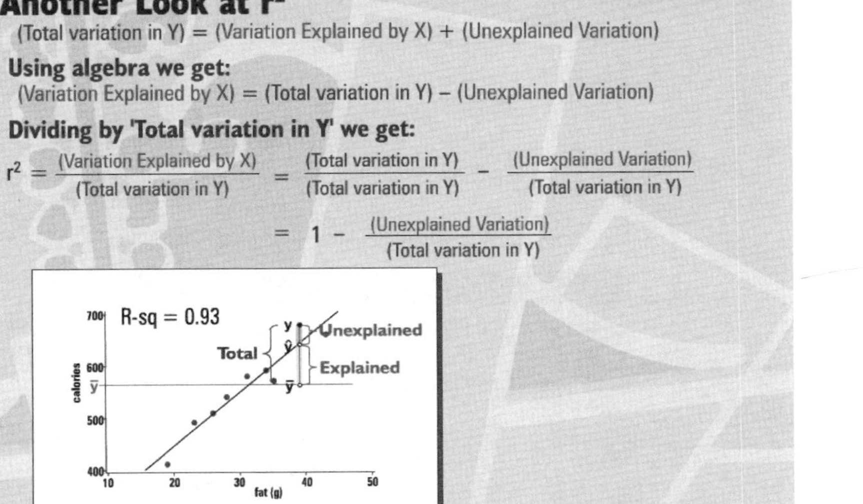


## Another Look at $r^2$

(Total variation in Y) = (Variation Explained by X) + (Unexplained Variation)

**Using algebra we get:**
(Variation Explained by X) = (Total variation in Y) – (Unexplained Variation)

**Dividing by 'Total variation in Y' we get:**

$$r^2 = \frac{\text{(Variation Explained by X)}}{\text{(Total variation in Y)}} = \frac{\text{(Total variation in Y)}}{\text{(Total variation in Y)}} - \frac{\text{(Unexplained Variation)}}{\text{(Total variation in Y)}}$$

$$= 1 - \frac{\text{(Unexplained Variation)}}{\text{(Total variation in Y)}}$$

14-18

## Another Look at $r^2$

What is *total variation*? = Sum of Squared Deviations about $\bar{y}$

What is *unexplained variation*? = Sum of Squared Residuals

R-sq = 0.93

$$r^2 = 1 - \frac{\text{(Unexplained Variation)}}{\text{(Total variation in Y)}}$$

= 1 –

= 1 – 0.07 = 0.93

Are they as far from deviation line than mean.

14-19

## What is the best predictor for graduating GPA?

ACT scores explain 49% of the variation in graduating GPA's.
High school GPA's explain 16% of the variation in graduating GPA's.

**Conclusion: ACT score is a better predictor; it accounts for three times more variation in graduating GPA than does high school GPA.**

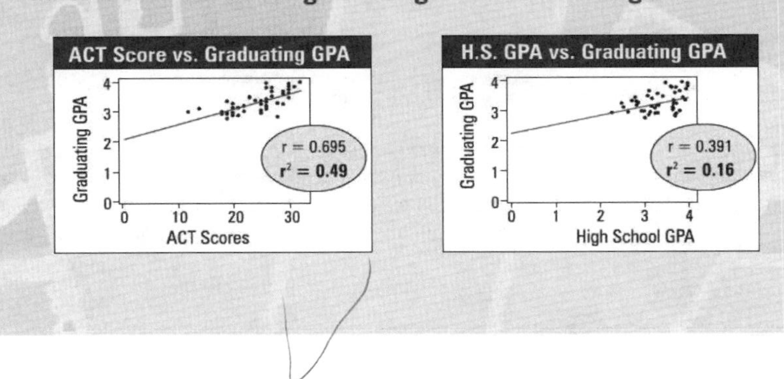


14-20

## Residuals

Basic Practice of Statistics Chapter 5

14-21

*Residuals*

? Kickoff Question

Fuel consumption strongly depends on the outside temperature. Officials at the American Manufacturing Company want to know how much coal they should order each week to heat its nine-building complex. Can they use outside temperature to make predictions?

X = average hourly temperature (°F)

Y = tons of coal burned

Fuel Consumption vs. Temperature

Fuel Consumption (tons)

Temperature (F)

Least-Squares Regression Line

14-22

*Residual Plots*

## Residuals and Residual Plots

**Residual:** The difference between observed y value and $\hat{y}$, the value predicted by the regression line; i.e., residual = $y - \hat{y}$

**Residual Plot:** A scatterplot of the residuals versus the observed x values (or the $\hat{y}$'s).

Fuel Consumption vs. Temperature

Residuals

Fuel Consumption (tons)

Temperature (F)

14-23

*Residual Plots*

## Regression Assumptions

- The relationship between X and Y can be modeled by a straight line. (Residuals show randomness around line.)
- Variation in Y's about the line does not depend on the value of X. (Residuals are similar in size for all X's.)

**If assumptions are met, there is no pattern in the residuals.**

Residual Plot

Residuals

Temperature (F)

14-24

*Residual Plots*

## Residual Plot Diagnostics

**Patterns in residual plots that identify violations of assumptions:**

- Smile or frown indicating non-linear relationship.
- Megaphone indicating non-constant variation (variation in Y is dependent on X.)
- Shoe box with point outside indicating outlier in X or Y direction.

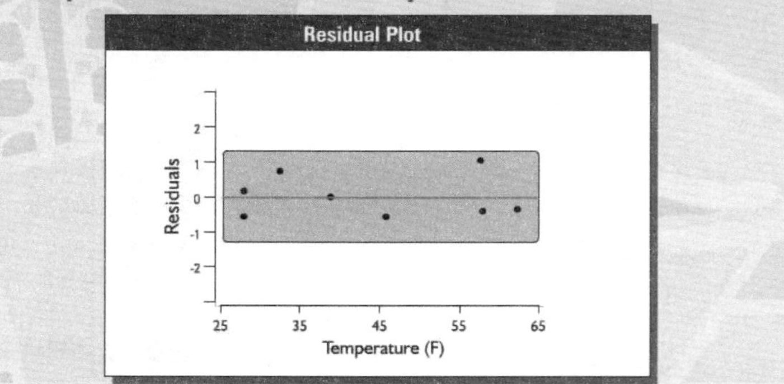

14-25



## Verifying Assumptions Example I

Data: Graduating GPA's and entering ACT scores for college students

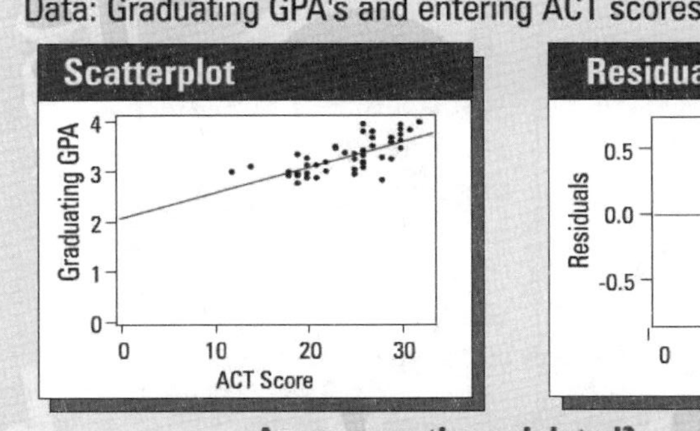


**Are assumptions violated?**

Residuals appear random with a shoe box form.

Assumptions are not violated.

14-26



## Verifying Assumptions Example 2

Data: Weight/length ratio vs. age in months for pre-schoolers

Scatterplot

Residual Plot

Frown Pattern

**Conclusion: Relationship between X & Y should not be modeled with a straight line.**

14-27



## Verifying Assumptions Example 3

Data: Previous years property tax versus selling price for 117 Albuquerque homes in 1993.

Scatterplot

Residual Plot

Megaphone

**Conclusion: Variation in the Y's about the line is increasing as X increases.**

14-28



## Verifying Assumptions Example 4

Data: Gesell test scores versus age at first word for infants.

Scatterplot

Residual Plot

Outlier in the X Direction

14-29

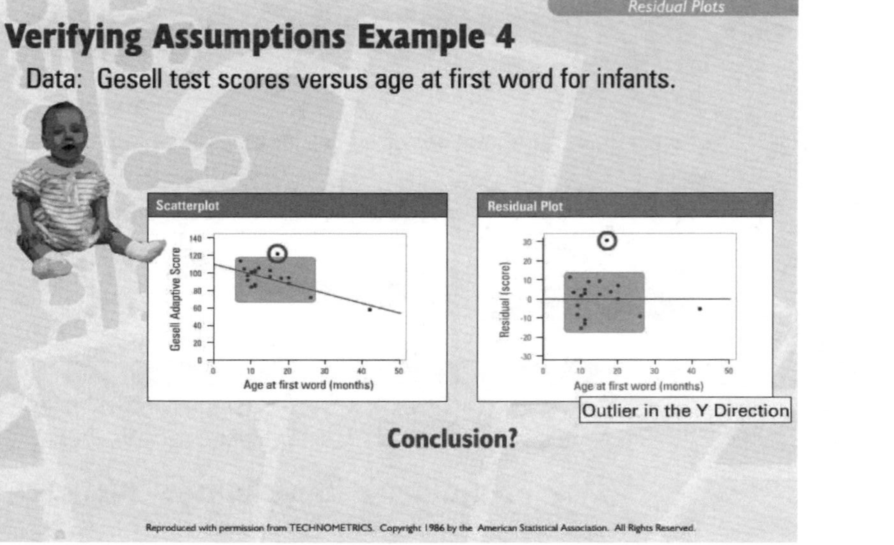


14-30

Residual Plots

## Residual Plot Applet

**Make a scatterplot that produces a residual plot with:**

- A smile or a frown
- A megaphone
- An outlier in X or Y direction

**View Applet**

14-31

## Vocabulary

**Residual**
**Sum of Squared Deviations about $\bar{y}$**
**Sum of Squared Residuals**
**$r^2$**
**Total Variation in Y**
**Variation Explained by X**
**Unexplained Variation**
**Regression Assumptions**
**Residual**
**Residual Plot**

15-1

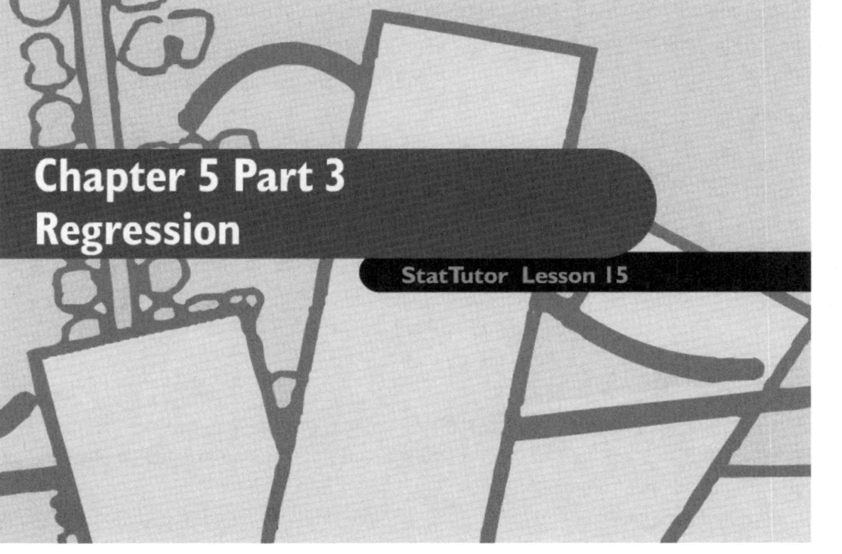
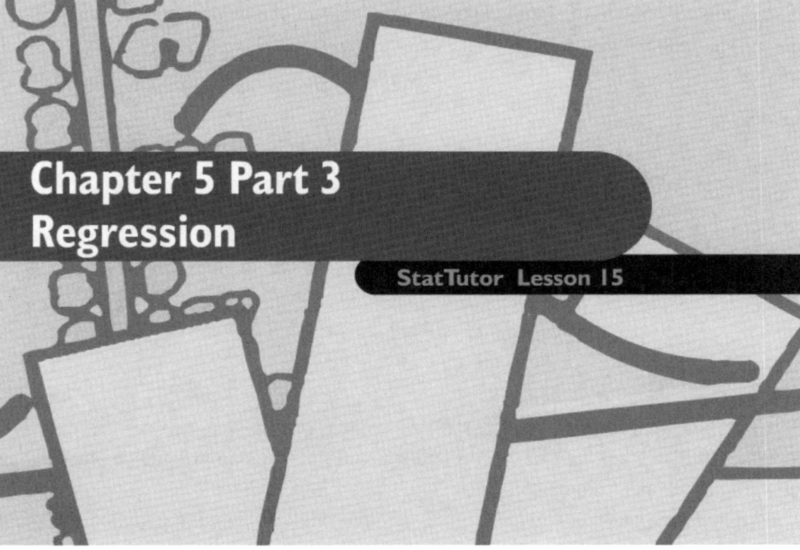

# Chapter 5 Part 3
# Regression

StatTutor Lesson 15

15-2

## Lesson Objectives

1. Evaluate the effect of outliers and influential observations on the least-squares regression equation.
2. Explain that correlation and regression describe only linear relationships.
3. Describe how correlation, r, and the least squares regression line are not resistant to outliers.
4. Warn about extrapolation.
5. Evaluate the effect of lurking variables in correlation and least-squares regression.
6. Recognize when association is not causation.

15-3



# Influential Observations

Basic Practice of Statistics Chapter 5

15-4



**Influential Observation:** An outlier in either the X or Y direction which, if removed, would markedly change the value of the slope and Y-intercept.

**Example 1** Outlier in direction of relationship that is influential

15-5



**Influential Observation:** An outlier in either the X or Y direction which, if removed, would markedly change the value of the slope and Y-intercept.

**Example 2** Outlier outside direction of relationship that is influential

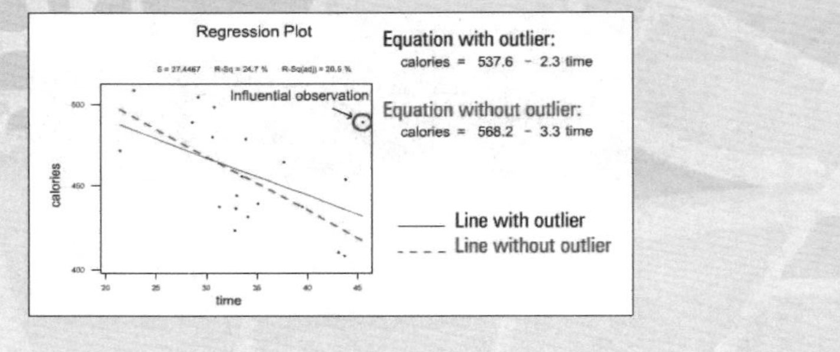


15-6



**Influential Observation:** An outlier in either the X or Y direction which, if removed, would markedly change the value of the slope and Y-intercept.

**Example 3** Point in direction of relationship that is not influential

Regression Plot

Non-influential point

Equation with point:
calories = 560.7 - 3.08 time

Equation without point:
calories = 562.2 - 3.10 time

Line with point
Line without point

15-7



**Influential Observation:** An outlier in either the X or Y direction which, if removed, would markedly change the value of the slope and Y-intercept.

- Outliers in the X direction are often influential.
- Influential observations may have small residuals.
- Not all outliers are influential observations.

15-8



## Influential Observations

- Make a scatterplot; then add an outlier in the X-direction and observe changes in the slope and Y-intercept.
- Repeat except add an outlier in the Y-direction.

**View Applet**

Feb 10

15-9

Linear Relationships

# Cautions about Correlation and Regression

Basic Practice of Statistics Chapter 5

Look at Plot!

15-10

Linear Relationships

## r and $\hat{y} = a + bx$ describe only linear relationships.

- r measures scatter of points about a straight line.
- The least-squares regression line models a straight line relationship.

Age and weight/height ratio have a curved relationship.

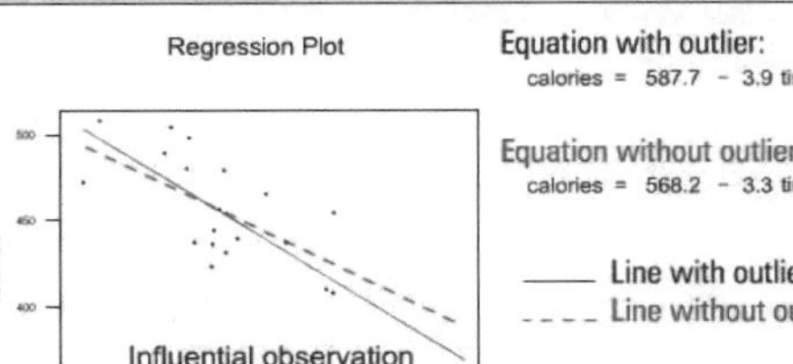

Scatterplot

r= .84

r is misleading.

$\hat{y} = a + bx$ models a straight line relationship, not the curved relationship.

It's complicated

15-11

Outliers & Influential Observations

## Outliers

The correlation coefficient (r) is not resistant to outliers in either the X or Y directions.

X-Direction: r = 0.90; r = 0.83 with outlier

Y-Direction: r = −0.66; r = −0.57 with outlier

- influential observation = outlier that greatly changes a and b if removed. (not just weakens)

Plot data!

15-12

Outliers & Influential Observations

## Influential Observations

**Influential Observation:** An outlier in either the X or Y direction which, if removed, would markedly change the value of the slope and Y-intercept.

- Outliers in the X direction are often influential.
- Influential observations may have small residuals.
- Not all outliers are influential observations.

Regression Plot

Equation with outlier: calories = 587.7 − 3.9 time

Equation without outlier: calories = 568.2 − 3.3 time

Line with outlier

Line without outlier

Influential observation

- $\hat{y} = a + bx$ fairly resistant, if outliers are in the y direction
- often not resistent when outliers are far from regression line and beyond the ends of football

15-13

## Avoid Extrapolation



Predicting **for an x value** outside the range of observed x values used to obtain the line.

Data: Annual world crude oil production in billions of barrels from 1900-1945 (Y = barrels; X = time)
Use linear regression to predict crude oil production for x = 1994.

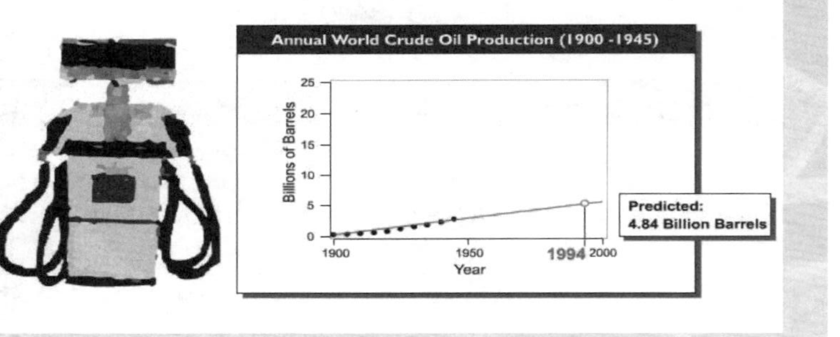


15-14

## Avoid Extrapolation



Oil production was not linear after about 1950.
Using a linear model to predict for 1994 gives incorrect results.

When making predictions, limit predictions to the range of observed x values.

Annual World Crude Oil Production (1900 -1945)

Actual: 22.23 Billion Barrels

Predicted: 4.84 Billion Barrels

Be aware of lurking variables - when..

15-15

## Extrapolation



= use of regression line to predict Y for X far outside x-range
- all relationships have to bend somewhere
- interpolation fine.

**View Movie Clip**

All models are wrong - but some are useful.

15-16

## Lurking variables



A variable that potentially affects the relationship among the variables in a study which is not included among the variables studied.

Data: MPG vs. Car Weight
What other variables could affect MPG?
"Is engine size a lurking variable?"

MPG vs. Weight for '78 - '79 Automobiles (n = 37)

$r^2 = 0.83$

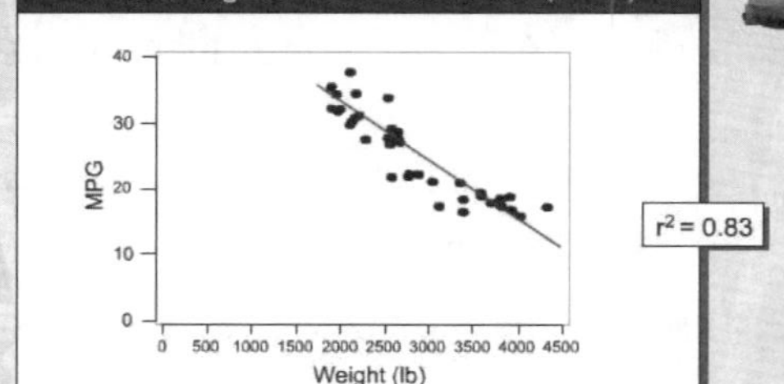

Feb 10

15-17

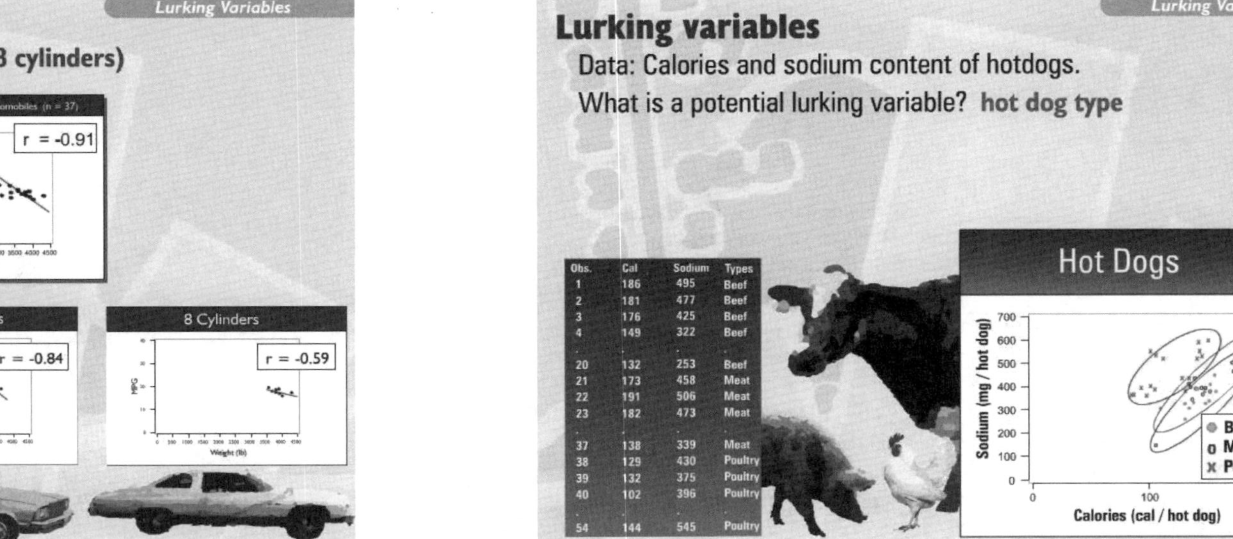



15-18

Lurking Variables

## Lurking variables

Data: Calories and sodium content of hotdogs.

What is a potential lurking variable? **hot dog type**

| Obs. | Cal | Sodium | Types |
|---|---|---|---|
| 1 | 186 | 495 | Beef |
| 2 | 181 | 477 | Beef |
| 3 | 176 | 425 | Beef |
| 4 | 149 | 322 | Beef |
| . | | | |
| 20 | 132 | 253 | Beef |
| 21 | 173 | 458 | Meat |
| 22 | 191 | 506 | Meat |
| 23 | 182 | 473 | Meat |
| . | | | |
| 37 | 138 | 339 | Meat |
| 38 | 129 | 430 | Poultry |
| 39 | 132 | 375 | Poultry |
| 40 | 102 | 396 | Poultry |
| . | | | |
| 54 | 144 | 545 | Poultry |

Hot Dogs

Overall r = .47

Beef r = .89
Meat r = .86
Poultry r = .66

Sodium (mg / hot dog)

Calories (cal / hot dog)

15-19

Association / Causation

# Association Does Not Imply Causation

Basic Practice of Statistics Chapter 5

- 1 problem: lurking variable; nearly confunded with x might cause changes in y.
- Confunding can only be ruled out if x values randomly assigned to individuals.

15-20

Association / Causation

## Association does not imply causation

**Does increasing fat in the diet cause cancer?**

Data: Fat intake vs. cancer death rate. The individual is country.

Possible lurking variables: dietary differences, medical care, lifestyle, sugar consumption, pollution, etc.

**To prove that X causes changes in Y, do an experiment.**

Fat Intake vs. Cancer Death Rate

r = 0.95

Cancer Death Rate (per 100,000)

Fat Intake per Capita per Day (Grams)

R. I. P.

Be careful about associating causation with observational studies.

15-21



## Association does not imply causation

**Is golf handicap related to stock ratings?**

X = Golf handicap of CEOs responsible for investments

Y = Stock rating for investments managed by those CEOs

Lurking variables: Company size, company recreation policy, type of company

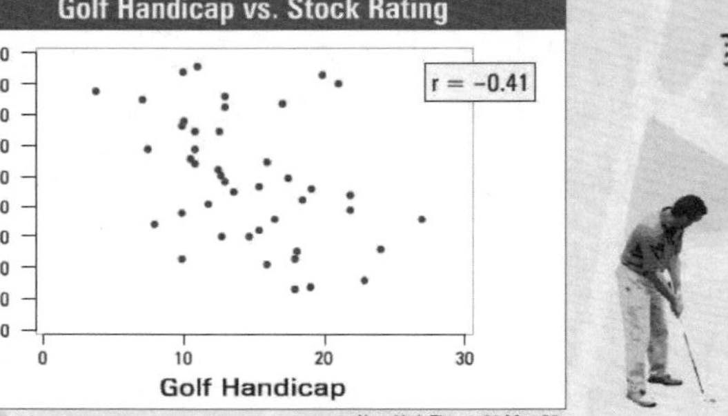

15-22



## Drawbacks of Observational Studies

1. **Cannot systematically change X and observe change in Y.**
   Example: Cannot systematically change golf handicaps
2. **Cannot randomize**
   Example: Cannot randomly assign golf handicaps to CEOs
3. **Cannot conclude causation**
   Example: Cannot conclude that higher golf handicaps *cause* lower stock ratings.

**To get good evidence of causation:**
**DO AN EXPERIMENT**

15-23



## Supporting Causation Without Experimentation

**Criteria:**

1. Strong association
2. Association consistent across studies
3. Higher doses associated with stronger responses
4. Alleged cause precedes the effect in time
5. Alleged cause is plausible

**More criteria met → Stronger case for causation**

15-24



## Smoking and Lung Cancer

Without ever experimenting on human subjects, U.S. Surgeon Generals have long stated that smoking causes lung cancer. This statement can be made because the relationship meets the criteria for establishing causation.

1. Very strong measures of association between smoking and lung cancer found in observational studies.
2. Multiple studies show same outcome across time and geographic boundaries.
3. Heavy smoking has greater risk than light smoking.
4. Smoking predates contracting lung cancer.
5. Connection between tars and lung cancer has been proven in animal experiments making cause plausible.

15-25

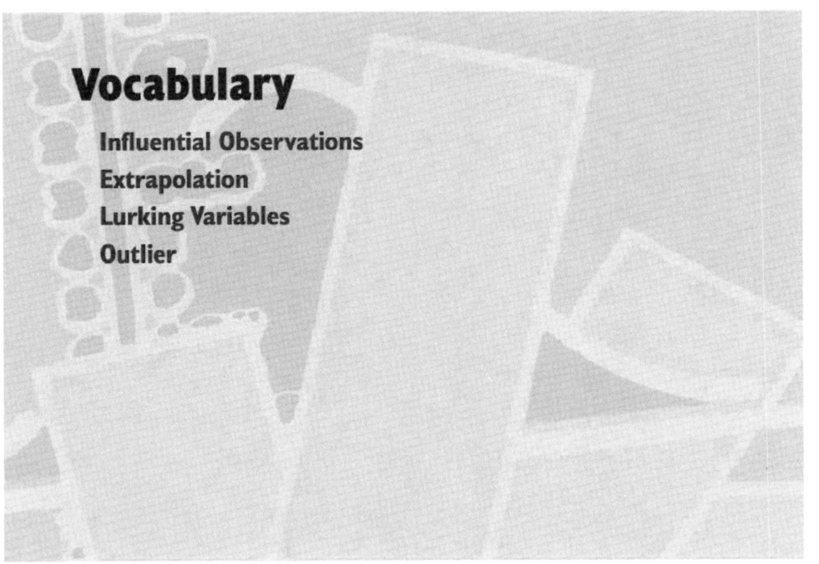


To trust observation

1. strong relationship
2. consistent relationship across different studies
3. logical dose-response relationship
4. alleged cause precede the effect in time
5. alleged

12 Feb

16-1

1. designate 1 var as 'row var' other as 'column var'

5. compare sets of row percentages
each set of row percentages called
"conditional distribution...

16-2

## Objectives

1. Contrast quantitative bivariate and categorical bivariate data.
2. Summarize a set of categorical bivariate data in a two-way table.
3. Identify marginal and conditional distributions in a two-way table.
4. Identify and interpret patterns that suggest association between variables in a two-way table.
5. Evaluate the effects of a third variable on the association between two variables and determine if Simpson's paradox is present.
6. Interpret a scatterplot of two quantitative variables and one categorical variable.

16-3

# Introduction to Chapter 6

Basic Practice of Statistics Chapter 6

16-4

## Exit Poll Survey

? Kickoff Question

Is there an association between voting choice and political ideology? What do the results from this survey tell us about voting behavior?

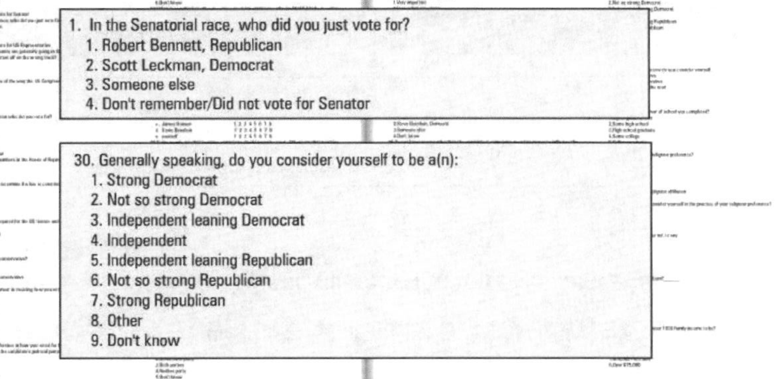
1. In the Senatorial race, who did you just vote for?
   1. Robert Bennett, Republican
   2. Scott Leckman, Democrat
   3. Someone else
   4. Don't remember/Did not vote for Senator

30. Generally speaking, do you consider yourself to be a(n):
   1. Strong Democrat
   2. Not so strong Democrat
   3. Independent leaning Democrat
   4. Independent
   5. Independent leaning Republican
   6. Not so strong Republican
   7. Strong Republican
   8. Other
   9. Don't know

12 Feb

16-5

*Categorical vs. Quantitative*

## Arithmetic Properties of Categorical Variables

Counting is the only arithmetic operation that makes sense for categorical data.

1. In the Senatorial race, who did you just vote for?
   1. Robert Bennett, Republican
   2. Scott Leckman, Democrat
   3. Someone else
   4. Don't remember/Did not vote for Senator

| Data (n=5838) | | | | | |
|---|---|---|---|---|---|
| 1 | 4 | 3 | 2 | 4 | 1 |
| 4 | 3 | 3 | 2 | 1 | 4 |
| 4 | 1 | 3 | 3 | 3 | 4 |
| 3 | 4 | 3 | 2 | 4 | . |
| 4 | 2 | 1 | 3 | 2 | . |
| 4 | 4 | 4 | 1 | 3 | . |

| Counts | |
|---|---|
| 1. (Bennett) | 3583 |
| 2. (Leckman) | 2007 |
| 3. (Another) | 174 |
| 4. (Unknown) | 74 |
| Total | 5838 |

| Operation | Interpretation |
|---|---|
| Add the first and second responses: 1 + 4 = 5 | ? |
| Average the first and second responses: $\frac{1+4}{2} = 2.5$ | ? |

Make sure causation is not confused with relation.

16-6

*Categorical vs. Quantitative*

## Arithmetic Properties of Categorical Variables

Counting is the only arithmetic operation that makes sense for categorical data.

1. In the Senatorial race, who did you just vote for?
   1. Robert Bennett, Republican
   2. Scott Leckman, Democrat
   3. Someone else
   4. Don't remember/Did not vote for Senator

| Data (n=5838) | | | | | |
|---|---|---|---|---|---|
| 1 | 4 | 3 | 2 | 4 | 1 |
| 4 | 3 | 3 | 2 | 1 | 4 |
| 4 | 1 | 3 | 3 | 3 | 4 |
| 3 | 4 | 3 | 2 | 4 | . |
| 4 | 2 | 1 | 3 | 2 | . |
| 4 | 4 | 4 | 1 | 3 | . |

| Counts | |
|---|---|
| 1. (Bennett) | 3583 |
| 2. (Leckman) | 2007 |
| 3. (Another) | 174 |
| 4. (Unknown) | 74 |
| Total | 5838 |

| Operation | Interpretation |
|---|---|
| Add the first and second responses: 1 + 4 = 5 | ? |
| Average the first and second responses: $\frac{1+4}{2} = 2.5$ | ? |

Caution: lurking variables!!
Smokers - older non-smokers when study started. Thus more surviving smokers in 20 years!

16-7

*Two-Way Table*

**Two-Way Table**

A table giving counts (or percents) for two categorical variables.

**Example:**

Row variable:
Political Ideology

Column variable:
Candidate preference

**Table**

| Political Ideology | Candidate | | | |
|---|---|---|---|---|
| | Bennett | Leckman | Other | Don't know |
| Strong Conservative | 831 | 115 | 49 | 6 |
| Moderate Conservative | 1771 | 497 | 48 | 17 |
| Middle | 638 | 561 | 34 | 20 |
| Moderate Liberal | 203 | 601 | 22 | 7 |
| Strong Liberal | 27 | 158 | 11 | 5 |
| Don't Know | 113 | 75 | 10 | 19 |

16-8

*Two-Way Table*

## Marginal Distributions

Basic Practice of Statistics Chapter 6

Feb 12

16-9

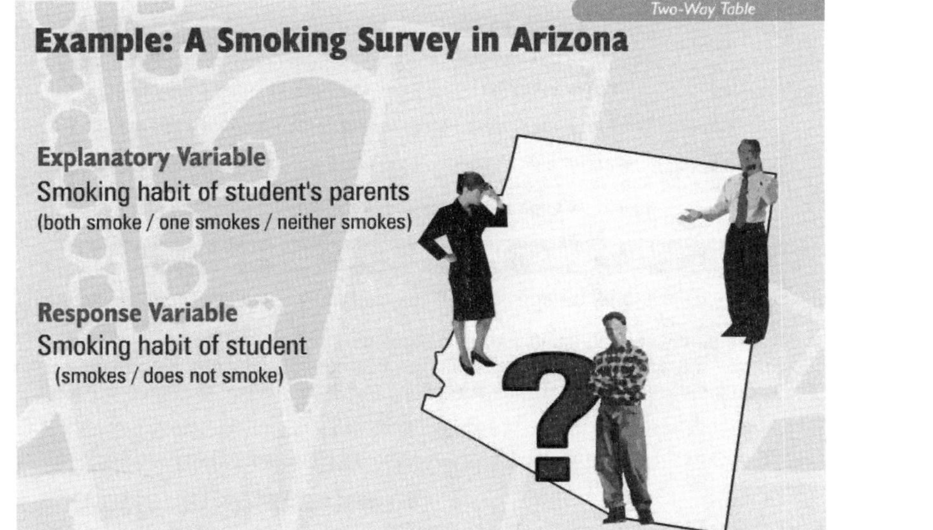


16-10

*Two-Way Table*

## Example: A Smoking Survey in Arizona

**Explanatory (Row) Variable:** Smoking habit of student's parents

**Response (Column) Variable:** Smoking habit of student

**Students' Smoking Habits vs. Parents' Smoking Habits**

| | Student smokes | Student does not smoke |
|---|---|---|
| Both parents smoke | 400 | 1380 |
| One parent smokes | 416 | 1823 |
| Neither parent smokes | 188 | 1168 |

This 3x2 two-way table has three rows and two columns. Numbers are counts or frequencies.

16-11

*Marginal Distributions*

## Margins

Margins show totals for each column and each row.
Both margins sum to the same overall total.

**Students' Smoking Habits vs. Parents' Smoking Habits**

| | Student smokes | Student does not smoke | Total |
|---|---|---|---|
| Both parents smoke | 400 | 1380 | 1780 |
| One parent smokes | 416 | 1823 | 2239 |
| Neither parent smokes | 188 | 1168 | 1356 |
| Total | 1004 | 4371 | 5375 |

16-12

*Marginal Distributions*

## Margins

**Marginal Distribution:** Distribution of **column variable** separately (or row variable separately) expressed in counts or percents.

Marginal distribution of students' smoking behavior: 18.7%, 81.3%

What percentage of the students smoke? 18.7%

**Students' Smoking Habits vs. Parents' Smoking Habits**

| | Student smokes | Student does not smoke | |
|---|---|---|---|
| Both parents smoke | 400 | 1380 | 1780 |
| One parent smokes | 416 | 1823 | 2239 |
| Neither parent smokes | 188 | 1168 | 1356 |
| Marginal % | 1004 / 5375 ⇒ 18.7% | 4371 / 5375 = 81.3 % | 100 % |

16-13



## Margins

**Marginal Distribution:** Distribution of column variable separately (or **row variable** separately) expressed in counts or percents.

Marginal distribution of parents' smoking habits: 33.1%, 41.7%, 25.2%

What percent of the students have parents who both smoke? 33.1%

**Students' Smoking Habits vs. Parents' Smoking Habits**

| | Student smokes | Student does not smoke | Marginal % |
|---|---|---|---|
| Both parents smoke | 400 | 1380 | $\frac{1780}{5375}$ = 33.1 % |
| One parent smokes | 416 | 1823 | $\frac{2239}{5375}$ ⇒ 41.7% |
| Neither parent smokes | 188 | 1168 | $\frac{1356}{5375}$ = 25.2 % |
| Total | 1004 | 4371 | 100 % |

16-14



## Relationships between Categorical Variables

Basic Practice of Statistics Chapter 6

relationship between gender and music preference
not male and rock

16-15



## Conditional Distributions

Given that

**Conditional Distributions (Rows):** Distribution of percents under a specific condition, namely the row category.

Row 1: Conditional for students' smoking behavior given both parents smoke
Row 2: Conditional for students' smoking behavior given one parent smokes
Row 3: Conditional for students' smoking behavior given neither parent smokes

If neither parent smokes, what percent of the students smoke? 13.9%

**Students' Smoking Habits vs. Parents' Smoking Habits**

| | Student smokes | Student does not smoke | Total |
|---|---|---|---|
| Both parents smoke % | 400 / 1780 ⇒ 22.5% | 1380 / 1780 ⇒ 77.5% | 100 % |
| One parent smokes % | 416 / 2239 ⇒ 18.6% | 1823 / 2239 ⇒ 81.4% | 100 % |
| Neither parent smokes% | 188 / 1356 ⇒ 13.9% | 1168 / 1356 ⇒ 86.1% | 100 % |
| Total | 1004 | 4371 | 5375 |

categories

Can't say it's causal but demonstrate a relationship

16-16



**Conditional Distributions (Columns):**

Column 1: Conditional for parents' smoking behavior given student smokes
Column 2: Conditional for parents' smoking behavior given student doesn't smoke

Of those students who smoke, what percentage have parents who both smoke? 39.8%

**Students' Smoking Habits vs. Parents' Smoking Habits**

| | Student smokes % | Student does not smoke % | Total |
|---|---|---|---|
| Both parents smoke | $\frac{400}{1004}$ ⇒ 39.8% | $\frac{1380}{4371}$ ⇒ 31.6% | 1780 |
| One parent smokes | $\frac{416}{1004}$ ⇒ 41.4% | $\frac{1823}{4371}$ ⇒ 41.7% | 2239 |
| Neither parent smokes | $\frac{188}{1004}$ ⇒ 18.7% | $\frac{1168}{4371}$ ⇒ 26.7% | 1356 |
| Total | 100 % | 100 % | 5375 |

16-17

*Conditional Distributions*

**Which conditional distributions (row or column) are easier to interpret?**

**Row**

| Students' Smoking Habits vs. Parents' Smoking Habits | Student smokes | Student does not smoke | Total |
|---|---|---|---|
| Both parents smoke | 22.5 % | 77.5 % | 100 % |
| One parent smokes | 18.6 % | 81.4 % | 100 % |
| Neither parent smokes | 13.9% | 86.1 % | 100 % |
| Total | 1004 | 4371 | 5375 |

**Column**

| Students' Smoking Habits vs. Parents' Smoking Habits | Student smokes | Student does not smoke | Total |
|---|---|---|---|
| Both parents smoke | 39.8 % | 31.6 % | 1780 |
| One parent smokes | 41.4 % | 41.7 % | 2239 |
| Neither parent smokes | 18.7 % | 26.7 % | 1356 |
| Total | 100 % | 100 % | 5375 |

16-18

*Association*

## Detecting Association Between Categorical Variables

**No association:** all conditional distributions look like the marginal distribution.

**Potential association:** one or more of the conditional distributions look very different from the marginal distribution (or each other).

Compare each conditional distribution with corresponding marginal distribution.

| Students' Smoking Habits vs. Parents' Smoking Habits | Student smokes | Student does not smoke | Total |
|---|---|---|---|
| Both parents smoke | 400 / 1780 ( 22.5 %) | 1380 / 1780 ( 77.5 %) | ( 100 %) |
| One parent smokes | 416 / 2239 ( 18.6 %) | 1823 / 2239 ( 81.4 %) | ( 100 %) |
| Neither parent smokes | 188 / 1356 ( 13.9 %) | 1168 / 1356 ( 86.1 %) | ( 100 %) |
| Total | 1004 / 5375 ( 18.7 %) | 4371 / 5375 ( 81.3 %) | ( 100 %) |

16-19

*Association*

## Detecting Association Between Categorical Variables

The conditional distributions for "Both parents smoke" and "Neither parent smokes" look different from the marginal distribution.

**Conclusion: Potential association**

Are the differences statistically significant?

| Students' Smoking Habits vs. Parents' Smoking Habits | Student smokes | Student does not smoke | Total |
|---|---|---|---|
| Both parents smoke | 400 / 1780 ( 22.5 %) | 1380 / 1780 ( 77.5 %) | ( 100 %) |
| One parent smokes | 416 / 2239 ( 18.6 %) | 1823 / 2239 ( 81.4 %) | ( 100 %) |
| Neither parent smokes | 188 / 1356 ( 13.9 %) | 1168 / 1356 ( 86.1 %) | ( 100 %) |
| Total | 1004 / 5375 ( 18.7 %) | 4371 / 5375 ( 81.3 %) | ( 100 %) |

16-20

*Two-Way Table*

## Interactive Two Way Tables

**Possible Associations**

- Gender and Music Preference Applet
- Handedness and Gender Applet
- Missionary Service and Music Preference Applet

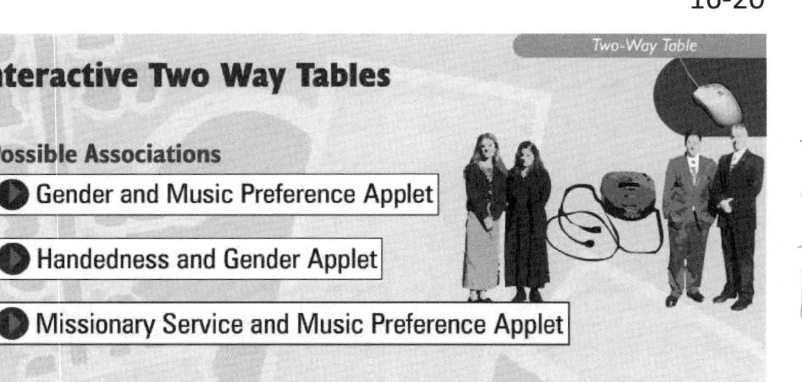

Feb 12

16-21



## Additional Example: Two-way Table

**Are age and education level related?**

Data gathered by U.S. Census Bureau 1991.

**Explanatory Variable:**

- 25-34
- 35-44
- 45-54
- 55-64
- 65+

} Age Group

**Response Variable:**

- Did not complete high school
- Completed high school only
- 1-3 years of college only
- 4+ years of college

} Education Level

Display data in a 5x4 two-way table

16-22



## Additional Example: Two-way Table

**Are age and education level related?**

Convert to row percentages (row conditionals).

**Age vs. Education Level**

| Age Group | Did not complete H.S. | Completed H. S. | 1-3 years of college | 4+ years of college | Total |
|---|---|---|---|---|---|
| | 1 | 2 | 3 | 4 | |
| 25-34 | 14% | 41% | 21% | 24% | 100% |
| 35-44 | 12% | 37% | 23% | 28% | 100% |
| 45-54 | 19% | 40% | 18% | 23% | 100% |
| 55-64 | 28% | 41% | 14% | 17% | 100% |
| 65 plus | 42% | 34% | 11% | 12% | 100% |
| Total | 22% | 39% | 18% | 21% | 100% |

16-23



## Additional Example: Two-way Table

**Are age and education level related?**

Convert to row percentages (row conditionals).

Compare using bar charts.

Are the differences large enough to be statistically significant?

**Age vs. Education Level**

| Bar Charts for Conditional Dist. (1 2 3 4) | Age Group | Did not complete H.S. | Completed H. S. | 1-3 years of college | 4+ years of college | Total |
|---|---|---|---|---|---|---|
| | | 1 | 2 | 3 | 4 | |
| | 25-34 | 14% | 41% | 21% | 24% | 100% |
| | 35-44 | 12% | 37% | 23% | 28% | 100% |
| | 45-54 | 19% | 40% | 18% | 23% | 100% |
| | 55-64 | 28% | 41% | 14% | 17% | 100% |
| | 65 plus | 42% | 34% | 11% | 12% | 100% |
| | Total | 22% | 39% | 18% | 21% | 100% |



16-24



## Simpson's Paradox

Basic Practice of Statistics Chapter 6

16-25



## Simpson's Paradox Example

Is the "hot hand" theory in basketball evident at the free throw line? i.e., after making the first free throw, does a player have a better chance of making the second?

**Three Variables**

**Variable 1 (explanatory)**
Player (Larry Bird, Rick Robey)

**Variable 2 (explanatory)**
Outcome of first free throw (make, miss)

**Variable 3 (response)**
Outcome of second free throw (make, miss)

Summarize results in a three-way table.



16-26



## Simpson's Paradox Example

Compute and compare the conditional distributions for rows for each player.

For both players, the percentage of free throws made after missing the first is higher than the percentage of free throws made after making the first; this gives evidence **against** the "hot hand" theory.

**Three-Way Table**

| Player | First Free Throw | Second Free Throw: Made | Second Free Throw: Missed | Total |
|---|---|---|---|---|
| Larry Bird | Made | 88.07% | 11.93% | 100.00% |
| | Missed | 90.57% | 9.43% | 100.00% |
| | Total | 88.46% | 11.54% | 100.00% |
| Rick Robey | Made | 59.34% | 40.66% | 100.00% |
| | Missed | 61.25% | 38.75% | 100.00% |
| | Total | 60.23% | 39.77% | 100.00% |



16-27



## Simpson's Paradox Example

What happens if we combine the data for Bird and Robey by summing across the third variable (player)?

**Three-Way Table**

| Player | First Free Throw | Second Free Throw: Made | Second Free Throw: Missed | Total |
|---|---|---|---|---|
| Larry Bird | Made | 251 | 34 | 285 |
| | Missed | 48 | 5 | 53 |
| | Total | 299 | 39 | 338 |
| Rick Robey | Made | 54 | 37 | 91 |
| | Missed | 49 | 31 | 80 |
| | Total | 103 | 68 | 171 |

**Two-Way Table**

| | First Free Throw | Second Free Throw: Made | Second Free Throw: Missed | Total |
|---|---|---|---|---|
| Both Players | Made | 305 | 71 | 376 |
| | Missed | 97 | 36 | 133 |
| | Total | 402 | 107 | 509 |



16-28



## Simpson's Paradox Example

What effect does the third variable (player) have on the association?

With the third variable, we see evidence against the "hot hand" theory.

Without it, we see evidence in favor of the "hot hand" theory.

**Three-Way Table**

| Player | First Free Throw | Second Free Throw: Made | Second Free Throw: Missed | Total |
|---|---|---|---|---|
| Larry Bird | Made | 88.07% | 11.93% | 100.00% |
| | Missed | 90.57% | 9.43% | 100.00% |
| | Total | 88.46% | 11.54% | 100.00% |
| Rick Robey | Made | 59.34% | 40.66% | 100.00% |
| | Missed | 61.25% | 38.75% | 100.00% |
| | Total | 60.23% | 39.77% | 100.00% |

**Two-Way Table**

| | First Free Throw | Second Free Throw: Made | Second Free Throw: Missed | Total |
|---|---|---|---|---|
| Both Players | Made | 81.12% | 18.88% | 100.00% |
| | Missed | 72.93% | 27.07% | 100.00% |
| | Total | 78.98% | 21.02% | 100.00% |

16-29

*Simpson's Paradox*

## Simpson's Paradox Example

This type of reversal is called **Simpson's Paradox.**

**Three-Way Table**

| Player | First Free Throw | Second Free Throw | | Total |
|---|---|---|---|---|
| | | Made | Missed | Total |
| Larry Bird | Made | 88.07% | 11.93% | 100.00% |
| | Missed | 90.57% | 9.43% | 100.00% |
| | Total | 88.46% | 11.54% | 100.00% |
| | | Made | Missed | Total |
| Rick Robey | Made | 59.34% | 40.66% | 100.00% |
| | Missed | 61.25% | 38.75% | 100.00% |
| | Total | 60.23% | 39.77% | 100.00% |

**Two-Way Table**

| | First Free Throw | Second Free Throw | | |
|---|---|---|---|---|
| | | Made | Missed | Total |
| Both Players | Made | 81.12% | 18.88% | 100.00% |
| | Missed | 72.93% | 27.07% | 100.00% |
| | Total | 78.98% | 21.02% | 100.00% |



16-30

*Simpson's Paradox*

## Summary of Simpson's Paradox:

- Association between two variables ignoring a third variable leads to a specific conclusion.
- Association between two variables including that third variable leads to the opposite conclusion.

**This happens when the third lurking variable is associated with the other two.**

16-31

*Simpson's Paradox*

## Optional Example: Simpson's Paradox

**Do non-smokers live longer than smokers?**

Results from a 1972-1974 survey in Wickham, England and a follow-up survey 20 years later.

Table gives survival status in follow-up survey.

**Three Variables**

**Variable 1:** Smoking status from 1972-74 (smoker/nonsmoker)

**Variable 2:** Survival status 20 years later (alive/dead)

**Variable 3:** Age group at time of 1972-74 survey

| Age Group | Smoking Status | ALIVE | DEAD | TOTAL |
|---|---|---|---|---|
| 18-24 | Smoker | 53 | 2 | 55 |
| | Non-Smoker | 61 | 1 | 62 |
| 25-34 | Smoker | 121 | 3 | 124 |
| | Non-Smoker | 152 | 5 | 157 |
| 35-44 | Smoker | 95 | 14 | 109 |
| | Non-Smoker | 114 | 7 | 121 |
| 45-54 | Smoker | 103 | 27 | 130 |
| | Non-Smoker | 66 | 12 | 78 |
| 55-64 | Smoker | 64 | 51 | 115 |
| | Non-Smoker | 81 | 40 | 121 |
| 65-74 | Smoker | 7 | 29 | 36 |
| | Non-Smoker | 28 | 101 | 129 |
| 75+ | Smoker | 0 | 13 | 13 |
| | Non-Smoker | 0 | 64 | 64 |

| Age Group | Smoking Status | ALIVE | DEAD | TOTAL |
|---|---|---|---|---|
| ALL | Smoker | 443 | 139 | 582 |
| | Non-Smoker | 502 | 230 | 732 |
| | Total | 945 | 369 | 1314 |

16-32

*Simpson's Paradox*

## Optional Example: Simpson's Paradox

**Do non-smokers live longer than smokers?**

Obtain conditional percentages for smokers and non-smokers.

What is the association between smoking habits and survival rates in the three-way table?
In the two-way table?

Ignoring third variable (age) in the two-way table obscures the true association between smoking habits and survival rates.

| Age Group | Smoking Status | ALIVE | DEAD | TOTAL |
|---|---|---|---|---|
| 18-24 | Smoker | 96.36% | 3.64% | 100% |
| | Non-Smoker | 98.39% | 1.61% | 100% |
| 25-34 | Smoker | 97.58% | 2.42% | 100% |
| | Non-Smoker | 96.82% | 3.19% | 100% |
| 35-44 | Smoker | 87.16% | 12.84% | 100% |
| | Non-Smoker | 94.21% | 5.79% | 100% |
| 45-54 | Smoker | 79.23% | 20.77% | 100% |
| | Non-Smoker | 84.62% | 15.39% | 100% |
| 55-64 | Smoker | 55.65% | 44.35% | 100% |
| | Non-Smoker | 66.94% | 33.06% | 100% |
| 65-74 | Smoker | 19.44% | 80.56% | 100% |
| | Non-Smoker | 21.71% | 78.30% | 100% |
| 75+ | Smoker | 0.00% | 100.00% | 100% |
| | Non-Smoker | 0.00% | 100.00% | 100% |

| Age Group | Smoking Status | ALIVE | DEAD | TOTAL |
|---|---|---|---|---|
| ALL | Smoker | 76.12% | 23.88% | 100% |
| | Non-Smoker | 68.58% | 31.42% | 100% |
| | Total | 71.92% | 28.08% | 100% |

Feb 12

16-33

Simpson's Paradox

# Optional Example: Simpson's Paradox

**Do non-smokers live longer than smokers?**

Age Distribution at the Beginning of the Study

| Age Group | Smoking Status | ALIVE | DEAD | TOTAL |
|---|---|---|---|---|
| 18-24 | Smoker | 96.36% | 3.64% | 100% |
| | Non-Smoker | 98.39% | 1.61% | 100% |
| 25-34 | Smoker | 97.58% | 2.42% | 100% |
| | Non-Smoker | 96.82% | 3.19% | 100% |
| 35-44 | Smoker | 87.16% | 12.84% | 100% |
| | Non-Smoker | 94.21% | 5.79% | 100% |
| 45-54 | Smoker | 79.23% | 20.77% | 100% |
| | Non-Smoker | 84.62% | 15.39% | 100% |
| 55-64 | Smoker | 55.65% | 44.35% | 100% |
| | Non-Smoker | 66.94% | 33.06% | 100% |
| 65-74 | Smoker | 19.44% | 80.56% | 100% |
| | Non-Smoker | 21.71% | 78.30% | 100% |
| 75+ | Smoker | 0.00% | 100.00% | 100% |
| | Non-Smoker | 0.00% | 100.00% | 100% |

| Age Group | Smoking Status | ALIVE | DEAD | TOTAL |
|---|---|---|---|---|
| ALL | Smoker | 76.12% | 23.88% | 100% |
| | Non-Smoker | 68.58% | 31.42% | 100% |
| | Total | 71.92% | 28.08% | 100% |

Ignoring third variable (age) in the two-way table obscures the true association between smoking habits and survival rates.

16-34

Objective 5: Detecting Association

# Interactive Two Way Tables

**Possible Associations**

- Gender and Music Preference Applet
- Handedness and Gender Applet
- Missionary Service and Music Preference Applet

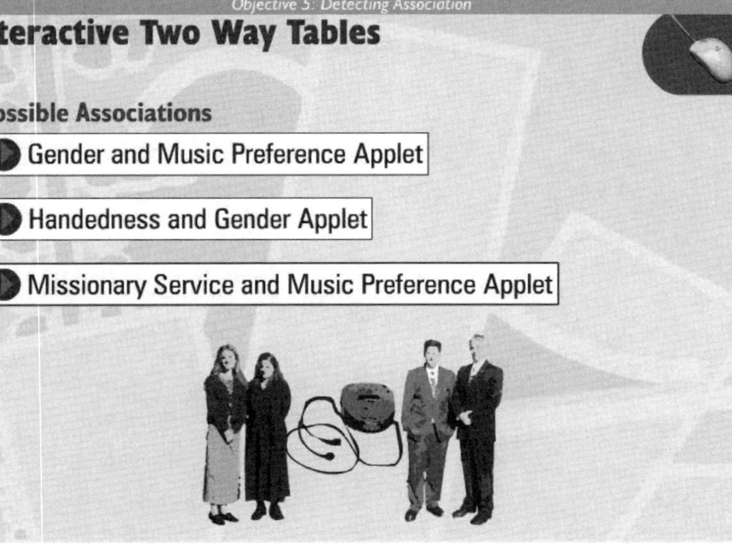

16-35

# Vocabulary

**Association**
**Conditional Distribution**
**Marginal Distribution**
**Simpson's Paradox**
**Two-way Table**

17-1

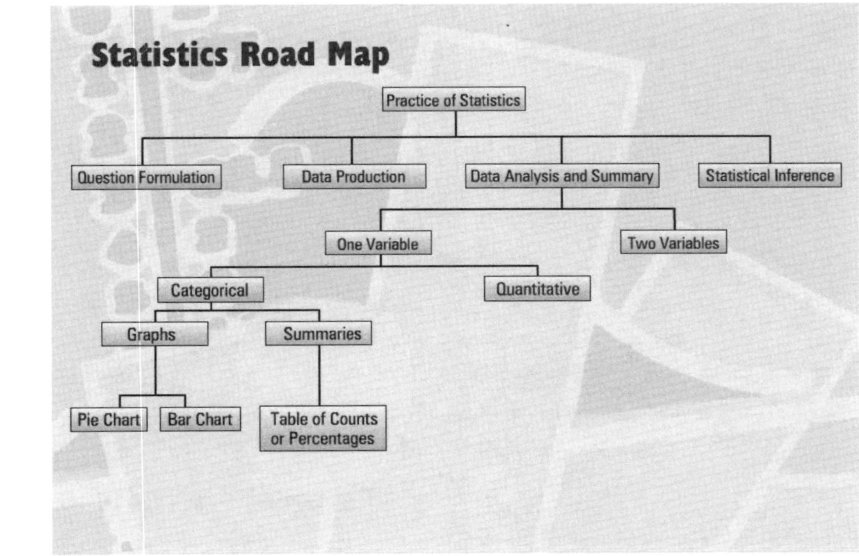


17-2

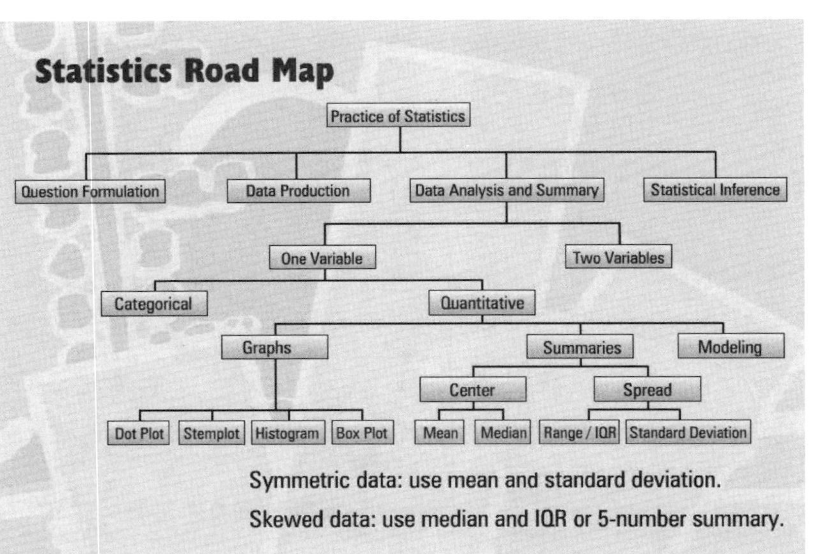


17-3

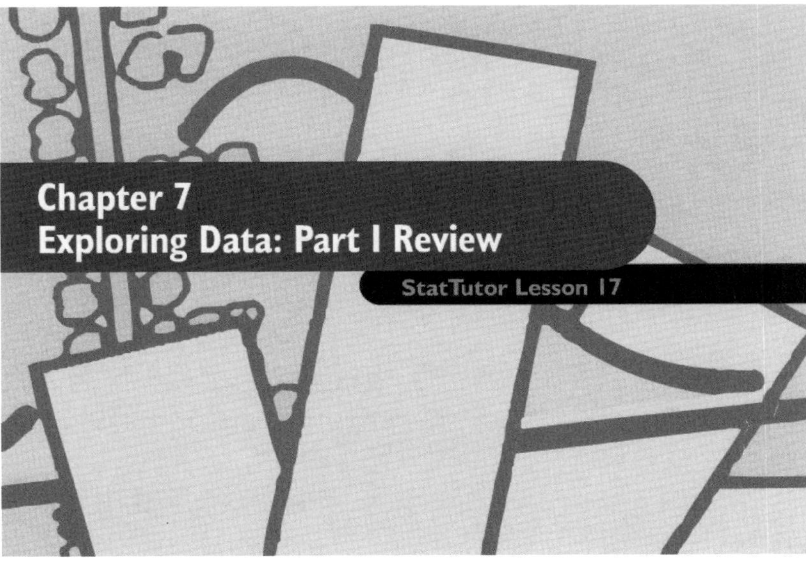


17-4

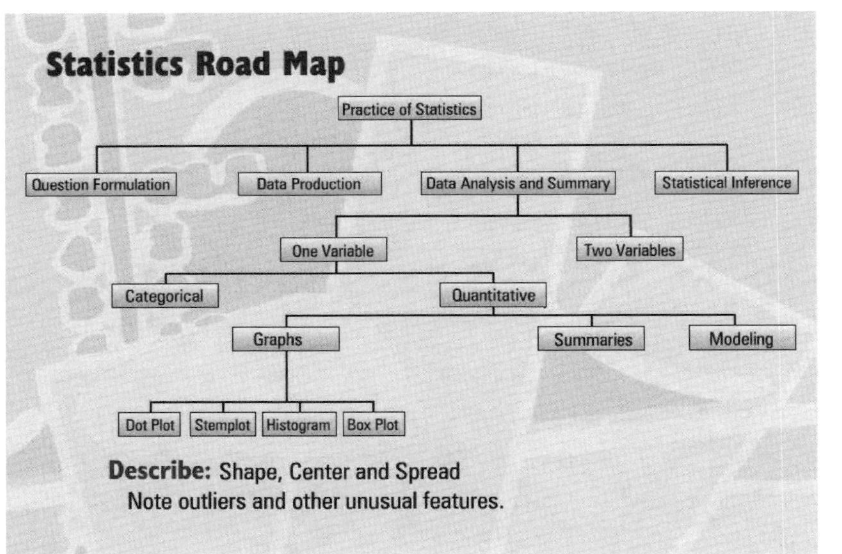


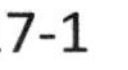

17-5

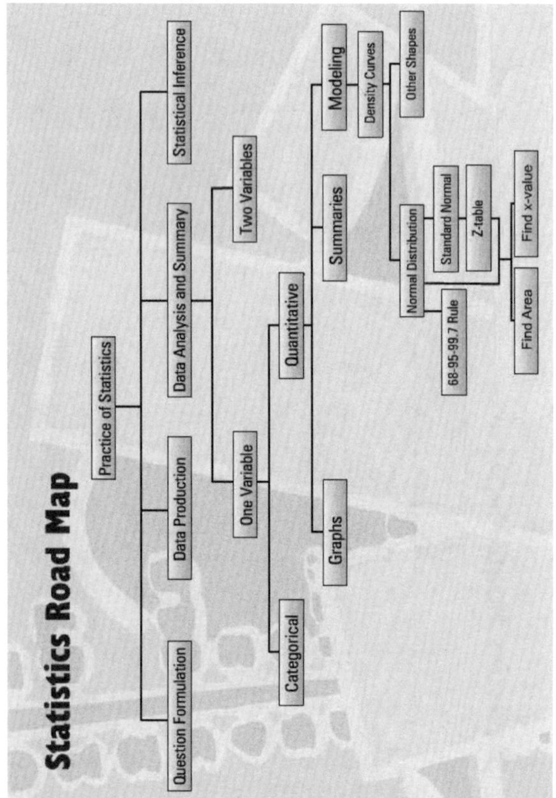


17-6

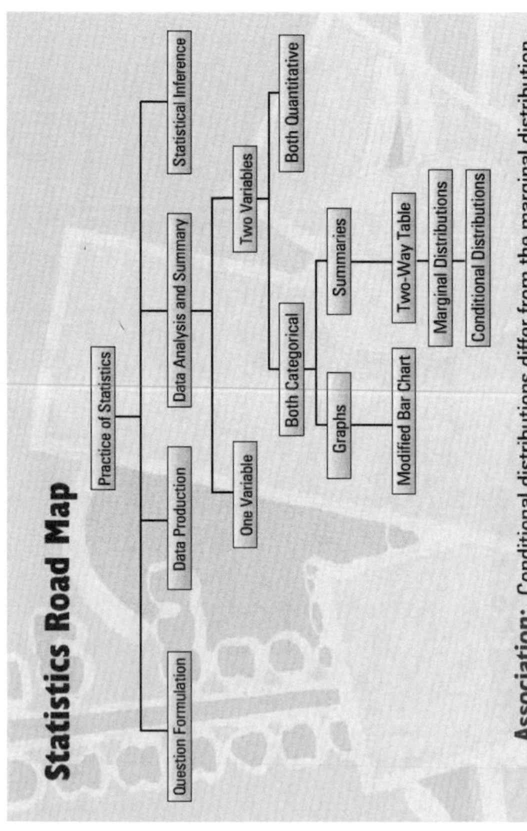


17-7

**Statistics Road Map**

Practice of Statistics

Question Formulation | Data Production | Data Analysis and Summary | Statistical Inference

One Variable | Two Variables

Both Categorical | Both Quantitative

Graphs | Summaries | Modeling

Scatterplot | Residual Plot | Correlation | $r^2$ | Least Squares Regression Line | Slope | y-intercept

**Describe:** Direction, form and strength for scatterplot.

**Look for:** Unusual patterns in residual plot.

17-8

**Statistics Road Map**

Practice of Statistics

Question Formulation | Data Production | Data Analysis and Summary | Statistical Inference

One Variable | Two Variables

Both Categorical | Both Quantitative

Graphs | Summaries | Modeling

Scatterplot | Residual Plot | Correlation | $r^2$ | Least Squares Regression Line | Slope | y-intercept

Interpret $r^2$ in context.

17-9

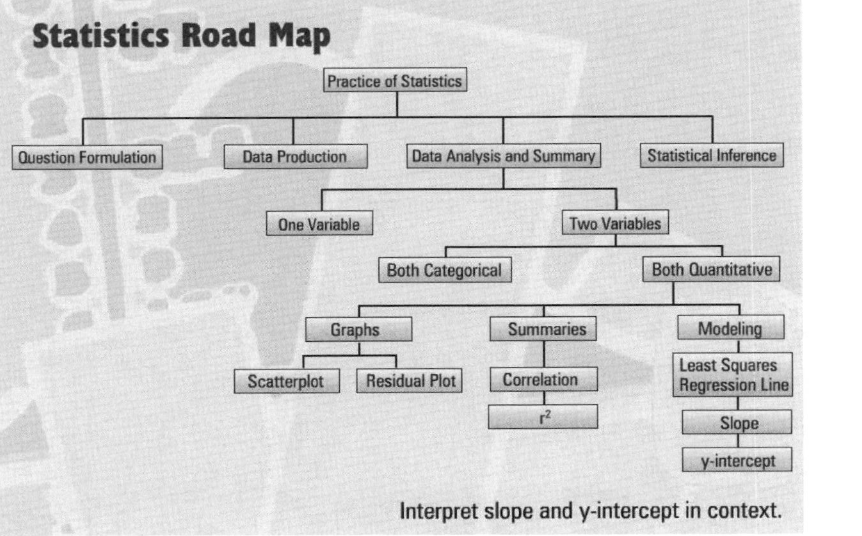


17-10

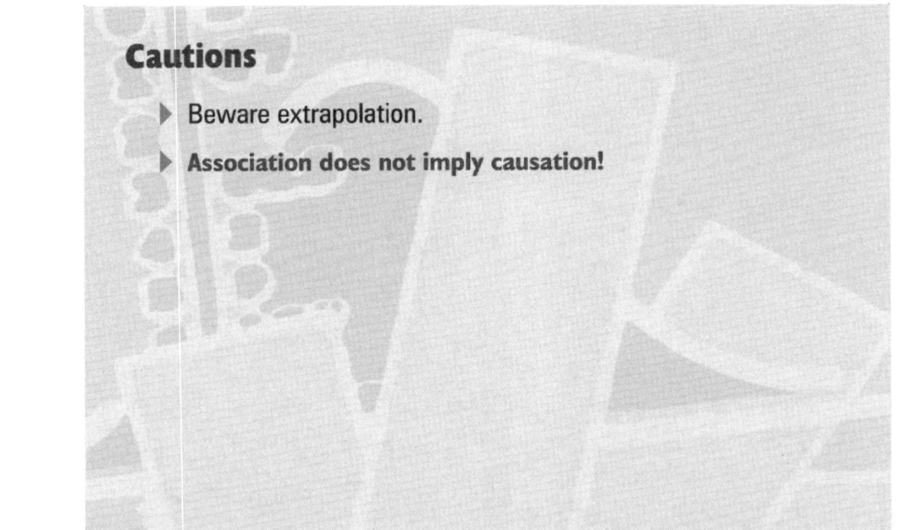


17-11

## Measures Affected by Outliers

- Mean
- Standard deviation
- Correlation
- $r^2$
- Slope and y-intercept

17-12

## Cautions

- Beware extrapolation.
- **Association does not imply causation!**

17-13

## Vocabulary

- Bar Graph
- Boxplot
- Categorical Data
- Conditional Distribution
- Correlation Coefficient
- Density Curve
- Histogram
- Interquartile Range
- Least-Squares Line
- Marginal Distribution
- Mean
- Median
- Normal Distribution
- $Q_1$
- $Q_3$
- Quantitative Data
- Pie Chart
- Range
- Residual
- Residual Plot
- $r^2$
- Scatterplot
- Slope
- Standard Normal Distribution
- Standard Deviation
- Stemplot
- Two-way Table
- y-intercept

18-1

# Chapter 10 Introducing Probability

StatTutor Lesson 18

18-2

## Lesson Objectives

1. Simulate playing games of chance to obtain probabilities.
2. Tabulate and interpret results from repeatedly "playing the game".
3. Propose a simulation using a "playing the game" strategy to approximate the probability distribution of $\bar{x}$ from an SRS.
4. List questions that can be answered by playing the SRS simulation game many, many times.
5. Define random phenomenon, probability, and probability model and apply to real life situations.
6. Compute probabilities based on a sample space.
7. Apply probability rules to calculate basic probabilities.

18-3

Why Study Probability

## Introducing Probability

Basic Practice of Statistics Chapter 10

18-4

Why Study Probability

## Research Question

**Assess the Dating Habits of Students at Your School**

What is the average cost of a typical weekend date?

**No one knows.**

Can you estimate it?

**Yes.**

How?

**Take a simple random sample of size $n = 50$, compute $\bar{x}$ and infer to all students.**

18-5

Why Study Probability

## Research Question

**Statistical Questions:**

- Can $\bar{x}$ from a simple random sample reliably tell us the average cost of a typical date? **Depends on variability.**
- If we take a second simple random sample, would we get the same value for $\bar{x}$? **No--$\bar{x}$ varies from sample to sample.**

**Because chance is used to choose simple random samples, the laws of probability govern the behavior of sample statistics.**

**Need to study probability!!**

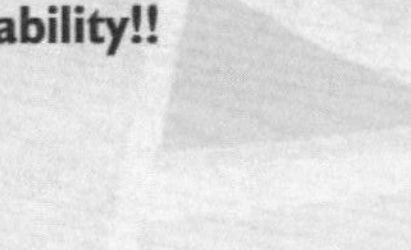

18-6

Simulating Probability

## The Idea of Probability

Basic Practice of Statistics Chapter 10

18-7

Simulating Probability

## Modeling a Game of Chance by "Playing the Game" Using Simulation

You "win" the crazy clay game if you get "rose" colored clay. What is the probability of winning?

Play the game many times and find out!

Play Crazy Clay!

Probability

Win Lose

18-8

"Playing the Game"

18-9

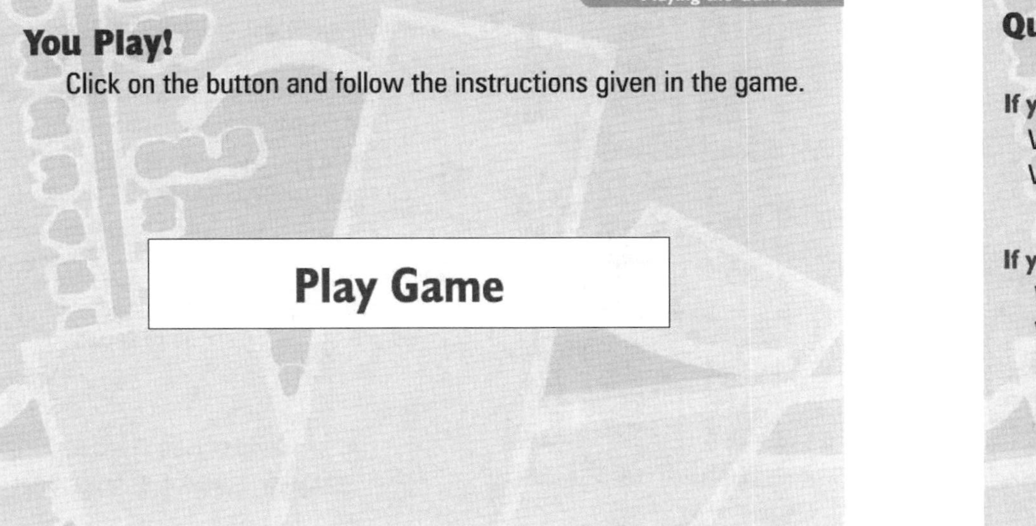



## You Play!

Click on the button and follow the instructions given in the game.

**Play Game**

18-10



## Question: Which Strategy is Best?

**If you switch doors:**

What is probability of winning a car?
What is probability of getting a goat?

**If you don't switch doors:**

What is probability of winning a car?
What is probability of getting a goat?

**Should I switch?**

**Should I not switch?**

18-11



## One Way to Answer the Question

**Model game of chance using simulation**

**Play the Game:**

Not once, but many times.
Use the same strategy each time!

18-12



## Simulating "Play the Game"

**Rules of Play for Never Switch**

**Strategy: Never Switch**

1. Place a car randomly behind a door for each game.
2. Choose a door.
3. When a goat is revealed, do not switch.
4. Play the game many times; tabulate wins and losses.

**Rules of Play for Always Switch**

**Strategy: Always Switch**

1. Place a car randomly behind a door for each game.
2. Choose a door.
3. When a goat is revealed, always switch.
4. Play the game many times; tabulate wins and losses.

**These rules are applied in the simulation game.**

18-13

"Playing the Game"

## Simulating "Play the Game"

Follow the instructions given in the simulation applet. Simulate both "always switch" and "never switch."
Maximum number of trials is 9999.

**Simulation**

18-14

"Playing the Game" Results

## Results from Web Site Playing the Game

Web site visitors using "Always Switch" strategy.

Strategy: Always Switch

| Outcome | Count | Percent |
|---|---|---|
| Win | 2451 | 67.34% |
| Lose | 1189 | 32.66% |
| Total | 3640 | 100.00% |

Web site visitors using "Never Switch" strategy.

Strategy: Never Switch

| Outcome | Count | Percent |
|---|---|---|
| Win | 886 | 33.15% |
| Lose | 1787 | 66.85% |
| Total | 2673 | 100.00% |

How do these estimates compare with the exact probabilities?

18-15

Exact Probabilities

## The Exact Probabilities

The car is behind door 1, 2 or 3.

Strategy: Never Switch

Chances of choosing the door with the car are one out of three or 1/3.

Strategy: Always Switch

- If you choose the door with the car and then switch, you will lose.
- If you choose a door with a goat and then switch, you will win.
- Chances of winning the car with switching are two out of three or 2/3.

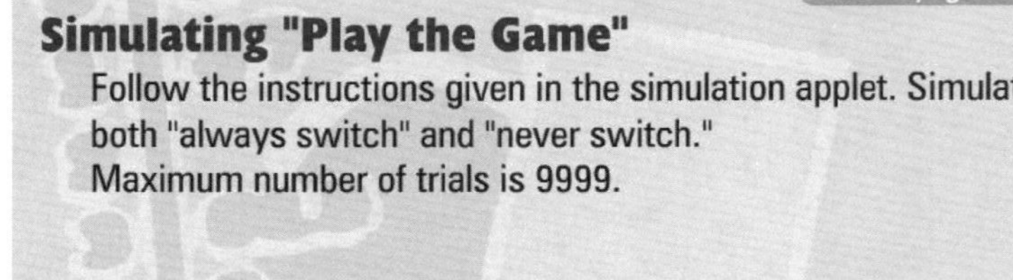

18-16

Comparing Probabilities

## Compare Exact and "Simulated" Probabilities

Strategy: Always Switch

| | Exact Probability | Simulated Probability |
|---|---|---|
| WIN | 0.6667 (2/3) | 0.6734 |
| LOSE | 0.3333 (1/3) | 0.3266 |
| Total | 1.0000 | 1.0000 |

Strategy: Never Switch

| | Exact Probability | Simulated Probability |
|---|---|---|
| WIN | 0.3333 (1/3) | 0.3315 |
| LOSE | 0.6667 (2/3) | 0.6685 |
| Total | 1.0000 | 1.0000 |

18-17

Interpretation of Probability

## Questions Answered with Certainty

Can you answer the question with certainty:

**"Will I win if I play the game once?"**

**Play Once**

Win a car? Win a goat?

Can't predict with certainty!

After many plays of the game, can you answer the question with certainty:

**"What's the probability I'll win?"**

**Yes, because with the results of many plays, you can estimate the probability!**

**Chance behavior is unpredictable in the short run, but has a regular and predictable pattern in the long run.**
**--David S. Moore**

18-18

Definitions

## Definitions

**Random phenomenon**

A phenomenon where the outcome of one play is unpredictable, but the outcomes from many plays form a distribution.

**Probability of an outcome**

The proportion of times that an outcome occurs in many, many repetitions (plays) of the random phenomenon.

18-19

Randomness

## Thinking about Randomness

- Single random phenomenon: outcome is uncertain.
- Many repetitions: proportion of specific outcome is predictable.

**Random does NOT mean haphazard.**

**Example: On-time Departures**

**Uncertain outcome:** Will the next flight to New York City leave on time?

**Estimable probability:** What proportion of flights to New York City leave on time?

18-20

Randomness

## Thinking about Randomness

- Single random phenomenon: outcome is uncertain.
- Many repetitions: proportion of specific outcome is predictable.

**Random does NOT mean haphazard.**

**Example: Allergic reactions of new medication**

**Uncertain outcome:** Will a randomly selected individual have an allergic reaction to the medication?

**Estimable probability:** What proportion of patients will have an allergic reaction to the medication?

18-21

*General Process of Simulation*

## General Process of "Playing the Game" (Simulation)

| Let's Make a Deal | General Process |
|---|---|
| 1. Rules for one play: Door selected for car with probability = 1/3. Goats placed behind the other two doors. Player picks door; host reveals goat and player switches; record outcome of win or lose. | 1. Establish rules for one play of the game using probability. Simulate one play; record result. |
| 2. Play the game many times. Tabulate wins and losses: Number of wins 2451 out of 3640 plays. | 2. Play the game many times. Tabulate results. |
| 3. Percentage of wins: 67.3% Percentage of losses: 32.7% | 3. Estimate probabilities |

18-22

*Simulation of SRS*

## Recall: Research Question

**What is the average cost of a typical weekend date for students at your school?**

**To answer: Take a simple random sample of size n = 50, compute $\bar{x}$ and infer to all students.**

Need to know:
How accurately does $\bar{x}$ estimate $\mu$?
How reliable is our measure of accuracy?

**Need to study the behavior of $\bar{x}$ using simulation!!**

18-23

*Simulation of SRS*

## Obtain Probability Model for $\bar{x}$'s from SRS's

We will "Play the Game" many times to assess the accuracy of $\bar{x}$ from a SRS of n = 50 and to measure reliability.

**Step I:**

One play of the game: Select a SRS of 50 students. Record the cost of a typical date for each student; compute $\bar{x}$.

**What produces the element of chance?**

Using SRS. (Imposes equal chance of selection for each individual in the population.)

18-24

*Simulation of SRS*

## Obtain Probability Model for $\bar{x}$'s from SRS's

**Step 2:**

Play the game many times. Record $\bar{x}$ for each sample.

**Step 3:**

Construct histogram of the $\bar{x}$'s and note shape, center and spread.

18-25



## Questions We Can Answer about $\bar{x}$ Outcomes from Simulation

1) **Center:** What value do $\bar{x}$'s tend to cluster about? Is bias present?

2) **Spread:** How much do $\bar{x}$'s vary from sample to sample? (What is the precision of the sampling process?)

3) **Shape:** What overall pattern is displayed by $\bar{x}$'s from SRS's?

**What density curve is suggested by shape?**

18-26



# Probability Models

Basic Practice of Statistics Chapter 10

18-27



## Probability Model

**Let's Make a Deal Game**

| Outcomes for switching | Probabilities for switching |
| --- | --- |
| ▶ Win a car<br>▶ Win a goat (lose) | ▶ 2/3 for winning a car<br>▶ 1/3 for winning a goat (losing) |

**Need a list of all possible outcomes and the probability of each outcome for a probability model.**

18-28



## Probability Terminology

**Sample space** The list of all possible outcomes of a random phenomenon.

**Event** A single outcome or a subset of outcomes from the sample space.

**Probability Model** A mathematical description of a random phenomenon consisting of a sample space and a way of assigning probabilities to events.

18-29

Applications of Probability

## Computing Probabilities Using Probability Model

**IF all outcomes are equally likely:**

**COUNT**

- number of outcomes in event of interest
- number of outcomes in sample space

$$\textbf{Probability} = \frac{\text{Count of outcomes in event of interest}}{\text{Count of outcomes in sample space}}$$

18-30

Applications of Probability

## Computing Probabilities Using Probability Model

**Example: Gender of children in family of three children**

Assume birth of boy (b) or girl (g) is equally likely.

$\boldsymbol{S} = \{ggg, ggb, gbg, gbb, bgg, bgb, bbg, bbb\}$

Assume all outcomes are equally likely.

What is the probability of two boys and one girl?

$$P(\text{two boys, one girl}) = \frac{\text{Count(E)}}{\text{Count}(\boldsymbol{S})} = \frac{3}{8} = 0.375$$

What is the probability that the oldest child and youngest child are the same gender?

$$P(\text{oldest \& youngest same gender}) = \frac{\text{Count(E)}}{\text{Count}(\boldsymbol{S})} = \frac{4}{8} = 0.5$$

18-31

Probability Rules

# Probability Rules

Basic Practice of Statistics Chapter 10

18-32

Probability Rules

## Review

**Random phenomenon**

A phenomenon where the outcome of one play is unpredictable, but the outcomes from many plays form a distribution.

**Probability of an outcome**

The proportion of times that an outcome occurs in many, many repetitions (plays) of the random phenomenon.

1 2 3

18-33



## Probability Rules

- A probability must be a number between 0 and 1.
- The sum of probabilities from all possible outcomes must equal 1.
- If two events cannot occur simultaneously, the probability either one or the other occurs equals the sum of their probabilities.
- The probability that an event does not occur equals 1 minus the probability that the event does occur.

18-34



## New Definition

**Disjoint Events**

Two events that have no outcomes in common and, thus, cannot both occur simultaneously.

18-35



## Applying Probability Rules

**Example: Blood Types**

Sample Space: Blood types = {A, B, AB, O}
Possible Events: Person has type A, Person has type B, etc.
A person has only one blood type ⟶ all blood types are disjoint.

**Probability Model:**

| Blood Type | A | B | AB | O |
|---|---|---|---|---|
| Probability | 0.40 | 0.10 | 0.04 | 0.46 |

- P(A) = 0.40
- P(not A) = 1 – P(A) = 1 – 0.40 = 0.60
- P(A or O) = 0.40 + 0.46 = 0.86
- P(***S***) = P(A) + P(B) + P(AB) + P(O)
  = 0.40 + 0.10 + 0.04 + 0.46 = 1.00

18-36



## Applying Probability Rules

**Example: Customer Preference**

Sample Space: Customer's Choice = {Brand X, Brand Y, Another Brand}
Possible Events: Customer chooses Brand X, Brand Y or another brand.
Customer chooses only one brand ⟶ All brands choices are disjoint.

**Probability Model:**

| Customer's Choice | Brand X | Brand Y | All other brands |
|---|---|---|---|
| Probability | 0.30 | 0.45 | 0.25 |

- What is the probability that a customer does not choose Brand X? P(not Brand X) = 1 – 0.30 = 0.70
- What is the probability that a customer does not choose Brand X or Brand Y?
  P[not (Brand X or Brand Y)] = 1 –

18-37

# Vocabulary

- Event
- Outcome
- "Playing the Game"
- Probability
- Probability Model
- Random Phenomenon
- Sample Mean
- Sample Space
- Simulation
- Simple Random Sample
- Random Phenomenon

Parameter numerical fact about the population (eg. $\mu$) - the the we want to know but can't

Statistic corresponding numerical fact in the sample (eg. $\bar{x}$) the thing we can know.

Feb 18, 2014

19-1

## Chapter 11 Part I
## Sampling Distributions

StatTutor Lesson 19

~~Amdatal~~ picture: try to estimate average height in this class $\mu$
– a sample of 5 persons

19-2

## Lesson Objectives

1. Determine whether a mean or a proportion is a statistic or parameter.
2. Explain the law of large numbers.
3. Explain the need for sampling distribution of $\bar{x}$ and give its definition.
4. Propose and carry out a "playing the game" strategy to approximate the distribution of $\bar{x}$'s.
5. Compare the center, spread and shape of the sampling distribution of $\bar{x}$ with center, spread and shape of the population.
6. Explain the effect of increasing sample size on the sampling distribution of $\bar{x}$.
7. Use a sampling distribution to solve probability problems on $\bar{x}$.
8. Answer questions about $\bar{x}$ using the sampling distribution of $\bar{x}$.

19-3

## Introduction to Chapter 11:
## Sampling Distributions

Basic Practice of Statistics Chapter 11

19-4

## Why do we need sampling distributions?

**Statistical Inference**

**Census:** An examination of entire population (no sampling)

**Disadvantages:**

1. Very Time Consuming
2. Very Expensive
3. Often impractical

**Alternative: Sample part of population**

1. Select SRS from population and compute $\bar{x} = 64$ inches.
2. Make inference: Population average is approximately 64 inches.

19-5

## Why do we need sampling distributions?

**Statistical Inference**

**Census:** An examination of entire population (no sampling)

**Disadvantages:**

1. Very Time Consuming
2. Very Expensive
3. Often impractical

**Alternative: Sample part of population**

1. Select SRS from population and compute $\bar{x} = 64$ inches.
2. Make inference: Population average is approximately 64 inches.

**Questions**

- How accurate is our inference?
- How often will this method give correct answers?
- What will happen if we used this method many times?

**We use facts about sampling distributions to answer these questions.**

19-6



## Parameters and Statistics

Basic Practice of Statistics Chapter 11

19-7



## Vocabulary

**Parameter:** A number describing a characteristic of the population (usually unknown).

| Name | Symbol | Example |
|---|---|---|
| Mean | $\mu$ | Mean number of cigarettes smoked per day by all teenagers |
| Proportion | $p$ | Proportion of all teenagers who used tobacco in the last 30 days |

**Statistic:** A number, computed from sample data, estimating an unknown parameter.

| Name | Symbol | Example |
|---|---|---|
| Sample Mean | $\bar{x}$ | Mean number of cigarettes smoked per day **in a sample** of teenagers |
| Sample Proportion | $\hat{p}$ | Proportion **of a sample** of teenagers who used tobacco in the last 30 days |

19-8



## Vocabulary

**Parameter:** A number describing a characteristic of the population (usually unknown).

| Name | Symbol | Example |
|---|---|---|
| Mean | $\mu$ | Mean number of cigarettes smoked per day by all teenagers |
| Proportion | $p$ | Proportion of all teenagers who used tobacco in the last 30 days |

**Statistic:** A number, computed from sample data, estimating an unknown parameter.

In inference we use statistics to estimate parameters.

| Name | Symbol | Example |
|---|---|---|
| Mean | | in a sample of teenagers |
| Sample Proportion | $\hat{p}$ | Proportion **of a sample** of teenagers who used tobacco in the last 30 days |

19-9



## Parameter or Statistic?

| | | |
|---|---|---|
| Proportion of all students who attended the last home football game. | **Parameter** | $p$ |
| Proportion of registered voters who voted in November | **Parameter** | $p$ |
| Mean height of a sample of NBA basketball players | **Statistic** | $\bar{x}$ |
| Mean SAT of entering freshmen | **Parameter** | $\mu$ |
| Proportion of people who prefer Coke over Pepsi in a sample of mall shoppers | **Statistic** | $\hat{p}$ |
| Mean number of pepperoni slices on a 12" pizza from a sample of a certain brand of pepperoni pizzas | **Statistic** | $\bar{x}$ |

19-10



# Statistical Estimation and the Law of Large Numbers

Basic Practice of Statistics Chapter 11

19-11



## Statistical Estimation

Using sample statistic value to estimate population parameter value.

**Example**

A new variety of corn is being tested to determine its yield in bushels per acre.

$\mu$ = mean yield of the corn variety in bushels per acre

Fifteen plots have these yields:

| | | | | | | | |
|---|---|---|---|---|---|---|---|
| 138.0 | 139.1 | 113.0 | 132.5 | 140.7 | 109.7 | 118.9 | 134.8 |
| 109.6 | 127.3 | 115.6 | 130.4 | 130.2 | 111.7 | 105.5 | |

$\bar{x} = 123.8$ estimates $\mu$.

- $\bar{x}$ not expected to equal $\mu$.
- Different plots and conditions give different yields $\longrightarrow$ different $\bar{x}$'s.
- $\bar{x}$ varies from one sample of plots to another sample of plots.
- The larger the sample size, the closer $\bar{x}$ should be to $\mu$.

19-12



## Law of Large Numbers

**IF**

- Population has a finite mean $\mu$.
- $\bar{x}$, the mean of a random sample, is used to estimate $\mu$.

**THEN**

As the sample size increases, $\bar{x}$ gets closer and closer to $\mu$.

**The Law of Large Numbers can be proven mathematically.**

19-13

# Sampling Distributions

Basic Practice of Statistics Chapter 11

tells us how reliable is $\bar{x}$?
mean of sampling dist. of $\bar{x}$ always $\mu$, regardless of n
standard deviation of $\bar{x}$ always $\sigma/\sqrt{n}$

19-14

## Review

**Statistical estimation**

Using the value of a sample statistic to estimate a parameter value.

**Sample statistic facts:**

1. Value of statistic varies from sample to sample.
2. Value of statistic almost always differs from parameter value.
3. Statistic approaches parameter value as sample size increases.

**Question: How do we investigate the behavior of the statistic?**

Population Average Height $\mu = ?$

Sample Statistic Average Height $\bar{x} = 64$

19-15

Questions about $\bar{x}$

## Questions about $\bar{x}$

1. How well does $\bar{x}$ (statistic) estimate $\mu$ (parameter)?
2. Does $\bar{x}$ vary about $\mu$?
3. By how much could $\bar{x}$ differ from $\mu$?
4. How much does $\bar{x}$ vary from sample to sample?
5. Can we compute probabilities on $\bar{x}$?

19-16

Questions about $\bar{x}$

## How to Answer Questions

1. Simulate the sampling process by taking many SRS's from a population with known parameter value, $\mu$.
2. Compute $\bar{x}$ for every sample.
3. Construct a histogram of the $\bar{x}$'s.
4. Compare the $\bar{x}$'s with the value of $\mu$, measure variation of the $\bar{x}$'s, and model the histogram of the $\bar{x}$'s.

**In other words, simulate the sampling distribution of $\bar{x}$.**

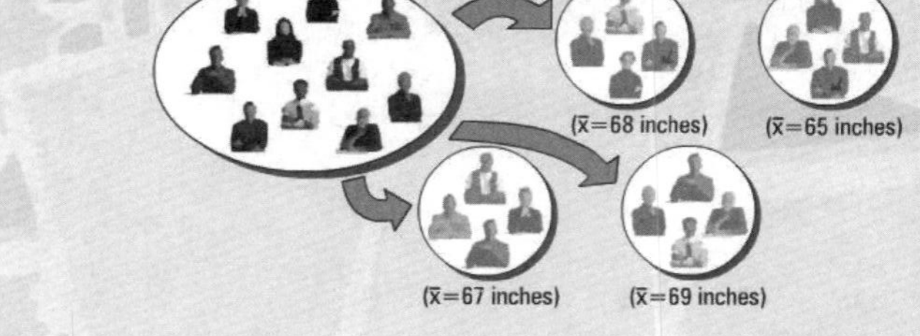

19-17

*Sampling Distribution of $\bar{x}$*

## What is the Sampling Distribution of $\bar{x}$?

**Theoretical sampling distribution of $\bar{x}$:**

The distribution of all $\bar{x}$-values from **all possible samples** of the same size from the same population.

**Can we take all possible samples?**

Maybe

If population size = 100 and n = 10

⟶ over 17,300,000,000,000 possible samples.

**What can we do instead?**

- Take many, many SRS's.
- Compute $\bar{x}$ for each.
- Approximate the theoretical sampling distribution of $\bar{x}$.

19-18

*Sampling Distribution of $\bar{x}$*

## What is the Sampling Distribution of $\bar{x}$?

**Approximate sampling distribution of $\bar{x}$:**

The distribution of $\bar{x}$-values obtained from repeatedly taking SRS's of the same size from the same population.

**Can we model the approximate sampling distribution of $\bar{x}$? Yes!!!**

**Theoretical and Approximate Sampling Distributions**

19-19

*Simulating $\bar{x}$'s from SRS's*

## Average Stock Price of NYSE from SRS

19-20

*Simulating $\bar{x}$'s from SRS's*

## Average Stock Price of NYSE from SRS

**Stock Population**

N=1228; $\mu$=\$26; $\sigma$=\$20

**Population:** 1228 New York Stock Exchange (NYSE) stocks

**Response Variable:** Closing price of a stock

**Population Properties:**

Shape: Right skewed

Center: $\mu$ = \$26, mean closing price for all 1228 stocks

Spread: $\sigma$ = \$20, standard deviation of all closing prices

19-21

*Simulating $\bar{x}$'s from SRS's*

## Simulating Average Stock Price from SRS's (n = 4)

**To estimate the average closing stock price,**

- Take SRS of 4 stocks and record closing price of each stock.
- Compute the sample mean, $\bar{x}$.

**To determine how accurate this sample mean is as an estimator of $\mu$, the average of all stocks,**

"Play the game" many times (i.e., simulate the sampling process):

- Take many, many SRS's; compute $\bar{x}$ for each sample.
- Construct histogram of $\bar{x}$'s to display the approximate sampling distribution of $\bar{x}$.
- Note center, spread, and shape.

19-22

*Simulating $\bar{x}$'s from SRS's*

## Simulating the Sampling Distribution of the Mean

**Step I:**

- Take SRS of 4 stocks; record closing price of each stock.

| BearStearn pfE | KenCole A | ParTch | RylandGp |
|---|---|---|---|
| \$43 1/4 | \$34 3/4 | \$7 5/8 | \$27 1/4 |

- Compute $\bar{x}$, the mean closing price of this sample of stocks.

$$\bar{x} = \$28.22$$

19-23

*Simulating $\bar{x}$'s from SRS's*

## Simulating the Sampling Distribution of the Mean

**Step 2:**

- Take many SRS's--a different SRS of 4 stocks each time.
- Compute $\bar{x}$ for each sample.

**Step 3:**

- Construct histogram of $\bar{x}$'s.

**The histogram of $\bar{x}$'s displays the estimated sampling distribution of $\bar{x}$.**

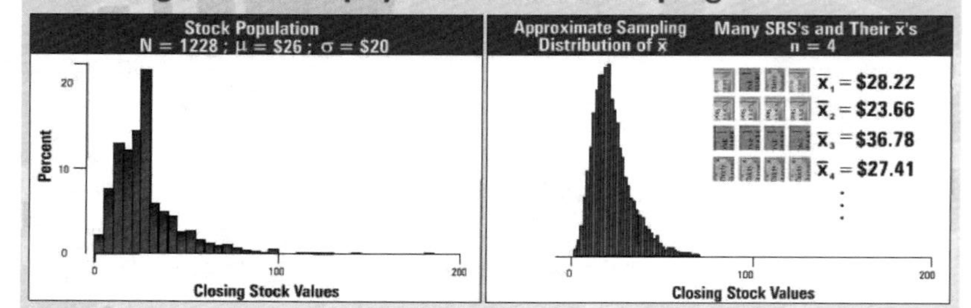


19-24

*Center, Spread and Shape*

## Center, Spread and Shape

**Center**
**\$26**
**(Equal to population center)**

**Shape**
**Slightly right skewed**
**(Closer to normal than population)**

**Spread**
**\$5 to \$75**
**SD ≅ 10 (Less than population spread)**

**Smooth curve represents theoretical sampling distribution of $\bar{x}$**

Stock Population
N = 1228 ; $\mu$ = \$26 ; $\sigma$ = \$20

Approximate Sampling Distribution of $\bar{x}$ — Many SRS's and Their $\bar{x}$'s, n = 4

$\bar{x}_1$ = \$28.22
$\bar{x}_2$ = \$23.66
$\bar{x}_3$ = \$26.78
$\bar{x}_4$ = \$37.41

Closing Stock Values

19-25

*Effect of Sample Size*

**How does the sampling distribution of $\bar{x}$ composed of $\bar{x}$'s from SRS's where n = 16 stocks differ from the sampling distribution of $\bar{x}$ composed of $\bar{x}$'s from SRS's where n = 4 stocks?**

SIMPLE RANDOM SAMPLE n=4

SIMPLE RANDOM SAMPLE n=16

- Will the center be different from $26?
- Will the spread be greater or smaller?
- Will the shape be more normal?

19-26

*Effect of Sample Size*

## Approximate Sampling Distribution of $\bar{x}$, n = 16

**Step 1:**
- Take SRS of 16 stocks.
- Record closing price of each stock.
- Compute the sample mean, $\bar{x}$.

**Step 2:**
- Take many SRS's; compute $\bar{x}$ for each sample.

**Step 3:**
- Construct histogram to display approximate sampling distribution of $\bar{x}$.

Note scale differences

Stock Population
N = 1228 ; μ = $26 ; σ = $20
Percent
Closing Stock Values

Approximate Sampling Distribution of $\bar{x}$

Many SRS's and Their $\bar{x}$'s, n = 16

$\bar{x}_1$ = $20.99
$\bar{x}_2$ = $33.85
$\bar{x}_3$ = $16.17
$\bar{x}_4$ = $21.46
⋮

Closing Stock Values

19-27

*Effect of Sample Size*

## Approximate Sampling Distribution of $\bar{x}$, n = 16

**Center**
$26
(Equal to population center)

**Shape**
Slightly right skewed
(Much more normal than population; more normal than sampling distribution of $\bar{x}$ with n = 4)

**Spread**
$11 to $41
SD ≅ 5 (Less than population spread)

Smooth curve represents theoretical sampling distribution of $\bar{x}$

Stock Population
N = 1228 ; μ = $26 ; σ = $20
Percent
Closing Stock Values

Approximate Sampling Distribution of $\bar{x}$

Many SRS's and Their $\bar{x}$'s, n = 16

$\bar{x}_1$ = $20.99
$\bar{x}_2$ = $33.85
$\bar{x}_3$ = $16.17
$\bar{x}_4$ = $21.46
⋮

Closing Stock Values

19-28

*Effect of Sample Size*

## Comparing Sampling Distributions: n=4 & n=16

1. Mean of sampling distribution of $\bar{x}$ = Mean of population
   Note: A statistic is unbiased when the mean of all possible values of that statistic equals the parameter; hence, $\bar{x}$ is unbiased.
2. As *n* increases, spread of sampling distribution of $\bar{x}$ decreases.
3. As *n* increases, shape of sampling distribution of $\bar{x}$ becomes more normal.

Note scale differences

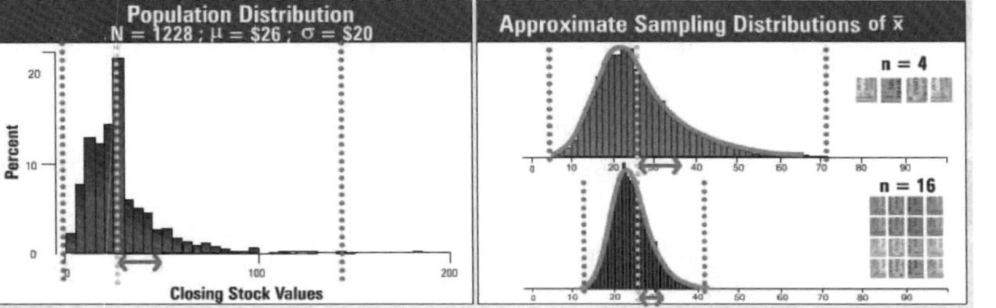

19-29

*Effect of Sample Size*

## Comparing Sampling Distributions: n=4, 16, 32, 64

**Center**
Equal to population center regardless of sample size.

**Spread**
Decreases as n increases

**Shape**
Becomes more normal as n increases.

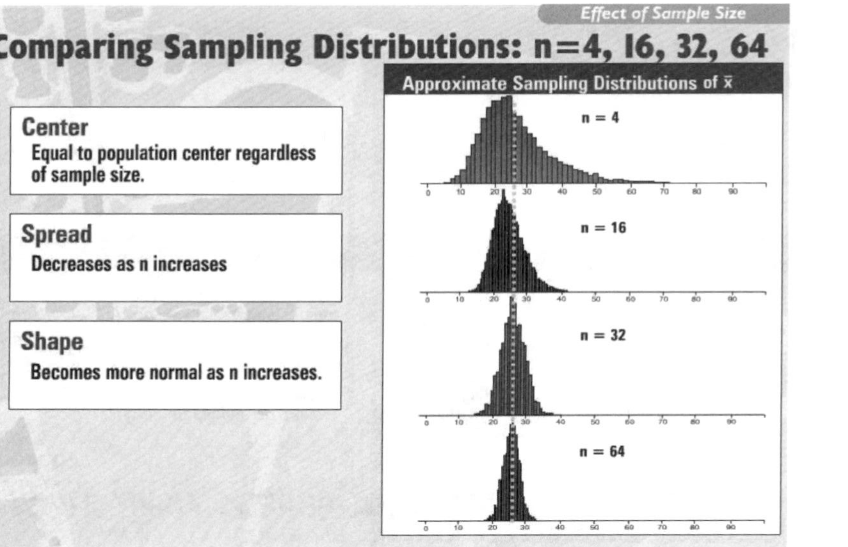


19-30

*Probabilities on Sampling Dist.*

## Estimating Probability of $\bar{x}$ Using Approximate Sampling Distribution with n = 4

**Probability Question:**
What is the probability of getting an average stock value, $\bar{x}$, less than \$20 when population mean is \$26 when n = 4?
$P(\bar{x} < \$20 \text{ when } \mu = \$26)$ = Proportion of $\bar{x}$'s in the sampling distribution less than \$20

**Estimated Answer:**

$$\frac{\text{Number of simulated } \bar{x}\text{'s less than \$20}}{\text{Total number of simulated } \bar{x}\text{'s}} = .30$$

**Interpretation Question:**
When n = 4, is an $\bar{x}$ value of \$20 reasonable? **Yes**

Is an $\bar{x}$ value of \$10 possible? **Yes**

Sampling Distribution of $\bar{x}$
n = 4
Proportion = 0.30

19-31

*Probabilities on Sampling Dist.*

## Estimating Probability of $\bar{x}$ Using Approximate Sampling Distribution with n = 16

**Probability Question:**
What is the probability of getting an average stock value, $\bar{x}$, less than \$20 when population mean is \$26 when n = 16?
$P(\bar{x} < \$20 \text{ when } \mu = \$26)$ = Proportion of $\bar{x}$'s in the sampling distribution less than \$20

**Estimated Answer:**

$$\frac{\text{Number of simulated } \bar{x}\text{'s less than \$20}}{\text{Total number of simulated } \bar{x}\text{'s}} = .1003$$

**Interpretation Question:**
When n = 16, is an $\bar{x}$ value of \$20 reasonable? **Yes**

Is an $\bar{x}$ value of \$10 possible? **No!**

Sampling Distribution of $\bar{x}$
n = 16
Proportion = 0.1003

19-32

*Probabilities on Sampling Dist.*

## Estimating Probability of $\bar{x}$ Using Approximate Sampling Distribution with n = 4 and n = 16

**Compare:** $P(\bar{x} < \$20)$

**Conclusion:** As sample size increases, $P(\bar{x} < \$20)$ decreases.

**Implications?**

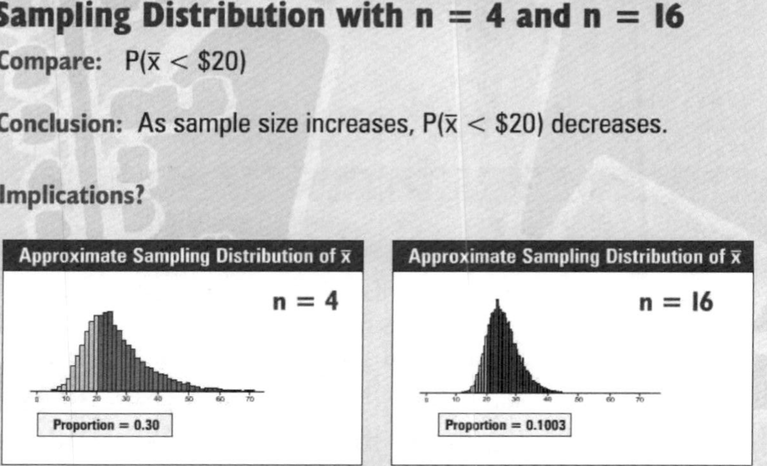

19-33

Questions and Answers

## Questions about Sampling Distribution of $\bar{x}$

1. How well does $\bar{x}$ estimate $\mu$? **Quite well for large SRS's**
2. Does $\bar{x}$ vary about $\mu$? **Yes**
3. By how much could $\bar{x}$ differ from $\mu$? **Stay tuned for next lesson**
4. How much does $\bar{x}$ vary from sample to sample? **Next lesson**
5. Can we compute probabilities on $\bar{x}$? **Yes, but we'll learn an easier method in next lesson.**

19-34

Applet

## Sampling Distribution Applet

**View Applet**

Sample mean of all people will be exactly $\bar{x} = \mu$

n=5 sigma (median?)

$\sigma_{\bar{x}} = \frac{4.49}{\sqrt{5}} = 2.01$ – standard deviation

- mean of sampling distribution of $\bar{x}$ is alway $\mu$ regardless of n
  - standard deviation of $\bar{x}$ always $\sigma/\sqrt{n}$

19-35

## Vocabulary

**Parameter**
**Statistic**
**Theoretical Sampling Distribution**
**Approximate Sampling Distribution**
**Simulation**
**Random Variable**

20-1

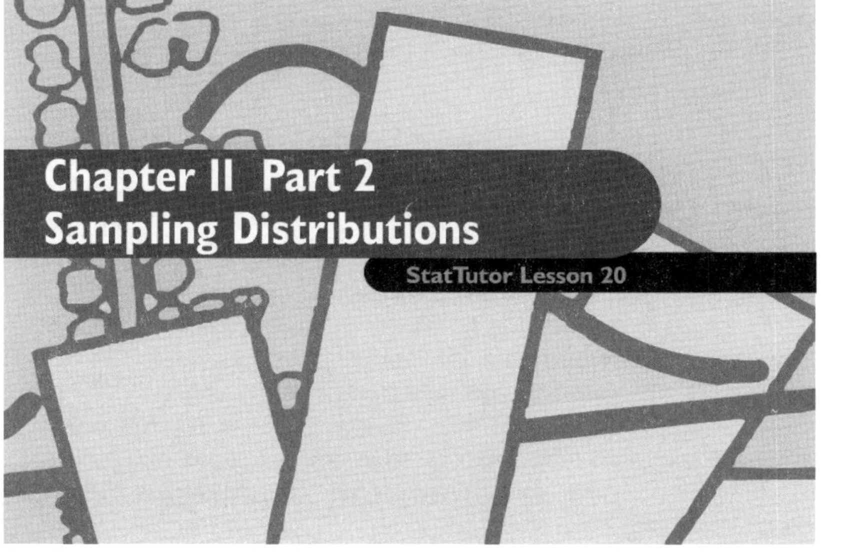


20-2

## Lesson Objectives

1. List the characteristics of the sampling distribution of $\bar{x}$ when the population is normal and when it is non-normal.
2. State the Central Limit Theorem and the special case for normal populations; explain why both are important.
3. Contrast means, standard deviations and shapes of four sampling distributions of $\bar{x}$ with different sample sizes.
4. Compare estimated probabilities on $\bar{x}$ with approximate probabilities on $\bar{x}$ found by applying the Central Limit Theorem.
5. Explain why the Central Limit Theorem justifies taking one SRS of size n to make inferences about $\mu$.

20-3

*Characteristics*

## Sampling Distribution of $\bar{x}$

Basic Practice of Statistics Chapter 11

20-4

*Characteristics*

## Review: Sampling Distribution of $\bar{x}$

**Theoretical sampling distribution of $\bar{x}$:**
The distribution of all $\bar{x}$-values from **all possible samples** of the same size from the same population.

**Approximate sampling distribution of $\bar{x}$:**
The distribution of $\bar{x}$-values obtained from repeatedly taking SRS's of the same size from the same population.

**What are the characteristics of the (theoretical) sampling distribution of $\bar{x}$?**

20-5

Characteristics

## Center of Sampling Distribution of $\bar{x}$

For $\bar{x}$, the mean of an SRS of size *n* from a large population with mean, $\mu$, and standard deviation, $\sigma$, . . .

**Center:** The mean of the sampling distribution of $\bar{x}$ equals the population mean, $\mu$.

$$\text{Mean} = \mu$$

**Valid for all sample sizes and populations of all shapes.**

**Applied to Stock Example:**

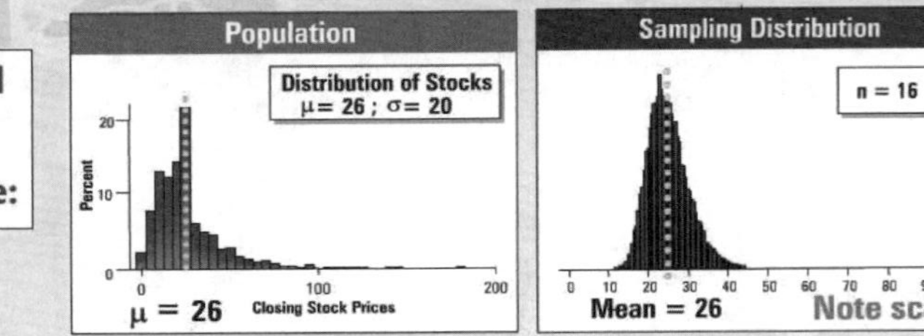


20-6

Characteristics

## Spread of Sampling Distribution of $\bar{x}$

For $\bar{x}$, the mean of an SRS of size *n* from a large population with mean, $\mu$, and standard deviation, $\sigma$, . . .

**Spread:** The standard deviation of the sampling distribution of $\bar{x}$ equals the standard deviation of the population divided by the square root of *n*.

$$\text{Standard deviation of } \bar{x} = \frac{\sigma}{\sqrt{n}}$$

**Valid for all sample sizes and populations of all shapes.**

**Applied to Stock Example:**

Population: Distribution of Stocks $\mu = 26$ ; $\sigma = 20$; $\sigma = 20$; $\mu = 26$; Closing Stock Prices

Sampling Distribution: n = 16; $\frac{20}{\sqrt{16}} = 5$; Mean = 26; Note scales

20-7

Characteristics

## Shape of Sampling Distribution of $\bar{x}$

For $\bar{x}$, the mean of an SRS of size *n* from a large population with mean, $\mu$, and standard deviation, $\sigma$, . . .

**Shape:** **Case I: Non-Normal population** Shape of the sampling distribution of $\bar{x}$ is approximately normal when *n* is large.

**Case 2: Normal population** Shape of the sampling distribution of $\bar{x}$ is exactly normal for any *n*.

**Implication:** Use Normal curve to compute probabilities on $\bar{x}$.

**Applied to Stock Example:**

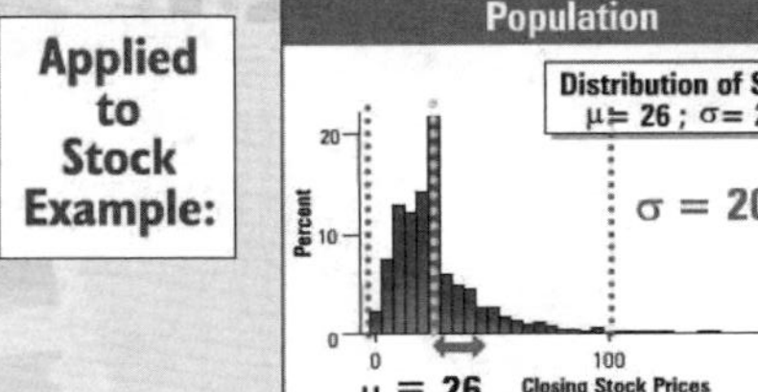

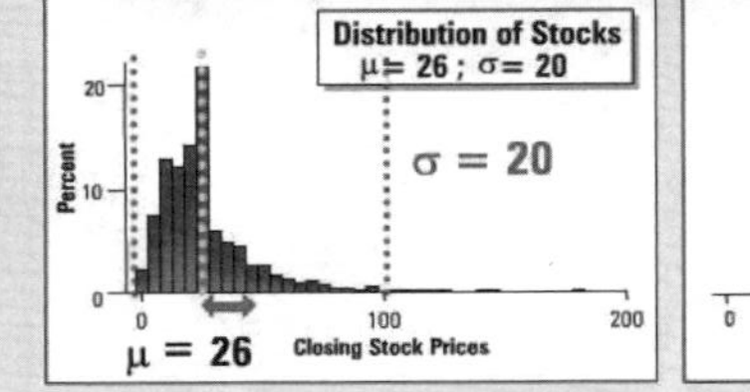

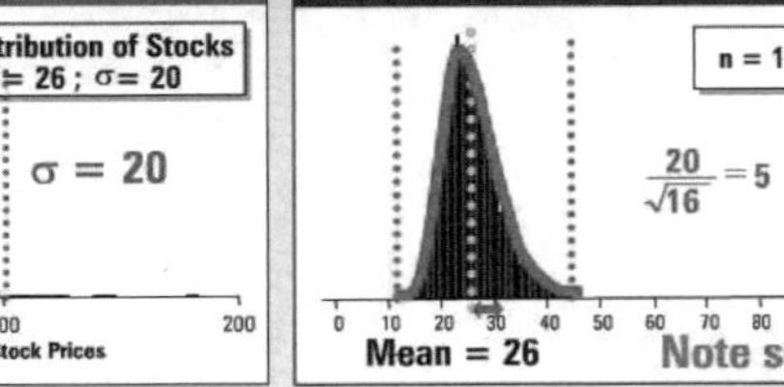


20-8

Characteristics

## Shape of Sampling Distribution of $\bar{x}$

**Case 2: Sampling from a Normal Population** (Case I next section.)

Take an SRS of any size *n* from a *Normal* population with mean $\mu$ and standard deviation $\sigma$ [i.e., $N(\mu, \sigma)$ using notation]. Then, the sampling distribution of $\bar{x}$ is *Normal* with mean $= \mu$, and standard deviation of $\bar{x} = \sigma/\sqrt{n}$ [i.e., $N(\mu, \sigma/\sqrt{n})$ using notation].

**Valid for any sample size n.**

- Can compute probabilities on $\bar{x}$ for any n when population is Normal.

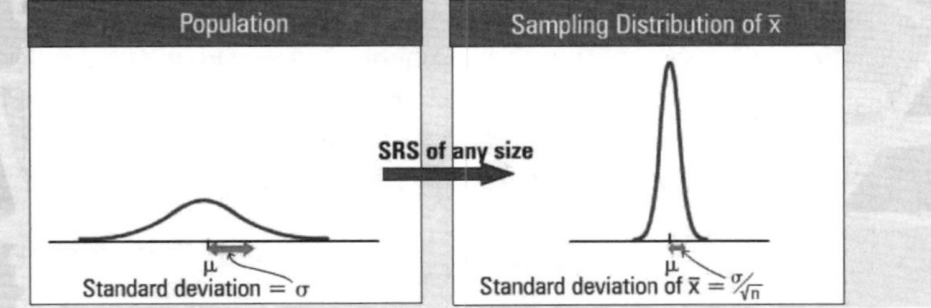

Feb 19

20-9

*Characteristics*

## Facts about Sampling Distribution of $\bar{x}$

**Sampling must be SRS.**

- Mean exactly equals $\mu$ regardless of population shape or sample size.
- Standard deviation of $\bar{x}$ is always less than the standard deviation of the population for samples of any size where $n > 1$.
- Standard deviation of $\bar{x}$ gets smaller as n increases at rate $\sqrt{n}$. To cut standard deviation in half, quadruple sample size.
- Shape is normal if population is normal for any sample size.
- Shape is approximately normal if we take a large random sample from a non-normal population. **Topic of our next section.**

20-10

*Characteristics*

# The Central Limit Theorem

Basic Practice of Statistics Chapter 11

enough people - follow nice normal shape
(good enough n)
In testing center n=30 is good enough

20-11

*Characteristics*

## Review: Sampling Distribution of $\bar{x}$

**The distribution of values taken by $\bar{x}$ from all possible samples of the same size from the same population.**

20-12

*Characteristics*

## Review: Sampling Distribution of $\bar{x}$

For $\bar{x}$, the mean of an SRS of size *n* from a large population with mean, $\mu$, and standard deviation, $\sigma$, . . .

**Center:** The mean of the sampling distribution of $\bar{x}$ equals the population mean, $\mu$.

**Spread:** The standard deviation of the sampling distribution of $\bar{x}$ equals $\sigma/\sqrt{n}$.

**Shape:**

**Case 1: Population Normal**
The shape of the sampling distribution of $\bar{x}$ is Normal.

**Case 2: Population Non-Normal**
The shape of the sampling distribution of $\bar{x}$ is approximately Normal when *n* is large. **Topic of this section.**

20-13

*Central Limit Theorem*

## Shape of Sampling Distribution of $\bar{x}$

**Central Limit Theorem (CLT):**

If you take a <u>large</u> SRS of size n from *any* population.
Then, the sampling distribution of $\bar{x}$ is approximately Normal.

**Shape gets more normal as n increases.**

$n > 30$ is considered large

- CLT allows us to use the standard Normal table to compute approximate probabilities on $\bar{x}$.

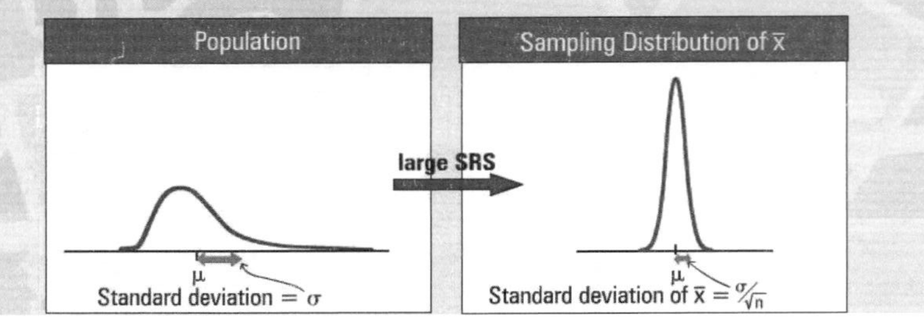


20-14

*Central Limit Theorem*

## Sampling Distribution of $\bar{x}$

These facts:

- mean of sampling distribution of $\bar{x} = \mu$
- standard deviation of sampling distribution of $\bar{x} = \sigma/\sqrt{n}$

are not part of the Central Limit Theorem.

Population — Standard deviation = $\sigma$

large SRS

Sampling Distribution of $\bar{x}$ — Standard deviation of $\bar{x} = \sigma/\sqrt{n}$

20-15

*Comparing Characteristics*

## Comparing Distributions

Population — Distribution of Stocks $\mu = 26$ ; $\sigma = 20$ — Percent — Closing Stock Prices

Sampling Distributions of $\bar{x}$ — n = 4, n = 16, n = 32, n = 64

| Center | Spread | Shape |
|---|---|---|
| $\mu = 26$ | $\sigma = 20$ | Very Right skewed |
| $\mu = 26$ | $\frac{\sigma}{\sqrt{n}} = \frac{20}{\sqrt{4}} = 10$ | Right skewed |
| $\mu = 26$ | $\frac{\sigma}{\sqrt{n}} = \frac{20}{\sqrt{16}} = 5$ | Slightly Right skewed |
| $\mu = 26$ | $\frac{\sigma}{\sqrt{n}} = \frac{20}{\sqrt{32}} = 3.5$ | Approximately Normal |
| $\mu = 26$ | $\frac{\sigma}{\sqrt{n}} = \frac{20}{\sqrt{64}} = 2.5$ | Essentially Normal |

20-16

*Comparing Characteristics*

## Comparing Distributions

Population — Distribution of Stocks $\mu = 26$ ; $\sigma = 20$ — Percent — Closing Stock Prices

Sampling Distributions of $\bar{x}$

**Summary:**

Means are equal for all n.

Standard deviation of $\bar{x}$ decreases as n increases.

Shape of sampling distribution of $\bar{x}$ becomes more Normal as n increases.

| Center | Spread | Shape |
|---|---|---|
| $\mu = 26$ | $\sigma = 20$ | Very Right skewed |
| $\mu = 26$ | $\frac{\sigma}{\sqrt{n}} = \frac{20}{\sqrt{4}} = 10$ | Right skewed |
| $\mu = 26$ | $\frac{\sigma}{\sqrt{n}} = \frac{20}{\sqrt{16}} = 5$ | Slightly Right skewed |
| $\mu = 26$ | $\frac{\sigma}{\sqrt{n}} = \frac{20}{\sqrt{32}} = 3.5$ | Approximately Normal |
| $\mu = 26$ | $\frac{\sigma}{\sqrt{n}} = \frac{20}{\sqrt{64}} = 2.5$ | Essentially Normal |

*Approximating Probabilities*

**Question:**
Do we have to create the sampling distribution of $\bar{x}$ every time we want to compute probabilities on $\bar{x}$?

**Answer:**
No! We can apply the central limit theorem and use the standard normal table!

Recall: $z = \frac{x - \mu}{\sigma}$

Basic formula: $z = \frac{\text{variable value} - \text{mean}}{\text{standard deviation}}$

For $\bar{x}$: $z = \frac{\bar{x}\text{-value} - \text{mean of } \bar{x}}{\text{standard deviation of } \bar{x}} = \frac{\bar{x} - \mu}{\sigma/\sqrt{n}}$



*Approximating Probabilities*

## Why We Apply Central Limit Theorem

Probabilities are much easier and quicker to compute using the standard normal table than by "playing the game" many times.

Approximation gets closer to the exact answer as *n* increases.

**Population**

Closing Stock Values

$\mu = \$26$

$\sigma = \$20$

**Sampling Distribution of $\bar{x}$**

n = 32

Estimated probability = 0.1281

**Normal Approximation**

$z = \frac{\bar{x} - \mu}{\sigma/\sqrt{n}}$

$= \frac{22 - 26}{20/\sqrt{32}} = -1.13$

$P(z < -1.13) = 0.1292$

Approximate probability = 0.1292

| z | .03 | .04 |
|---|---|---|
| -1.3 | .0918 | .0901 |
| -1.2 | .1093 | .1075 |
| -1.1 | .1292 | .1271 |
| -1.0 | .1515 | .1492 |
| -0.9 | .1762 | .1736 |

If n is large (bigger than 30ish) We can calculate probabilities on $\bar{x}$ obtained





*Taking One SRS in Practice*

## Predicting Sampling Distribution of $\bar{x}$

**In Statistical Practice:**

- Take only one sample of size n.
- Use sample results to make inference about the population.

**Why don't we need to create sampling distribution of $\bar{x}$?**

We know:

- Mean = $\mu$ and standard deviation of $\bar{x} = \sigma/\sqrt{n}$.
- Shape is approximately normal if sample is large and SRS by CLT.

→ **These facts allow us to specify the sampling distribution of $\bar{x}$ without creating it!**

- Don't need to know shape of population!
- Can do inference on $\mu$ based on $\bar{x}$ from one sample!



*Taking One SRS in Practice*

## Comparing Three Distributions

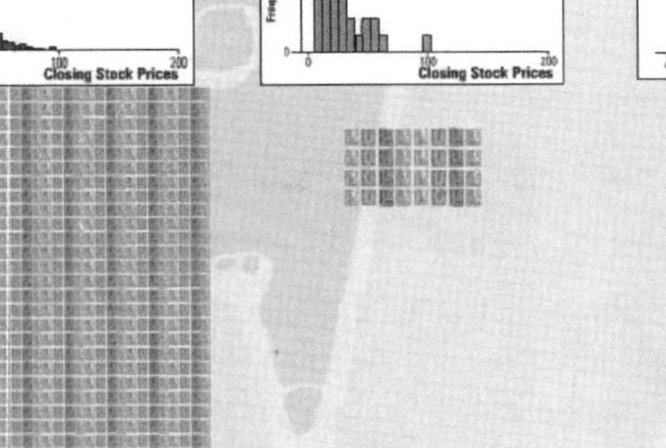


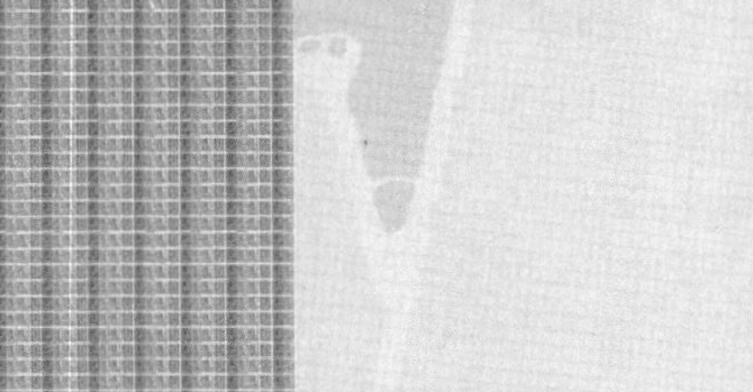

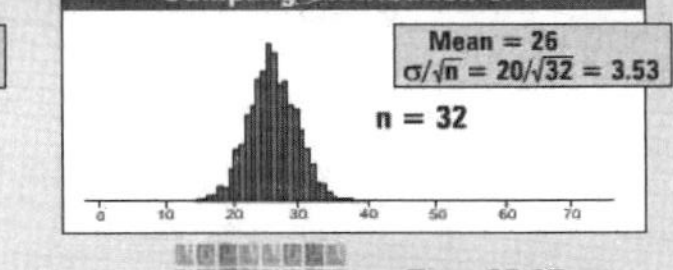

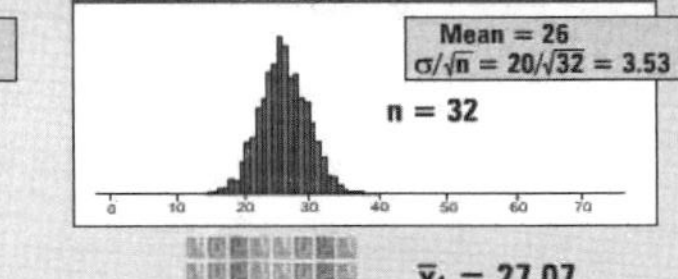

$\bar{x}_1 = 27.07$

$\bar{x}_2 = 21.78$

$\bar{x}_3 = 20.38$

$\bar{x}_4 = 30.51$

$\bar{x}_5 = 26.43$

$\bar{x}_6 = 19.44$

⋮

Feb 21

20-21



## Summary of Three Distributions

### Three Different Distributions

| | Population | Sample | Sampling Distribution of $\bar{x}$ |
|---|---|---|---|
| Center | $\mu$ | $\bar{x}$ | $\mu$ |
| Spread | $\sigma$ | s | $\sigma/\sqrt{n}$ |
| Shape | Non-normal or Normal | Gets closer to population shape as n increases. | Approx. normal if n is large ***OR*** normal if pop. is normal. |
| Probability using Normal Table | Only if population is normal. | ⊘ | Only if sampling dist. is approx. or exactly normal. |

20-22



## Computing Probabilities

**Example I (Review):** The BYU Creamery sells bottles of chocolate milk with a mean weight of 1.0875 pounds ($\mu$) and a standard deviation of 0.015 pounds ($\sigma$). The weights of these bottles are normally distributed. What is the probability that a randomly selected bottle weighs more than 1.1 pounds?

What is the distribution of weights? N(1.0875, 0.015)

How do we compute the probability? Given x ⟶ z ⟶ Area

Which z-score formula should we use?

**A.** $z = \frac{x-\mu}{\sigma}$ **B.** $z = \frac{\bar{x}-\mu}{\sigma/\sqrt{n}}$ **C.** Neither

20-23



## Computing Probabilities

**Example I (Review):** The BYU Creamery sells bottles of chocolate milk with a mean weight of 1.0875 pounds ($\mu$) and a standard deviation of 0.015 pounds ($\sigma$). The weights of these bottles are normally distributed. What is the probability that a randomly selected bottle weighs more than 1.1 pounds?

What is the distribution of weights? N(1.0875, 0.015)

Given x ⟶ z ⟶ Area

1. Draw and label normal curve.
2. Compute appropriate z-score.

$$z = \frac{x-\mu}{\sigma} = \frac{1.1-1.0875}{0.015} = 0.83$$

3. Look up z-score in table to get probability. $P(x > 1.1) = P(z > 0.83)$

$= 1 - P(z < 0.83) = 1 - .7967 = .2033$

1.1

TABLE A Standard Normal Probabilities

| z | .01 | .02 | .03 |
|---|---|---|---|
| 0.6 | .7291 | .7324 | .7357 |
| 0.7 | .7611 | .7642 | .7673 |
| 0.8 | .7910 | .7939 | .7967 |
| 0.9 | .8186 | .8212 | .8238 |

20-24



## Computing Probabilities

**Example I (Review):** The BYU Creamery sells bottles of chocolate milk with a mean weight of 1.0875 pounds ($\mu$) and a standard deviation of 0.015 pounds ($\sigma$). The weights of these bottles are normally distributed. What is the probability that a randomly selected bottle weighs more than 1.1 pounds?

What is the distribution of

The probability that a randomly selected bottle weighs more than 1.1 pounds is 0.2033.

1. Draw and label normal
2. Compute appropriate z-score.

$$z = \frac{x-\mu}{\sigma} = \frac{1.1-1.0875}{0.015} = 0.83$$

3. Look up z-score in table to get probability. $P(x > 1.1) = P(z > 0.83)$

$= 1 - P(z < 0.83) = 1 - .7967 = .2033$

1.1

TABLE A Standard Normal Probabilities

| z | .01 | .02 | .03 |
|---|---|---|---|
| 0.6 | .7291 | .7324 | .7357 |
| 0.7 | .7611 | .7642 | .7673 |
| 0.8 | .7910 | .7939 | .7967 |
| 0.9 | .8186 | .8212 | .8238 |

20-25

Computing Probabilities

## Computing Probabilities (Case 2 problem.)

**Example 2:** Weights of bottles of chocolate milk are N(1.0875, 0.015). What is the probability that the mean of a random sample of eight bottles of chocolate milk ($\bar{x}$) exceeds 1.1 pounds?

What is the distribution of $\bar{x}$? N(1.0875, 0.0053)
Why? Population is normal ⇨ Sampling distribution of $\bar{x}$ is normal
mean = $\mu$ = 1.0875 standard deviation = $\sigma/\sqrt{n}$ = $0.015/\sqrt{8}$ = 0.0053
How do we compute the probability? Given $\bar{x} \rightarrow z \rightarrow$ Area

Which z-score formula should we use?

**A.** $z = \frac{x-\mu}{\sigma}$ **B.** $z = \frac{\bar{x}-\mu}{\sigma/\sqrt{n}}$ **C.** Neither

20-26

Computing Probabilities

## Computing Probabilities (Case 2 problem.)

**Example 2:** Weights of bottles of chocolate milk are N(1.0875, 0.015). What is the probability that the mean of a random sample of eight bottles of chocolate milk ($\bar{x}$) exceeds 1.1 pounds?

What is the distribution of $\bar{x}$? N(1.0875, 0.0053)
Why? Population is normal ⇨ Sampling distribution of $\bar{x}$ is normal
mean = $\mu$ = 1.0875 standard deviation = $\sigma/\sqrt{n}$ = $0.015/\sqrt{8}$ = 0.0053
Given $\bar{x} \rightarrow z \rightarrow$ Area

1. Draw and label normal curve.
2. Compute appropriate z-score.
$z = \frac{\bar{x}-\mu}{\sigma/\sqrt{n}} = \frac{1.1 - 1.0875}{0.015/\sqrt{8}} = 2.36$
3. Look up z-score in table to get probability. $P(\bar{x} > 1.1) = P(z > 2.36)$
$= 1 - P(z < 2.36) = 1 - .9909 = .0091$

TABLE A Standard Normal Probabilities

| z | .05 | .06 | .07 |
|---|---|---|---|
| 2.1 | .9842 | .9846 | .9850 |
| 2.2 | .9878 | .9881 | .9884 |
| 2.3 | .9906 | .9909 | .9911 |
| 2.4 | .9929 | .9931 | .9932 |

20-27

Computing Probabilities

## Computing Probabilities (Case 2 problem.)

**Example 2:** Weights of bottles of chocolate milk are N(1.0875, 0.015). What is the probability that the mean of a random sample of eight bottles of chocolate milk ($\bar{x}$) exceeds 1.1 pounds?

What is the distribution of $\bar{x}$?
Why? Population is normal
mean = $\mu$ = 1.0875 standa

The probability that the average of a random sample of eight bottles is more than 1.1 pounds is 0.0091.

1. Draw and label normal curve.
2. Compute appropriate z-score.
$z = \frac{\bar{x}-\mu}{\sigma/\sqrt{n}} = \frac{1.1 - 1.0875}{0.015/\sqrt{8}} = 2.36$
3. Look up z-score in table to get probability. $P(\bar{x} > 1.1) = P(z > 2.36)$
$= 1 - P(z < 2.36) = 1 - .9909 = .0091$

TABLE A Standard Normal Probabilities

| z | .05 | .06 | .07 |
|---|---|---|---|
| 2.1 | .9842 | .9846 | .9850 |
| 2.2 | .9878 | .9881 | .9884 |
| 2.3 | .9906 | .9909 | .9911 |
| 2.4 | .9929 | .9931 | .9932 |

20-28

Computing Probabilities

## Computing Probabilities (Case 2 problem.)

**Example I (Review):** The BYU Creamery sells bottles of chocolate milk with a mean weight of 1.0875 pounds ($\mu$) and a standard deviation of 0.015 pounds ($\sigma$). The weights of these bottles are normally distributed. What is the probability that a randomly selected bottle weighs more than 1.1 pounds?

$z = \frac{x-\mu}{\sigma}$

**Example 2:** Weights of bottles of chocolate milk are N(1.0875, 0.015). What is the probability that the mean of a random sample of eight bottles of chocolate milk ($\bar{x}$) exceeds 1.1 pounds?

$z = \frac{\bar{x}-\mu}{\sigma/\sqrt{n}}$

20-29

*Computing Probabilities*

## Computing Probabilities

**Example 3:** Closing prices of stocks have a right skewed distribution with $\mu = 26$ and $\sigma = 20$. What is the probability of randomly selecting a closing stock whose value is less than \$15?

What is the distribution of closing stock prices?

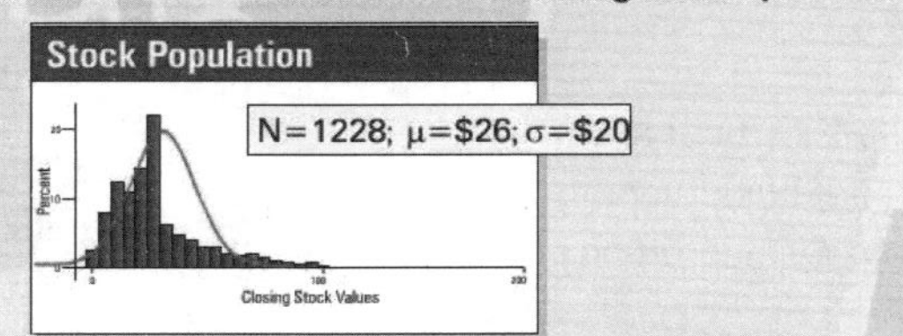


Should we compute a z-score and use the standard normal table to find $P(x < \$15)$?

**NO! The distribution of closing stock prices is not normal. If we did, the approximation would be poor.**

20-30

*Computing Probabilities*

## Computing Probabilities Apply Central Limit Theorem

**Example 4:** Closing prices of stocks have a right skewed distribution with $\mu = 26$ and $\sigma = 20$. What is the probability that the mean price of a random sample of $n = 32$ closing stocks is less than \$15?

What is the distribution of $\bar{x}$? $\approx N(26, 3.54)$

Why? CLT and large n ⇨ Sampling distribution of $\bar{x}$ is $\approx$ Normal.

mean $= \mu = 26$ and standard deviation $= \sigma/\sqrt{n} = 20/\sqrt{32} = 3.54$

How do we compute the probability? Given $\bar{x}$ ⟶ z ⟶ Area

Which z-score formula should we use?

**A.** $z = \frac{x - \mu}{\sigma}$  **B.** $z = \frac{\bar{x} - \mu}{\sigma/\sqrt{n}}$  **C.** Neither

20-31

*Computing Probabilities*

## Computing Probabilities Apply Central Limit Theorem

**Example 4:** Closing prices of stocks have a right skewed distribution with $\mu = 26$ and $\sigma = 20$. What is the probability that the mean price of a random sample of $n = 32$ closing stocks is less than \$15?

What is the distribution of $\bar{x}$? $\approx N(26, 3.54)$

Why? CLT and large n ⇨ Sampling distribution of $\bar{x}$ is $\approx$ Normal.

mean $= \mu = 26$ and standard deviation $= \sigma/\sqrt{n} = 20/\sqrt{32} = 3.54$

1. Draw and label normal curve.
2. Compute appropriate z-score.
   $z = \frac{\bar{x} - \mu}{\sigma/\sqrt{n}} = \frac{15 - 26}{20/\sqrt{32}} = -3.11$
3. Look up z-score in table to get probability.
   $P(\bar{x} < 15) = P(z < -3.11) = .0009$

TABLE A Standard Normal Probabilities

| z | .00 | .01 | .02 |
|---|---|---|---|
| -3.2 | .0007 | .0007 | .0006 |
| -3.1 | .0010 | .0009 | .0009 |
| -3.0 | .0013 | .0013 | .0013 |
| -2.9 | .0019 | .0018 | .0018 |

20-32

*Computing Probabilities*

## Computing Probabilities Apply Central Limit Theorem

**Example 4:** Closing prices of stocks have a right skewed distribution with $\mu = 26$ and $\sigma = 20$. What is the probability that the mean price of a random sample of $n = 32$ closing stocks is less than \$15?

What is the distribution of $\bar{x}$
Why? CLT and large n ⇨ Sa
mean $= \mu = 26$ and stand

The probability that the mean index of a random sample of 32 stocks is less than \$15 is approximately 0.0009.

1. Draw and label normal curve.
2. Compute appropriate z-score.
   $z = \frac{\bar{x} - \mu}{\sigma/\sqrt{n}} = \frac{15 - 26}{20/\sqrt{32}} = -3.11$
3. Look up z-score in table to get probability.
   $P(\bar{x} < 15) = P(z < -3.11) = .0009$

TABLE A Standard Normal Probabilities

| z | .00 | .01 | .02 |
|---|---|---|---|
| -3.2 | .0007 | .0007 | .0006 |
| -3.1 | .0010 | .0009 | .0009 |
| -3.0 | .0013 | .0013 | .0013 |
| -2.9 | .0019 | .0018 | .0018 |

20-33



## Computing Probabilities on $\bar{x}$

**Method I:**

Population Normal ⇨ Sampling distribution of $\bar{x}$ is Normal.

**Method 2:** **Apply Central Limit Theorem**

Population non-Normal ⇨ Sampling distribution of $\bar{x}$ is approximately Normal if large random sample.

**Same z-score and process for both:** $z = \frac{\bar{x} - \mu}{\sigma/\sqrt{n}}$

20-34



## Sampling Distribution Applet

**View Applet**

if n "large" (30 is ample), shape of sampling distribution of $\bar{x}$ is close to the normal curve
- shape of original

68%

$\sigma = 1$

0

20-35

## Vocabulary

**Central Limit Theorem**
**Sample**
**Population Distribution**
**Sampling Distribution of $\bar{x}$**
**Standard Deviation of $\bar{x}$**

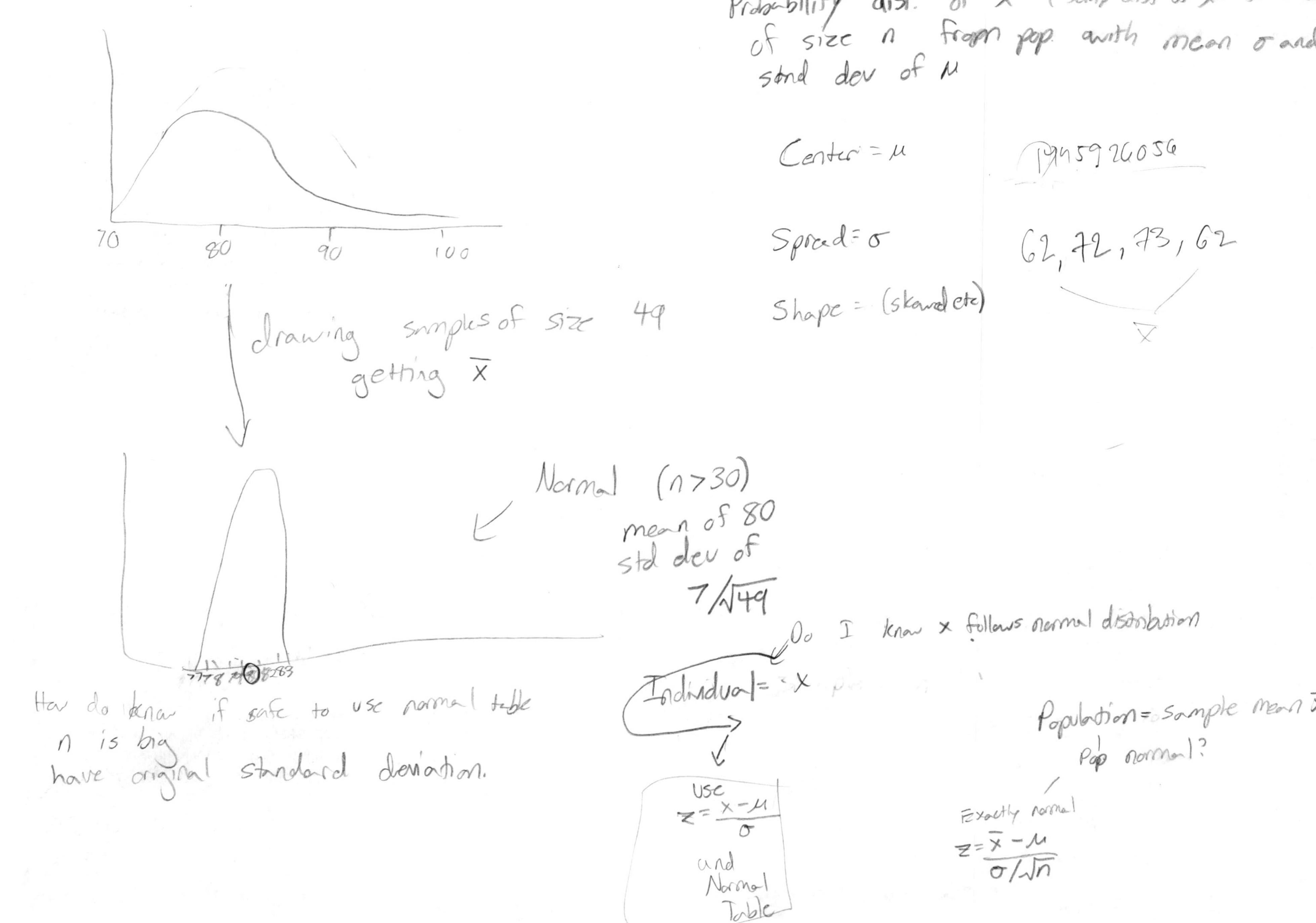
Probability dist. of $\bar{x}$ (samp dist of $\bar{x}$) for SRS
of size n from pop with mean σ and
stnd dev of μ
Center = μ
Spread = σ
Shape = (skewed etc)
1945926056
62, 72, 73, 62
$\bar{x}$
70
80
90
100
drawing samples of size 49
getting $\bar{x}$
Normal (n > 30)
mean of 80
std dev of
$7/\sqrt{49}$
Do I know x follows normal distribution
Individual = x
use
$z = \frac{x - \mu}{\sigma}$
and
Normal
Table
Population = sample mean $\bar{x}$
Pop normal?
Exactly normal
$z = \frac{\bar{x} - \mu}{\sigma/\sqrt{n}}$
How do know if safe to use normal table
n is big
have original standard deviation.

Feb 21

21-1

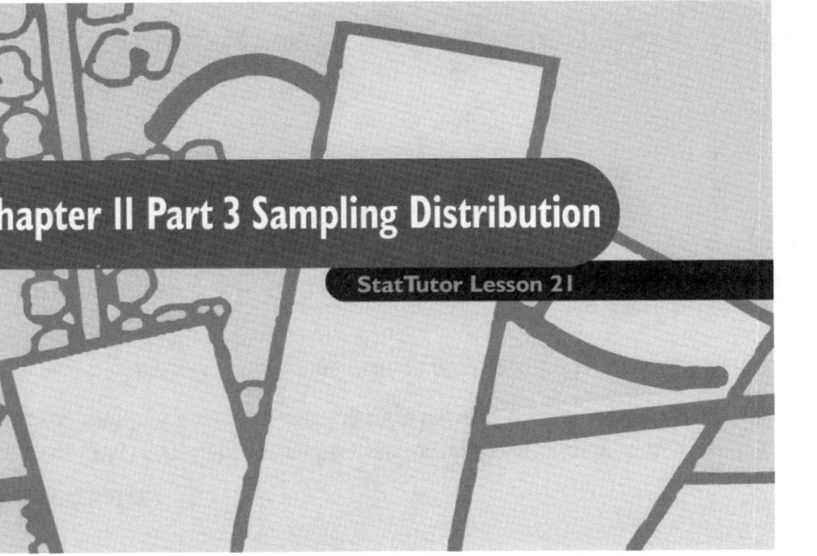


21-2

## Lesson Objectives

1. Describe process variation.
2. Explain the purpose of a control chart and how process variation is manifested in it.
3. Construct a control chart for sample means.
4. Determine whether a process is "in control" using a control chart.

21-3

*Process Variation*

## Statistical Process Control

Basic Practice of Statistics Chapter 11

**This section is NOT found in the textbook--only on StatsPortal at the end of chapter 11 in the eBook.**

21-4

*Process Variation*

## Processes and Variation

**All processes have variation; to monitor variation we measure characteristics of process input and output.**

In the video, identify:
- the process--making potato chips
- the monitored variable--salt content

**View Movie Clip.**

21-5



## Process: Making Potato Chips

| Input | Processing | Output |
|---|---|---|
| ▶ Potatoes from<br>--different farms<br>(moisture, soil, fertilizer)<br>--different farmers<br>--different regions | ▶ Sorting | ▶ Salt content of chips |
| | ▶ Washing | ▶ Color of chips |
| | ▶ Slicing | ▶ Taste of chips |
| | ▶ Deep frying | ▶ Weight of package |
| | ▶ Packaging | ▶ Volume of package |
| ▶ Oil | | |
| ▶ Salt | | |

**Each output has variability--need to distinguish between natural (ordinary) variation and variation due to a problem.**

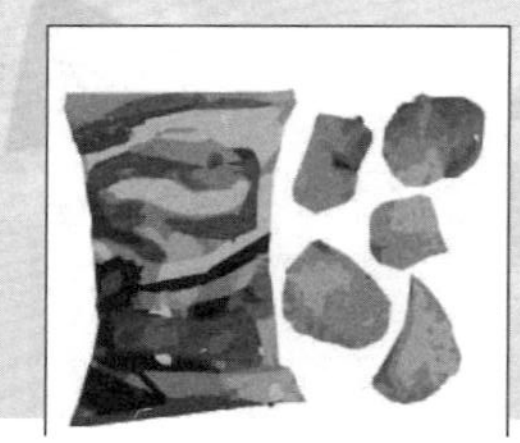

21-6



## Natural Variation vs. Variation Due to a Problem

Plot: Sample statistics from process vs. time.
Which plot shows natural variation?

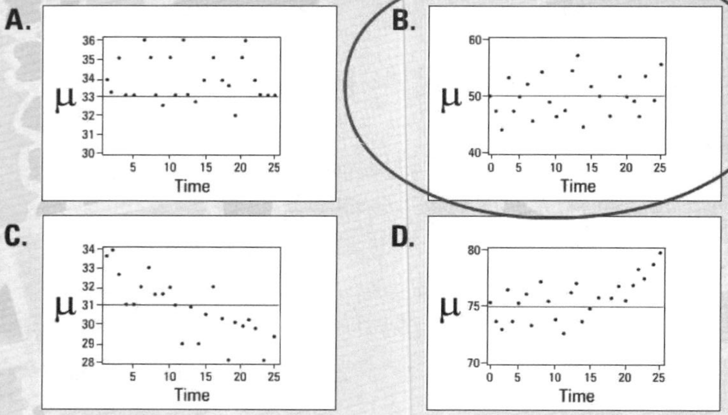

A. B. C. D.



21-7



## Definitions

**Control Chart:** Statistical tool for monitoring an input or an output of a process that has variation, alerting us when a problem has occurred.

**Process:** Sequence of operations used in production, manufacturing, etc....

**Process *in* Statistical Control:** A process whose inputs and outputs exhibit natural variation when observed over time.

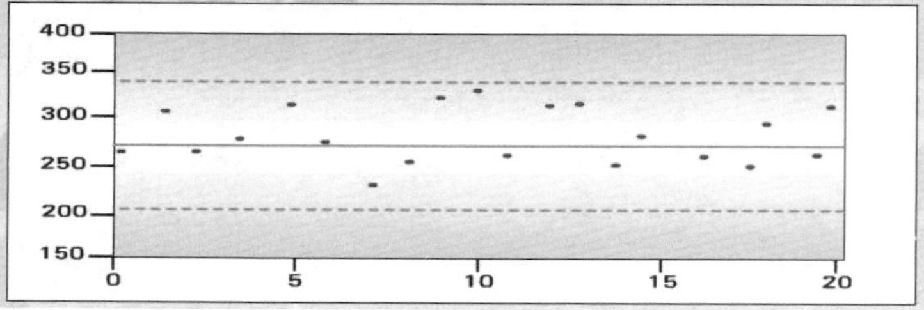

21-8



## Advantages of Using Control Charts to Monitor Processes

- Assess variability of statistics from samples of inputs and outputs of the process.
- Avoid over-reacting to natural variation.

**Caution: A process in control does not guarantee good quality.**

21-9

# $\bar{x}$ Charts

**This section is NOT found in the textbook--only on StatsPortal at the end of chapter II in the eBook.**

21-10

## Review of Sampling Distribution of $\bar{x}$

If we take an SRS of any size *n* from a ***normal*** population with mean, $\mu$, and standard deviation, $\sigma$, . . .

**The sampling distribution of $\bar{x}$ has:** Shape: *Normal*

Center: Mean = $\mu$ Spread: Standard deviation = $\sigma/\sqrt{n}$



In the population, what percentage of the x's are between $\mu - 3\sigma$ and $\mu + 3\sigma$? *99.7%*

In the sampling distribution of $\bar{x}$, what percentage of the $\bar{x}$'s are between $\mu - 3\sigma/\sqrt{n}$ and $\mu + 3\sigma/\sqrt{n}$ ? *99.7%*

21-11

*Constructing Control Charts*

## Reasoning Behind Control Charts



Sampling distribution of $\bar{x}$ predicts values for $\bar{x}$ if SRS is from target population.

21-12

*Constructing Control Charts*

## Constructing Control Chart for $\bar{x}$



**Make a control chart for $\bar{x}$ as follows**

1. Draw a horizontal centerline at m
2. Draw horizontal control limits at $\mu \pm 3\sigma/\sqrt{n}$
3. Plot the means ($\bar{x}$'s) from samples of size $n$ against time.

Sampling distribution of $\bar{x}$ predicts values for $\bar{x}$ if SRS is from target population.

21-13



**Out-of-Control Signals**

- One point above the upper control limit or below the lower control limit.
- Run of 9 points in a row on same side of the centerline. (As unlikely as one point outside the control limits.)

As soon as an "out-of-control" signal is observed, STOP the process and look for a cause.

21-14



## Control charts with out-of-control signals?

$\mu+3\frac{\sigma}{\sqrt{n}}$, $\mu$, centerline, $\mu-3\frac{\sigma}{\sqrt{n}}$; 0, 5, 10, 15, 20; TIME OF SAMPLE

One point outside control limits

$\mu+3\frac{\sigma}{\sqrt{n}}$, $\mu$, centerline, $\mu-3\frac{\sigma}{\sqrt{n}}$; 0, 5, 10, 15, 20; TIME OF SAMPLE

Run of 9 points above centerline

21-15



## Example: BYU Creamery

**View Movie Clip.**

21-16



## Out-of-Control Causes

**What can cause out-of-control signal?**

Clogged filters

Settings

Changes in Milk Quality

Defective Containers

Feb 21

21-17

Out-of-Control Signals

## In-Control and Out-of-Control Signals

What do you do when the control chart signals filling machine is:

- In-Control? ⟶ Continue to operate
- Out-of-Control? ⟶ Stop, identify cause, adjust, and restart

**Remember: We expect natural variation around target weight.**

21-18

Creamery Control Limits

## Control Limits: Filling Chocolate Milk Containers

Control Limits $= \mu \pm 3\frac{\sigma}{\sqrt{n}}$

Target Wt. = $\mu = 1.0875$ lb.
$\sigma = 0.015$ lb.
$n = 8$ bottles every ten minutes

Upper Control Limit = $\mu + 3(\sigma / \sqrt{n})$
$= 1.0875 + 3(0.015/\sqrt{8})$
UCL = 1.103 lb.

Lower Control Limit = $\mu - 3(\sigma / \sqrt{n})$
$= 1.0875 - 3(0.015/\sqrt{8})$
LCL = 1.072 lb.

21-19

Creamery Control Chart

## BYU Creamery Example

**What signal is suggested by this pattern of nine points in a row above the centerline?**

| Sample | Mean |
|---|---|
| 1 | 1.0813 |
| 2 | 1.0866 |
| 3 | 1.0986 |
| 4 | 1.0962 |
| 5 | 1.0843 |
| 6 | 1.0947 |
| 7 | 1.0889 |
| 8 | 1.0967 |
| 9 | 1.1015 |
| 10 | 1.0896 |
| 11 | 1.1062 |
| 12 | 1.0946 |
| 13 | 1.0957 |
| 14 | 1.0985 |

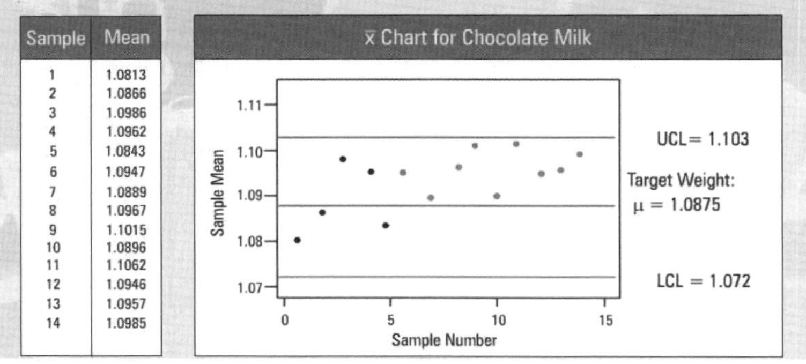


21-20

## Vocabulary

**Control Charts**
**Control Limits**
**Natural Variation**
**Out-of-Control Signals**
**Statistical Control**
**Variation Due to a Problem**
**Target Value**
**$\bar{x}$-Charts**

Closing prices of stocks have a right skewed distribution with $\mu = \$26$ and $\sigma = \$20$
what is probability that $\bar{x}$ for a random sample of $n=10$ closing stocks < \$10.

Cannot use normal table!

probabi

1 Draw picture

2 Find Z-score

3. look up in A table.

.0009

15 26 u

Z: —

$$\frac{\bar{x}-u}{\sigma/\sqrt{n}} \qquad \frac{15-26}{20/\sqrt{32}}$$

32 stocks

σ

= -3.111

look up undere Z column

End of Exam 2

Feb 26

22-1

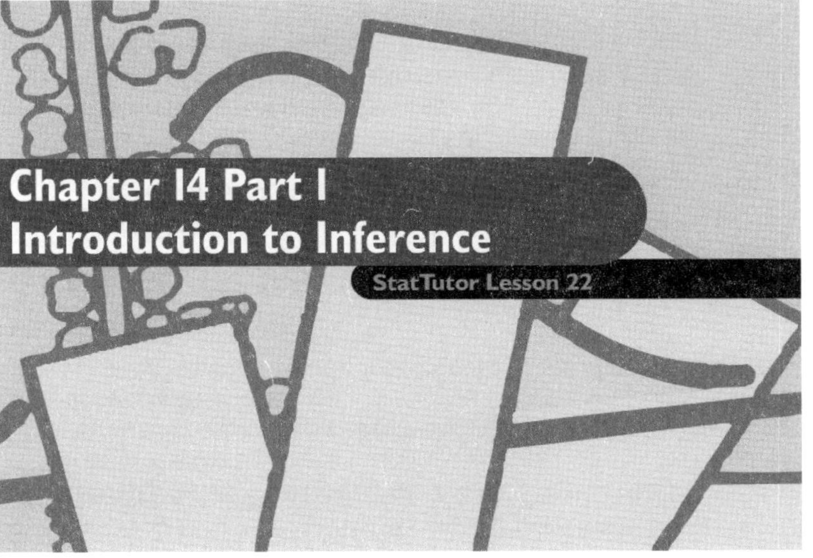


22-2

## Lesson Objectives

1. Explain what is meant by ***inference***.
2. Describe the simple conditions for inference.
3. Explain need for margin of error and how it is obtained from sampling distribution of $\bar{x}$.
4. Explain level of confidence.
5. Explain purpose of confidence interval; compute and interpret confidence interval for $\mu$ using four steps.
6. Describe formula for computing a confidence interval for $\mu$.
7. Compute and interpret confidence intervals for $\mu$ in context.

22-3

22-4

Statistical Inference

**Statistical Inference:** Drawing conclusions about a population parameter from a sample statistic.

With a measure of uncertainty

**Because of sampling variability:**
the sample statistic usually differs from the population parameter.

**Because of SRS and knowledge about sampling distributions:**
we can predict the expected maximum size of the difference.

22-5



## An Example of Inference

DESERET MORNING NEWS/KSL-TV

POLL

| How concerned are you about the following: | VERY CONCERNED | SOMEWHAT CONCERNED | NOT VERY CONCERNED | NOT AT ALL CONCERNED | DON'T KNOW |
|---|---|---|---|---|---|
| Having your home broken into? | 17% | 42% | 33% | 7% | 0% |
| Having your car broken into? | 19% | 39% | 33% | 8% | 1% |
| Being physically assaulted? | 14% | 26% | 46% | 13% | 1% |
| Being sexually assaulted? | 15% | 18% | 36% | 31% | 1% |
| Being a victim of domestic violence? | 8% | 4% | 15% | 72% | 1% |
| Being a victim of identity theft? | 36% | 50% | 9% | 4% | 1% |

A poll of 411 Utah residents was conducted Jan. 15-17, 2004, by Dan Jones & Associates. It has a margin of error of +/-5 percent.
©2004 Deseret Morning News / KSL-TV

Sample Statistics

Sample Size

Estimated Maximum Error

Margin of Error: +/−5 percent

No measure of confidence reported

22-6



## Statistical Inference

Two basic types:

- Estimating the value of a parameter with a confidence interval.
- Assessing evidence for a claim about a parameter value using a test of significance.

**--Both require random samples.**

**--Both are based on sampling distributions.**

**--Both use probabilities based on what would happen if we used the inferential procedure many times.**

22-7



## All Inferential Procedures Have Conditions

**Three examples:**

- A mean describes center effectively unless there are outliers or strong skewness.
  -- Need to plot data and check for outliers and strong skewness before computing a mean.
- A correlation coefficient measures strength of only linear relationships.
  -- Need to plot data in a scatterplot and check for outliers and linear relationship before computing correlation.
- A linear regression equation models the linear relationship between two quantitative variables.
  -- Need to plot data in a scatterplot and check for outliers and linear relationship before obtaining equation.

22-8



## All Inferential Procedures Have Conditions

"It is not enough to be able to 'do' the routine (either by hand or on the computer); one must know why one has chosen it, what its application tells one, and what limitations one must place upon its conclusions."

A.E. Kelly, et al. in *Simple Approaches to Assessing Underlying Understanding of Statistical Concepts.*

22-9

Simple Conditions

## Simple Conditions for Inference on $\mu$, $\sigma$ Known

- The data are from a perfect SRS.
- The variable measured has a perfectly Normal distribution.
- $\sigma$ is known, (but $\mu$ is unknown.)

**All three conditions are unrealistic.**

**Inference based on these conditions allows us to focus on the reasoning of inference without lots of details.**

22-10

Simple Conditions

## Simple Conditions for Inference on $\mu$, $\sigma$ Known

**Consider: Data are from a perfect SRS.**

-- Most samples suffer from some type of bias: undercoverage, non-response, measurement, interviewer, question wording, etc.

-- Obtaining a complete and accurate listing of the entire population is often difficult.

-- In real life, we base inference on data from samples that are reasonably close to an SRS.

**No analysis, no matter how sophisticated, can compensate for poorly collected data.**

22-11

Simple Conditions

## Simple Conditions for Inference on $\mu$, $\sigma$ Known

**Consider: Variable measured has a perfectly Normal distribution.**

-- In practice, no population is exactly Normal.

-- In a later chapter we will learn how to practically deal with this condition.

**Outliers are always problematic; always plot data and check for outliers, removing them if appropriate.**

22-12

Simple Conditions

## Simple Conditions for Inference on $\mu$, $\sigma$ Known

**Consider: $\sigma$ is known while $\mu$ is unknown.**

-- In practice, $\sigma$ is almost never known.

-- In a later chapter we will learn how to practically deal with this condition by estimating $\sigma$ with s.

**We only use these simple conditions as we introduce inference so that we can focus on the reasoning of inference.**

22-13

Estimating $\mu$

# The Reasoning of Statistical Estimation

Basic Practice of Statistics Chapter 14

☆ Confidence interval: range of likely values for unknown parameter

22-14

Estimating $\mu$

## Estimating $\mu$ with confidence

**Problem: population with unknown mean, $\mu$**

**Solution:** Estimate $\mu$ with $\bar{x}$

- But $\bar{x}$ does not exactly equal $\mu$.
- How accurately does $\bar{x}$ estimate $\mu$?

**Needed:** A measure of error (*ME*) so that $\mu$ is between:

$\bar{x}$ – *ME* and $\bar{x}$ + *ME*

Statistic

with 95% confidence.

**Note: 95% confidence was pre-selected--what does it mean?**

22-15

95% confidence

## Meaning of 95% Confidence

**Sampling Distribution of $\bar{x}$**

About 95% of the area

$\mu-3\sigma/\sqrt{n}$ $\mu-2\sigma/\sqrt{n}$ $\mu-\sigma/\sqrt{n}$ $\mu$ $\mu+\sigma/\sqrt{n}$ $\mu+2\sigma/\sqrt{n}$ $\mu+3\sigma/\sqrt{n}$

≈ 95% of all possible $\bar{x}$ values will be between $\mu - 2\sigma/\sqrt{n}$ and $\mu + 2\sigma/\sqrt{n}$.

What is the probability of taking an SRS of size n and getting an $\bar{x}$ between $\mu - 2\sigma/\sqrt{n}$ and $\mu + 2\sigma/\sqrt{n}$? ≈**0.95**

Take one SRS and get $\bar{x} = 32$.

**Language of confidence after selecting a sample:**

We are 95% confident that 32 is within $2\sigma/\sqrt{n}$ of $\mu$.

**We say "probability" before the sample is taken, "confidence" after.**

22-16

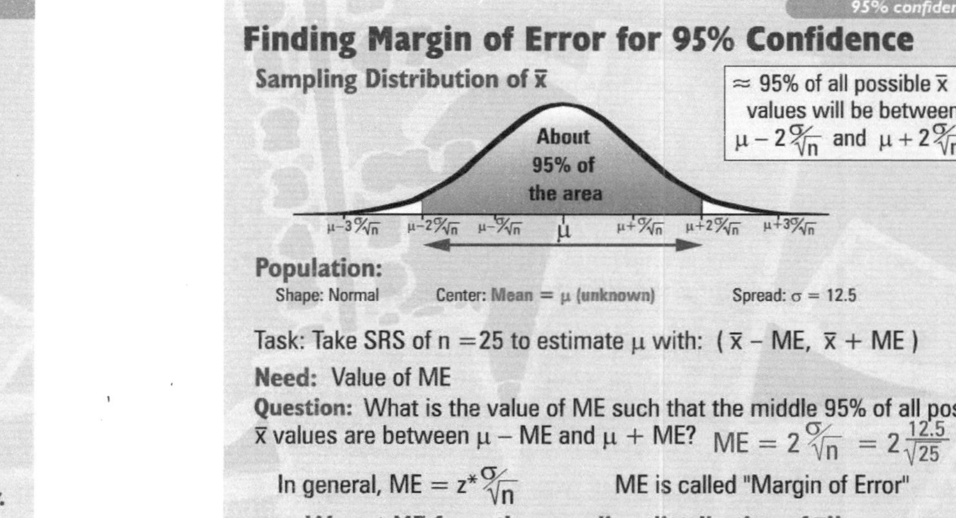

22-17

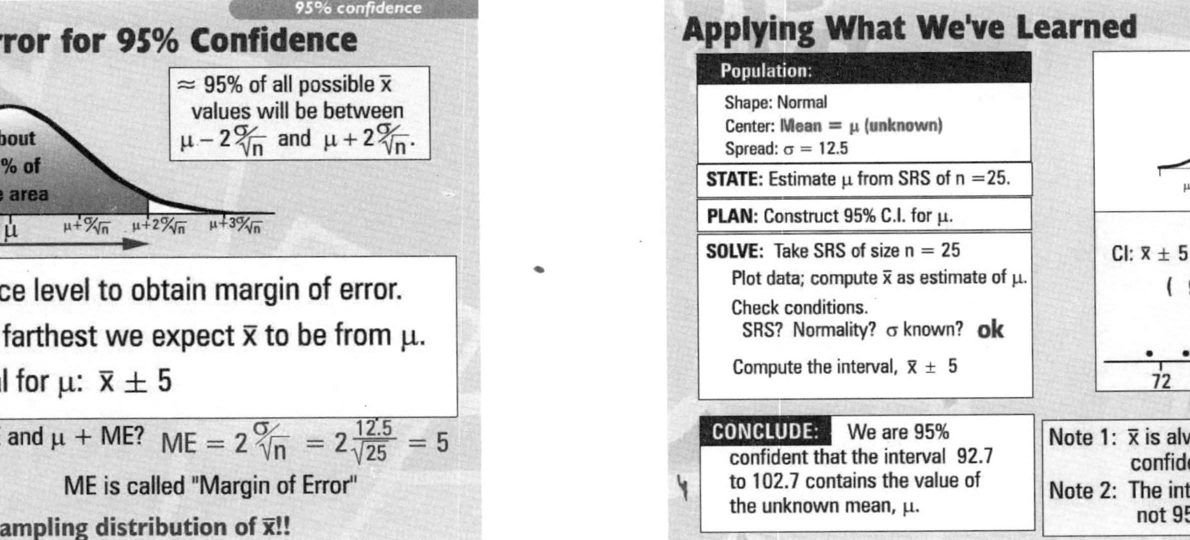

*95% confidence*

## Finding Margin of Error for 95% Confidence

**Sampling Distribution of $\bar{x}$**



$\approx$ 95% of all possible $\bar{x}$ values will be between $\mu - 2\sigma/\sqrt{n}$ and $\mu + 2\sigma/\sqrt{n}$.

We used 95% confidence level to obtain margin of error.
Margin of error tells us farthest we expect $\bar{x}$ to be from $\mu$.
95% confidence interval for $\mu$: $\bar{x} \pm 5$

$\bar{x}$ values are between $\mu$ – ME and $\mu$ + ME? $ME = 2\sigma/\sqrt{n} = 2\frac{12.5}{\sqrt{25}} = 5$

In general, $ME = z^*\sigma/\sqrt{n}$ ME is called "Margin of Error"

**We get ME from the sampling distribution of $\bar{x}$!!**

22-18

*Estimating $\mu$*

## Applying What We've Learned

**Population:**
Shape: Normal
Center: **Mean = $\mu$ (unknown)**
Spread: $\sigma = 12.5$

**STATE:** Estimate $\mu$ from SRS of n = 25.

**PLAN:** Construct 95% C.I. for $\mu$.

**SOLVE:** Take SRS of size n = 25
Plot data; compute $\bar{x}$ as estimate of $\mu$.
Check conditions.
SRS? Normality? $\sigma$ known? **ok**
Compute the interval, $\bar{x} \pm 5$



**CONCLUDE:** We are 95% confident that the interval 92.7 to 102.7 contains the value of the unknown mean, $\mu$.

Note 1: $\bar{x}$ is always in the center of a confidence interval for $\mu$.
Note 2: The interval contains some, but not 95% of the data.

22-19

*Estimating $\mu$*

## Why the interval, $\bar{x} \pm 5$, gives feasible values for $\mu$

**Question**
When does the interval ($\bar{x}$ – 5, $\bar{x}$ + 5) contain the value of the unknown mean, $\mu$?

**Answer**
Whenever $\bar{x}$ is between $\mu$ – 5 and $\mu$ + 5.



22-20

*Estimating $\mu$*

## Why the interval, $\bar{x} \pm 5$, gives feasible values for $\mu$

**Applet demonstrates: The interval ($\bar{x}$ – 5, $\bar{x}$ + 5) contains $\mu$ whenever $\bar{x}$ is between $\mu$ – ME and $\mu$ + ME.**

22-21



## Summary

**Results based on the sampling distribution of $\bar{x}$ :**

- Before sampling, the probability of getting a sample mean, $\bar{x}$, that will be between $\mu - 5$ and $\mu + 5$ is 0.95.
- **If** the interval $(\mu - 5, \mu + 5)$ contains the value of $\bar{x}$, **then** the interval $(\bar{x} - 5, \bar{x} + 5)$ will contain the value of $\mu$.

**Definitions:**

- With 95% confidence, the interval $(\bar{x} - 5, \bar{x} + 5)$ is called: ***a 95% confidence interval estimate for $\mu$.***
- Since the procedure of using $(\bar{x} - ME, \bar{x} + ME)$ to estimate $\mu$ gives intervals that contain $\mu$ for 95% of all possible $\bar{x}$-values, we say: ***level of confidence is 95%.***

  --Level of confidence is subjectively chosen by researcher before data are collected.

22-22



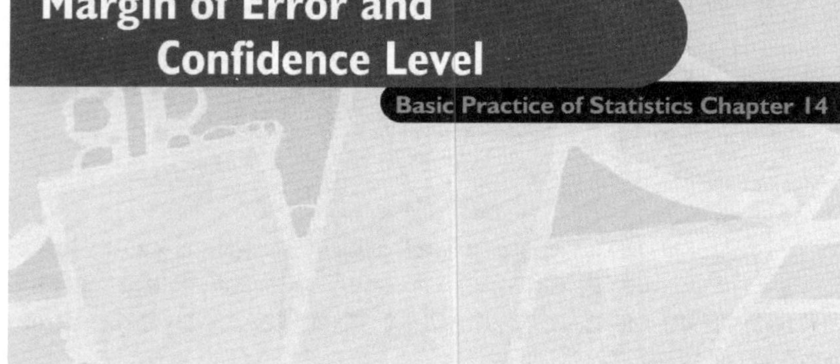

## Margin of Error and Confidence Level

Basic Practice of Statistics Chapter 14

22-23



## Confidence Interval Estimate

**General Form:** estimate $\pm$ margin of error

**Example:**
In a study of the effect of font on reading speed, twenty-five adults read four paragraphs of text in an ornate font called Gigi. The average time of these 25 adults was 22.6 seconds and the margin of error was 2.4 seconds at 95% confidence.

**What is $\mu$?**
The true mean time for all adults to read four paragraphs in Gigi font.

**What is a 95% confidence interval for $\mu$?**

estimate $\pm$ margin of error

$22.6 \pm 2.4$

or (20.2 seconds, 25.0 seconds)

We are 95% confident that the true mean time ($\mu$) is between 20.2 seconds and 25.0 seconds.

22-24



## Facts about Margin of Error for 95% Confidence

**Margin of error:**

- A measure of how accurately $\bar{x}$ estimates $\mu$.
- Tells us the most $\bar{x}$ could differ from $\mu$ for the middle 95% of all possible $\bar{x}$-values.
- For this example, $\bar{x}$ differs from $\mu$ by no more than 2.4 seconds provided $\bar{x} = 22.6$ is in the middle 95% of all possible $\bar{x}$-values.
- We obtain margin of error using facts about the sampling distribution of $\bar{x}$.

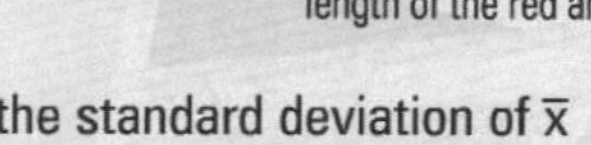


Margin of error equals the length of the red arrow.

$ME = z^* \frac{\sigma}{\sqrt{n}}$ where $\frac{\sigma}{\sqrt{n}}$ is the standard deviation of $\bar{x}$ and $z^*$ is determined by level of confidence.

**For 95% confidence, $z^*$ is approximately 2.**

22-25

*Level of Confidence*

## Understanding Level of Confidence

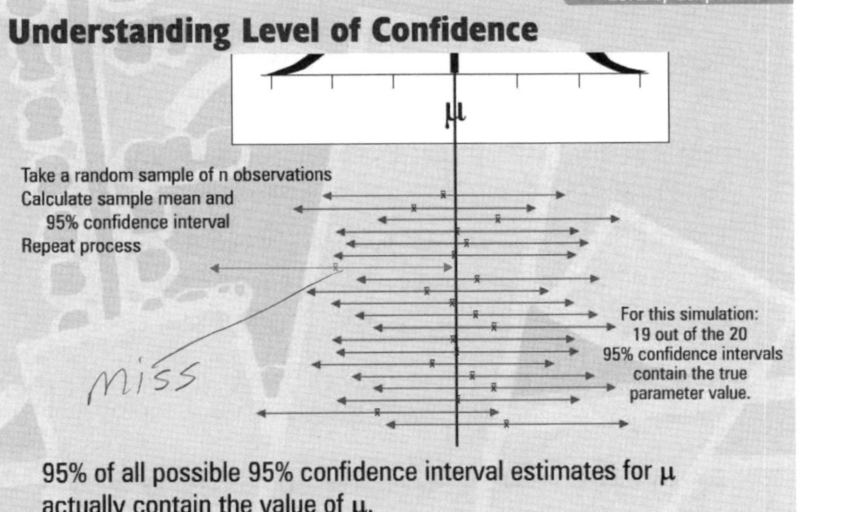


95% of all possible 95% confidence interval estimates for μ actually contain the value of μ.

22-26

*Level of Confidence*

## More on Understanding Level of Confidence

**Recall: our 95% interval is** 22.6 ± 2.4 **or** 20.4 —— 25.0

**Question:** Does the interval (20.2, 25.0) contain the value of the population mean, μ?

**Answer:** We are 95% confident that the value of μ is somewhere between 20.2 and 25.0, but we are not positive.

**Question:** What exactly is level of confidence?

**Answer:** It's the percentage of confidence intervals that could be produced by the procedure that actually contain the value of μ.

**Question:** What is the probability that μ is between 20.2 and 25.0?

**Answer:** Either zero or one--we don't know which.

Note: We say ***probability*** before taking a sample and ***confidence*** after.

22-27

*Level of Confidence*

## Choosing Level of Confidence

- Typically, 90%, 95%, 98% or 99%.
- Chosen by researcher before data are collected.

22-28

*Level of Confidence*

## Choosing Level of Confidence

**The higher the level of confidence you choose**

- The more "sure" you can be that μ will be in the confidence interval.
- The less precise (wider) your interval will be. (ME will be larger.)

90% μ      95% μ

Conclusion: Larger C ⟶ Larger ME ⟶ Wider interval

**Very important decision ⟶ Select higher confidence level**

I am 100% confident that the mean cost of a gallon of oil is between 0 and a hundred million dollars.

22-29

*Components of Confidence Interv*

## Confidence Interval Terms

**Point Estimate for $\mu$:** $\bar{x} = 22.6$

**95% Confidence Interval Estimate for $\mu$:** $22.6 \pm 2.4$ (ME = 2.4)

**Margin of error:** 2.4 is the most that an $\bar{x}$ could differ from the unknown value of $\mu$ for the middle 95% of all possible $\bar{x}$-values.

**Confidence interval interpretation:** We are 95% confident that the interval (20.2, 25.0) contains the true mean time ($\mu$) of all adults.

**Level of confidence:** The percentage of confidence intervals the procedure produces that actually contain the value of $\mu$. (Note: Level of confidence is based on the procedure, not the interval (20.2, 25.0).)

**"95% confidence" interpretation:** 95% of all possible samples yield intervals containing the value of $\mu$ when computed by the same method used to obtain the 95% confidence interval (20.2, 25.0).

22-30

*Confidence Intervals*

## Confidence Intervals for the Mean $\mu$

Basic Practice of Statistics Chapter 14

22-31

*Confidence Intervals*

## Confidence Intervals for Estimating Parameters

**Confidence Interval:** An interval within which we have confidence that the value of the population parameter can be found.

Confidence interval has two parts:

1. An interval estimate of a population parameter of the form:

   estimate $\pm$ margin of error

2. A level of confidence *C*, which gives the success rate of the confidence interval method for capturing the parameter value.

**Purpose of a Confidence Interval:** To give a range of reasonable values for the unknown population parameter (i.e., to estimate the value of the unknown parameter.)

22-32

*Confidence Intervals*

**View Video**

Two parts of confidence interval:

1. Estimate $\pm$ Margin of Error: $7.5 \pm 0.33$

   Estimate: $\bar{x} = 7.5$ hours

   Margin of error: 20 minutes (0.33 hours)

2. Level of Confidence: 95%

22-33

Confidence Intervals

## General Procedure of Confidence Interval for $\mu$:

**Duracell Example**

Step 1 **STATE** the problem. What is the average lifetime of batteries?

Step 2 **PLAN:** Recognize need to estimate $\mu$ with a confidence interval; specify level of confidence. 95%

Step 3 **SOLVE:** Collect data with SRS. Random sample of batteries

Plot data; compute $\bar{x}$ as an estimate of $\mu$.

(No plot available.) $\bar{x} = 7.5$

Checks: SRS, population normally distributed and $\sigma$ known.

SRS? Seems ok Lifetimes normal? Assumption ok $\sigma$ known? ✓

Calculate interval: $\bar{x} \pm$ ME → 7.5 ± 0.33 → (7.17, 7.83)

since ME was given as 0.33 hours (20 minutes).

Step 4 **CONCLUDE:** Interpret confidence interval in context.

We are 95% confident that the mean number of hours, $\mu$, that all Duracell batteries last is somewhere between 7.17 hours and 7.83 hours.

22-34

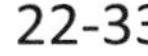

Confidence Intervals

**Confidence Interval Formula:**

$$\bar{x} \pm z^* \cdot \frac{\sigma}{\sqrt{n}}$$

- $\bar{x}$: Estimate of $\mu$ from SRS
- $z^*$: Z-value for specified level of confidence
- $\frac{\sigma}{\sqrt{n}}$: Standard deviation of $\bar{x}$
- $\sigma$: Population standard deviation (Known)
- $n$: Sample size
- $z^* \cdot \frac{\sigma}{\sqrt{n}}$: Margin of Error

**Simple Conditions:**

1. SRS of size n
2. Population normal
3. Known value of $\sigma$

22-35

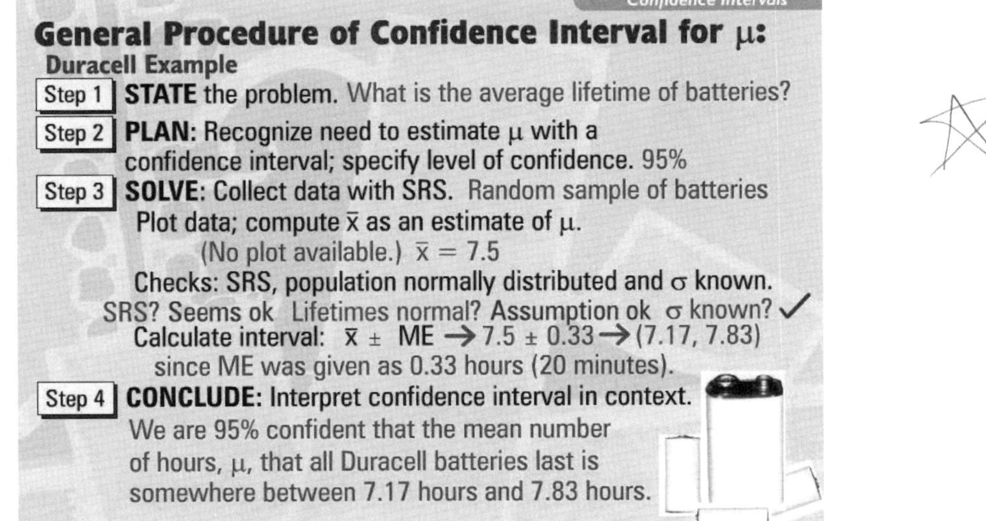


22-36

Different Levels of Confidence

## $z^*$ for the Most Common Confidence Levels

| Confidence Level | $z^*$ |
|---|---|
| 90% | 1.645 |
| 95% | 1.960 |
| 98% | 2.326 |
| 99% | 2.576 |

| | Confidence level $C$ | | | | | | | | | | | |
|---|---|---|---|---|---|---|---|---|---|---|---|---|
| | 50% | 60% | 70% | 80% | 90% | 95% | 96% | 98% | 99% | 99.5% | 99.8% | 99.9% |
| $z^*$ | 0.674 | 0.841 | 1.036 | 1.282 | 1.645 | 1.960 | 2.054 | 2.326 | 2.576 | 2.807 | 3.091 | 3.291 |

Near bottom of Table C.

Heading of Table C.

22-37

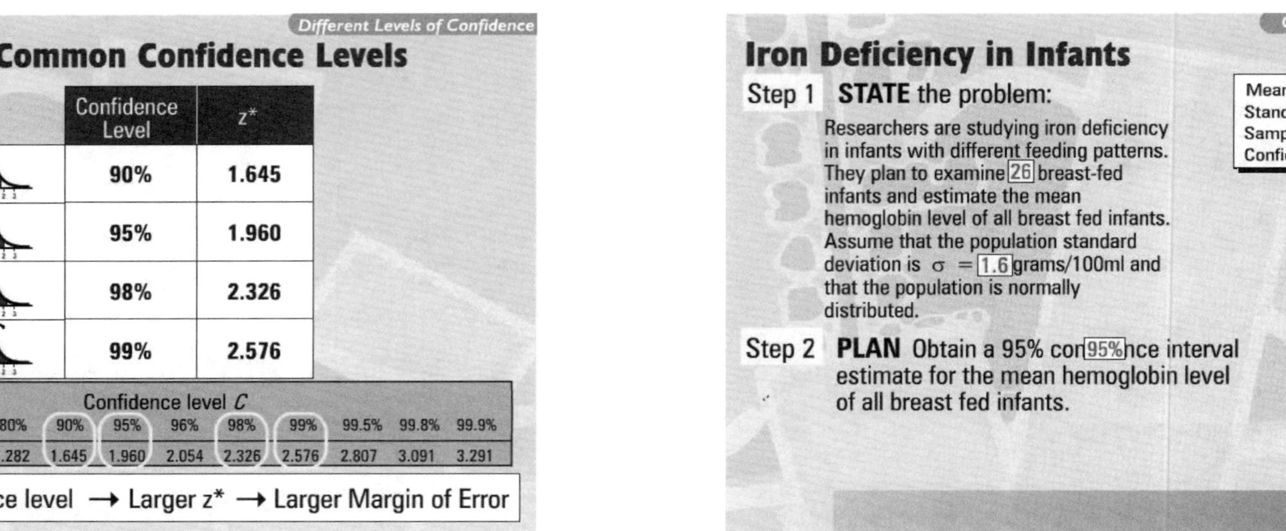

*Different Levels of Confidence*

## z* for the Most Common Confidence Levels

| | Confidence Level | z* |
|---|---|---|
| 90% | 90% | 1.645 |
| 95% | 95% | 1.960 |
| 98% | 98% | 2.326 |
| 99% | 99% | 2.576 |

| | Confidence level *C* | | | | | | | | | | | |
|---|---|---|---|---|---|---|---|---|---|---|---|---|
| | 50% | 60% | 70% | 80% | 90% | 95% | 96% | 98% | 99% | 99.5% | 99.8% | 99.9% |
| z* | 0.674 | 0.841 | 1.036 | 1.282 | 1.645 | 1.960 | 2.054 | 2.326 | 2.576 | 2.807 | 3.091 | 3.291 |

Note: Larger confidence level → Larger z* → Larger Margin of Error

90% = .0495 or .0505
.05 or .04

22-38

*Obtaining Confidence Intervals*

## Iron Deficiency in Infants

| | |
|---|---|
| Mean, $\bar{x}$: | |
| Standard Deviation ($\sigma$): | 1.6 |
| Sample Size: | 26 |
| Confidence Level: | 95% |

**Step 1** **STATE** the problem:

Researchers are studying iron deficiency in infants with different feeding patterns. They plan to examine 26 breast-fed infants and estimate the mean hemoglobin level of all breast fed infants. Assume that the population standard deviation is $\sigma$ = 1.6 grams/100ml and that the population is normally distributed.

**Step 2** **PLAN** Obtain a 95% confidence interval estimate for the mean hemoglobin level of all breast fed infants.

22-39

*Obtaining Confidence Intervals*

## Iron Deficiency in Infants

| | |
|---|---|
| Mean, $\bar{x}$: | 12.9 |
| Standard Deviation ($\sigma$): | 1.6 |
| Sample Size: | 26 |
| Confidence Level: | 95% |

**Step 3** **SOLVE:** Collect data

Plot data; compute $\bar{x}$ as an estimate of $\mu$.

13 13 11 12 1 3 13
13 15 14 13 1 12
16 13 14 11
14 14 14

$\bar{x}$ = 12.9 grams/100ml

Check: SRS? Normal population? $\sigma$ known?

Data can be assumed from an SRS.
Plot is not skewed; no outliers. No evidence of non-normality.
$\sigma$ is known.
Ok to proceed.

22-40

*Obtaining Confidence Intervals*

## Iron Deficiency in Infants

| | |
|---|---|
| Mean, $\bar{x}$: | 12.9 |
| Standard Deviation ($\sigma$): | 1.6 |
| Sample Size: | 26 |
| Confidence Level: | 95% |

**Step 3** **SOLVE:** (cont.) Compute interval.

- Input $\bar{x}$
- Input $\sigma$
- Input *n*
- Find and input z*

12.9 ± 0.62 → (12.28, 13.52)

22-41

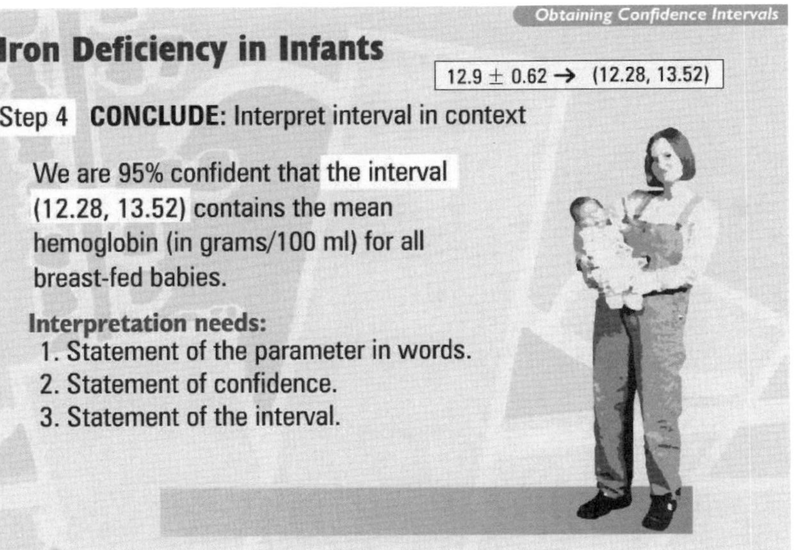
Obtaining Confidence Intervals
Iron Deficiency in Infants
12.9 ± 0.62 → (12.28, 13.52)
Step 4 CONCLUDE: Interpret interval in context
We are 95% confident that the interval (12.28, 13.52) contains the mean hemoglobin (in grams/100 ml) for all breast-fed babies.
Interpretation needs:
1. Statement of the parameter in words.
2. Statement of confidence.
3. Statement of the interval.

22-42

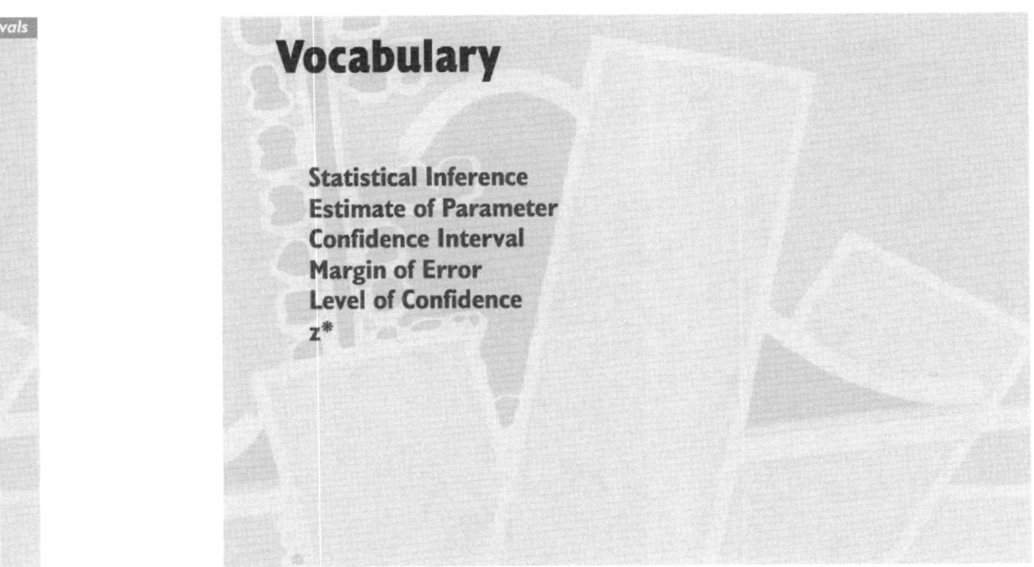
Vocabulary
Statistical Inference
Estimate of Parameter
Confidence Interval
Margin of Error
Level of Confidence
z*

23-1

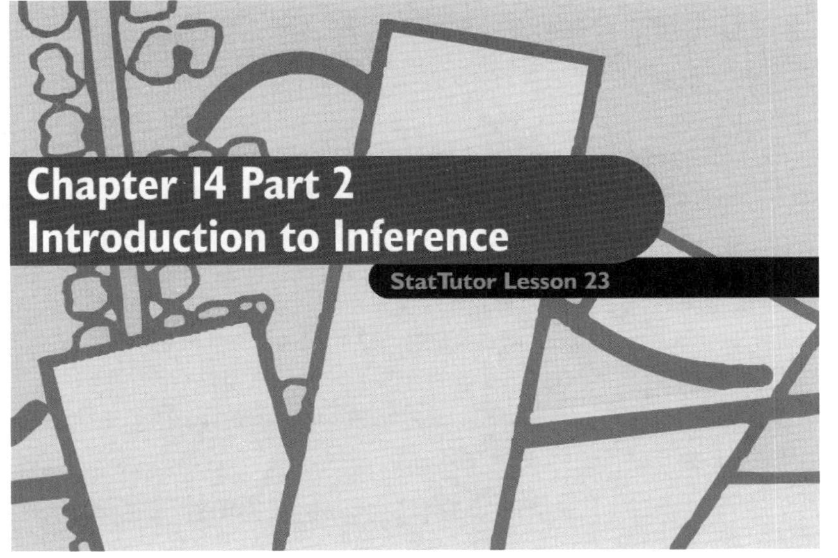


23-2

## Lesson Objectives

1. Compute and interpret confidence intervals for $\mu$ in context.
2. Make correct interpretations of confidence intervals in context.
3. Recognize a problem that compares a sample mean with a claimed value for the population mean.
4. Apply the properties of the sampling distribution of $\bar{x}$ to conduct a test of significance.
5. Explain the reasoning behind a test of significance.

23-3

*Obtaining Confidence Intervals*

## Confidence Intervals for the Mean $\mu$
(Continued)

Basic Practice of Statistics Chapter 14

23-4

*Obtaining Confidence Intervals*

## Average Dating Time to Engagement

Step 1 **STATE:** the problem.

For a class assignment, students at a large church sponsored university decided to take a survey of 121 married students to find out how long these students had dated on average before becoming engaged. The population standard deviation is assumed to be about 10 months.

| | |
|---|---|
| Mean: | |
| Standard Deviation: | 10 |
| Sample Size: | 121 |
| Confidence Level: | 90% |

Step 2 **PLAN:** Students recognized a need for a 90% confidence interval for the mean number of months students at this university dated before becoming engaged.

23-5

*Obtaining Confidence Intervals*

## Average Dating Time to Engagement

**Step 3** **SOLVE:** Contacted random sample of 121 married students and asked how long they dated before becoming engaged.

Plot data; compute $\bar{x}$ as an estimate of $\mu$.

| | |
|---|---|
| Mean: | 9.34 |
| Standard Deviation: | 10 |
| Sample Size: | 121 |
| Confidence Level: | 90% |

# of months married students dated before engagement

$\bar{x} = 9.34$

0 5 10 15 20 25 30 35 40 45 50 55 60

**Warning: The distribution is skewed right with outliers.**

Check: SRS? Normal population? $\sigma$ known?

**What should we do when the data are clearly NOT normally distributed?** Answer: Try to apply the Central Limit Theorem.

- $n$ is large (121), so we can apply CLT.
- OK to proceed.
- Remember: confidence level will be *approximate.*

23-6

*Obtaining Confidence Intervals*

## Average Dating Time to Engagement

**Step 3** **SOLVE:** (cont.) Compute interval.

- Input $\bar{x}$
- Input $\sigma$
- Input $n$
- Find and input z*

| | |
|---|---|
| Mean, $\bar{x}$: | **9.34** |
| Standard Deviation: | **10** |
| Sample Size: | **121** |
| Confidence Level: | **90%** |

$$9.34 \pm 1.645 \cdot \frac{10}{\sqrt{121}}$$

Table C t distribution critical values

| | Confidence level *C* | | | | | | | | | | | |
|---|---|---|---|---|---|---|---|---|---|---|---|---|
| | 50% | 60% | 70% | 80% | 90% | 95% | 96% | 98% | 99% | 99.5% | 99.8% | 99.9% |
| z* | 0.674 | 0.841 | 1.036 | 1.282 | 1.645 | 1.960 | 2.054 | 2.326 | 2.576 | 2.807 | 3.091 | 3.291 |

23-7

*Obtaining Confidence Intervals*

## Average Dating Time to Engagement

$9.34 \pm 1.50 \rightarrow (7.845, 10.836)$

**Step 4** **CONCLUDE:** Interpret interval in context

We are approximately 90% confident that the interval (7.8 months, 10.8 months) contains the true mean number of months married students at this church sponsored university dated before getting engaged.

**OR**

We are approximately 90% confident that our estimate of 9.34 months differs from the true mean length of time dating before getting engaged by no more than 1.5 months.

23-8

*Interpreting Confidence Intervals*

## How to Give a Correct Interpretation

1. State the true parameter in words.
2. Report the interval.
3. Report the confidence of getting a "good" interval (called the confidence level).
4. Summarize all three in a statement.

**Example: Gallup's Phillip Morris Poll**

A Gallup poll on smoking, conducted September 23-26, 1999, shows that today virtually all Americans -- 95% -- think cigarette smoking is harmful. "For results based on this sample, one can say with 95 percent confidence that the maximum error attributable to sampling and other random effects is plus or minus 3 percentage points."

23-9



## Examples of Good Interpretations

"I am 90% confident that the interval (119.5, 128.1) captures the true mean yield in bushels per acre."

"The interval (22.7 degrees, 26.8 degrees) gives a range of reasonable values for the average angle of deformity for all patients having HAV, a deformity of the big toe. We are 95% confident of this."

"The mean IQ of all seventh-grade girls in the school district is somewhere between 95.3 and 109.2 with 99% confidence."

23-10



## Examples of Incorrect Interpretations

"99% of the IQ's are contained in the interval (95.3, 109.2)."

"The probability that the interval (119.5, 128.1) captures the true mean yield in bushels per acre is .90"

"We are 95% confident that the interval (22.7 degrees, 26.8 degrees) contains the sample average angle of deformity for the 38 patients having HAV, a deformity of the big toe."

"99% of the time, the mean IQ's of all seventh-grade girls will be contained in the interval (95.3, 109.2)."

"We are 90% confident that the interval (119.5, 128.1) captures the yields in bushels per acre."

23-11



# The Reasoning of Tests of Significance

Basic Practice of Statistics Chapter 14

23-12



## Review: Statistical Significance

- Inference is drawing conclusions about a population parameter based on the value of a sample statistic.
- Two types of inference:
  --Confidence interval estimation of the value of a parameter
  --Testing a claim about the value of a parameter.

23-13



## Review: Statistical Significance

- Begin with claim about the value of a parameter.
- Observed Effect = Observed Statistic – Claimed Parameter Value

**Statistically Significant:**

An observed effect that is "*too large*" to plausibly be due to chance variation.

- To decide if an observed effect is "too large" (i.e., statistically significant), use the sampling distribution of the statistic.

**Reasoning of a Statistical Test**

***An outcome that would rarely happen if the claim about the parameter value were true is good evidence that the claim is not true.***

23-14



## Matt Perez vs. FBI Movie Clip

**View Movie Clip.**

23-15



## Comparing Observed Statistic with Claimed Value

**Example I: Matt Perez vs. FBI**



**The judge declared the observed effect statistically significant.**

The observed Hispanic promotion rate would rarely happen by chance IF Hispanics were promoted at the same rate as all FBI agents.

--good evidence that the FBI rate is not true for Hispanics.

23-16



## Comparing Observed Statistic with Expected Value

**Example 2: No women on the jury?**

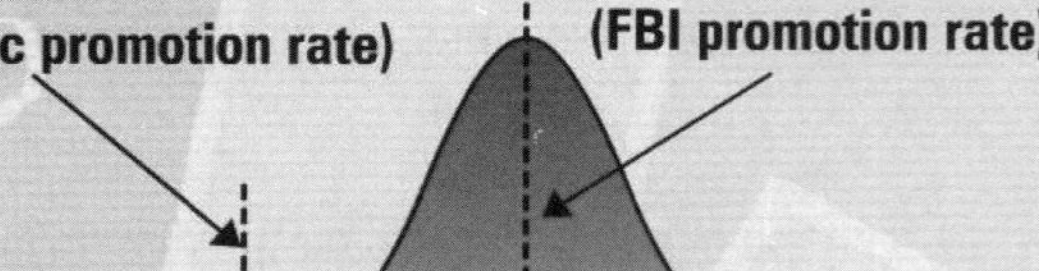

- 12 people chosen to be on jury--all male
- Defense attorney argued that selection was biased as 50% of city population is male.

**Claim:** Percent of jury members that are male reflects percent of males in population.

**What are the chances of randomly selecting males as all 12 jury members when 50% of the population is male?** Answer: 0.0002

**Conclusion:** Randomly selecting males as all 12 jury members would rarely happen if population has 50% males.

--good evidence that the claim is not true.

--good evidence that jury selection is biased.

## Summary

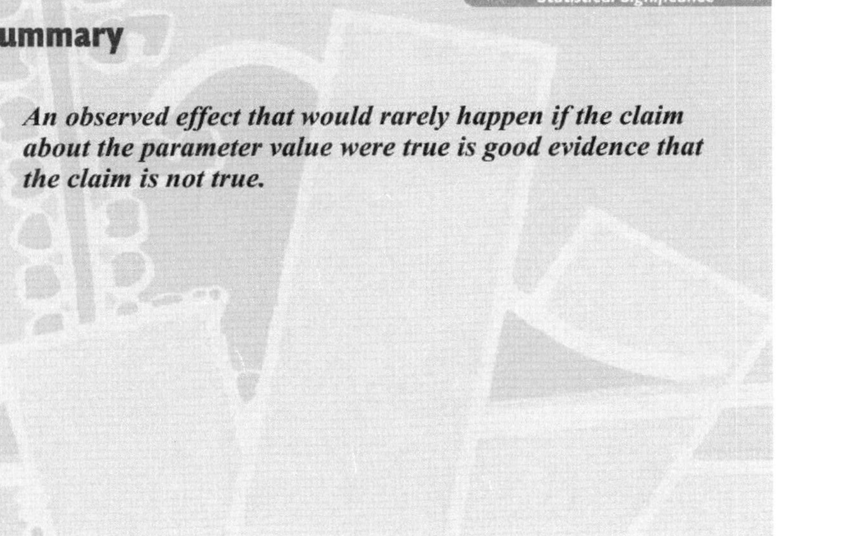

***An observed effect that would rarely happen if the claim about the parameter value were true is good evidence that the claim is not true.***





## Comparing Observed Statistic with Claimed Value

**Example 3: University Creamery**

A machine fills bottles of chocolate milk that should weigh 16 oz. with $\sigma = 0.22$ oz.

**Claim:** Mean weight of bottles is $\mu = 16$ oz.

To test claim: take SRS of 8 bottles and compute $\bar{x}$



**An outcome this large would rarely happen by chance if $\mu = 16$ oz.**

If $\bar{x} = 16.3$? Observed effect too large to be chance ➡ statistically significant

"*$\bar{x} = 16.3$ would rarely happen if $\mu = 16$*" is good evidence that the mean weight of the bottles is not 16.





## Comparing Observed Statistic with Claimed Value

**Example 3: University Creamery**

A machine fills bottles of chocolate milk that should weigh 16 oz. with $\sigma = 0.22$ oz.

**Claim:** Mean weight of bottles is $\mu = 16$ oz.

To test claim: take SRS of 8 bottles and compute $\bar{x}$

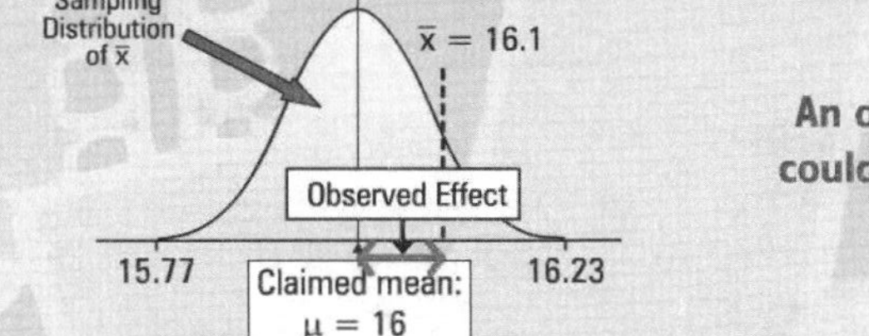



**An outcome this small could happen by chance if $\mu = 16$.**

If $\bar{x} = 16.1$? Observed effect due to chance variation ➡ Not significant

"*$\bar{x} = 16.1$ could happen if $\mu = 16$*" does not give evidence to conclude that the mean weight of the bottles is not 16 oz.





**Just for fun--a real life example:**

1. Does he love me?
2. Evidence: He sent me two dozen long stem red roses.
3. Therefore, he loves me.

**Same question from a statistician's view:**

1. CLAIM: "He loves me not."
2. Evidence: He sent me two dozen long stem red roses.
3. What is the probability that he would send me two dozen long stemmed red roses if "He loves me not"? Very small
4. Since probability is very small, the CLAIM that "He loves me not" is not true. ⟶ Therefore, he must love me.

**In summary, an outcome that would rarely happen if a claim were true is good evidence that the claim is not true.**

23-21

# Vocabulary

- Confidence Interval
- Estimate of Parameter
- Level of Confidence
- Margin of Error
- Sample Size
- Statistical Inference
- z*
- Claimed Parameter Value
- Observed Effect
- Observed Statistic
- Statistical Significance

24-1

# Chapter 14 Part 3
# Introduction to Inference

StatTutor Lesson 24

24-2

## Objectives

1. State null and alternative hypotheses (in PLAN step 2).
2. Define and compute a test statistic in Step 3, the SOLVE step.
3. Define and obtain *P*-value in Step 3, the SOLVE step.
4. State a value for significance level, $\alpha$, (in PLAN step 2) and compare it with *P*-value to determine whether results are significant (in CONCLUDE step 4).

24-3

*Review*

# Stating Hypotheses

Basic Practice of Statistics Chapter 14

24-4

*Review*

## Review: Reasoning in the Test of Significance

- Begin with a claim about the value of a parameter.
- Take a random sample and compute the statistic value.
- Using sampling distribution of the statistic with center equal to the claimed parameter value, decide whether the statistic value is likely or unlikely.
- If the statistic value is unlikely, then conclude that the claim about the parameter value is incorrect.

**In this lesson we formalize stating our claim about the parameter value.**

24-5

*Null and Alternative Hypotheses*

## Formalizing Steps One and Two

Step 1 **STATE** a question about a parameter and specify the claimed parameter value.

Step 2 **PLAN** by deciding to perform a test of significance and determine $H_0$ and $H_a$.

What are $H_0$ and $H_a$?

$H_0$ is the symbol for the null hypothesis.

$H_a$ is the symbol for the alternative hypothesis.

**The null and alternative hypotheses are contradictory statements about the value of the parameter.**

24-6

*Null and Alternative Hypotheses*

## Example: Bottles of Chocolate Milk

Step 1 **STATE the problem.**

A machine fills bottles of chocolate milk that should weigh 16 oz. with $\sigma = 0.22$ oz.

**QUESTION:** Is the mean weight of bottles greater than 16 oz?

**Claim to be tested:**

Mean weight of bottles is $\mu = 16$ oz.

| All bottles (Population) | Response Variable |
|---|---|
| $\mu = 16$ $\sigma = 0.22$ (15.77, 16, 16.23) | Weight of bottle |

24-7

*Null and Alternative Hypotheses*

Step 2 **PLAN: Decide to perform a test of significance and determine $H_0$ and $H_a$.**

**The Null Hypothesis**

- A statement of ***no difference (or no change)*** in the parameter value.
- Gives parameter as equal to its claimed value with an "equal" sign.
- The claim you usually wish to find evidence **against**.
- Denoted by $H_0$; written using parameter symbols such as $\mu$.

---

**Creamery Example:**

A machine fills bottles of chocolate milk that should weigh 16 oz. with $\sigma = 0.22$ oz. If machine is functioning properly, $\mu = 16$.

"No difference" or "no problem": Mean weight = 16 oz.

In symbols:

**$H_0$: $\mu = 16$** "The mean weight of bottles is 16 oz."

24-8

*Null and Alternative Hypotheses*

Step 2 **PLAN: Decide to perform a test of significance and determine $H_0$ and $H_a$.**

**The Alternative Hypothesis**

- A statement of ***difference (or change)*** in the parameter value.
- Compares parameter with its claimed value using: "$<$", "$>$", or "$\neq$".
- The claim about the population you usually wish to find evidence **for**.
- Denoted by $H_a$; written using parameter symbols such as $\mu$.

---

**Creamery Example of "$>$" in $H_a$:**

Intention: To decide whether the machine is overfilling bottles; i.e., is the mean weight of the bottles greater than 16 oz?

In symbols:

**$H_a : \mu > 16$** "Mean weight of bottles is greater than 16 oz."

**A test with "$>$" in $H_a$ is called a one-sided test.**

24-9



**Step 2** **PLAN: Decide to perform a test of significance and determine $H_0$ and $H_a$.**

**The Alternative Hypothesis**

- A statement of ***difference (or change)*** in the parameter value.
- Compares parameter with its claimed value using: "<", ">", or "≠".
- The claim about the population you usually wish to find evidence **for**.
- Denoted by $H_a$; written using parameter symbols such as $\mu$.

**Creamery Example of "<" in $H_a$:**

Intention: To decide whether the machine is underfilling bottles; i.e., is the mean weight of the bottles less than 16 oz?

In symbols:

**$H_a : \mu < 16$** "Mean weight of bottles is less than 16 oz."

**A test with "<" in $H_a$ is called a one-sided test.**

24-10



**Step 2** **PLAN: Decide to perform a test of significance and determine $H_0$ and $H_a$.**

**The Alternative Hypothesis**

- A statement of ***difference (or change)*** in the parameter value.
- Compares parameter with its claimed value using: "<", ">", or "≠".
- The claim about the population you usually wish to find evidence **for**.
- Denoted by $H_a$; written using parameter symbols such as $\mu$.

**Creamery Example of "≠" in $H_a$:**

Intention: To decide whether the machine is improperly filling bottles; i.e., has the mean weight of the bottles changed from 16 oz?

In symbols:

**$H_a : \mu \neq 16$** "Mean weight of bottles not equal to 16 oz."

**A test with "≠" in $H_a$ is called a two-sided test.**

24-11



## Null and Alternative Hypotheses Graphically

**Null Hypothesis**

**In symbols:** $H_0$: $\mu = 16$ **In words:** $H_0$: Mean weight of bottles is 16 oz. False

**Alternative Hypothesis**

**In symbols:** $H_a$: $\mu > 16$ **In words:** $H_a$: Mean weight of bottles is greater than 16. True

| Population ($H_0$) |
|---|
| $\mu = 16 \quad \sigma = .22$ |

| Population ($H_a$) |
|---|
| $\mu > 16 \quad \sigma = .22$ |

Weight of chocolate milk bottles (Population Distribution)



24-12



## More Examples

**Example I: Safety apptitude test**

An insurance company tests the safety aptitude of their insured drivers using a driving simulator. The mean score for their insured drivers is 75.6 points. Officials suspect that teenagers will score lower on average.

**Research Question**

Is the mean for teenage drivers less than 75.6 points?

**Claim to be tested:**

Mean score for all teenagers is the same as for all insured drivers.

$H_0$: $\mu = 75.6$ points

**Research Hypothesis:**

$H_a$: $\mu < 75.6$ points **This is a one-sided test.**

24-13

*Null and Alternative Hypotheses*

## More Examples

**Example 2: Average time spent doing homework**

The teacher of a very large introductory statistics class planned for her students to spend an average of three hours on a homework assignment. When the students turned in their homework, a few complained that it took a lot longer than three hours. She decides to randomly sample twenty students, ask them how long they spent, and perform a test of significance.

**Research Question**

Was the mean time spent doing the homework assignment greater than three hours?

**Claim to be tested:**

Mean time spent on homework was 3 hours. $H_0$: $\mu = 3$ hours

**Research Hypothesis:**

$H_a$: $\mu > 3$ hours **This is a one-sided test.**

24-14

*Null and Alternative Hypotheses*

## More Examples

**Example 3: Mean cost per customer at Sam's Eatery**

At Sam's Eatery, Sam changed the menu and prices of the menu items. Before the change, it cost the eatery $11.50 per customer for ingredients and labor to prepare their meals. Now Sam wants to know if the cost per customer has changed.

**Research Question**

Has the mean cost per customer changed?

**Claim to be tested:**

Mean cost per customer is $11.50. $H_0$: $\mu = \$11.50$

**Research Hypothesis:**

$H_a$: $\mu \neq \$11.50$

**A test with "≠" in $H_a$ is called a two-sided test.**

24-15

*Null and Alternative Hypotheses*

## More Examples

**Example 3: Mean cost per customer at Sam's Eatery**

At Sam's Eatery, Sam changed the menu and prices of the menu items. Before the change, it cost the eatery $11.50 per customer for ingredients and labor to prepare their meals. Now Sam wants to know if the cost per customer has changed.

**Research Question**

Has the mean cost per customer changed?

**Claim to be tested:**

Mean cost per customer is $11.50. $H_0$: $\mu = \$11.50$

**Research Hypothesis:**

$H_a$: $\mu \neq \$11.50$

**A test with "≠" in $H_a$ is called a two-sided test.**

24-16

*Summary*

## Summary

**Null Hypothesis ($H_0$)**

Describes status quo in the parameter value--no effect, no change, no difference, nothing's there.
(Usually the hypothesis we want to disprove.)

**Alternative Hypothesis ($H_a$)**

Describes a difference or change from the status quo in the parameter value.
(Usually the research hypothesis we want to prove.)

- Always put the "equal" sign in $H_0$.
- Never put the $\bar{x}$ symbol or an $\bar{x}$ value in $H_0$ or $H_a$.

**Hypotheses should always be specified before examining data.**

24-17

Test of Significance

# *P*-values and Statistical Significance

Basic Practice of Statistics Chapter 14

24-18

Test of Significance

## A Test of Significance Answers the Question:

Is the observed effect "too large" to be due to chance variation?

**An Outline of Test of Significance**

Step 1 **STATE** a research question in terms of a parameter and specify the claimed parameter value.

Step 2 **PLAN** solution by deciding to do a test of significance and stating $H_0$ and $H_a$.

Step 3 **SOLVE** by Collecting data

Checking conditions

Computing test statistic and probability on test statistic using sampling distribution of statistic with center = claimed parameter value.

Step 4 **CONCLUDE** by declaring the claim is not true if the probability on the observed statistic is small.

**An observed statistic that would rarely happen if a claim about a parameter value were true is good evidence that the claim is not true.**

24-19

Test Statistic

## What is a Test Statistic?

- A number that summarizes the data for a test of significance.
- Compares estimate of the parameter from sample data (i.e., the statistic) with the parameter value given in the null hypothesis.
  --Measures how far statistic is from claimed parameter value.
  --Large values are not consistent with $H_0$ (i.e., large values give evidence against $H_0$.)
- Used to find probability of obtaining statistic **IF** $H_0$ were true.
- Test statistic formula for testing $\mu$ assuming $\sigma$ known:

$$z = \frac{\bar{x} - \mu_0}{\sigma/\sqrt{n}}$$

where $\mu_0$ is the value of the parameter given in the null hypothesis.

24-20

Calculate Test Statistic

## Examples of Calculating Test Statistic

**Suppose we are testing:**

$H_0$: $\mu = 16$

$H_a$: $\mu > 16$

and we know $\sigma = 0.22$

**From the sample we learn:**

Sample Size: $n = 8$

Sample Mean: $\bar{x} = 16.1$

**Calculate Test Statistic:**

Standardized Test Statistic

$$z = \frac{\bar{x} - \mu_0}{\sigma/\sqrt{n}} = \frac{16.1 - 16}{0.22/\sqrt{8}} = 1.29$$

- Test statistic value $z = 1.29$ is not large; observed effect is approximately equal to chance variation.
- Test statistic value $z = 1.29$ does not provide evidence against $H_0$.

24-21

Calculate Test Statistic

## Examples of Calculating Test Statistic

**Suppose we are testing:**

$H_0$: $\mu = 16$

$H_a$: $\mu > 16$

and we know $\sigma = 0.22$

**(Same hypotheses and $\sigma$.)**

**From the sample we learn:**

Sample Size: $n = 8$

Sample Mean: $\bar{x} = 16.3$

**(Same n; different $\bar{x}$ value)**

**Calculate Test Statistic:**

Standardized Test Statistic

$$z = \frac{\bar{x} - \mu_0}{\sigma/\sqrt{n}} = \frac{16.3 - 16}{0.22/\sqrt{8}} = 3.86$$

- Test statistic value $z = 3.86$ is large; observed effect is much greater than chance variation.
- Test statistic value $z = 3.86$ provides strong evidence against $H_0$.

24-22

Calculate Test Statistic

## Compare Test Statistics

| If $\bar{x} = 16.1$? | If $\bar{x} = 16.3$? |
|---|---|
| Test statistic value $z = 1.29$ | Test statistic value $z = 3.86$ |

**Why are these test statistics different?**

**Because $\bar{x} = 16.3$ is significantly farther from $\mu_0$ of 16 than $\bar{x} = 16.1$.**



- $\bar{x} = 16.1$ is not significantly far from $\mu = 16$.
- $\bar{x} = 16.3$ is significantly far from $\mu = 16$.

24-23

What is P-value?

## What is *P*-value?

**In a test of significance:**

- The null hypothesis, $H_0$, specifies a claim about the parameter value.
- The test statistic measures how far the sample statistic diverges from the claimed parameter value given in $H_0$.
- If test statistic is large, then the statistic is unlikely if $H_0$ were true.
- But how unlikely is a large test statistic?

**Needed: a measure of how unlikely the statistic is if $H_0$ were true.**

- Compute the probability of obtaining a test statistic as extreme or more extreme than observed if $H_0$ were true.
- Call the probability: *P*-value.

24-24

Finding P-value

## Examples of Finding *P*-value

$\bar{x} = 16.1$

$H_0$: $\mu = 16$

$H_a$: $\mu > 16$

Assume $H_0$: $\mu = 16$ is true.

Using the sampling distribution of $\bar{x}$, calculate probability of getting a statistic as extreme or more extreme than the observed $\bar{x}$ value of 16.1.

Call probability the *P*-value.

***P*-value** = Probability that $\bar{x} \geq 16.1$ ***IF*** $\mu = 16$

= Area under curve above 16.1 = **0.0985**

Table A

| z | .09 |
|---|---|
| 1.0 | .8621 |
| 1.1 | .8830 |
| 1.2 | .9015 |
| 1.3 | .9177 |
| 1.4 | .9319 |

Test statistic

$$z = \frac{16.1 - 16}{.22/\sqrt{8}} = 1.29$$

Area

$P(z \geq 1.29) = 1 - 0.9015 = 0.0985$



Population (Under $H_0$)

$\mu = 16$ $\sigma = 0.22$

Sampling Distribution of $\bar{x}$

$\mu = 16$

$s/\sqrt{n} = 0.22/\sqrt{8} = 0.078$

24-25

*Finding P-value*

## Examples of Finding *P*-value

$\bar{x} = 16.1$ $H_0: \mu = 16$

***Interpretation of P-value***
If the mean weight of all bottles of chocolate milk is $\mu = 16$ oz., the probability of getting a mean weight from a random sample of eight bottles of 16.1 or greater is 0.0985.

***P*-value** = Probability that $\bar{x} \geq 16.1$ ***IF*** $\mu = 16$
= Area under curve above 16.1 = **0.0985**

| Table A | |
|---|---|
| z | .09 |
| 1.0 | .8621 |
| 1.1 | .8830 |
| 1.2 | .9015 |
| 1.3 | .9177 |
| 1.4 | .9319 |

Sampling Distribution assuming $H_0$ is true.
n = 8
***P*-value**
15.77 16 16.1 16.23

Test statistic
$z = \frac{16.1 - 16}{.22/\sqrt{8}} = 1.29$
Area
$P(z \geq 1.29) =$
$1 - 0.9015 = 0.0985$

Population (Under $H_0$)
$\mu = 16$ $\sigma = 0.22$
Sampling Distribution of $\bar{x}$
$\mu = 16$
$s/\sqrt{n} = 0.22/\sqrt{8} = 0.078$

24-26

*Finding P-value*

## Examples of Finding *P*-value

$\bar{x} = 16.3$ $H_0: \mu = 16$
$H_a: \mu > 16$

Assume $H_0: \mu = 16$ is true.

***P*-value** = Probability that $\bar{x} \geq 16.3$ ***IF*** $\mu = 16$
= Area under curve above 16.3
= Probability that $z \geq 3.86$
= **0.000**

3.86 is OFF the chart!!!

| Table A | |
|---|---|
| z | .09 |
| 3.0 | .9990 |
| 3.1 | .9993 |
| 3.2 | .9995 |
| 3.3 | .9997 |
| 3.4 | .9998 |

Sampling Distribution assuming $H_0$ is true.
n = 8
***P*-value**
15.77 16 16.3 16.23

Test statistic
$z = \frac{16.3 - 16}{0.22/\sqrt{8}} = 3.86$
Area
$P(z \geq 3.86) =$
$1 - 1.000 = 0.000$

Population (Under $H_0$)
$\mu = 16$ $\sigma = 0.22$
Sampling Distribution of $\bar{x}$
$\mu = 16$
$s/\sqrt{n} = 0.22/\sqrt{8} = 0.078$

24-27

*Finding P-value*

## Examples of Finding *P*-value

$\bar{x} = 16.3$ $H_0: \mu = 16$

***Interpretation of P-value in context***
If the mean weight of all bottles is $\mu = 16$ ounces, the probability of getting a sample mean greater than or equal to 16.3 ounces from a random sample of eight bottles is 0.000.

= **0.000**

3.86 is OFF the chart!!!

| Table A | |
|---|---|
| z | .09 |
| 3.0 | .9990 |
| 3.1 | .9993 |
| 3.2 | .9995 |
| 3.3 | .9997 |
| 3.4 | .9998 |

Sampling Distribution assuming $H_0$ is true.
n = 8
***P*-value**
15.77 16 16.3 16.23

Test statistic
$z = \frac{16.3 - 16}{0.22/\sqrt{8}} = 3.86$
Area
$P(z \geq 3.86) =$
$1 - 1.000 = 0.000$

Population (Under $H_0$)
$\mu = 16$ $\sigma = 0.22$
Sampling Distribution of $\bar{x}$
$\mu = 16$
$s/\sqrt{n} = 0.22/\sqrt{8} = 0.078$

24-28

*Finding P-value*

## Examples of Finding *P*-value

**Compare results:**

| | |
|---|---|
| Sample Size: n = 8 | Sample Size: n = 8 |
| Test statistic value $z = 1.29$ | Test statistic value $z = 3.86$ |
| *P*-value = .0985 | *P*-value = .000 |

**Why are the *P*-values different?**
**Because $\bar{x} = 16.3$ is significantly farther from $\mu_0$ of 16 than $\bar{x} = 16.1$.**

$\bar{x} = 16.1$
*P*-value = .0985

$\bar{x} = 16.3$
*P*-value = .000

**Note: the farther $\bar{x}$ is from $\mu$ on the curve, the smaller the *P*-value.**

24-29

Finding P-value

## *P*-value Facts

- A number between 0 and 1: $0 \le P\text{-value} \le 1$
- A measure of the strength of disagreement between the observed test statistic and $H_0$ (i.e., measures evidence *against* $H_0$).
- Probability of getting a test statistic as extreme or more extreme than observed if $H_0$ were true. (*Key parts: (1) probability is on the statistic, not $H_0$; (2) probability is conditional on $H_0$ being true.*)

**A small *P*-value gives evidence against $H_0$ in support of $H_a$.**
**Rule to remember: *P* low--reject "H" "oh"!**

good evidence that $H_0$ is not true; evidence *for* $H_a$ — no evidence that $H_0$ is not true; no evidence *for* $H_a$

Strength of evidence against $H_0$

0 — .5 — 1

*P*-value

24-30

P-value

## Reporting *P*-value in Literature

The time to complete resolution of symptoms was significantly shorter in the zinc group than in the placebo group (median, 4.4 days compared with 7.6 days; P < 0.001). The zinc group had significantly fewer days with coughing (median, 2.0 days compared with 4.5 days; P = 0.04), Headache (2.0 days and 3.0 days; P = 0.02), hoarseness (2.0 days and 3.0 days; P = 0.02), nasal congestion (4.0 days and 6.0 days; P = 0.002), nasal drainage (4.0 days and 7.0 days; P < 0.001), and sore throat (1.0 days and 3.0 days; P < 0.001)...

**Note**

Large differences → small *P*-values

24-31

Statistical Significance

## When Are Results Statistically Significant?

**An observed effect that would rarely happen if a claim about a parameter value were true is good evidence that the claim is not true.**

- If *P*-value is really low, then we have evidence that $H_0$ is incorrect.
  --Distance between observed statistic value and the claimed parameter value is statistically significant.
- If *P*-value is NOT really low, then we do NOT have evidence that $H_0$ is incorrect. *(Neither do we have evidence that $H_0$ is correct.)*
  --Distance between observed statistic value and the claimed parameter value is NOT statistically significant.

When is *P*-value low?

**Needed: A more decisive method for determining whether *P*-value is low.**

24-32

Level of Significance

## What Is Level Of Significance?

- Denoted by the Greek letter: $\alpha$
- Subjectively chosen by researcher in PLAN step
- Defined as: Risk of rejecting $H_0$ when $H_0$ is actually correct
- Typically small, usually 0.05 or smaller
- Cut-off that divides *P*-values into two regions:

| ***P*-value $\le \alpha$** | ***P*-value $> \alpha$** |
|---|---|
| **Data inconsistent with $H_0$** | **Data consistent with $H_0$** |
| **Reject $H_0$** | **Do not reject $H_0$** |
| **Results are statistically significant.** | **Results are NOT statistically significant** |

***P*-value:** 0 — $\alpha$ — .5 — 1

**Conclusion: Believe $H_a$ — Insufficient evidence to believe $H_a$**

24-33

Comparing P-value with $\alpha$

## Examples of Using *P*-value & Level of Significance

If *P*-value $\leq \alpha$, reject $H_0$; declare results to be statistically significant; conclude sufficient evidence to believe $H_a$.

If *P*-value $> \alpha$, don't reject $H_0$; declare results NOT statistically significant; conclude insufficient evidence to believe $H_a$.

**Specify $\alpha = 0.05$:** $\bar{x} = 16.1$ $H_0: \mu = 16$

*P*-value $= 0.0985 > 0.05 = \alpha$ $H_a: \mu > 16$

| Reject $H_0$ Results are statistically significant. | Do not reject $H_0$ Results are NOT statistically significant |
|---|---|

At $\alpha = .05$, we have insufficient evidence to conclude that the mean weight for all bottles is greater than 16 ounces.

**Conclusion: Believe $H_a$ | Insufficient evidence to believe $H_a$**

24-34

Comparing P-value with $\alpha$

## Examples of Using *P*-value & Level of Significance

If *P*-value $\leq \alpha$, reject $H_0$; declare results to be statistically significant; conclude sufficient evidence to believe $H_a$.

If *P*-value $> \alpha$, don't reject $H_0$; declare results NOT statistically significant; conclude insufficient evidence to believe $H_a$.

**Specify $\alpha = 0.05$:** $\bar{x} = 16.3$ $H_0: \mu = 16$

*P*-value $= 0.000 < 0.05 = \alpha$ $H_a: \mu > 16$

| Reject $H_0$ Results are statistically significant. | Do not reject $H_0$ Results are NOT statistically significant |
|---|---|

At $\alpha = .05$, we have sufficient evidence to conclude that the mean weight for all bottles of chocolate milk is significantly greater than 16 ounces.

**Conclusion: Believe $H_a$ | Insufficient evidence to believe $H_a$**

24-35

Summary

## Summary

***P*-value:**

**Definition**

Probability
of getting a test statistic
as extreme or more extreme than the observed value
assuming $H_0$ is true.

- Always an area under the curve of the sampling distribution of $\bar{x}$ defined by $H_0$.
- Always an area of the tail indicated by the direction in $H_a$.
- Always compared with $\alpha$ to determine statistical significance.

24-36

Summary

## Summary

**Level of Significance:**

**Definition**

Largest risk of *rejecting $H_0$ when it is correct* that researcher is willing to take.

- Set by researchers in Step 2: PLAN
- *P*-value $\leq \alpha$:
  - → Reject $H_0$ (***P low--reject $H_0$***)
  - → Results are statistically significant
  - → Conclude: sufficient evidence to believe $H_a$ to be correct.
- *P*-value $> \alpha$:
  - → Fail to reject $H_0$ (***P NOT low--do NOT reject $H_0$***)
  - → Results are NOT statistically significant
  - → Conclude: insufficient evidence believe $H_a$ to be correct.

24-37

# Vocabulary

**Alternative Hypothesis**
**Claimed Parameter Value**
**Null Hypothesis**
**Observed Effect**
**Observed Statistic**
***P*-value**
**Significance Level**
**Statistical Significance**
**Test of Significance**
**Test Statistic**

25-1

25-2

## Lesson Objectives

1. List outline of a test of significance.
2. Distinguish between one-sided (both left-tailed or right-tailed) and two-sided alternative hypotheses.
3. Do tests of hypotheses for one-sided left tailed tests; one-sided right tailed tests; and two-sided tests for different problem scenarios.
   - State hypotheses.
   - Check simple conditions.
   - Compute test statistic and determine *P*-value.
   - Use *P*-value to draw conclusions in the context of the problem.

25-3

# Tests for a Population Mean

Basic Practice of Statistics Chapter 14

25-4

## Outline of Tests of Significance

Step 1 **STATE** the problem.

Step 2 **PLAN:** Recognize need for a test on $\mu$.
Specify $H_0$ and $H_a$ and choose $\alpha$.

Step 3 **SOLVE:** Collect data with SRS.
Plot data; compute $\bar{x}$ as an estimate of $\mu$.
Check conditions: SRS, Normal population, $\sigma$ known
Calculate test statistic: $z = \frac{(\bar{x} - \mu_0)}{\sigma/\sqrt{n}}$
Find *P*-value.

Step 4 **CONCLUDE:** Compare *P*-value with $\alpha$ and draw conclusions in context.

If *P*-value $\leq \alpha$, reject $H_0$; declare results statistically significant.
If *P*-value $> \alpha$, don't reject $H_0$; conclude that the results are not statistically significant.

25-5



## Recognizing One or Two Sided Hypotheses

The null hypothesis, $H_0$

- Contains the equality sign "=".
- Gives $\mu_0$, the claimed parameter value or standard against which the observed $\bar{x}$ is compared.
- Specifies center of the sampling distribution of $\bar{x}$ for finding *P*-value.
- Is assumed to be true for computing test statistic and *P*-value.

| General Case | Specific Example |
|---|---|
| $H_0: \mu = \mu_0$ | $H_0: \mu = 75.6$ for safety aptitude scores of teenagers |

25-6



## Recognizing One or Two Sided Hypotheses

The alternative hypothesis, $H_a$

- Predicts where test statistic would fall if $H_a$ were true.
- Specifies tail for finding *P*-value.
- Has three possibilities.

| General Case | Specific Example | Name |
|---|---|---|
| $H_a: \mu < \mu_0$ | $H_a: \mu < 75.6$ | One sided: left-tailed |
| $H_a: \mu > \mu_0$ | $H_a: \mu > 75.6$ | One sided: right-tailed |
| $H_a: \mu \neq \mu_0$ | $H_a: \mu \neq 75.6$ | Two sided |

25-7



## Recognizing One or Two Sided Hypotheses

| Alternative hypothesis, $H_a$ | | Type | *P*-value Area |
|---|---|---|---|
| $H_a: \mu < \mu_0$ | $H_a: \mu < 75.6$ | One-sided (Left tail) | Area under curve less than observed $\bar{x}$ |
| $H_a: \mu > \mu_0$ | $H_a: \mu > 75.6$ | One-sided (Right tail) | Area under curve greater than observed $\bar{x}$ |
| $H_a: \mu = \mu_0$ | $H_a: \mu \neq 75.6$ | Two-sided | Area under curve farther away from $\mu_0$ than observed $\bar{x}$ (both directions) |

$H_0: \mu = 75.6$

$H_a: \mu \neq 75.6$



25-8



## Summary: General Case

| Null Hypothesis: | Alternative Hypotheses: | Type of Alternative: | *P*-value is area of: |
|---|---|---|---|
| $H_0: \mu = \mu_0$ | $H_a: \mu < \mu_0$ | One-sided | Left-Tail |
| | $H_a: \mu > \mu_0$ | One-sided | Right-Tail |
| | $H_a: \mu \neq \mu_0$ | Two-sided | Both Tails |

| | Alternative | Sampling Distribution of $\bar{x}$ | Predicted values for $\bar{x}$ under $H_a$ |
|---|---|---|---|
| Left tailed | $H_a: \mu < \mu_0$ | | $\bar{x}$ significantly less than $\mu_0$ ⟶ reject $H_0$ |
| Right tailed | $H_a: \mu > \mu_0$ | | $\bar{x}$ significantly greater than $\mu_0$ ⟶ reject $H_0$ |
| Two tailed | $H_a: \mu \neq \mu_0$ | | $\bar{x}$ significantly greater (or less) than $\mu_0$ ⟶ reject $H_0$ |

25-9

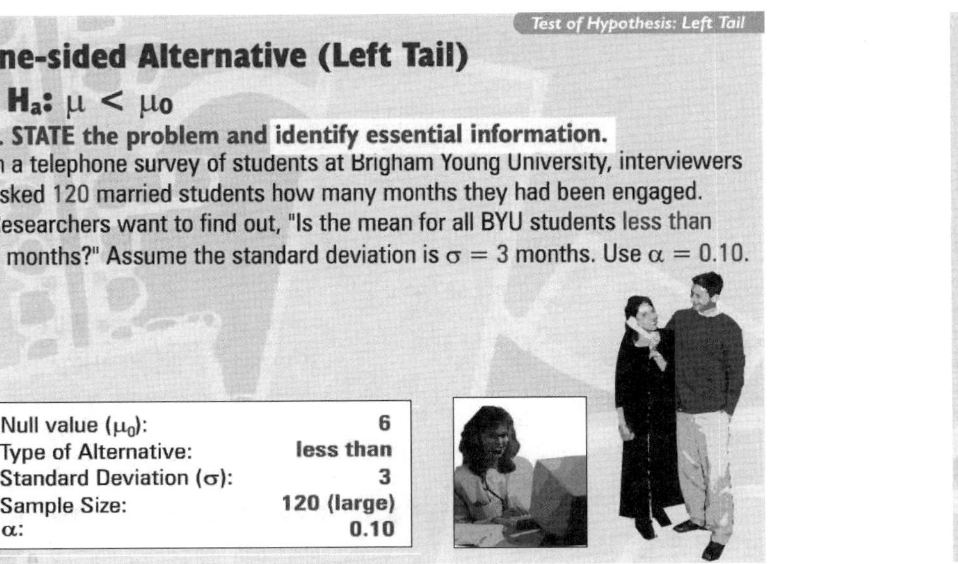


25-10

## One-sided Alternative (Left Tail)

Test of Hypothesis: Left Tail

**$H_a$: $\mu < \mu_0$**

**2. PLAN:**

**Decide to perform test on $\mu$;**

**Determine $H_0$, $H_a$; select $\alpha$**

| | |
|---|---|
| Null value ($\mu_0$): | 6 |
| Type of Alternative: | less than |
| Standard Deviation ($\sigma$): | 3 |
| Sample Size: | 120 (large) |
| $\alpha$: | 0.10 |

**The Null Hypothesis**

$H_0$: $\mu = 6$ months

$\mu$ = mean length of engagement for all married BYU students

**The Alternative Hypothesis**

$H_a$: $\mu < 6$ months

$\alpha = 0.10$

25-11

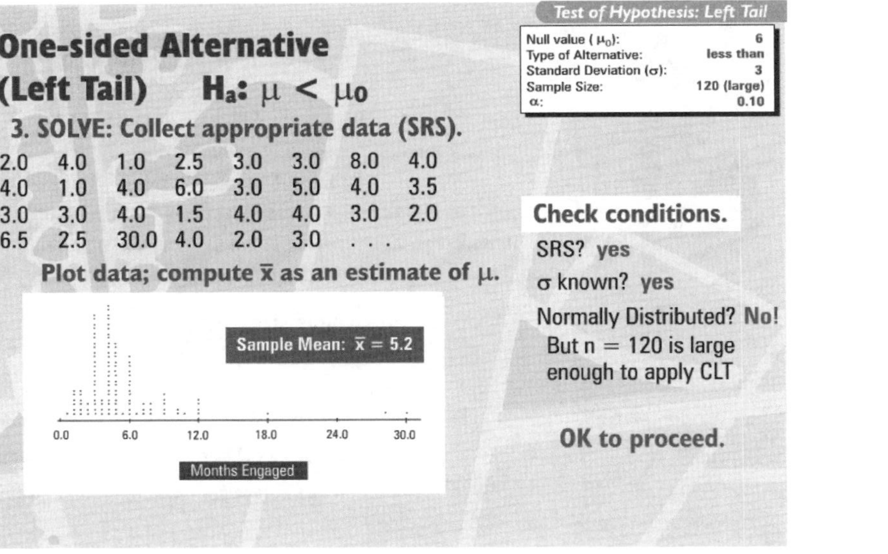


25-12

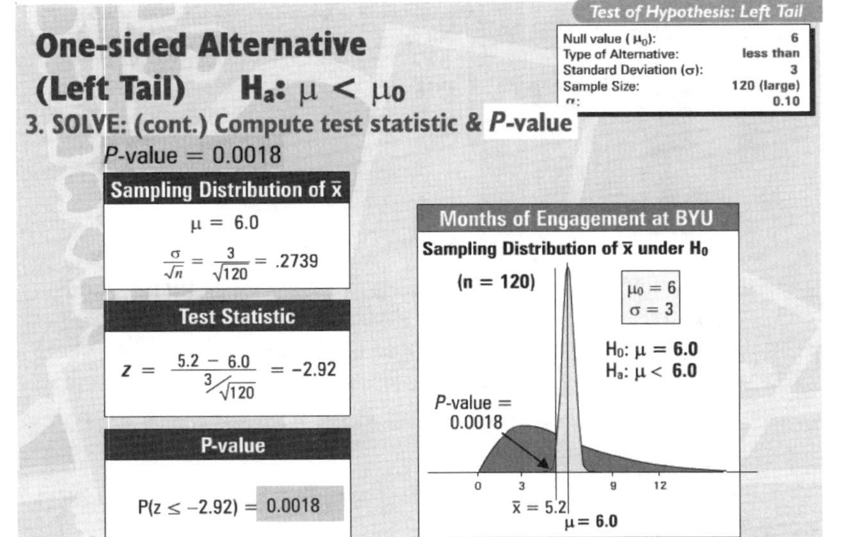

25-13



## One-sided Alternative (Left Tail) $H_a$: $\mu < \mu_0$

**4. CONCLUDE: Draw conclusions in context.**

*P*-value = 0.0018 < 0.10 = level of significance

Reject $H_0$. The observed effect is statistically significant.

**Conclusion in Context: Data give sufficient evidence to conclude that the mean number of months married BYU students were engaged is significantly less than 6 months at $\alpha = 0.10$.**

**The Null Hypothesis**
$H_0$: $\mu = 6$ months

**The Alternative Hypothesis**
$H_a$: $\mu < 6$ months

25-14



## One-sided Alternative Right Tail

**$H_a$: $\mu > \mu_0$**

**1. STATE the problem; identify essential information**

Scores on the SAT are approximately normally distributed with standard deviation $\sigma = 100$. A random sample of 20 students from a large school district took a training course before the SAT. Is there evidence that this training raised the mean above the district mean of 483? Use $\alpha = 0.05$.

470 540 530

| | |
|---|---|
| Null value ( $\mu_0$): | 483 |
| Type of Alternative: | greater than |
| Standard Deviation ($\sigma$): | 100 |
| Sample Size: | 20 |
| $\alpha$: | 0.05 |

25-15



## One-sided Alternative Right Tail

| | |
|---|---|
| Null value ( $\mu_0$): | 483 |
| Type of Alternative: | greater than |
| Standard Deviation ($\sigma$): | 100 |
| Sample Size: | 20 |
| $\alpha$: | 0.05 |

**$H_a$: $\mu > \mu_0$**

**2. PLAN:**

**Decide to perform test on $\mu$;**

**Determine $H_0$, $H_a$; select $\alpha$**

**The Null Hypothesis**
$H_0$: $\mu = 483$

**The Alternative Hypothesis**
$H_a$: $\mu > 483$

$\mu$ = mean score on SAT for all students in the large school district who took training course

$\alpha = 0.05$

25-16



## One-sided Alternative Right Tail

| | |
|---|---|
| Null value ( $\mu_0$): | 483 |
| Type of Alternative: | greater than |
| Standard Deviation ($\sigma$): | 100 |
| Sample Size: | 20 |
| $\alpha$: | 0.05 |

**$H_a$: $\mu > \mu_0$**

**3. SOLVE: Collect appropriate data (SRS).**

| | | | | | | |
|---|---|---|---|---|---|---|
| 452 | 438 | 577 | 421 | 508 | 450 | 698 |
| 498 | 540 | 396 | 743 | 398 | 449 | 593 |
| 514 | 520 | 483 | 328 | 429 | 547 | |

**Plot data; compute $\bar{x}$ as an estimate of $\mu$.**

$\bar{x} = 499.10$

300 400 500 600 700 800

**Check conditions.** **OK to proceed.**

SRS? **Yes** $\sigma$ known? **Yes**

Normally Distributed? **OK, since plot gives no evidence that it's not.**

25-17

Test of Hypothesis: Right Tail

## One-sided Alternative Right Tail

**$H_a$: $\mu > \mu_0$**

| | |
|---|---|
| Null value ($\mu_0$): | 483 |
| Type of Alternative: | greater than |
| Standard Deviation ($\sigma$): | 100 |
| Sample Size: | 20 |
| $\alpha$: | 0.05 |

**3. SOLVE: (cont.) Find Test Statistic & *P*-value.**

*P*-value = 0.2358

**Sampling Distribution of $\bar{x}$**

$\mu = 483$

$\frac{\sigma}{\sqrt{n}} = \frac{100}{\sqrt{20}} = 22.36$

**Test Statistic**

$z = \frac{499.10 - 483.00}{100/\sqrt{20}} = 0.72$

**P-value**

$P(z \geq 0.72) = 1 - P(z < 0.72)$
$= 1 - .7642 = 0.2358$

**All District's SAT Scores**

**Sampling Distribution of $\bar{x}$ under $H_0$**

(n = 20)

$\mu_0 = 483$
$\sigma = 100$

$H_0$: $\mu = 483$
$H_a$: $\mu > 483$

P-value = 0.2358

0 200 400 600 800 1000

$\bar{x} = 499.10$
$\mu = 483.00$

25-18

Test of Hypothesis: Right Tail

## One-sided Alternative Right Tail

**$H_a$: $\mu > \mu_0$**

| | |
|---|---|
| Null value ($\mu_0$): | 483 |
| Type of Alternative: | greater than |
| Standard Deviation ($\sigma$): | 100 |
| Sample Size: | 20 |
| $\alpha$: | 0.05 |

**4. CONCLUDE: Draw conclusions in context.**

*P*-value = 0.2358 > 0.05 = level of significance

Do not reject $H_0$. The observed effect is not statistically significant.

**Conclusion in Context: We have insufficient evidence to conclude that the training raised the mean above the district mean of 483 at $\alpha = 0.05$.**

**The Null Hypothesis**

$H_0$: $\mu = 483$

**The Alternative Hypothesis**

$H_a$: $\mu > 483$

**All District's SAT Scores**

$H_a$: $\mu > 483$

P-value = 0.2358

0 200 400 600 800 1000

$\bar{x} = 499.10$
$\mu = 483.00$

25-19

Test of Hypothesis: Both Tails

## Two-sided Alternative: Both Tails $H_a$: $\mu \neq \mu_0$

| | |
|---|---|
| Null value ($\mu_0$): | 128 |
| Type of Alternative: | not equal |
| Standard Deviation ($\sigma$): | 15 |
| Sample Size: | 72 (large) |
| $\alpha$: | 0.05 |

**I. STATE the problem; identify essential information.**

The National Center for Health Statistics reports that the mean systolic blood pressure for males, aged 25 to 44, is 128 with a standard deviation of 15. The medical director of a large company looked at medical records of 72 randomly selected executives to see if the mean systolic blood pressure of executives differed from that of the general population. Use significance level of 0.05 and assume that executives have the same standard deviation ($\sigma = 15$) as the general population.

25-20

Test of Hypothesis: Both Tails

## Two-sided Alternative: Both Tails $H_a$: $\mu \neq \mu_0$

| | |
|---|---|
| Null value ($\mu_0$): | 128 |
| Type of Alternative: | not equal |
| Standard Deviation ($\sigma$): | 15 |
| Sample Size: | 72 (large) |
| $\alpha$: | 0.05 |

**2. PLAN:**

**Decide to perform test on $\mu$;**

**Determine $H_0$, $H_a$; select $\alpha$**

**The Null Hypothesis**

$H_0$: $\mu = 128$

$\mu$ = mean systolic blood pressure for executives

**The Alternative Hypothesis**

$H_a$: $\mu \neq 128$

$\alpha = 0.05$

25-21

Test of Hypothesis: Both Tails

| Null value ($\mu_0$): | 128 |
| --- | --- |
| Type of Alternative: | not equal |
| Standard Deviation ($\sigma$): | 15 |
| Sample Size: | 72 (large) |
| $\alpha$: | 0.05 |

## Two-sided Alternative: Both Tails  $H_a$: $\mu \neq \mu_0$

**3. SOLVE: Collect appropriate data (SRS).** 120, 131, . . .

**Plot data; compute $\bar{x}$ as an estimate of $\mu$.**

$\bar{x} = 126.07$

**Check assumptions.** **Ok to proceed.**

SRS? yes  $\sigma$ known? yes

Normally Distributed? n = 72 is large enough to apply CLT

25-22

Test of Hypothesis: Both Tails

| Null value ($\mu_0$): | 128 |
| --- | --- |
| Type of Alternative: | not equal |
| Standard Deviation ($\sigma$): | 15 |
| Sample Size: | 72 (large) |
| $\alpha$: | 0.05 |

## Two-sided Alternative: $H_a$: $\mu \neq \mu_0$

**3. SOLVE: (cont.) Compute test statistic & *P*-value**

P-value = Probability of getting a sample mean as far or farther from 128 as 126.07 if $\mu = 128$.

**Sampling Distribution of $\bar{x}$**

$\mu = 128$

$$\frac{\sigma}{\sqrt{n}} = \frac{15}{\sqrt{72}} = 1.768$$

**Test Statistic**

$$z = \frac{126.07 - 128}{15/\sqrt{72}} = -1.09$$

**Tail Probability**

$P(z \leq -1.09) = 0.1379$

Warning: 0.1379 is not P-value

**Systolic Blood Pressure for Men Age 25 to 44**

**Sampling Distribution of $\bar{x}$ under $H_0$**

**(n = 72)**

$\mu_0 = 128$
$\sigma = 15$

$H_0$: $\mu = 128$
$H_a$: $\mu \neq 128$

0.1379

80 100 120 140 160

$\bar{x} = 126.07$  $\mu = 128.0$

25-23

Test of Hypothesis: Both Tails

| Null value ($\mu_0$): | 128 |
| --- | --- |
| Type of Alternative: | not equal |
| Standard Deviation ($\sigma$): | 15 |
| Sample Size: | 72 (large) |
| $\alpha$: | 0.05 |

## Two-sided Alternative: $H_a$: $\mu \neq \mu_0$

**3. SOLVE: (cont.) Compute test statistic & *P*-value**

$P(\bar{x} \leq 126.07) = P(z \leq -1.09) = 0.1379$

**Need for doubling the tail area to get *P*-value**

1. Under $H_a$: No prior expectation about which tail the statistic ($\bar{x}$) will fall into.
2. In practice, the statistic falls on one side or the other of $\mu_0$; in this example, $\bar{x} = 126.07$ fell to the left of $\mu_0 = 128$.
3. The value $\bar{x} = 129.93$ is just as far from $\mu_0 = 128$ as $\bar{x} = 126.07$. (Symmetry)
4. $\bar{x}$ values above 129.93 are just as unlikely as $\bar{x}$ values below 126.07.

*P*-value = area below 126.07
+ area above 129.93
= 2 * (area below 126.07)
= 2[0.1379]
= 0.2758

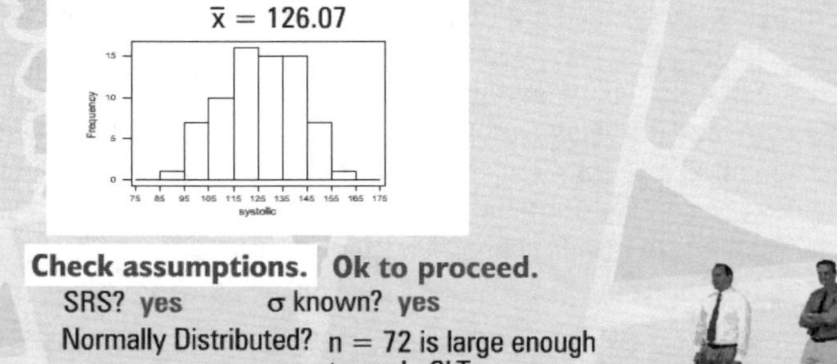


25-24

Test of Hypothesis: Both Tails

| Null value ($\mu_0$): | 128 |
| --- | --- |
| Type of Alternative: | not equal |
| Standard Deviation ($\sigma$): | 15 |
| Sample Size: | 72 (large) |
| $\alpha$: | 0.05 |

## Two-sided Alternative: $H_a$: $\mu \neq \mu_0$

**4. CONCLUDE: Draw conclusions in context.**

*P*-value = 0.2758 > 0.05 = $\alpha$

Do not reject $H_0$. Not statistically significant.

**Conclusion in Context: Data show no statistical evidence that the mean systolic blood pressure for the company's executives differs significantly from the general population mean at $\alpha = 0.05$.**

**The Null Hypothesis**

$H_0$: $\mu = 128$

**The Alternative Hypothesis**

$H_a$: $\mu \neq 128$

25-25

## Summary: One- and Two-Sided Tests

Null hypothesis: specifies the claimed parameter value.

Alternative hypothesis: specifies whether the test is one- or two-sided.

*P*-value computation depends on type of alternative.

| | | *P*-value |
|---|---|---|
| $H_0: \mu = \mu_0$ | | |
| $H_a: \mu < \mu_0$ | One-sided (Left tail) | $P(Z \leq z)$ |
| $\mu > \mu_0$ | One-sided (Right tail) | $P(Z \geq z)$ |
| $\mu \neq \mu_0$ | Two-sided | $2 \cdot P(Z \geq \lvert z \rvert)$ |

where $z$ = observed test statistic

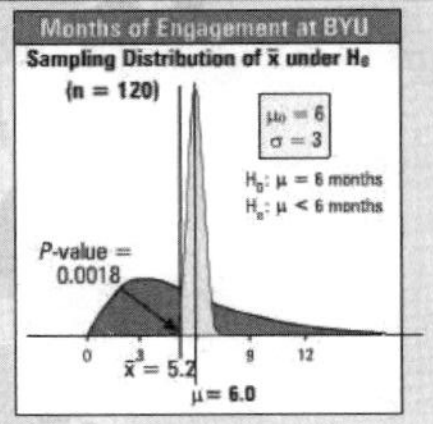

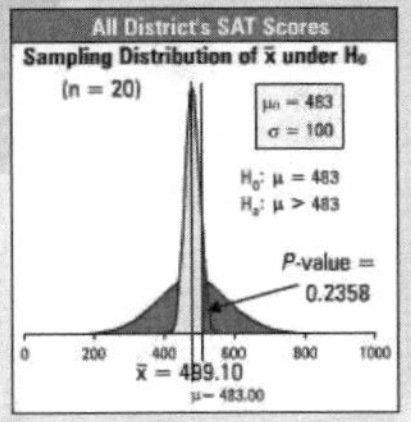

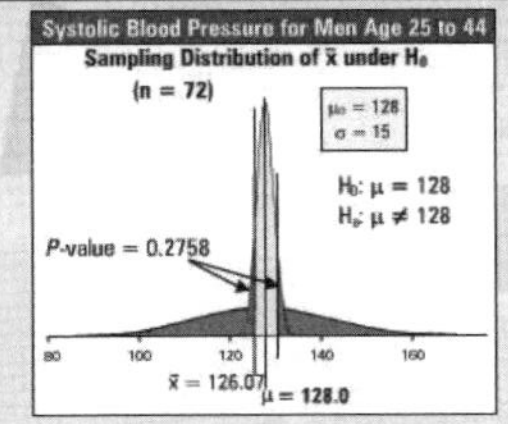

25-26

## Vocabulary

- Claimed Parameter Value
- One-Sided Alternative
  - Left Tail
  - Right Tail
- Observed Effect
- Observed Statistic Value
- *P*-value
- Significance Level
- Statistical Significance
- Test of Significance
- Test Statistic
- Two-Sided Alternative

26-1

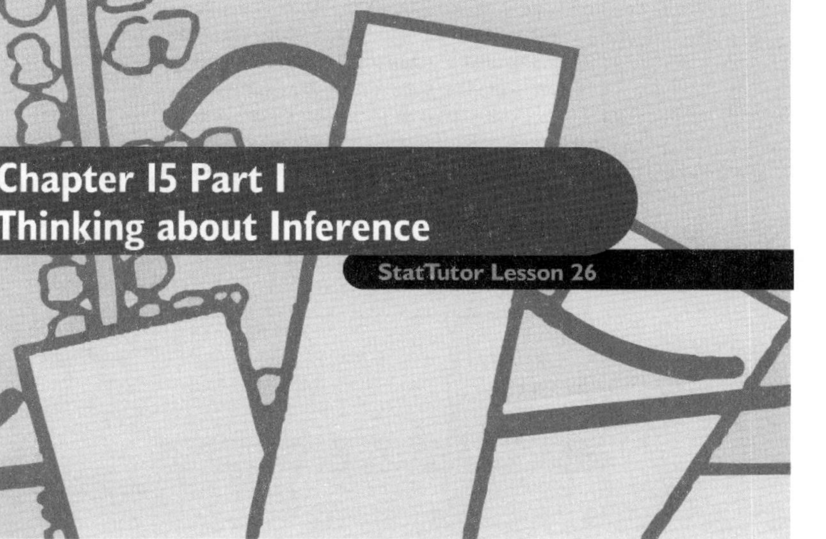


26-2

## Lesson Objectives:

1. Explain how a confidence interval can be used to perform a two-sided test of significance.
2. Explain why "How the data were obtained" matters.
3. Explain why checking shape of sampling distribution is necessary in inference.
4. Describe how level of confidence and sample size influence margin of error.
5. Give limitations of margin of error.

26-3

Test of Significance Using C.I.

## Tests from Confidence Intervals

Basic Practice of Statistics Chapter 15

**This section is NOT found in the textbook--only on StatsPortal at the end of chapter 14 in the eBook.**

26-4

Test of Significance Using C.I.

## A Problem

Eggs are sorted so that large eggs have a mean weight of 50 grams with a standard deviation of 2 grams ($\sigma = 2$). (Weights of eggs are known to be normally distributed.) Quality control inspectors frequently sample eggs to make sure that the average weight of large eggs is 50 grams. One random sample of 12 eggs ($n = 12$) had a sample mean of 48.65 grams ($\bar{x} = 48.65$). Two quality control inspectors are now going to use their own method of determining whether the mean weight is significantly different from 50.

26-5

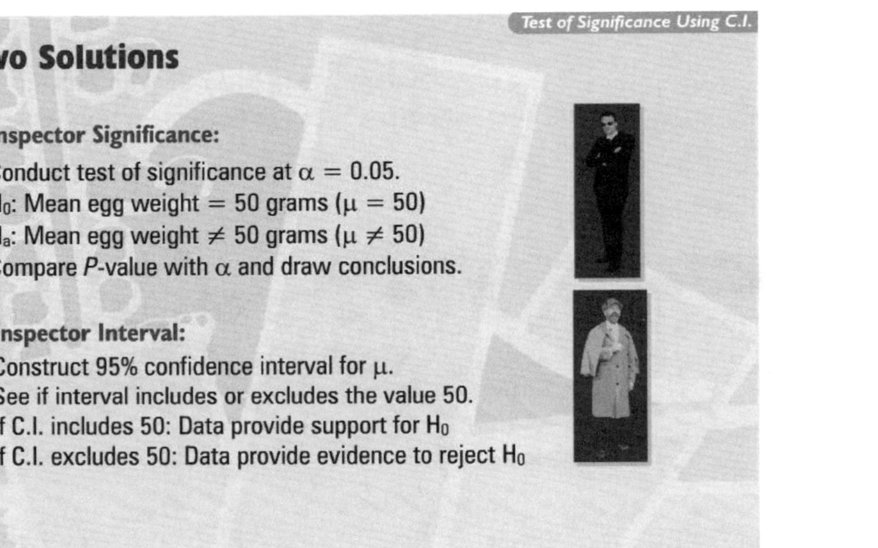

Test of Significance Using C.I.

## Two Solutions

1. **Inspector Significance:**
   Conduct test of significance at $\alpha = 0.05$.
   $H_0$: Mean egg weight = 50 grams ($\mu = 50$)
   $H_a$: Mean egg weight ≠ 50 grams ($\mu \neq 50$)
   Compare *P*-value with $\alpha$ and draw conclusions.

2. **Inspector Interval:**
   Construct 95% confidence interval for $\mu$.
   See if interval includes or excludes the value 50.
   If C.I. includes 50: Data provide support for $H_0$
   If C.I. excludes 50: Data provide evidence to reject $H_0$

26-6

Test of Significance Using C.I.

## Test of Significance

| Test of Significance | Given: |
|---|---|
| $H_0: \mu = 50$ <br> $H_a: \mu \neq 50$ <br> $\alpha = 0.05$ | $n = 12$ <br> $\bar{x} = 48.65$ <br> $\sigma = 2$ |

$$Z_{cal} = \frac{\bar{x} - \mu}{\sigma/\sqrt{n}} = \frac{48.65 - 50}{2/\sqrt{12}} = -2.34$$

$$P = 2(0.0096) = 0.0192 < 0.0500 = \alpha$$

**Conclusion:**

Reject the null hypothesis. The mean weight of all eggs is significantly different from 50 grams.

Dotplot for weight

Table A Standard Normal Probabilities

| z | .03 | .04 |
|---|---|---|
| -2.6 | .0043 | .0041 |
| -2.5 | .0057 | .0055 |
| -2.4 | .0075 | .0073 |
| -2.3 | .0099 | .0096 |
| -2.2 | .0129 | .0125 |
| -2.1 | .0166 | .0162 |
| -2.0 | .0212 | .0207 |

26-7

Test of Significance Using C.I.

## Confidence Interval

| 95% Confidence Interval: | Given: |
|---|---|
| $\bar{x} \pm z^* \frac{\sigma}{\sqrt{n}}$ <br> $48.65 \pm 1.96 \frac{2}{\sqrt{12}}$ <br> $48.65 \pm 1.13$ <br> (47.52, 49.78) | $n = 12$ <br> $\bar{x} = 48.65$ <br> $\sigma = 2$ <br> $z^* = 1.96$ |

Dotplot for weight

45.5 46.5 47.5 48.5 49.5 50.5 51.5 52.5

47.52 48.65 49.78 50.0

**Conclusion:**

The mean weight of all eggs is between 47.52 and 49.78 grams with 95% confidence. Interval excludes 50 grams. Reject $H_0$; the mean weight is not equal to 50 grams.

26-8

Test of Significance Using C.I.

## Confidence Interval vs. Test of Significance

**Conclusion**

A $(1 - \alpha)\cdot 100\%$ confidence interval can be used to perform a two-sided test of significance with the level of significance = $\alpha$.

If C. I. does not contain $\mu_0$ ⇨ test is statistically significant.
If C. I. contains $\mu_0$ ⇨ test is not statistically significant.

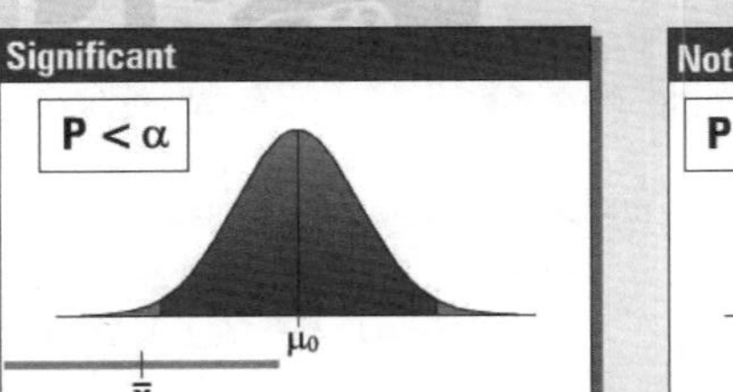

26-9



## Confidence Interval vs. Test of Significance

Drag black bar representing a confidence interval.

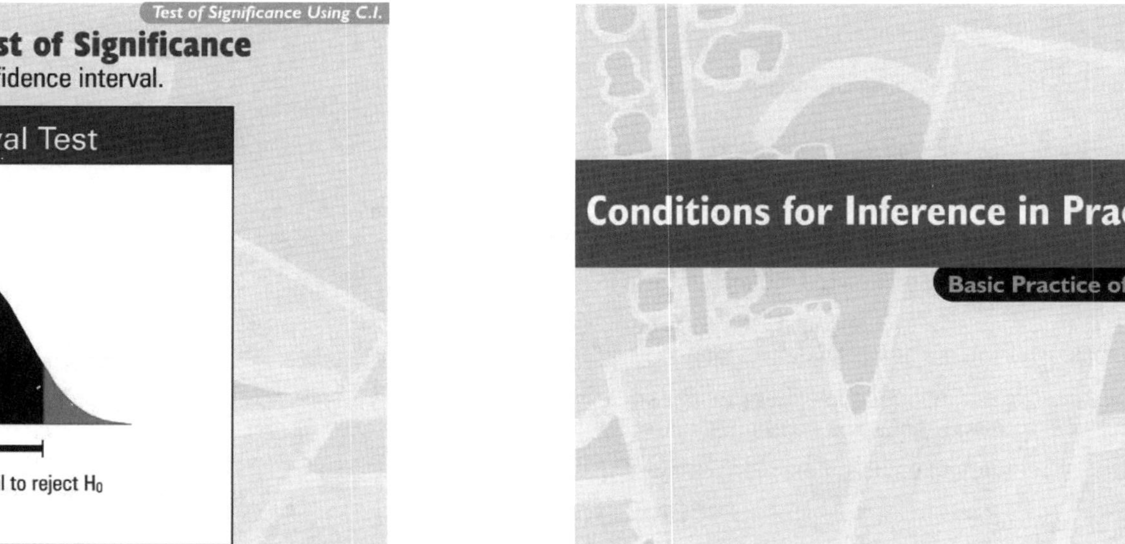


26-10



## Conditions for Inference in Practice

Basic Practice of Statistics Chapter 15

26-11



## Need to Check Conditions

**Statistical Inference depends on:**

1. Properly collected data
   --Experiments: Check random allocation of individuals to treatments
   --Sample Surveys: Check random sampling of individuals
2. Laws of probability and chance
   --Check shape of sampling distribution

26-12



## Where Did the Data Come from?

**Most important inference requirement:**

Data collected using a process to which laws of probability apply.

26-13



## Example: Call-In Opinion Poll

A question for a call-in opinion poll during the nightly news concerns a proposed gun-control ordinance. Of the 2,372 calls received, 1,921 oppose the new law (81%). The station, following procedures from standard statistical practice, makes a confidence statement: "We can be 95% confident that the proportion of all viewers who oppose the law is 81% plus or minus 1.6%."

**Is the station's conclusion justified?**
**No, sample was not random, but voluntary response so 81% is biased.**

**Reporting a "margin of error" is inappropriate; station should only report 81% and warn listeners of bias.**

*Data did not come from a process to which the laws of probability apply!!*

26-14



## Where Did the Data Come from?

**Without randomization/random sampling:**

1. Laws of probability cannot correctly be applied.
2. Confidence level may be smaller (or larger) than stated.
3. P-value may be larger (or smaller) than computed.

**If statistical inference is done without randomization/random sampling:**

1. Apply statistical procedures cautiously, knowing that good statistics cannot overcome bad data.
2. Ask whether conclusion can legitimately be based on data.
3. Consult subject-matter experts.

26-15



## What Is the Shape of the Sampling Distribution?

**Inference on Means Requires:**

--Normal shape of population **OR**

--Large sample size to apply Central Limit Theorem

**Sample mean not resistant to outliers**
**--always plot data when n small**
**--check for outliers or strong skewness**

**All Inferential Procedures Require:**

A certain shape of either population or sampling distribution of statistic

26-16

## Summary

1. How the data are collected matters.
2. When performing statistical inference, your data must come from a random sample or a randomized experiment.
3. Confidence intervals and tests of significance cannot remedy flaws in data collection.
4. If your data are not properly collected, your conclusions may not be valid.
5. For confidence levels and *P*-values to be correct, the distributional requirement of your inferential procedure must be met.

**Most important condition: properly collected data**

26-17

26-18

## Review

**Formula for a Confidence Interval for Mean**

$$\bar{x} \pm z^* \cdot \frac{\sigma}{\sqrt{n}}$$

**Estimate of $\mu$ from SRS** — Margin of Error

Properties of this formula are shared with all confidence intervals, even though formula uses $z^*$ and requires $\sigma$ known.

26-19

## How Do We Get a Small Margin of Error?

$$ME = z^* \cdot \frac{\sigma}{\sqrt{n}}$$

**Some questions to consider:**

- How does decreasing level of confidence affect Margin of Error?
- How does increasing sample size affect Margin of Error?
- How does standard deviation affect Margin of Error?

26-20

*Factors Affecting Margin of Error*

**Desired Properties of Confidence Interval**

- High confidence
- Small margin of error

$$\text{Margin of Error} = z^* \cdot \frac{\sigma}{\sqrt{n}}$$

When:
- Level of confidence increases ($z^*$ increases): ME increases
- Sample size n increases: ME decreases
- Population standard deviation is large: ME will be large.

**Researcher selects:**

- Level of Confidence
- Sample size

**Researcher cannot control:**

- Population standard deviation, $\sigma$

26-21

*Factors Affecting Margin of Error*

## Effects of n and Confidence Level on Width of C.I.

$$\bar{x} \pm z^* \cdot \frac{s}{\sqrt{n}}$$

| ME: | Assume: | Change: | | C.I. Width |
|---|---|---|---|---|
| $z^* \cdot \frac{s}{\sqrt{n}}$ | The higher the level of confidence, the wider the confidence interval. | Level of confidence | $z^*$ | |
| | | 80% | 1.282 | |
| | | 90% | 1.645 | |
| | | 95% | 1.960 | |
| | | 98% | 2.326 | |
| | | 99% | 2.576 | |
| | The larger the sample size, the narrower the confidence interval. | Sample Size | $1/\sqrt{n}$ | |
| | | 10 | .32 | |
| | | 20 | .22 | |
| | | 30 | .18 | |
| | | 40 | .16 | |
| | | 50 | .14 | |

26-22

*Factors Affecting Margin of Error*

## Margin of Error Calculator

Margin of Error

Clear All

ME= 00000 $z^*$ $\frac{0\ (\sigma)}{\sqrt{0\ (n)}}$ = 00000

| | | | | | | | |
|---|---|---|---|---|---|---|---|
| Level of Confidence | 80% | 90% | 95% | 96% | 98% | 99% | 99.9% |
| Population Standard Deviation | 5 | 10 | 15 | 20 | 25 | 30 | 35 |
| Sample Size | 10 | 20 | 40 | 80 | 100 | 1000 | 2000 |

26-23

*Summary*

## How Do We Get a Small Margin of Error?

$$ME = z^* \cdot \frac{\sigma}{\sqrt{n}}$$

**Answers to questions we considered:**

- How does decreasing level of confidence affect Margin of Error?
  Decreasing level of confidence decreases Margin of Error.
- How does increasing sample size affect Margin of Error?
  Increasing sample size decreases Margin of Error.
- How does standard deviation affect Margin of Error?
  The smaller the standard deviation, the smaller the Margin of Error.

26-24

*Confidence Interval Cautions*

## Limitations of Margin of Error

**Margin of Error**

- Accounts only for random sampling error (i.e., variation from random sampling).
- Does not account for measurement errors, undercoverage or nonresponse.

**Example:**

Americans agree with Phillip Morris: Smoking is harmful

"For results based on this sample, one can say with 95 percent confidence that the maximum error attributable to sampling and other random effects is plus or minus 3 percentage points. In addition to sampling error, question wording and practical difficulties in conducting surveys can introduce error or bias into the findings of public opinion polls."

http://www.gallup.com/poll/releases/pr991014.asp

## Limitations of Margin of Error

**Margin of Error**

- Accounts only for random sampling error (i.e., variation from random sampling).
- Does not account for measurement errors, undercoverage or nonresponse.

--These practical difficulties can be more serious than random sampling error.

**Always consider practical difficulties before trusting results of a survey.**

Mean is fixed
want to be sure to contain $\mu$
bigger margin, more confidence
have to lose confidence to be more useful. (more accurate)
(smaller confidence, smaller margin)

Four steps Conf I
1. Specify parameter of interest → state
2 choose procedure, level of confidence → Plan
3 Carry out procedure → solve
4. Conclude → claim Mean in interval } not probability because not random mean. about Parameter
We are 90% confident the mean lies between ( ) interval



## Vocabulary

**Confidence Interval**
**Estimate of Parameter**
**Level of Confidence**
**Margin of Error**
**Random Samples**
**Randomized Experiment**
**Shape of Population**
**Shape of Sampling Distribution**
**Statistical Inference**



Conditions
1. Data gathered using SRS
2 σ known
3. normality of samp dist of $\bar{x}$?

Check
1. random device? nonresponse?
2. for sure? how?
3. cannot check directly
n large? serious outliers?
sample histogram normalish?

27-1

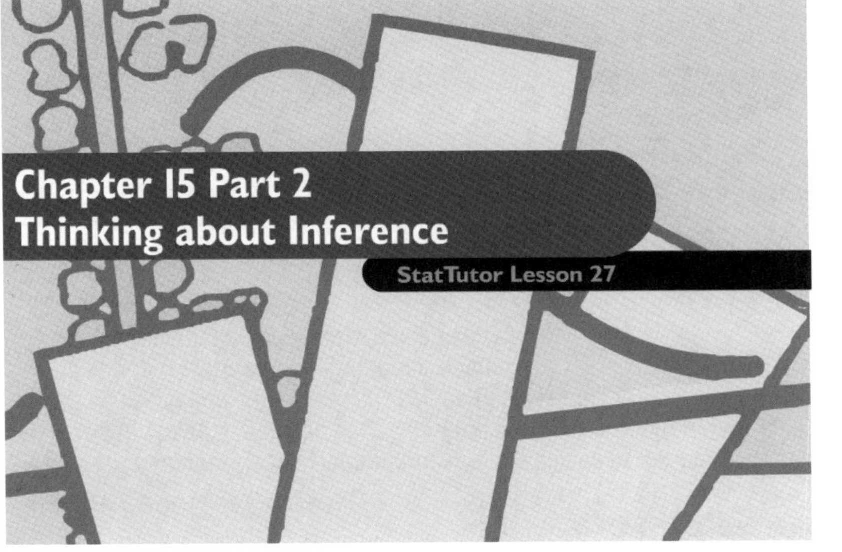


27-2

## Lesson Objectives:

1. Describe how the plausibility of $H_0$ and/or the cost of rejecting $H_0$ influences the choice of $\alpha$. Explain that $\alpha$ is a guide and not a sharp cutoff between "significant" and "not significant".
2. Distinguish between statistical significance and practical significance.
3. Describe how multiple analyses affect the overall significance level and proscribe proper usage of multiple analyses.
4. Compute the sample size necessary to estimate $\mu$ when both the margin of error and confidence level are specified.

27-3

Significance Tests Cautions

## How Significance Tests Behave

Basic Practice of Statistics Chapter 15

27-4

Significance Tests Cautions

**Statistically significant:**
An observed effect that is unlikely to occur simply by chance **IF** the claim about the parameter were true.

**Purpose of test of significance:**
To make a clear statement about strength of evidence against $H_0$ provided by the data.

**Purpose of significance level, $\alpha$:**
To designate how small a P-value is convincing evidence against $H_0$.

- Largest risk of rejecting a correct $H_0$.

**Most current studies report P-values rather than specified $\alpha$.**

ed mice nearly doubled the HNE content in the arterial wall in comparison with the control mice (7.1 ± 1.8% vs. 3.9 ± 1.3%, respectively; *P* = 0.028). Treatment with Zopolrestat resulted in a threefold increase in HNE-stained areas (Figure 5e; 13.1 ± 4.6% vs. 4.4 ± 4.6%; *P* = 0.002).
HNE can function as a cytopathic substance for almost

27-5



## How Small a *P* is Convincing? i.e., Choosing $\alpha$

**How plausible is $H_0$?**

If $H_0$ is widely held belief, need strong evidence to reject $H_0$:

$\longrightarrow$ need small $\alpha$ (and smaller ***P***)

**Example:** Herbs have recently received attention as alternatives to prescription drugs. Some manufacturers hail St. John's Wort, an antidepressant herb, as a safe alternative to Prozac. Sales of St. John's Wort continue to increase, despite doctors' skepticism of its effectiveness. If a clinical trial tested the effectiveness of St. John's Wort, what $\alpha$ level might a skeptical doctor set? The general public?

27-6



## How Small a *P* is Convincing? i.e., Choosing $\alpha$

**What are the consequences of rejecting a correct $H_0$?**

If rejecting a correct $H_0$ has serious consequences, we need really strong evidence against $H_0$; use small $\alpha$ like 0.01.

If failing to reject a false $H_0$ has serious consequences, use a large $\alpha$ like point 0.10 or 0.15 to avoid making this error.

Possible errors:

1. Reject $H_0$ when shouldn't
2. Fail to reject $H_0$ when should reject $H_0$

27-7



## Example: Pool Chlorine

The Utah County Health Department sets guidelines for proper levels of chlorine in public pools. Too much chlorine irritates the skin, but too little chlorine won't kill the germs in the pool, leading to a greater risk of waterborne diseases. The Utah County recommended level is one part per million.

Recommended level: $\mu = 1$ ppm

27-8



## Example: Pool Chlorine

| **Hypotheses:** | **Policy:** |
|---|---|
| $H_0$: $\mu = 1$ppm | Fail to Reject $H_0 \Rightarrow$ don't add chlorine |
| $H_a$: $\mu < 1$ppm | Reject $H_0 \Rightarrow$ add chlorine |
| $\alpha = ?$ | |

**Implications:**

"Small" $\alpha$ (i.e. $\alpha \le 0.01$):

- Rarely reject $H_0$ (rarely add chlorine).
- Lower risk of skin irritation; increased risk of disease.

"Large" $\alpha$ (i.e., $0.05 \le \alpha \le 0.10$):

- Reject $H_0$ more often (add chlorine more often)
- Greater risk of skin irritation; less risk of disease.

**What $\alpha$ would you choose?**

27-9

Choosing α

## Choosing α

Standard α levels: 0.10, 0.05, 0.01.

(α = 0.05 accepted in discrimination cases in court.)

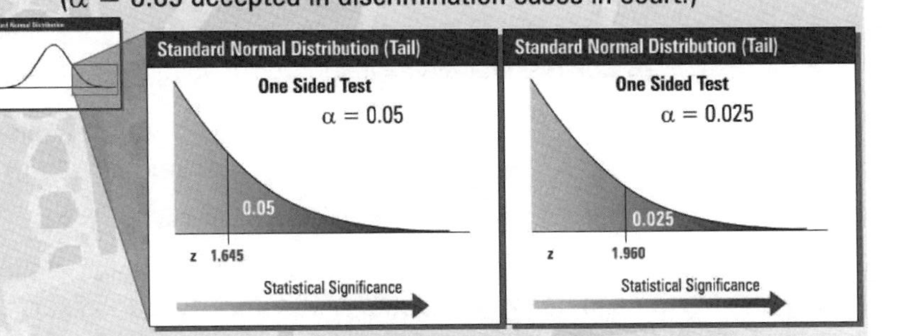


- As *P*-value decreases ⇨ evidence against $H_0$ increases.
- No sharp border between "significant" and "not significant"
- Use α as a guide, not as a sharp cutoff between "significant" and "not significant."

27-10

Significance Tests Cautions

## Significance Depends on Alternative Hypothesis

***P*-value for one-sided test:**

P-value

***P*-value for two-sided test:**

P-value

P-value for a two-sided test = 2 times P-value for a one-sided test.

⟶ Two-sided test requires stronger evidence than one-sided test.

27-11

Significance Tests Cautions

## Significance Depends on Sample Size

**Test Statistic:** $$z = \frac{\overline{x} - \mu_0}{\sigma / \sqrt{n}} = \sqrt{n}\,\frac{\overline{x} - \mu_0}{\sigma}$$

**Significance depends on:**

- Size of the observed effect (numerator of test statistic): $\overline{x} - \mu_0$

  $\overline{x} - \mu_0$: measures how far the sample mean deviates from the hypothesized mean value $\mu_0$

  **The "larger" the observed effect, the smaller the *P*-value**

- Size of the sample: $\sqrt{n}$

  $\sigma / \sqrt{n}$ : measures how much random variation we expect

  **The larger the sample size, the smaller the *P*-value**

  ⟶ Sample size may be too small to detect significance.

  ⟶ Sample size may be so large results are always significant.

27-12

Statistical vs. Practical Significance

**When sample size is large, check for practical significance:**

- Results are declared *statistically significant* when *P*-value ≤ α.
- Results are declared *practically significant* when the observed effect (numerator of test statistic) is large enough to matter.

**Practical significance is not the same as statistical significance.**

27-13

Statistical vs. Practical Significance

**Example:**

The Health Examination Survey used a nation-wide probability sample of children age 6 to 11 to study the relationship between test scores and the type of community in which the parents lived. The sample included 2500 big-city children and 2500 rural children. Big-city children averaged 26 points on the test, but rural children averaged only 25 points. The one-point difference in means produced a P-value of 0.0004.

**Are these results statistically significant?**
**YES, because *P*-value $< \alpha$**
**Are these results practically significant?**
**Discussion follows**

27-14

Practical Significance

## The result is statistically significant, but is it important?

**Analysis**

Total score possible = 80 points    Two points per question
Average test scores: Big city ($\bar{x} = 26$), Rural ($\bar{x} = 25$)
Difference: One point (a partial understanding of one question).
**Conclusion:** One point is NOT large enough to matter; result is NOT practically significant!

**Facts**

Large samples ⇨ Unimportant differences can be statistically significant.
Small samples ⇨ Important difference may not be statistically significant.

**Recommendations**

Look for evidence of effect in plots of data.
Report the *P*-value and give a confidence interval.
Always ask whether a statistically significant effect is "large enough to matter."

27-15

Practical Significance

## Summary of Practical Significance

- Declare results statistically significant when *P*-value $\leq \alpha$.
- Consider results practically significant when observed effect is large enough to matter and has practical value.
  **Recall:** Observed effect = numerator of test statistic
- Check for practical significance only ***after*** observing statistical significance.
- Especially check for practical significance when sample sizes are very large.
- **Recommended:** Give a confidence interval of the parameter that you are testing.

27-16

Multiple Analyses

## Beware of Multiple Analyses

**What do we mean by "multiple analyses"?**

Performing more than one test of significance on one set of data.

- Performing multiple analyses increases the risk of rejecting $H_0$ when $H_0$ is correct for at least one of the many tests.
- If you perform twenty tests at $\alpha = 0.05$, the probability of rejecting at least one correct $H_0$ due to chance is 0.64.

27-17

Multiple Analyses

## Beware of Multiple Analyses

**Example I: Study comparing farmers' marriages with their sons'**

- Marriage counselor performed twenty-two tests at $\alpha = 0.05$. Two were statistically significant.
- $20 \cdot (0.05) = 1.1 \Rightarrow$ expect one or two significant due to chance
- Two significant tests likely due to chance

27-18

Multiple Analyses

## Beware of Multiple Analyses

**Example 2: 2004 Utah Colleges Exit Poll**

This poll contains almost 200 questions. When looking for association between the responses for any two questions, thousands of tests are possible. If we use $\alpha = 0.05$, we expect 5% of all the tests to be statistically significant due to chance alone when $H_0$ is correct.

**Consequence: $\alpha$ is much greater than 0.05 for the overall analysis.**

**Solution: Collect new data and retest the hypotheses of the significant tests.**

27-19

Multiple Analyses

## Beware of Multiple Analyses

**Example 2 (cont.):** One of the significance tests on the 1988 exit poll data showed a significant association between time of day and voting patterns. Democrats tended to vote earlier in the day than Republicans.

The same hypothesis was investigated in the exit polls for 1990 and 1992 election years. For these two years, the association was not significant.

Subsequent tests on new data did not yield the same results.

**The significance result on the 1988 exit poll data was most likely due to chance.**

27-20

Multiple Analyses

## Confidence Interval View of Multiple Analyses

A significance level of $\alpha = 0.05$ means that, out of many tests, you expect to find 5% statistically significant due to chance alone.

The same principle applies to confidence intervals.

Beware multiple analyses: Performing many tests on one set of data **INFLATES** the overall level of significance.

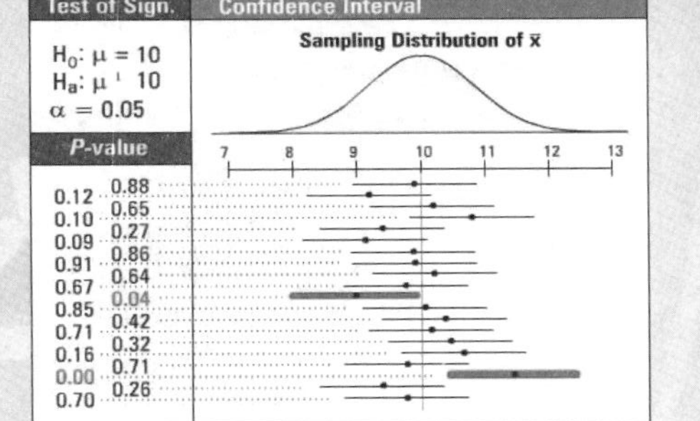

27-21

Multiple Analyses

## How to Properly Use Multiple Analyses

**Questionable Procedure (AKA "Data Snooping")**

Using multiple analyses to find statistical significance and then publishing the results. ("Torturing the data until they confess.")

**Acceptable Procedure for Multiple Analyses**

1. Use multiple analyses to find statistical significance. Use the significant results to define new hypotheses.
2. Collect new data using the same survey instrument / same treatments to test these new hypotheses.
3. Perform tests of significance on the new hypotheses using the new data to verify previous statistical significance.

27-22

## Summary

1. Selection of $\alpha$ depends on
   - the plausibility of $H_0$.
   - consequences of rejecting a correct $H_0$.
   - consequences of failing to reject an incorrect $H_0$.
2. Significance depends on
   - the alternative hypothesis $H_a$.
   - the sample size.
3. Sample size may be so large significant results are not practically significant.
4. Sample size may be too small to detect real population effects.
5. Beware multiple analyses: some significant results may be due to chance and not real population effects.

27-23

## Planning Studies: Sample Size for Confidence Intervals

Basic Practice of Statistics Chapter 15

27-24

## Review The Formula for a Confidence Interval for Mean

$$\bar{x} \pm z^* \cdot \frac{\sigma}{\sqrt{n}}$$

Estimate of $\mu$ from SRS

Margin of Error

Population standard deviation

Sample size

27-25



**Can we find a sample size to give us desired margin of error?**

$$\textbf{Margin of Error} = z^* \cdot \frac{\sigma}{\sqrt{n}}$$

Yes! We can

- Choose level of confidence.
- Set margin of error as desired.
- Determine $\sigma$.
- Then, find corresponding sample size, n.

27-26



## Solving for n

$$ME = z^* \cdot \frac{\sigma}{\sqrt{n}}$$

Square both sides:

$$(ME)^2 = \frac{(z^* \cdot \sigma)^2}{n}$$

Multiply by n and divide by $(ME)^2$:

$$n = \frac{(z^* \cdot \sigma)^2}{(ME)^2} = \left(\frac{z^* \cdot \sigma}{ME}\right)^2$$

1. Set desired value for margin of error (ME).
2. Choose level of confidence and input corresponding $z^*$.
3. Input a value of population standard deviation, $\sigma$.
4. Compute n from the formula.

27-27



## Scale Accuracy Example

| | |
|---|---|
| Margin of Error: | .0001 |
| Standard Deviation: | .0002 |
| Confidence Level: | 98% |

To assess the accuracy of a laboratory scale, we weigh a standard weight (known to weigh 10 grams) repeatedly and compute the mean. The scale readings are normally distributed with unknown mean (which should be 10 grams if the scale is accurate). The standard deviation of the scale readings is .0002 grams. How many measurements must we take to get a ± 0.0001 margin of error with 98% confidence?

27-28



## Scale Accuracy Example

**Find sample size, n**

**Use n = 22**

| | |
|---|---|
| Margin of Error: | **.0001** |
| Standard Deviation: | **.0002** |
| Confidence Level: | **98%** |

$$n = 21.641$$

Table C t distribution critical values

| | Confidence level *C* | | | | | | | | | | | |
|---|---|---|---|---|---|---|---|---|---|---|---|---|
| | 50% | 60% | 70% | 80% | 90% | 95% | 96% | 98% | 99% | 99.5% | 99.8% | 99.9% |
| $z^*$ | 0.674 | 0.841 | 1.036 | 1.282 | 1.645 | 1.960 | 2.054 | 2.326 | 2.576 | 2.807 | 3.091 | 3.291 |

27-29

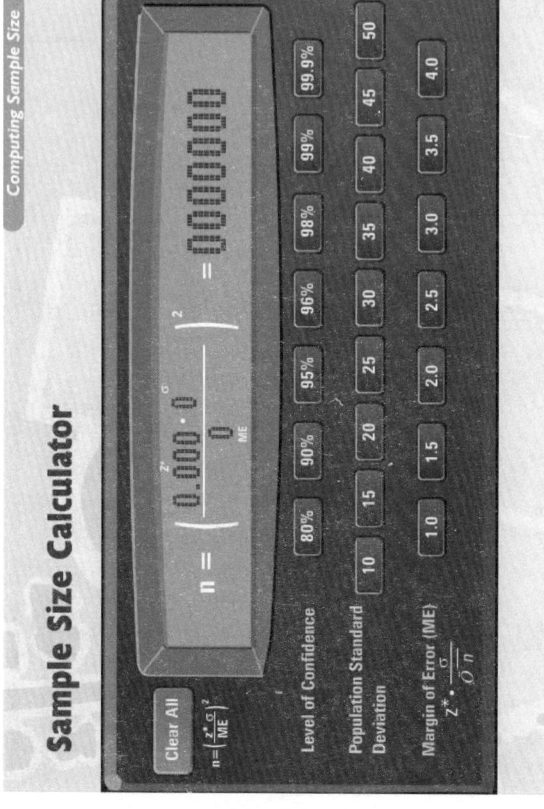

Computing Sample Size
Sample Size Calculator
Clear All
$n = \left(\frac{z^* \cdot \sigma}{ME}\right)^2$
n = ( 0.000 · 0 / 0 )² = 0.000000
Level of Confidence
80% 90% 95% 96% 98% 99% 99.9%
Population Standard Deviation
10 15 20 25 30 35 40 45 50
Margin of Error (ME) $z^* \cdot \frac{\sigma}{\sqrt{n}}$
1.0 1.5 2.0 2.5 3.0 3.5 4.0


27-30

Vocabulary
Level of Confidence
Level of Significance
Margin of Error
Multiple analyses
Observed Effect
Practical Significance
Sample Size
Statistical Significance
z*

28-1

# Chapter 15 Part 3
# Thinking about Inference

StatTutor Lesson 28

28-2

## Objectives

1. Connect significance tests with discovering truth.
2. Discuss potential errors in any decision process.
3. Describe type I and type II errors in problem context.
4. Connect $\alpha$ and $\beta$ with probabilities of type I and type II errors.
5. Discuss the relationship between $\alpha$, power and sample size.

28-3

Decision Making Significance Tests

## Planning Studies:
## Type I and Type II Errors

Basic Practice of Statistics Chapter 15

28-4

Decision Making Significance Tests

In science, business, and industry, we want to know the truth.
For example:

- Does a newly developed prescription drug work?
- Will a proposed marketing scheme increase drug sales?
- Does drug quality meet manufacturing specifications?

A test of significance can help answer these questions.

Unfortunately, errors are possible in any decision making process.

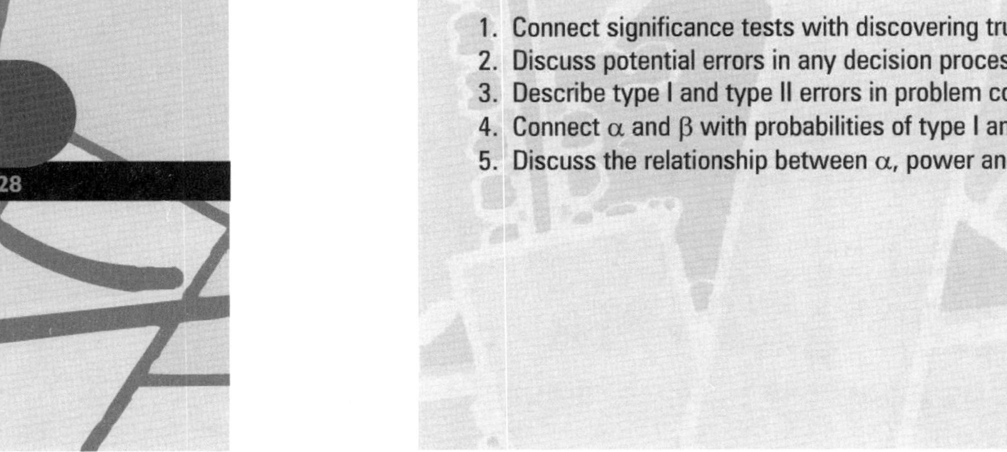

28-5

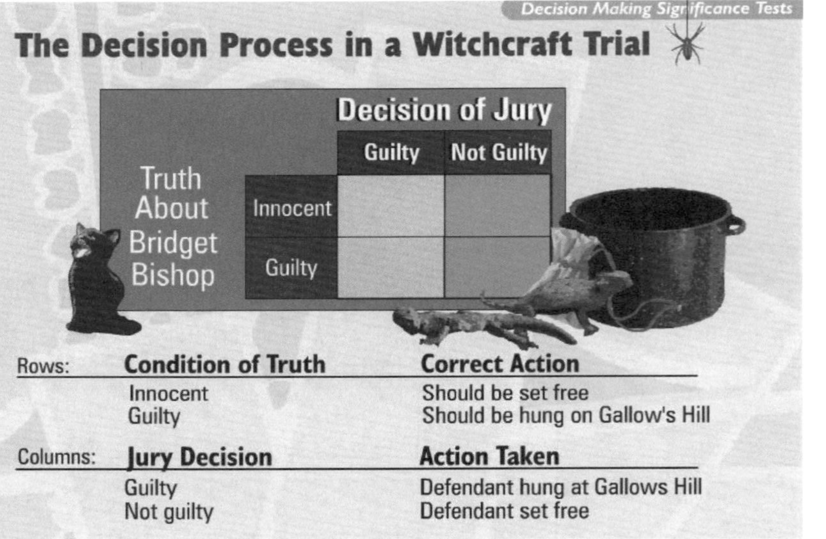


28-6

*Decision Making Significance Tests*

## The Courtroom Decision Process as a Test of Significance

| Truth About Bridget Bishop | Decision of Jury: Guilty (Reject $H_0$) | Decision of Jury: Not Guilty (Don't Reject $H_0$) |
|---|---|---|
| $H_0$: Innocent | | |
| $H_a$: Guilty | | |

The null and alternative hypotheses are:

$H_0$: Bishop is innocent vs. $H_a$: Bishop is guilty

**The jury made a decision about Bridget's guilt or innocence based on evidence.**

**Possible Jury Decisions**

(1) Reject $H_0$: Evidence sufficiently strong to prove guilt beyond reasonable doubt.

(2) Fail to reject $H_0$: Evidence not strong enough to establish guilt.

28-7

*Potential Errors*

## Implications of Decisions

| Truth About Bridget Bishop | Decision of Jury: Guilty (Reject $H_0$) | Decision of Jury: Not Guilty (Don't Reject $H_0$) |
|---|---|---|
| $H_0$: Innocent | Incorrect Decision | Correct Decision |
| $H_a$: Guilty | Correct Decision | Incorrect Decision |

**CONSEQUENCES OF FOUR CELLS:**

1. A guilty person receives "guilty" verdict from jury.
2. An innocent person receives "not guilty" verdict from jury.
3. An innocent person receives "guilty" verdict from jury.
4. A guilty person receives "not guilty" verdict from jury.

28-8

*Type I and Type II Errors*

## Definitions of Type I and Type II Errors

| Truth About Bridget Bishop | Decision of Jury: Guilty (Reject $H_0$) | Decision of Jury: Not Guilty (Don't Reject $H_0$) |
|---|---|---|
| $H_0$: Innocent | Type I Error | Correct Decision |
| $H_a$: Guilty | Correct Decision | Type II Error |

**Type I Error:** Reject $H_0$ when $H_0$ is true

In trial context: Pronounce guilty when defendant is innocent.

**Type II Error:** Fail to reject $H_0$ when $H_a$ is true

In trial context: Pronounce not guilty when defendant is guilty.

Which error is more serious? Current jury system assumes defendant is innocent until evidence proves them guilty. Hence, type I error is viewed as more serious.

28-9



## Type I and Type II Errors in Practice

| Truth About Bridget Bishop | Decision of Jury: Guilty (Reject $H_0$) | Decision of Jury: Not Guilty (Don't Reject $H_0$) |
|---|---|---|
| $H_0$: Innocent | Type I Error | Correct Decision |
| $H_a$: Guilty | Correct Decision | Type II Error |

**WHAT REALLY HAPPENED AT BRIDGET BISHOP'S TRIAL?**

The jury's decision: Guilty

Implies: Correct decision or Type I error

Could a type II error also have been made? No

28-10



## Type I and Type II Errors in Practice

Suppose you have a strep (streptococcus) test at the doctor's office.

The hypotheses are:

$H_0$: You don't have strep vs. $H_a$: You have strep

**Type I Error:** Reject $H_0$ when $H_0$ is true

In context: Test result says you have strep when you don't.

- In other words, test is false positive.
- False positive rate = 2.0% for the Rapid Strep Test

**Consequence:** Doctor prescribes antibiotics when he/she shouldn't.

**Type II Error:** Fail to reject $H_0$ when $H_a$ is true

In context: Test result says you don't have strep when you do.

- In other words, test is false negative.

False negative rate = 30.0% for the Rapid Strep Test

**Consequence:** Doctor doesn't prescribe antibiotics when he/she should.

28-11



## Definitions of Probabilities of Errors

**α (Level of significance):**

$\alpha$ = P(type I error) = P(Reject $H_0$ when $H_0$ is true) — **Sampling distribution determined by $H_0$**

**β:**

$\beta$ = P(type II error) = P(Fail to reject $H_0$ when $H_a$ is true) — **Sampling distribution determined by $H_a$**

**Power:**

Power = P(Reject $H_0$ when $H_a$ is true) $= 1 - \beta$ — **Sampling distribution determined by $H_a$**

28-12



## Relationship between α and Power (Fixed n)

**Consider testing $H_0$: $\mu = 20$ versus $H_a$: $\mu > 20$**

What happens if $\alpha = 0.05$? **Sampling distribution under $H_0$: $\mu = 20$**

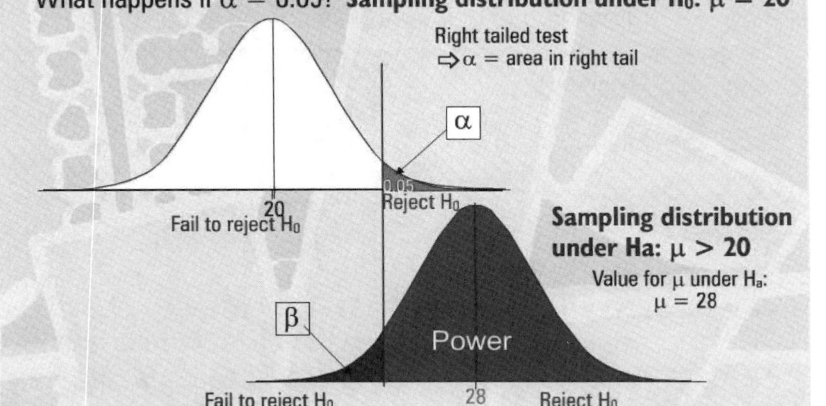

28-13

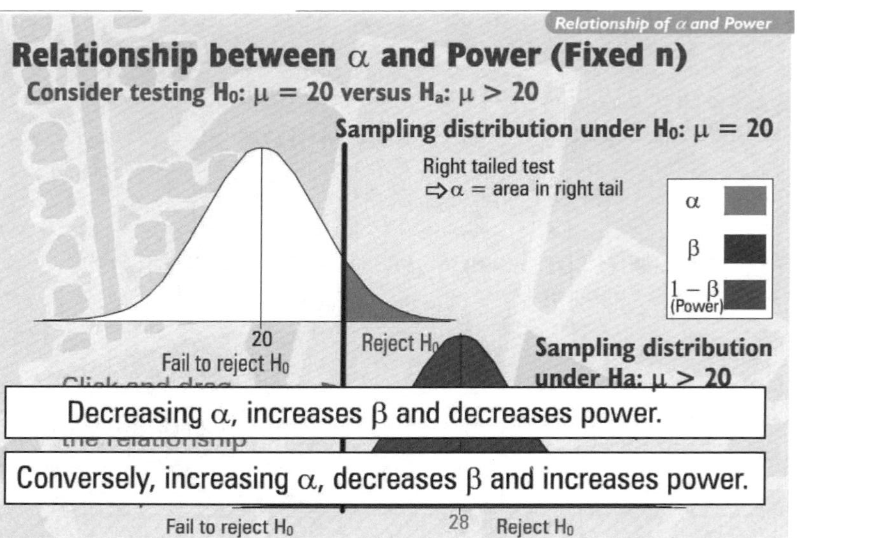


28-14

Relationship of n and β

## Relationship between n and Power (Fixed $\alpha$)

Consider testing $H_0$: $\mu = 20$ versus $H_a$: $\mu > 20$

Let $\alpha = 0.10$

Sampling distribution under $H_0$: $\mu = 20$

What happens if we increase n?

$\alpha$

0.10

20

Fail to reject $H_0$

Reject $H_0$

Sampling distribution under Ha: $\mu > 20$

Increasing n, increases power and decreases $\beta$.

$\beta$

Power

Fail to reject $H_0$ 24 Reject $H_0$

28-15

Relationship of Effect Size and Power

## Relationship between Effect Size & Power (Fixed $\alpha$)

Consider testing $H_0$: $\mu = 20$ versus $H_a$: $\mu > 20$

Let $\alpha = 0.10$

**Effect size:** Size of difference between hypothesized parameter value and closest parameter value we'd like to find significant

-- Equals $\mu_C - \mu_0$

**For a "small" effect size, what happens to power?**

**For a "large" effect size, what happens to power?**

| | Effect size: |
|---|---|
| What is power: if $\mu_C = 23$? | 23 – 20 = 3 |
| if $\mu_C = 24$? | 24 – 20 = 4 |
| if $\mu_T = 26$? | 26 – 20 = 6 |
| if $\mu_C = 28$? | 28 – 20 = 8 |

where $\mu_C$ = closest parameter value of interest

28-16

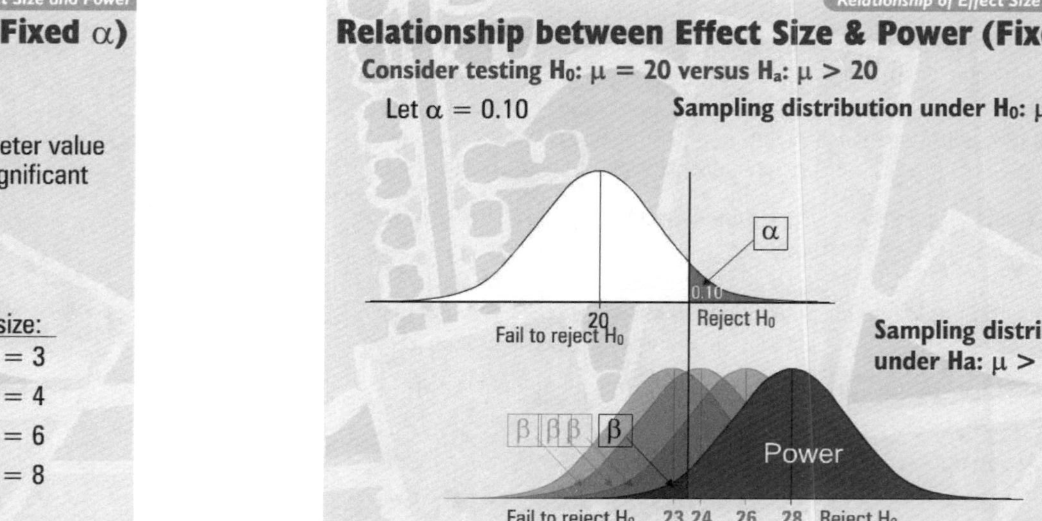

28-17



## Relationship between Power, $\beta$, and Actual $\mu$

Testing: $H_0$: $\mu = 2.00$ vs. $H_a$: $\mu \neq 2.00$

Setting $\alpha = 0.05$ determined the cutoff numbers 1.991 and 2.009.



Drag button on slider

28-18



## Factors influencing:

**How large a sample do I need?**

1. A small level of significance requires a larger sample.
2. Depending on the effect size, higher power requires a larger sample size.
3. Detecting a small effect size requires a larger sample size.
4. A two-sided test requires a larger sample size than a one-sided test.

**When planning a study, try to answer: "How large a sample do I need?"**

28-19

## Summary of Type I and Type II Errors

**Potential errors in a test of significance:**

**Type I Error:** Reject $H_0$ when $H_0$ is true
Believe $\mu \neq \mu_0$ when $\mu = \mu_0$

**Type II Error:** Fail to reject $H_0$ when $H_a$ is true
Fail to reject $\mu = \mu_0$ when $\mu \neq \mu_0$

| Truth About Population Mean | | Decision of Test: Reject $H_0$ Believe $H_a$ | Don't Reject $H_0$ Accept $H_0$ |
|---|---|---|---|
| | $H_0$: $\mu = \mu_0$ | Type I Error | Correct Decision |
| | $H_a$: $\mu \neq \mu_0$ | Correct Decision | Type II Error |

28-20



## Reminder!

**$\alpha$ is the probability of a Type I error.**

**$\beta$ is the probability of a Type II error.**

**Power is the probability of rejecting $H_0$ when it's false**

28-21



## Summary: Relationship between $\alpha$, Power and n

1. **For fixed n:**
   $\alpha$ and $\beta$ are inversely related.
   - **Increasing $\alpha$, increases power.**

   $\alpha$ — $\beta$
   Fixed n

2. **For fixed $\alpha$:**
   $\beta$ and n are inversely related.
   - **Increasing n, increases power.**

   $\beta$ — n
   Fixed $\alpha$

3. **The larger the effect size,**
   the smaller $\beta$ and the larger power.

28-22

## Planning Studies: Part 2
## The Power of a Statistical Test

Basic Practice of Statistics Chapter 15

28-23



## What sample size should we use?

- Sample size may be too small to detect real population effects.
- Consequence: Fail to reject $H_0$ when it is wrong.
- How large should the sample size be to prevent this error?
- With that sample size, what is our confidence in rejecting $H_0$ when it is wrong?

28-24



## What sample size should we use?

**Determining sample size depends on:**

1. Significance level: Risk of getting a significant result when no effect exists in the population (i.e., $H_0$ is correct)
2. Effect size: Size of difference between hypothesized parameter value and closest parameter value we'd like to find significant
3. Power: Confidence in detecting an effect of the size deemed important

**Definition of "Power"**

Probability of rejecting $H_0$ when it is wrong at a chosen significance level $\alpha$ for a specified value of the true parameter.

28-25

## What sample size should we use?

*Sample Size*

**Example**

Significance test on whether participating in a training course before taking SAT raised mean above district mean of 483. $H_0$: $\mu = 483$ versus $H_a$: $\mu > 483$, $\sigma = 100$, n = 20 students and $\alpha = 0.05$.

1. Significance level: 1 in 20 chance of concluding training course raised mean when it really didn't; i.e., $\alpha = 0.05$.
2. Effect size: District officials want to detect differences of 20 points or more; i.e., if the true mean of those taking training course is 503 or higher, officials want to find significance.
3. Power: District officials want to be 90% confident in rejecting $H_0$ when true mean is 503 or higher at $\alpha = 0.05$.

28-26

## What sample size should we use?

*Sample Size*

**Example**

Significance test on whether participating in a training course before taking SAT raised mean above district mean of 483. $H_0$: $\mu = 483$ versus $H_a$: $\mu > 483$, $\sigma = 100$, n = 20 students and $\alpha = 0.05$.

1. Significance level: $\alpha = 0.05$.
2. Effect size: 20 points or more
3. Power: 90%

**What sample size is required to met these criteria?**

Minitab results

```
Testing mean = null (versus > null)
Calculating power for mean = null + difference
Alpha = 0.05  Sigma = 100

             Sample  Target  Actual
Difference     Size   Power   Power
        20      215  0.9000  0.9011
```

28-27

## What sample size should we use?

*Sample Size*

**Example**

Significance test on whether participating in a training course before taking SAT raised mean above district mean of 483. $H_0$: $\mu = 483$ versus $H_a$: $\mu > 483$, $\sigma = 100$, n = 20 students and $\alpha = 0.05$.

1. Significance level: $\alpha = 0.05$.
2. Effect size: 20 points or more
3. Power: 90%

**What sample size is required to met these criteria?**

Why is the required sample size so large?

Because $\sigma = 100$ is so large; large $\sigma$ requires large n.

```
Alpha = 0.05  Sigma = 100

             Sample  Target  Actual
Difference     Size   Power   Power
        20      215  0.9000  0.9011
```

28-28

## What sample size should we use?

*Sample Size*

**Example**

Significance test on whether participating in a training course before taking SAT raised mean above district mean of 483. $H_0$: $\mu = 483$ versus $H_a$: $\mu > 483$, $\sigma = 100$, n = 20 students and $\alpha = 0.05$.

**What is power for n = 20 if true mean = 503?**

Minitab results

```
Testing mean = null (versus > null)
Calculating power for mean = null + difference
Alpha = 0.05  Sigma = 100

             Sample
Difference     Size    Power
        20       20    0.227
```

Why is power so small?

Because $\sigma = 100$ is so large; large $\sigma$ requires large n.

## Vocabulary

$\alpha$
$\beta$
**Power**
**Probability of a Type I Error**
**Probability of a Type II Error**
**Type I Error**
**Type II Error**

29-1

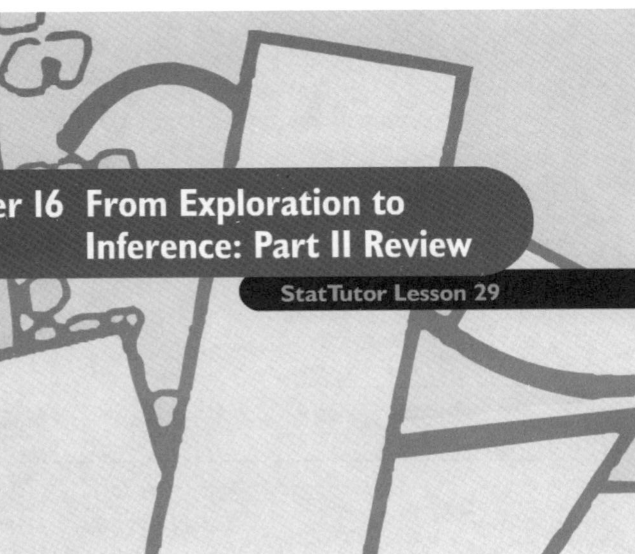


29-2

Practice of Statistics
Question Formulation
Data Production
Data Analysis and Summary
Statistical Inference
Sampling
Experimenting
Not Random
Convenience
Voluntary Response
Random
SRS
Stratified
Multistage

29-3

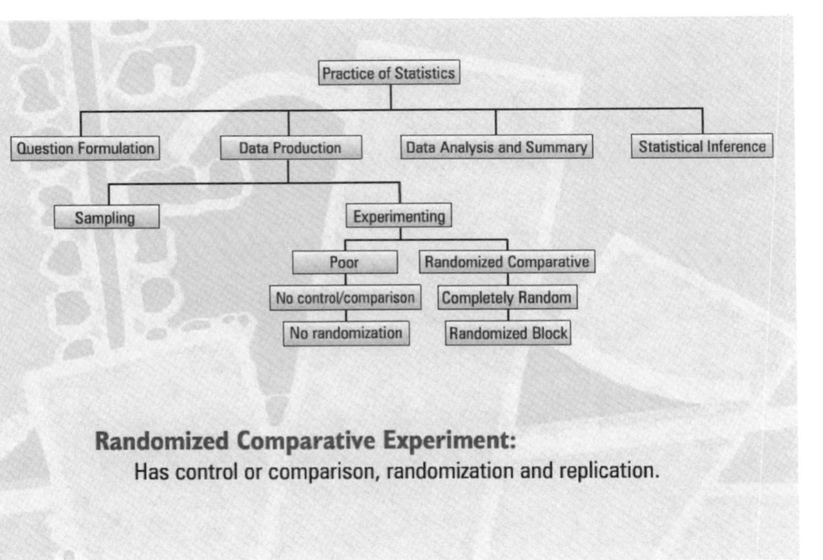


29-4

Practice of Statistics
Question Formulation
Data Production
Data Analysis and Summary
Statistical Inference
Probability
Definition & Facts
Disjoint Events
P(not A) = 1 − P(A)
P(Either A or B) = P(A) + P(B)

29-5

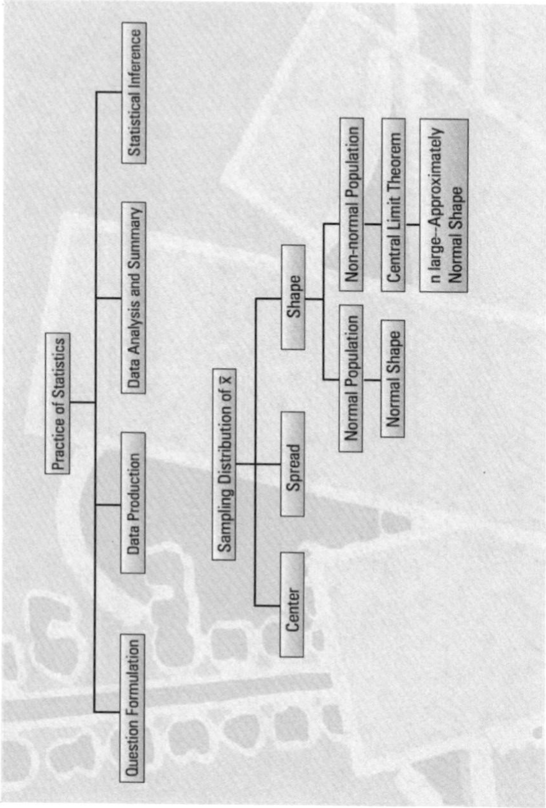

Practice of Statistics
Question Formulation
Data Production
Data Analysis and Summary
Statistical Inference
Sampling Distribution of $\bar{x}$
Center
Spread
Shape
Normal Population
Normal Shape
Non-normal Population
Central Limit Theorem
n large--Approximately Normal Shape

29-6

Practice of Statistics
Question Formulation
Data Production
Data Analysis and Summary
Statistical Inference
Estimating Parameter Value
Testing Parameter Value
Confidence Interval for $\mu$
Level of Confidence
Check conditions
Determining Sample Size
Always interpret Confidence Interval in context.

29-7

Practice of Statistics
Question Formulation
Data Production
Data Analysis and Summary
Statistical Inference
Estimating Parameter Value
Testing Parameter Value
State hypotheses about $\mu$
Specify Significance Level
Check conditions
Test Statistic & *P*-value
Always state conclusions in context.

29-8

Optional
Practice of Statistics
Question Formulation
Data Production
Data Analysis and Summary
Statistical Inference
Probability
Addition Rule
Multiplication Rule
Conditional Probability

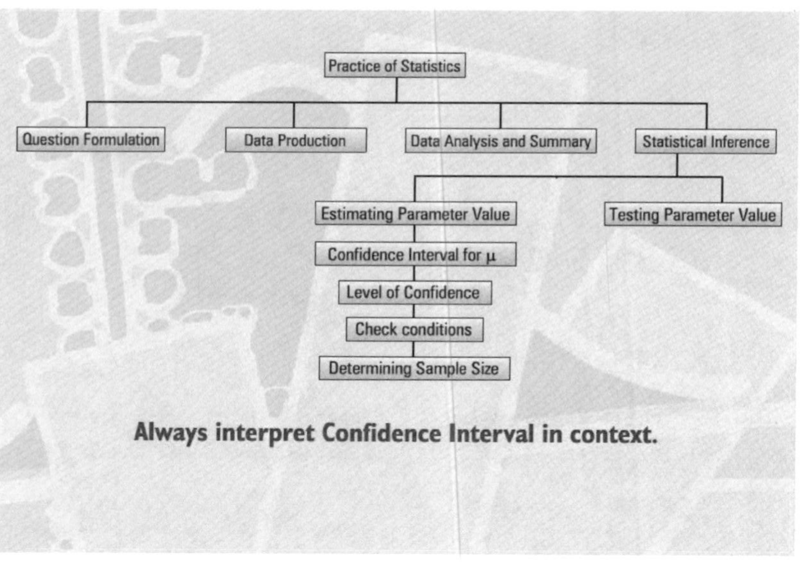

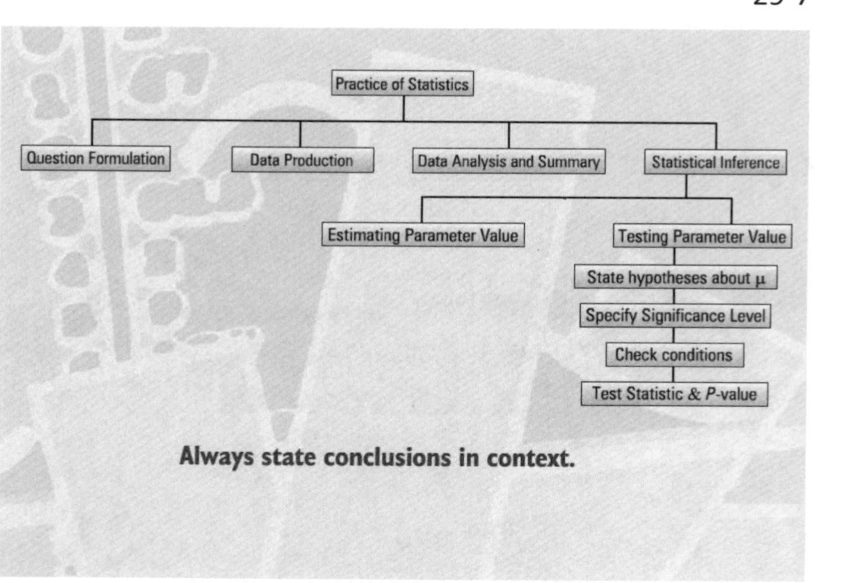

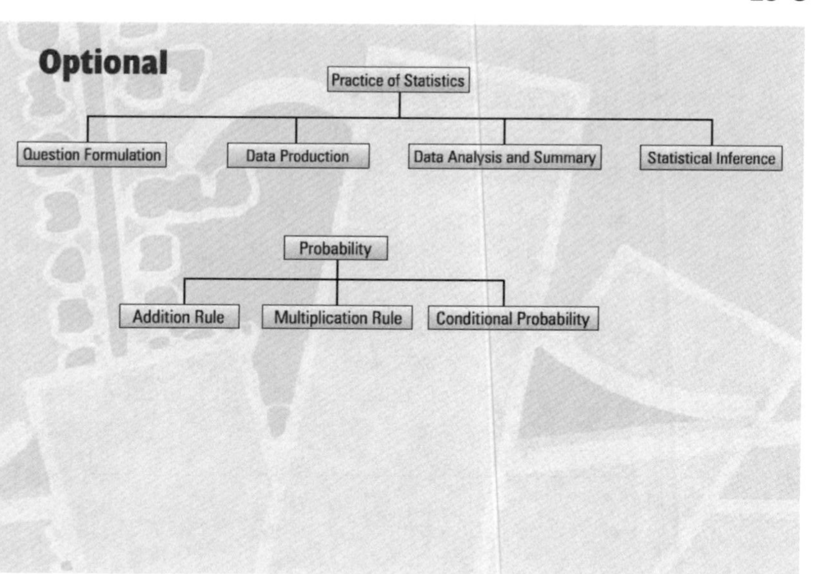

29-9

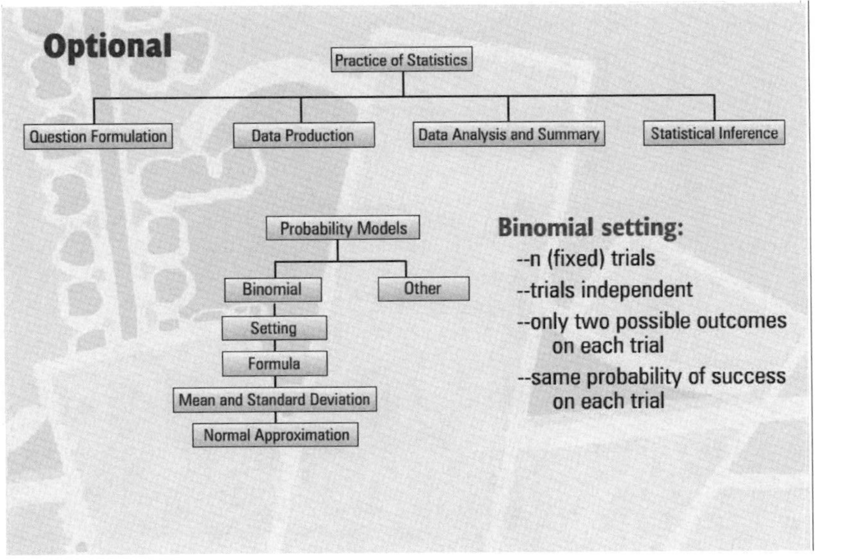


29-10

## Vocabulary

*Not covered in Statistics 221

- Addition Rule*
- Binomial Formula*
- Binomial Setting*
- Blocking
- Central Limit Theorem
- Comparison
- Conditional Probability*
- Confidence Interval
- Confidence Level
- Control
- Convenience Sampling
- Dependent Events*
- Disjoint Events
- Double Blind
- Experiment
- Independent Events*
- Hypotheses
- Margin of Error
- Matched Pairs
- Mean of Sampling Distribution of $\bar{x}$
- Multiplication Rule*
- Multi-Stage Sampling
- Placebo
- Probability
- P-value
- Randomization
- Random Sampling
- Sampling Distribution of $\bar{x}$
- Simple Random Sampling
- Significance Level
- Standard Deviation of $\bar{x}$
- Stratified Samping
- Test of Significance
- Test Statistic
- Tree Diagrams*
- Voluntary Response Sampling

30-1

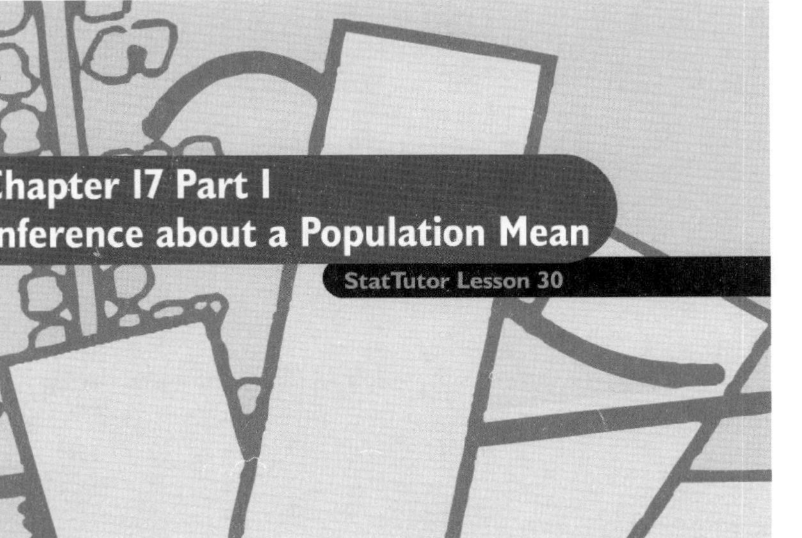


30-2

## Objectives

1. Explain that replacing $\sigma$ with $s$ in the standardized expression $\frac{\bar{x}-\mu_0}{\sigma/\sqrt{n}}$ changes the distribution from standard normal.
2. Name the distribution of $\frac{\bar{x}-\mu_0}{s/\sqrt{n}}$ and list its properties.
3. Compare the density curve of the $t$ distribution to the standard normal density curve.
4. Explain the components of the $t$ distribution table and show how it is used to find probabilities.
5. Using t distribution and $s$, obtain a confidence interval for $\mu$.
6. Using t distribution and $s$, perform a test of significance on $\mu$.

30-3

*Using s to estimate σ*

# Conditions for Inference

Basic Practice of Statistics Chapter 17

30-4

*Using s to estimate σ*

**Conditions for Inference:**

- SRS--need to be able to regard data as an SRS.
- Population is N($\mu$, $\sigma$)--distribution needs to be symmetric and single-peaked.

Standardized Test Statistic

$$t = \frac{(\bar{x}-\mu_0)}{s/\sqrt{n}}$$

where $s = \sqrt{\frac{\sum (x_i - \bar{x})^2}{n-1}}$

What should we do if $\sigma$ is not known? Estimate $\sigma$ with s!

**Does this test statistic have a standard normal distribution? NO!**

**It has a t-distribution!!!**

30-5



**Conditions for Inference:**

- SRS--need to be able to regard data as an SRS.
- Population is N(μ, σ)--distribution needs to be symmetric and single-peaked.

Standardized Test Statistic

$$t = \frac{(\bar{x} - \mu_0)}{s/\sqrt{n}}$$

Note: $s/\sqrt{n}$

- is called *standard error of the mean* (SEMean).
- estimates $\sigma/\sqrt{n}$, which is the standard deviation of the sampling distribution of $\bar{x}$.
- varies from sample to sample.

**It has a t-distribution!!!**

30-6



# The *t* Distributions

Basic Practice of Statistics Chapter 17

30-7



**When performing inference on μ, σ is usually unknown!!**

**Use a *t* procedure when σ is unknown.**

30-8



## Distributions of Test Statistics

| Population | Sample | |
|---|---|---|
| N(μ, σ) | Sample Size: | n |
| | Sample Mean: | $\bar{x}$ |
| | Sample Standard Deviation: | s |

| Test Statistic: | Distribution of Test Statistic: |
|---|---|
| $\bar{x}$ | $N(\mu, \sigma/\sqrt{n})$ |
| $z = \frac{\bar{x} - \mu_0}{\sigma/\sqrt{n}}$ | N(0,1) |
| $t = \frac{\bar{x} - \mu_0}{s/\sqrt{n}}$ | *t* with df = n − 1 |

**NOTE: A *t* distribution is specified by its degrees of freedom (df).**
Degrees of freedom: amount of sample information for estimating σ.

30-9



## Properties of *t* Distributions

- Symmetric
- Bell shaped
- Mean = zero
- The smaller the df, the larger the tail areas
- The smaller the df, the larger the spread

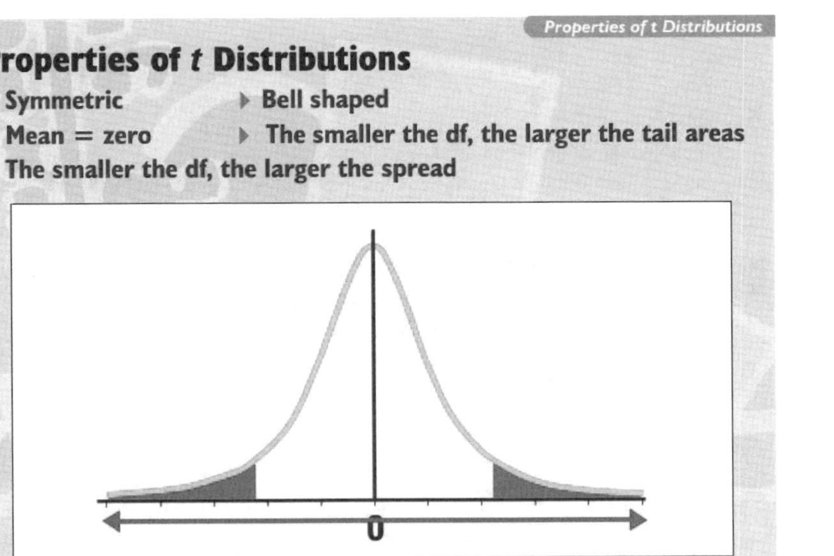


30-10



**View Applet**

**As degrees of freedom increase, the density curve of a *t* distribution approaches the standard normal curve, N(0,1).**

30-11



## Tail Area: *t* Distribution versus Standard Normal

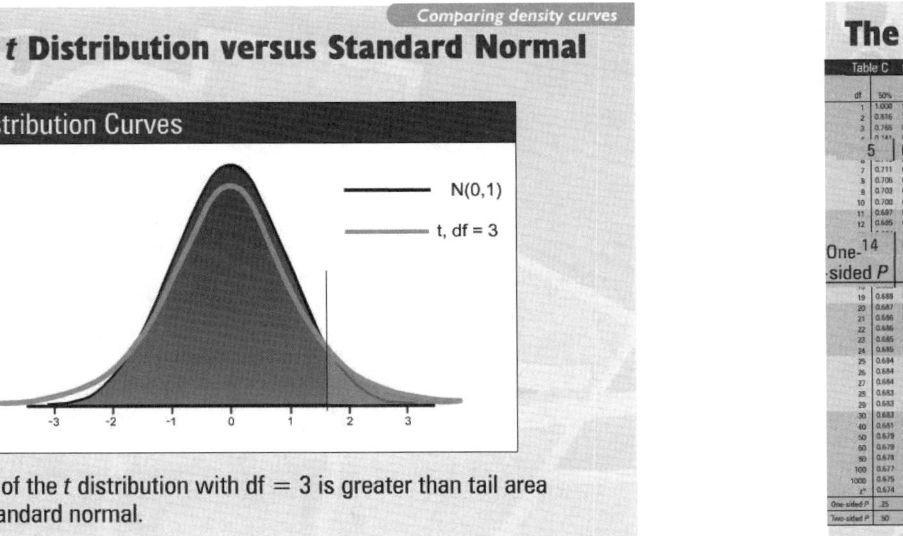


Tail area of the *t* distribution with df = 3 is greater than tail area of the standard normal.

30-12



## The *t* Table

One-sided *P* is area to the right of the table entry.

Each row = a different density curve.

*t* distribution is symmetric.

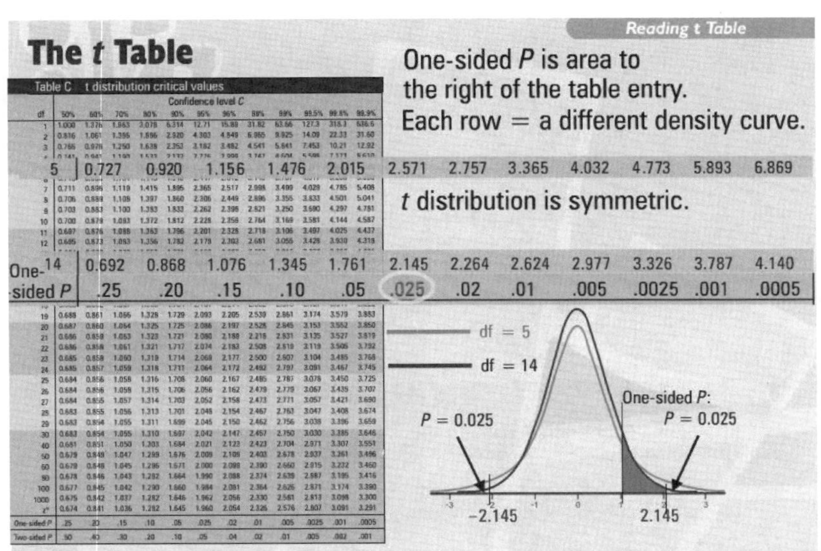

Table C t distribution critical values

| df | | | | | | | | | | | | |
|---|---|---|---|---|---|---|---|---|---|---|---|---|
| 5 | 0.727 | 0.920 | 1.156 | 1.476 | 2.015 | 2.571 | 2.757 | 3.365 | 4.032 | 4.773 | 5.893 | 6.869 |
| 14 | 0.692 | 0.868 | 1.076 | 1.345 | 1.761 | 2.145 | 2.264 | 2.624 | 2.977 | 3.326 | 3.787 | 4.140 |
| One-sided *P* | .25 | .20 | .15 | .10 | .05 | .025 | .02 | .01 | .005 | .0025 | .001 | .0005 |

30-13



## The *t* Table

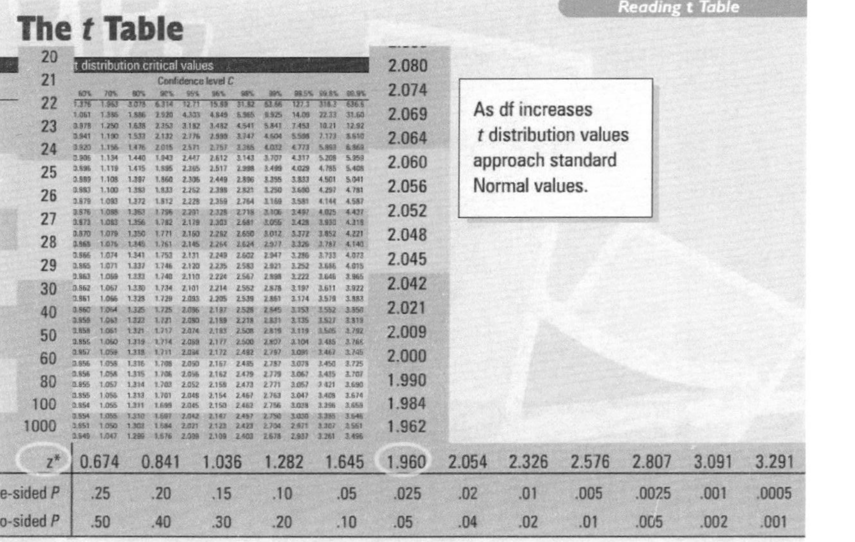

| df | $z^*$ value (right column) |
|---|---|
| 20 | |
| 21 | 2.080 |
| 22 | 2.074 |
| 23 | 2.069 |
| 24 | 2.064 |
| 25 | 2.060 |
| 26 | 2.056 |
| 27 | 2.052 |
| 28 | 2.048 |
| 29 | 2.045 |
| 30 | 2.042 |
| 40 | 2.021 |
| 50 | 2.009 |
| 60 | 2.000 |
| 80 | 1.990 |
| 100 | 1.984 |
| 1000 | 1.962 |

| $z^*$ | 0.674 | 0.841 | 1.036 | 1.282 | 1.645 | 1.960 | 2.054 | 2.326 | 2.576 | 2.807 | 3.091 | 3.291 |
|---|---|---|---|---|---|---|---|---|---|---|---|---|
| ne-sided *P* | .25 | .20 | .15 | .10 | .05 | .025 | .02 | .01 | .005 | .0025 | .001 | .0005 |
| vo-sided *P* | .50 | .40 | .30 | .20 | .10 | .05 | .04 | .02 | .01 | .005 | .002 | .001 |



As df increases *t* distribution values approach standard Normal values.

30-14



## Formulas for Statistical Inference about $\mu$

| | Confidence Interval for Estimating $\mu$ | Test Statistic for Testing $H_0$: $\mu = \mu_0$ | Table |
|---|---|---|---|
| $\sigma$ known | $\bar{x} \pm z^* \frac{\sigma}{\sqrt{n}}$ | $z = \frac{\bar{x} - \mu_0}{\sigma/\sqrt{n}}$ | Standard Normal Table |
| $\sigma$ unknown | $\bar{x} \pm t^* \frac{s}{\sqrt{n}}$ | $t = \frac{\bar{x} - \mu_0}{s/\sqrt{n}}$ | *t* Table $df = n - 1$ |

Find $t^*$ and *P*-value for *t* test statistic using Table C with $df = n - 1$.

**In summary, use *t* formulas not *z* formulas when $\sigma$ is unknown!**

30-15



# The One-Sample *t* Confidence Interval

Basic Practice of Statistics Chapter 17

30-16



## Confidence Intervals for $\mu$ using *t* Distributions

**Conditions:**
- SRS of size *n*,
- Normal population or large n, unknown $\sigma$.

Confidence Interval Formula for $\mu$:

$$\bar{x} \pm t^* \frac{s}{\sqrt{n}}$$

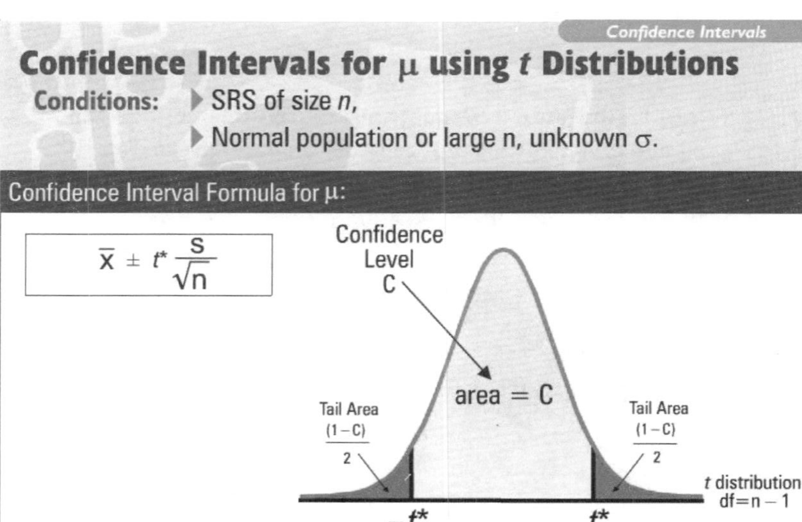

30-17



## Finding $t^*$ in $t$ Table

$$\bar{x} \pm 2.306 \frac{s}{\sqrt{n}}$$

Suppose confidence level = 95% and n = 9

df = n – 1 = 9 – 1 = 8

**Table C** *t* distribution critical values

| | Confidence level *C* | | | | | | | | | | | |
|---|---|---|---|---|---|---|---|---|---|---|---|---|
| | 50% | 60% | 70% | 80% | 90% | 95% | 96% | 98% | 99% | 99.5% | 99.8% | 99.9% |
| 1 | 1.000 | 1.376 | 1.963 | 3.078 | 6.314 | 12.71 | 15.89 | 31.82 | 63.66 | 127.3 | 318.3 | 636.6 |
| 2 | 0.816 | 1.061 | 1.386 | 1.886 | 2.920 | 4.303 | 4.849 | 6.965 | 9.925 | 14.09 | 22.33 | 31.60 |
| 3 | 0.765 | 0.978 | 1.250 | 1.638 | 2.353 | 3.182 | 3.482 | 4.541 | 5.841 | 7.453 | 10.21 | 12.92 |
| 4 | 0.741 | 0.941 | 1.190 | 1.533 | 2.132 | 2.776 | 2.999 | 3.747 | 4.604 | 5.598 | 7.173 | 8.610 |
| 5 | 0.727 | 0.920 | 1.156 | 1.476 | 2.015 | 2.571 | 2.757 | 3.365 | 4.032 | 4.773 | 5.893 | 6.869 |
| 6 | 0.718 | 0.906 | 1.134 | 1.440 | 1.943 | 2.447 | 2.612 | 3.143 | 3.707 | 4.317 | 5.208 | 5.959 |
| 7 | 0.711 | 0.896 | 1.119 | [illegible] | [illegible] | [illegible] | 2.517 | 2.998 | 3.499 | 4.029 | 4.785 | 5.408 |
| 8 | 0.706 | 0.889 | 1.108 | 1.397 | [illegible] | [illegible] | [illegible] | 2.896 | 3.355 | 3.833 | 4.501 | 5.041 |
| 9 | 0.703 | 0.883 | 1.100 | 1.383 | 1.833 | 2.262 | 2.398 | 2.821 | 3.250 | 3.690 | 4.297 | 4.781 |
| 10 | 0.700 | 0.879 | 1.093 | 1.372 | 1.812 | 2.228 | 2.359 | 2.764 | 3.169 | 3.581 | 4.144 | 4.587 |
| $z^*$ | 0.674 | 0.841 | 1.036 | 1.282 | 1.645 | 1.960 | 2.054 | 2.326 | 2.576 | 2.807 | 3.091 | 3.291 |
| One-sided *P* | .25 | .20 | .15 | .10 | .05 | .025 | .02 | .01 | .005 | .0025 | .001 | .0005 |
| Two-sided *P* | .50 | .40 | .30 | .20 | .10 | .05 | .04 | .02 | .01 | .005 | .002 | .001 |

$t^* = 2.306$

30-18



## Finding $t^*$ in $t$ Table

$$\bar{x} \pm 2.306 \frac{s}{\sqrt{n}}$$

Suppose confidence level = 95% and n = 9

df = n – 1 = 9 – 1 = 8

Note 1: If the actual degrees of freedom (df) are not in the table, use "The Price is Right" algorithm; i.e., use df closest to the actual df without going over.

Note 2: Unknown $\sigma$ means less information ⟶ less precision in our results ⟶ we need a larger multiplier ($t^*$). For a given level of confidence, $t^* > z^*$.

| | | | | | | | | | | | | |
|---|---|---|---|---|---|---|---|---|---|---|---|---|
| 10 | 0.700 | 0.879 | 1.093 | 1.372 | 1.812 | 2.228 | 2.359 | 2.764 | 3.169 | 3.581 | 4.144 | 4.587 |
| $z^*$ | 0.674 | 0.841 | 1.036 | 1.282 | 1.645 | 1.960 | 2.054 | 2.326 | 2.576 | 2.807 | 3.091 | 3.291 |
| One-sided *P* | .25 | .20 | .15 | .10 | .05 | .025 | .02 | .01 | .005 | .0025 | .001 | .0005 |
| Two-sided *P* | .50 | .40 | .30 | .20 | .10 | .05 | .04 | .02 | .01 | .005 | .002 | .001 |

30-19



**View Movie Clip**

30-20



## Steps for Creating Confidence Intervals

Step 1 **STATE** the problem.

Step 2 **PLAN:** Recognize need for a confidence interval for the mean using a one-sample *t* procedure; specify confidence level.

Step 3 **SOLVE:** Collect data with SRS.
Plot data; compute $\bar{x}$ and s as estimates of $\mu$ and $\sigma$.
Check conditions: need SRS and if n < 40, no outliers.
Calculate confidence interval for $\mu$:

$$\bar{x} \pm t^* \frac{s}{\sqrt{n}} \qquad df = n - 1$$

Step 4 **CONCLUDE:** Interpret confidence interval in context.

30-21

*Confidence Intervals*

## Example: Resting Pulse Rate

Step 1 **STATE** the problem.

**What is the true mean of resting pulse rates for male students?**

Step 2 **PLAN:**

How do we estimate the true mean?

- Select SRS of 92 male students and measure their resting pulse rates.
- Obtain a 95% confidence interval for $\mu$ using $\bar{x}$.
- Use a one-sample t procedure.

30-22

*Confidence Intervals*

## Example: Resting Pulse Rate

Level of confidence: 95%

| Mean: | $\bar{x}$ = 72.87 |
|---|---|
| Standard Deviation: | s = 11.01 |
| Sample Size: | 92 |
| Confidence Level: | 95% |

Step 3 **SOLVE:** Collect data: select SRS of **92**

Plot data; compute $\bar{x}$ and s as estimates of $\mu$ and $\sigma$

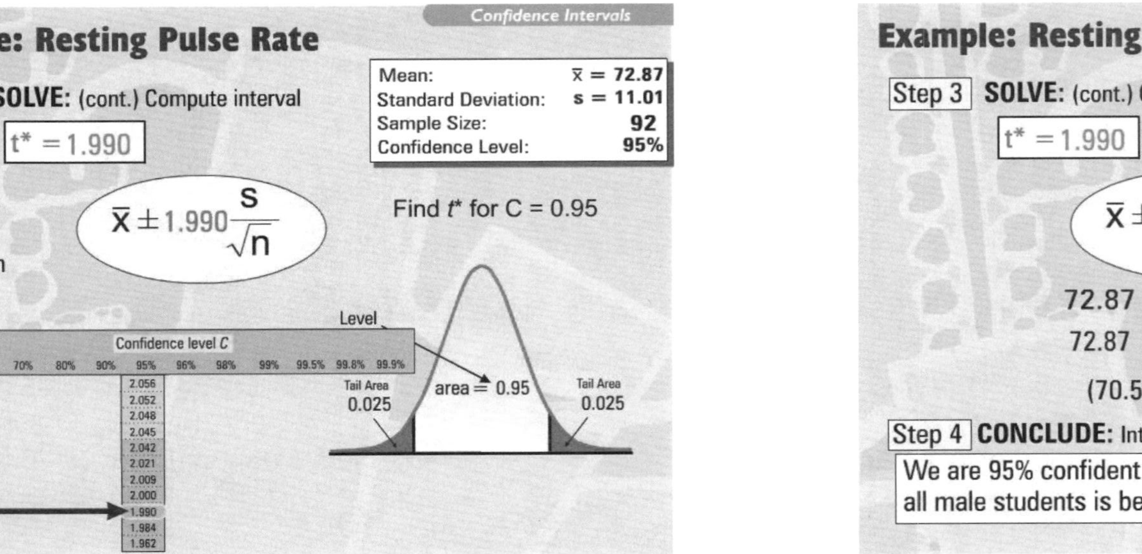

**Resting pulse rate from a random sample of 92 male students**

| | | | | | | | | | |
|---|---|---|---|---|---|---|---|---|---|
| 64 | 58 | 62 | 66 | 64 | 74 | 84 | 68 | 62 | 76 |
| 90 | 80 | 92 | 68 | 60 | 62 | 66 | 70 | 68 | 72 |
| 70 | 74 | 66 | 70 | 96 | 62 | 78 | 82 | 100 | 68 |
| 96 | 78 | 88 | 62 | 80 | 62 | 60 | 72 | 62 | 76 |
| 68 | 54 | 74 | 74 | 68 | 72 | 68 | 82 | 64 | 58 |
| 54 | 70 | 62 | 48 | 76 | 88 | 70 | 90 | 78 | 70 |
| 90 | 92 | 60 | 72 | 68 | 84 | 74 | 68 | 84 | 61 |
| 64 | 94 | 60 | 72 | 58 | 88 | 66 | 84 | 62 | 66 |
| 80 | 78 | 68 | 72 | 82 | 76 | 87 | 90 | 78 | 68 |
| 86 | 76 | | | | | | | | |



$\bar{x}$ = 72.87
s = 11.01

Check conditions; if ok, proceed

n large--ok to proceed.

30-23

*Confidence Intervals*

## Example: Resting Pulse Rate

Step 3 **SOLVE:** (cont.) Compute interval

| Mean: | $\bar{x}$ = 72.87 |
|---|---|
| Standard Deviation: | s = 11.01 |
| Sample Size: | 92 |
| Confidence Level: | 95% |

$t^* = 1.990$

$$\bar{x} \pm 1.990 \frac{s}{\sqrt{n}}$$

Find $t^*$ for C = 0.95

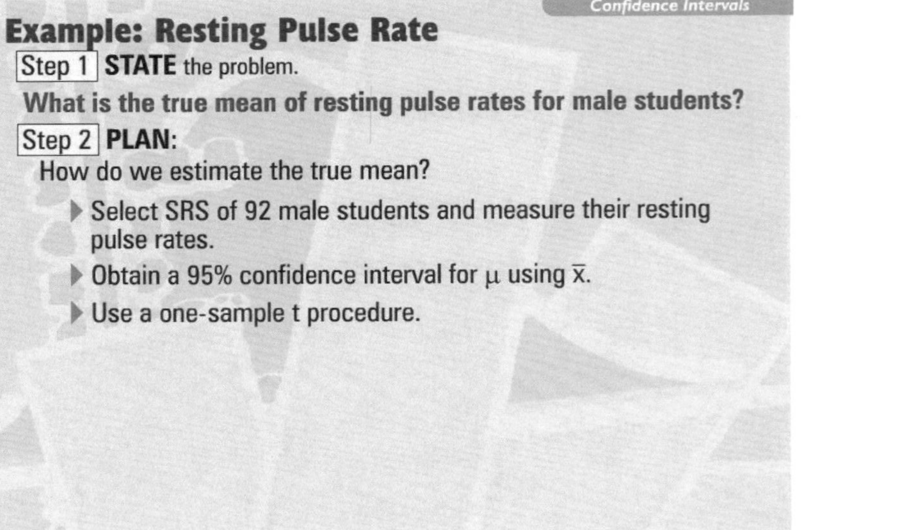



| df | 50% | 60% | 70% | 80% | 90% | 95% | 96% | 98% | 99% | 99.5% | 99.8% | 99.9% |
|---|---|---|---|---|---|---|---|---|---|---|---|---|
| 26 | | | | | | 2.056 | | | | | | |
| 27 | | | | | | 2.052 | | | | | | |
| 28 | | | | | | 2.048 | | | | | | |
| 29 | | | | | | 2.045 | | | | | | |
| 30 | | | | | | 2.042 | | | | | | |
| 40 | | | | | | 2.021 | | | | | | |
| 50 | | | | | | 2.009 | | | | | | |
| 60 | | | | | | 2.000 | | | | | | |
| 80 | | | | | | 1.990 | | | | | | |
| 100 | | | | | | 1.984 | | | | | | |
| 1000 | | | | | | 1.962 | | | | | | |

30-24

*Confidence Intervals*

## Example: Resting Pulse Rate

Step 3 **SOLVE:** (cont.) Compute interval

| Mean: | $\bar{x}$ = 72.87 |
|---|---|
| Standard Deviation: | s = 11.01 |
| Sample Size: | 92 |
| Confidence Level: | 95% |

$t^* = 1.990$

$$\bar{x} \pm 1.990 \frac{s}{\sqrt{n}}$$

$$72.87 \pm 1.990 \frac{11.01}{\sqrt{92}}$$

$$72.87 \pm 2.28$$

$$(70.59, 75.15)$$

Step 4 **CONCLUDE:** Interpretation in context.

We are 95% confident that the true mean resting pulse rate for all male students is between 70.59 and 75.15.

30-25

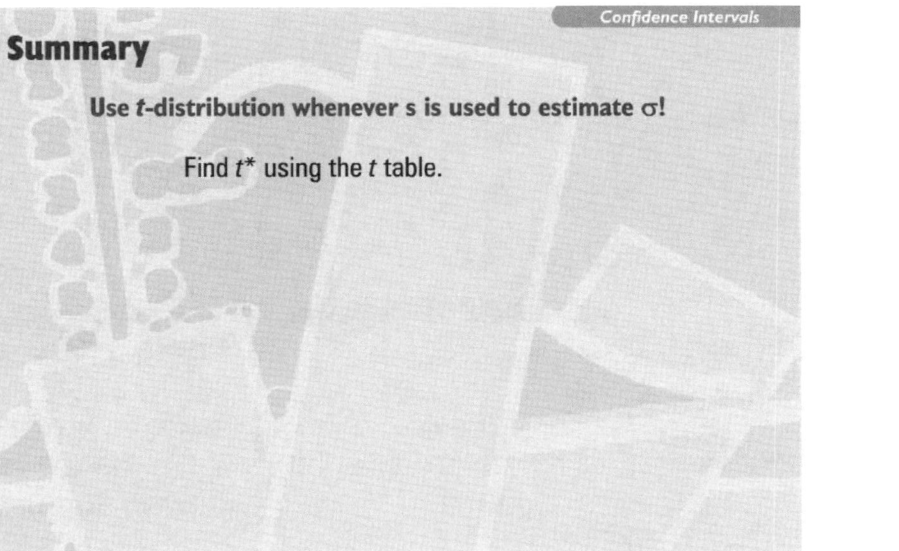


30-26

Test of Significance

# The One-Sample *t* Test

Basic Practice of Statistics Chapter 17

30-27

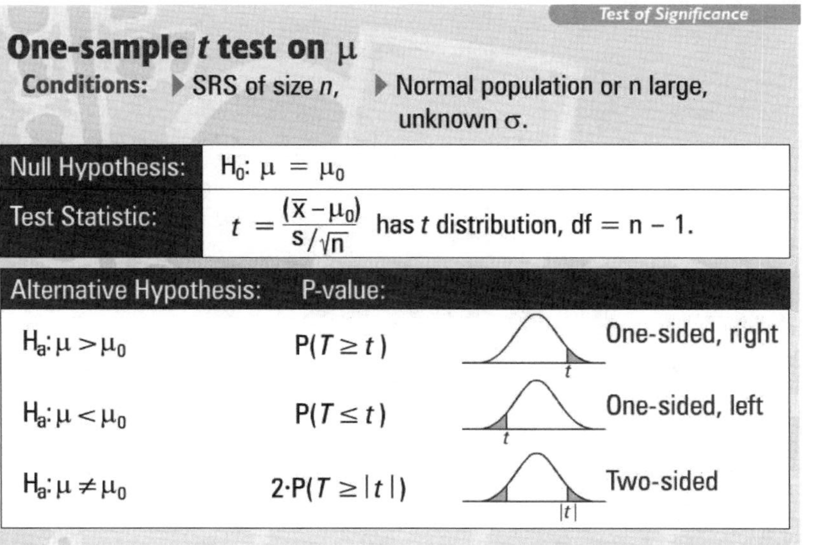


30-28

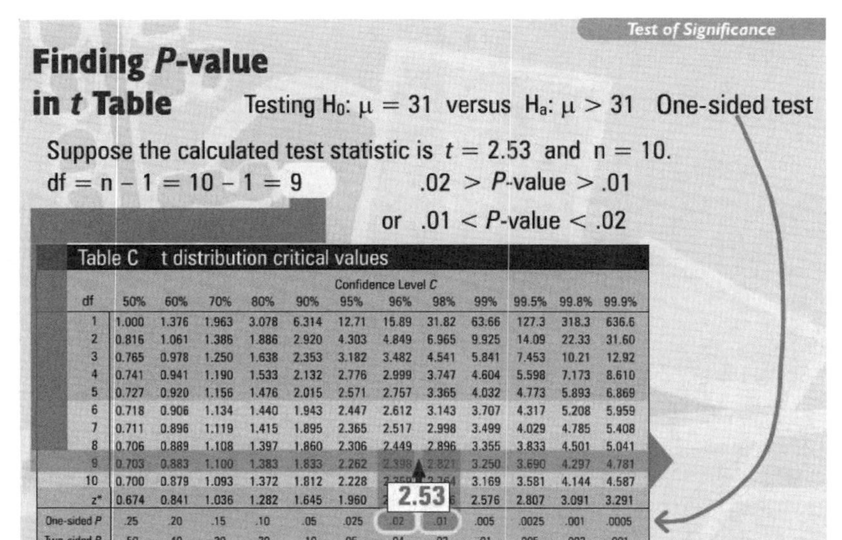


Table C t distribution critical values

| df | Confidence Level C | | | | | | | | | | | |
|---|---|---|---|---|---|---|---|---|---|---|---|---|
| | 50% | 60% | 70% | 80% | 90% | 95% | 96% | 98% | 99% | 99.5% | 99.8% | 99.9% |
| 1 | 1.000 | 1.376 | 1.963 | 3.078 | 6.314 | 12.71 | 15.89 | 31.82 | 63.66 | 127.3 | 318.3 | 636.6 |
| 2 | 0.816 | 1.061 | 1.386 | 1.886 | 2.920 | 4.303 | 4.849 | 6.965 | 9.925 | 14.09 | 22.33 | 31.60 |
| 3 | 0.765 | 0.978 | 1.250 | 1.638 | 2.353 | 3.182 | 3.482 | 4.541 | 5.841 | 7.453 | 10.21 | 12.92 |
| 4 | 0.741 | 0.941 | 1.190 | 1.533 | 2.132 | 2.776 | 2.999 | 3.747 | 4.604 | 5.598 | 7.173 | 8.610 |
| 5 | 0.727 | 0.920 | 1.156 | 1.476 | 2.015 | 2.571 | 2.757 | 3.365 | 4.032 | 4.773 | 5.893 | 6.869 |
| 6 | 0.718 | 0.906 | 1.134 | 1.440 | 1.943 | 2.447 | 2.612 | 3.143 | 3.707 | 4.317 | 5.208 | 5.959 |
| 7 | 0.711 | 0.896 | 1.119 | 1.415 | 1.895 | 2.365 | 2.517 | 2.998 | 3.499 | 4.029 | 4.785 | 5.408 |
| 8 | 0.706 | 0.889 | 1.108 | 1.397 | 1.860 | 2.306 | 2.449 | 2.896 | 3.355 | 3.833 | 4.501 | 5.041 |
| 9 | 0.703 | 0.883 | 1.100 | 1.383 | 1.833 | 2.262 | 2.398 | 2.821 | 3.250 | 3.690 | 4.297 | 4.781 |
| 10 | 0.700 | 0.879 | 1.093 | 1.372 | 1.812 | 2.228 | [illegible] | [illegible] | 3.169 | 3.581 | 4.144 | 4.587 |
| z* | 0.674 | 0.841 | 1.036 | 1.282 | 1.645 | 1.960 | [illegible] | [illegible] | 2.576 | 2.807 | 3.091 | 3.291 |
| One-sided P | .25 | .20 | .15 | .10 | .05 | .025 | .02 | .01 | .005 | .0025 | .001 | .0005 |
| Two-sided P | .50 | .40 | .30 | .20 | .10 | .05 | .04 | .02 | .01 | .005 | .002 | .001 |

30-29



## Finding *P*-value in *t* Table

Testing $H_0$: $\mu = 31$ versus $H_a$: $\mu > 31$ One-sided test

Suppose the calculated test statistic is $t = 2.53$ and $n = 10$.

$df = n - 1 = 10 - 1 = 9$ $.02 > P\text{-value} > .01$

or $.01 < P\text{-value} < .02$

Table C t distribution critical values

| df | 50% | 60% | 70% | 80% | 90% | 95% | 96% | 98% | 99% | 99.5% | 99.8% | 99.9% |
|---|---|---|---|---|---|---|---|---|---|---|---|---|
| | Confidence Level *C* | | | | | | | | | | | |
| 1 | 1.000 | 1.376 | 1.963 | 3.078 | 6.314 | 12.71 | 15.89 | 31.82 | 63.66 | 127.3 | 318.3 | 636.6 |
| 2 | 0.816 | 1.061 | 1.386 | 1.886 | 2.920 | 4.303 | 4.849 | 6.965 | 9.925 | 14.09 | 22.33 | 31.60 |
| 8 | 0.706 | 0.889 | 1.108 | 1.397 | 1.860 | 2.306 | 2.449 | 2.896 | 3.355 | 3.833 | 4.501 | 5.041 |
| Two-sided *P* | .50 | .40 | .30 | .20 | .10 | .05 | .04 | .02 | .01 | .005 | .002 | .001 |

*P*-values obtained from the *t*-distribution table are always reported as an interval. For more accurate *P*-values, use statistical software.

*P*-values are exact if the population is Normal and approximate for non-Normal populations with large n.

30-30



## Finding *P*-value in *t* Table

Testing $H_0$: $\mu = 50$ versus $H_a$: $\mu < 50$ One-sided test

Suppose the calculated test statistic is $t = -8.78$ and $n = 5$.

$df = n - 1 = 5 - 1 = 4$

*t* curve is symmetric: area below $t = -8.78$ equals area above $t = 8.78$

$.0005 > P\text{-value}$ or $P\text{-value} < .0005$

Table C t distribution critical values

| df | 50% | 60% | 70% | 80% | 90% | 95% | 96% | 98% | 99% | 99.5% | 99.8% | 99.9% |
|---|---|---|---|---|---|---|---|---|---|---|---|---|
| | Confidence Level *C* | | | | | | | | | | | |
| 1 | 1.000 | 1.376 | 1.963 | 3.078 | 6.314 | 12.71 | 15.89 | 31.82 | 63.66 | 127.3 | 318.3 | 636.6 |
| 2 | 0.816 | 1.061 | 1.386 | 1.886 | 2.920 | 4.303 | 4.849 | 6.965 | 9.925 | 14.09 | 22.33 | 31.60 |
| 3 | 0.765 | 0.978 | 1.250 | 1.638 | 2.353 | 3.182 | 3.482 | 4.541 | 5.841 | 7.453 | 10.21 | 12.92 |
| 4 | 0.741 | 0.941 | 1.190 | 1.533 | 2.132 | 2.776 | 2.999 | 3.747 | 4.604 | 5.598 | 7.173 | 8.610 |
| 5 | 0.727 | 0.920 | 1.156 | 1.476 | 2.015 | 2.571 | 2.757 | 3.365 | 4.032 | 4.773 | 5.893 | 6.869 |
| 6 | 0.718 | 0.906 | 1.134 | 1.440 | 1.943 | 2.447 | 2.612 | 3.143 | 3.707 | 4.317 | 5.208 | [illegible] |
| 7 | 0.711 | 0.896 | 1.119 | 1.415 | 1.895 | 2.365 | 2.517 | 2.998 | 3.499 | 4.029 | 4.785 | [illegible] |
| 8 | 0.706 | 0.889 | 1.108 | 1.397 | 1.860 | 2.306 | 2.449 | 2.896 | 3.355 | 3.833 | 4.501 | 5.041 |
| 9 | 0.703 | 0.883 | 1.100 | 1.383 | 1.833 | 2.262 | 2.398 | 2.821 | 3.250 | 3.690 | 4.297 | 4.781 |
| 10 | 0.700 | 0.879 | 1.093 | 1.372 | 1.812 | 2.228 | 2.359 | 2.764 | 3.169 | 3.581 | 4.144 | 4.587 |
| z* | 0.674 | 0.841 | 1.036 | 1.282 | 1.645 | 1.960 | 2.054 | 2.326 | 2.576 | 2.807 | 3.091 | 3.291 |
| One-sided *P* | .25 | .20 | .15 | .10 | .05 | .025 | .02 | .01 | .005 | .0025 | .001 | .0005 |
| Two-sided *P* | .50 | .40 | .30 | .20 | .10 | .05 | .04 | .02 | .01 | .005 | .002 | .001 |

8.78

30-31



## Finding *P*-value in *t* Table

Testing $H_0$: $\mu = 10$ versus $H_a$: $\mu \neq 10$ Two-sided test

Suppose the calculated test statistic is $t = 1.93$ and $n = 8$.

$df = n - 1 = 8 - 1 = 7$ $.10 > P\text{-value} > .05$

or $0.05 < P\text{-value} < 0.10$

Table C t distribution critical values

| df | 50% | 60% | 70% | 80% | 90% | 95% | 96% | 98% | 99% | 99.5% | 99.8% | 99.9% |
|---|---|---|---|---|---|---|---|---|---|---|---|---|
| | Confidence Level *C* | | | | | | | | | | | |
| 1 | 1.000 | 1.376 | 1.963 | 3.078 | 6.314 | 12.71 | 15.89 | 31.82 | 63.66 | 127.3 | 318.3 | 636.6 |
| 2 | 0.816 | 1.061 | 1.386 | 1.886 | 2.920 | 4.303 | 4.849 | 6.965 | 9.925 | 14.09 | 22.33 | 31.60 |
| 3 | 0.765 | 0.978 | 1.250 | 1.638 | 2.353 | 3.182 | 3.482 | 4.541 | 5.841 | 7.453 | 10.21 | 12.92 |
| 4 | 0.741 | 0.941 | 1.190 | 1.533 | 2.132 | 2.776 | 2.999 | 3.747 | 4.604 | 5.598 | 7.173 | 8.610 |
| 5 | 0.727 | 0.920 | 1.156 | 1.476 | 2.015 | 2.571 | 2.757 | 3.365 | 4.032 | 4.773 | 5.893 | 6.869 |
| 6 | 0.718 | 0.906 | 1.134 | 1.440 | 1.943 | 2.447 | 2.612 | 3.143 | 3.707 | 4.317 | 5.208 | 5.959 |
| 7 | 0.711 | 0.896 | 1.119 | 1.415 | 1.895 | 2.365 | 2.517 | 2.998 | 3.499 | 4.029 | 4.785 | 5.408 |
| 8 | 0.706 | 0.889 | 1.108 | 1.397 | 1.860 | 2.306 | 2.449 | 2.896 | 3.355 | 3.833 | 4.501 | 5.041 |
| 9 | 0.703 | 0.883 | 1.100 | 1.383 | [illegible] | [illegible] | 2.398 | 2.821 | 3.250 | 3.690 | 4.297 | 4.781 |
| 10 | 0.700 | 0.879 | 1.093 | 1.372 | [illegible] | [illegible] | 2.359 | 2.764 | 3.169 | 3.581 | 4.144 | 4.587 |
| z* | 0.674 | 0.841 | 1.036 | 1.282 | 1.645 | 1.960 | 2.054 | 2.326 | 2.576 | 2.807 | 3.091 | 3.291 |
| One-sided *P* | .25 | .20 | .15 | .10 | .05 | .025 | .02 | .01 | .005 | .0025 | .001 | .0005 |
| Two-sided *P* | .50 | .40 | .30 | .20 | .10 | .05 | .04 | .02 | .01 | .005 | .002 | .001 |

1.93

30-32



## General Outline for a One-Sample *t* Test

Step 1 **STATE** the problem.

Step 2 **PLAN:** Recognize need for a test on $\mu$ using a one-sample *t* procedure; specify $H_0$ and $H_a$ and choose $\alpha$.

Step 3 **SOLVE:** Collect data with SRS.

Plot data; compute $\bar{x}$ and s as estimates of $\mu$ and $\sigma$.

Check conditions: need SRS and if $n < 40$, no outliers.

Calculate test statistic: $t = \dfrac{(\bar{x} - \mu_0)}{s/\sqrt{n}}$ $df = n - 1$

Find *P*-value using *t* table.

Step 4 **CONCLUDE:** Interpret conclusions in context.

If *P*-value $\leq \alpha$, reject $H_0$ in favor of $H_a$; declare observed effect statistically significant.

If *P*-value $> \alpha$, fail to reject $H_0$; conclude observed effect is not statistically significant.

30-33

Test of Significance

## Example: Resting Pulse Rate

Step 1 **STATE** the problem.

Is the mean pulse rate for male students different from 72 beats per minute? (Adult males typically have a resting pulse rate of 72 bpm.)

Step 2 **PLAN:** Recognize a need to perform a test on $\mu$ using a one-sample *t*; specify $H_0$ and $H_a$ and choose $\alpha$.

- Plan to take a SRS of 92 students.
- Use level of significance = 0.05.

| | |
|---|---|
| Null value ($\mu_0$): | 72 |
| Type of Alternative: | not equal to |
| Standard Deviation ($\sigma$): | ? |
| Sample Size: | 92 |
| $\alpha$: | 0.05 |

$H_0$: $\mu = 72$ $H_a$: $\mu \neq 72$

$\alpha = 0.05$

Step 3 **SOLVE:** Collect data with SRS of 92 students.

30-34

Test of Significance

## Example: Resting Pulse Rate Test of Significance

Step 3 **SOLVE:** (cont.) Plot data; compute $\bar{x}$ and s.

50 60 70 80 90 100 Pulse Rate

$\bar{x} = 72.87$
$s = 11.01$

| | |
|---|---|
| Null value ($\mu_0$): | 72 |
| Type of Alternative: | not equal to |
| Standard Deviation ($\sigma$): | ? |
| Sample Size: | 92 |
| $\alpha$: | 0.05 |

Check conditions

SRS, no outliers and n large --ok to proceed.

Compute test statistic:

$$t = \frac{\bar{x} - \mu_0}{s/\sqrt{n}} = \frac{72.87 - 72}{11.01/\sqrt{92}} = 0.758$$

30-35

Test of Significance

## Example: Resting Pulse Rate Test of Significance

Step 3 **SOLVE:** (cont.) Find *P*-value for $t = 0.758$. df = 92 – 1 = 91

Table C t distribution critical values

| | | | | | | | | | | | | |
|---|---|---|---|---|---|---|---|---|---|---|---|---|
| 80 | 0.678 | 0.846 | 1.043 | 1.292 | 1.664 | 1.990 | 2.088 | 2.374 | 2.639 | 2.887 | 3.195 | 3.416 |
| 100 | 0.677 | 0.845 | 1.042 | 1.290 | 1.660 | 1.984 | 2.081 | 2.364 | 2.626 | 2.871 | 3.174 | 3.390 |
| One-sided *P* | .25 | .20 | .15 | .10 | .05 | .025 | .02 | .01 | .005 | .0025 | .001 | .0005 |
| Two-sided *P* | .50 | .40 | .30 | .20 | .10 | .05 | .04 | .02 | .01 | .005 | .002 | .001 |

Two-sided test →

$0.678 < 0.758 < 0.846$

$.50 > P\text{-value} > .40$

Step 4 **CONCLUDE:** Draw Conclusions in context.

$0.50 > P\text{-value} > 0.40 > 0.05 = \alpha$

Do not reject the null hypothesis.

Conclusion in context: Insufficient evidence to conclude that the mean pulse rate is significantly different from 72 beats per minute.

30-36

## Vocabulary

**Conditions for t**
**Standard Error of $\bar{x}$**
**t Distribution**
**t***
**t Test**
**Degrees of Freedom**

31-1

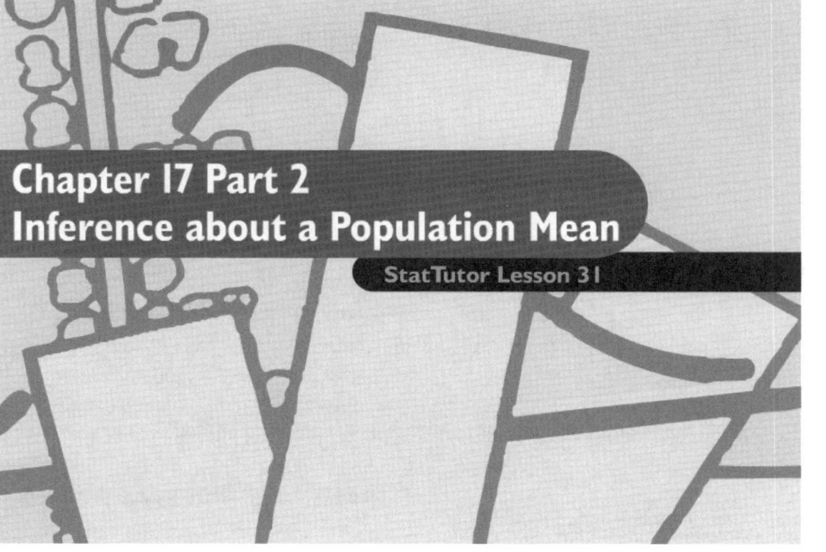


31-2

## Lesson Objectives

1. Examine assumptions of *t* procedures.
2. Define what a robust statistical procedure is and check to determine whether a *t* procedure is robust in a problem setting.
3. Demonstrate what a matched pairs design is and how it is used in experimentation.
4. Perform a one-sample *t* test on data from a matched pairs design using observed differences.
5. Compute and interpret a one-sample *t* confidence interval for $\mu_d$ using observed differences from a matched pairs design.

31-3

Conditions of *t* Procedure

# Robustness of *t* Procedures

Basic Practice of Statistics Chapter 17

31-4

Conditions of *t* Procedure

**Theoretical Conditions of *t* procedures:**

- SRS.
- Population must be Normally distributed.

If these two conditions are met, then *t* confidence intervals and *t* test *P*-values are exact.

**But what should we check in practice?**

31-5

*Conditions of t Procedure*

## In Practice

**No population is exactly Normal:**

- Thus, no $t$-procedure has an exact $t$-distribution.

**Questions:**

How are $t$-procedures affected by not having an SRS?

Confidence levels and $P$-values are off, but we don't know how much nor in what direction.

How are $t$-procedures affected by lack of Normality?

Confidence levels and $P$-values are approximately correct provided data are not strongly skewed and have no outliers!

31-6

*Robustness of t Procedures*

## Definition of Robust

**A statistical procedure (confidence interval or significance test) is *robust* if:** Confidence level or $P$-value does not change very much when conditions of procedure are not met.

**Are $t$ procedures *robust* with respect to:**

- Lack of SRS (randomization)? **Never**

  **Check:** Method of data collection for use of probability selection.

  Ask: Can data be regarded as an SRS?

- Lack of Normality? **Yes, but only IF data are not strongly skewed and have no outliers.**

  **Check:** Plot of data:

  Look for: Reasonable symmetry and single-peaked appearance

  Look out for: Strong skewness, outliers

**Sample size less than 40:**
OK to use $t$ procedures unless outliers or strong skewness are present.
**Sample size at least 40:**
OK to use $t$ procedures even when data are strongly skewed due to CLT.

31-7

*Checking conditions for t*

## Can a *t* Procedure Be Used?

**Case 1**

Researchers collected data on n = 143 bears in order to estimate the chest girth for all bears. Is using a $t$ confidence interval procedure appropriate? Why or why not?

**SRS?** **Seems reasonable to consider data as SRS.**

**Is $t$ robust with respect to Normality?** Examine plot of data.

**Yes, because sample size is sufficiently large to apply Central Limit Theorem.**

Use of $t$ procedure is appropriate.

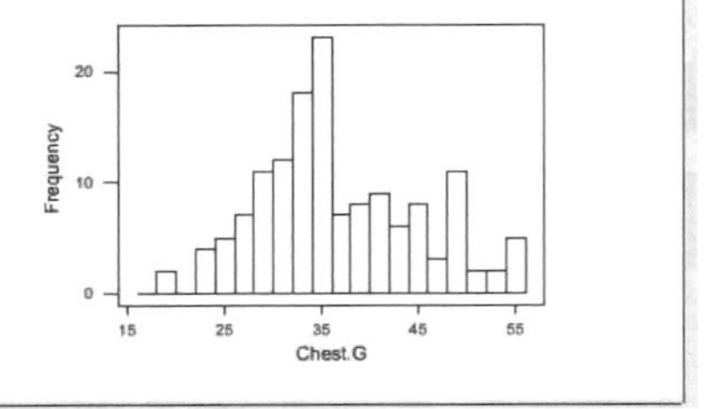


31-8

*Checking conditions for t*

## Can a *t* Procedure Be Used?

**Case 2**

Researchers at an agricultural station want to determine if the average yield of a variety of alfalfa exceeds three tons per acre; they randomly selected sixteen fields from those available for use in the experiment. Is using a $t$ significance test procedure appropriate? Why or why not?

**SRS?** **Fields were randomly selected.**

**Is $t$ robust with respect to Normality?**

Examine plot of data.

**Yes, because there are no outliers or strong skewness in the data.**

Use of $t$ procedure is appropriate.

Leaf Unit = 0.010

| Stem | Leaf |
|---|---|
| 29 | 3 |
| 29 | 9 |
| 30 | 4 |
| 30 | 69 |
| 31 | 1 |
| 31 | 79 |
| 32 | 023 |
| 32 | 567 |
| 33 | 1 |
| 33 | |
| 34 | 0 |

31-9

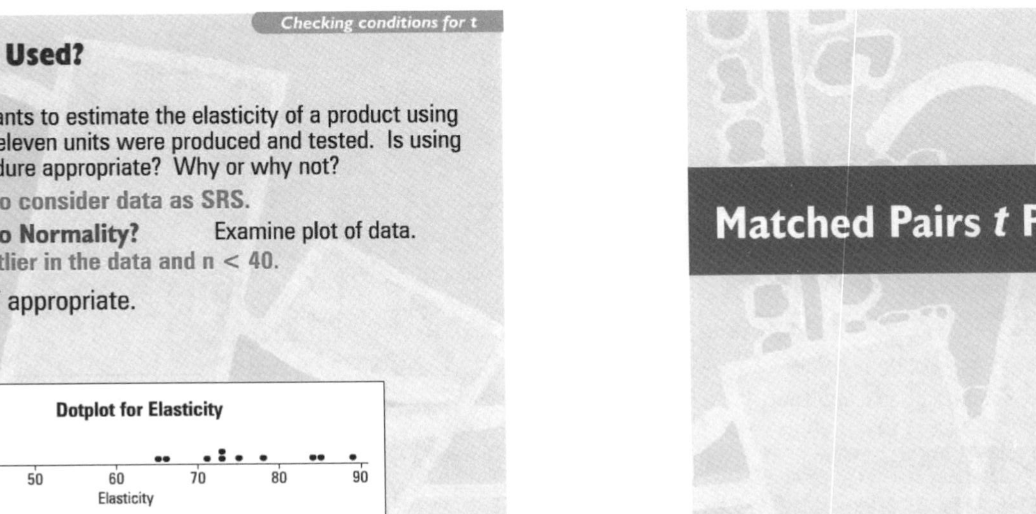


31-10

Matched Pairs Designs

# Matched Pairs $t$ Procedures

Basic Practice of Statistics Chapter 17

31-11

Matched Pairs Designs

## Matched Pairs Design

Randomized Block Design with 2 Treatments or 2 Measurements

| Blocks (Pairs) | Randomization |
|---|---|
| Two matched individuals | Randomly assign treatments to individuals within pair. |
| One individual: 2 treatments | Randomly assign order of treatments. |
| One individual: pre and post measurements | Randomly select individuals. |

**Analysis of data from a matched pairs design is the most common use of the one-sample *t* test.**

31-12

Matched Pairs Designs

## Matched Pairs: Two Subjects

Mean and standard deviation are computed from the differences.

| | Response | Difference |
|---|---|---|
| Treatment #1 | $x_{11}$ | $x_{11} - x_{21} = d_1$ |
| | $x_{12}$ | $x_{12} - x_{22} = d_2$ |
| | $x_{13}$ | $x_{13} - x_{23} = d_3$ |
| | $x_{14}$ | $x_{14} - x_{24} = d_4$ |
| | $x_{15}$ | $x_{15} - x_{25} = d_5$ |
| | $x_{16}$ | $x_{16} - x_{26} = d_6$ |
| | $x_{17}$ | $x_{17} - x_{27} = d_7$ |
| | $x_{18}$ | $x_{18} - x_{28} = d_8$ |
| Treatment #2 | $x_{21}$ | |
| | $x_{22}$ | |
| | $x_{23}$ | |
| | $x_{24}$ | |
| | $x_{25}$ | |
| | $x_{26}$ | |
| | $x_{27}$ | |
| | $x_{28}$ | |

31-13

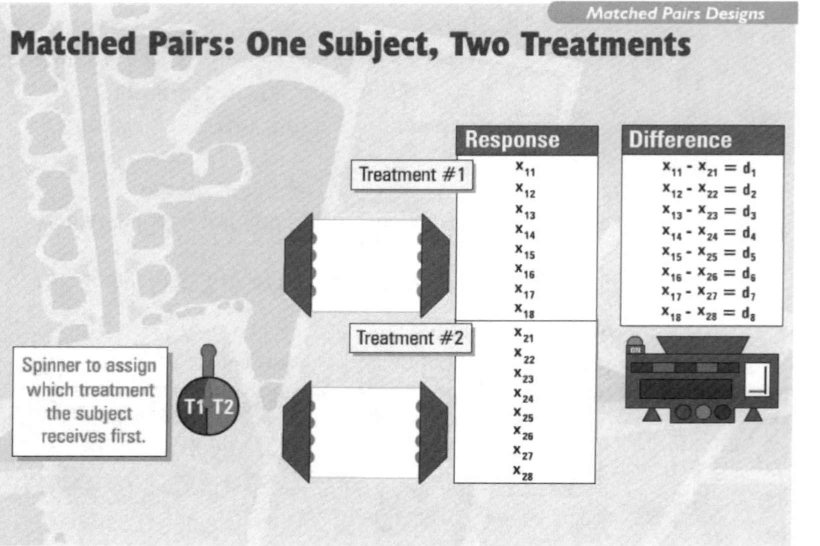


31-14

Matched Pairs Designs

## Post Responses

| Response *before* | Response *after* | Differences |
|---|---|---|
| $x_{11}$ | $x_{21}$ | $x_{11} - x_{21} = d_1$ |
| $x_{12}$ | $x_{22}$ | $x_{12} - x_{22} = d_2$ |
| $x_{13}$ | $x_{23}$ | $x_{13} - x_{23} = d_3$ |
| $x_{14}$ | $x_{24}$ | $x_{14} - x_{24} = d_4$ |
| $x_{15}$ | $x_{25}$ | $x_{15} - x_{25} = d_5$ |
| $x_{16}$ | $x_{26}$ | $x_{16} - x_{26} = d_6$ |
| $x_{17}$ | $x_{27}$ | $x_{17} - x_{27} = d_7$ |
| $x_{18}$ | $x_{28}$ | $x_{18} - x_{28} = d_8$ |

Treatment

Mean and standard deviation are computed from the differences.

* **Randomization:** ***In choosing subjects***

31-15

Matched Pairs Designs

**View Movie Clip.**

**What type of matched pairs?**

- Two Paired Individuals
- One Individual: Two Treatments
- One Individual: Pre-Post Responses

31-16

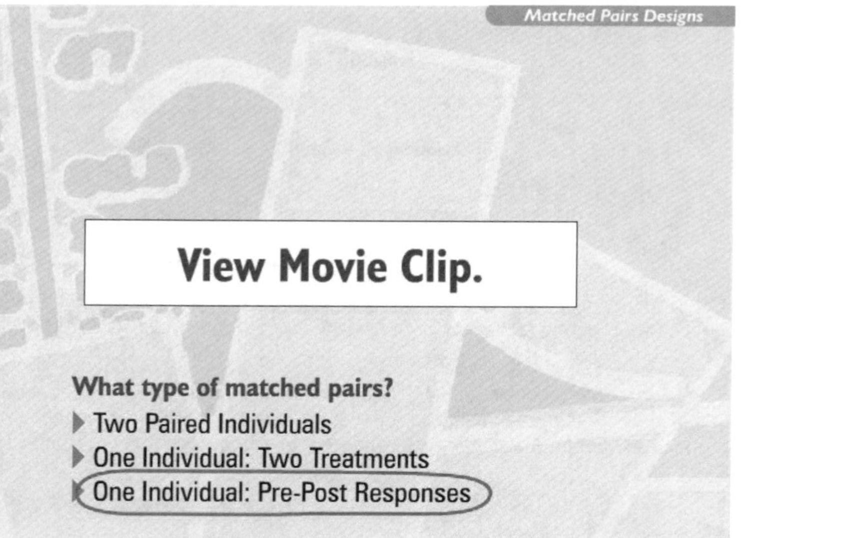

31-17



## Steps for Test of Significance--Matched Pairs *t*

Step 1 **STATE** the problem.

Step 2 **PLAN:** Recognize need for a matched pairs *t*-test.
Specify $H_0$ and $H_a$ in terms of $\mu_d$; choose $\alpha$.

Step 3 **SOLVE:** Collect data--random allocation or SRS for pre/post.
Plot differences; compute $\bar{d}$ and $s_d$.
Check: data collection ok and no outliers in differences ($n < 40$)
Calculate test statistic: $t = \frac{\bar{d} - 0}{\frac{s_d}{\sqrt{n}}}$

$\bar{d}$ = mean of differences
$s_d$ = standard deviation of differences
$n$ = # of pairs
df = $n - 1$

Obtain *P*-value from *t* table.

Step 4 **CONCLUDE:** Draw conclusions in context.

31-18



## Example: Matched Pairs t Test (Cola Sweetness)

Step 1 **STATE** the problem and identify essential information.

A cola maker tested an artificial sweetner in their cola recipe to see if the sweetness of this cola remains constant or decreases during storage.
Ten batches of cola were prepared using the artificial sweetner. Two bottles of cola from each batch were taste tested by a panel of experts to obtain a composite sweetness measure -- one immediately after the batch was produced and the other one month later. Is there evidence that the cola lost sweetness during storage?

| Type of Alternative: | One sided |
|---|---|
| Sample Size: | 10 |
| Null value ($\mu_0$): | 0 |

Step 2 **PLAN:** Two measurements on each batch: fresh and stored--perform a matched pairs *t* test.
Specify $H_0$ and $H_a$ in terms of $\mu_d$; choose $\alpha$.

**Let $d_i$ = fresh – stored** $H_0$: $\mu_d = 0$ vs. $H_a$: $\mu_d > 0$

31-19

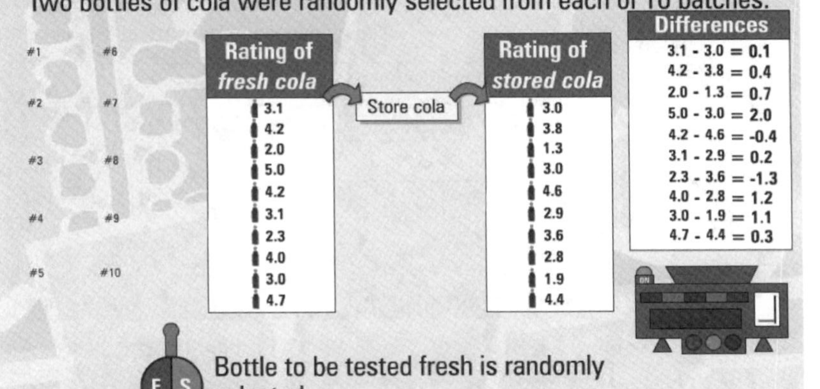



## Example: Matched Pairs t Test (Cola Sweetness)

Step 3 **SOLVE:** Collect data by conducting experiment
Two bottles of cola were randomly selected from each of 10 batches.

| Rating of *fresh cola* | Rating of *stored cola* | Differences |
|---|---|---|
| 3.1 | 3.0 | 3.1 - 3.0 = 0.1 |
| 4.2 | 3.8 | 4.2 - 3.8 = 0.4 |
| 2.0 | 1.3 | 2.0 - 1.3 = 0.7 |
| 5.0 | 3.0 | 5.0 - 3.0 = 2.0 |
| 4.2 | 4.6 | 4.2 - 4.6 = -0.4 |
| 3.1 | 2.9 | 3.1 - 2.9 = 0.2 |
| 2.3 | 3.6 | 2.3 - 3.6 = -1.3 |
| 4.0 | 2.8 | 4.0 - 2.8 = 1.2 |
| 3.0 | 1.9 | 3.0 - 1.9 = 1.1 |
| 4.7 | 4.4 | 4.7 - 4.4 = 0.3 |



Bottle to be tested fresh is randomly selected.

31-20



## Example: Matched Pairs t Test (Cola Sweetness)

Step 3 **SOLVE:** (cont.) Plot differences; compute $\bar{d}$ and $s_d$

-1.20 -0.60 0.00 0.60 1.20 1.80 Differences

| Differences |
|---|
| 0.1 |
| 0.4 |
| 0.7 |
| 2.0 |
| -0.4 |
| 0.2 |
| -1.3 |
| 1.2 |
| 1.1 |
| 0.3 |

Check conditions

**Data collection?** Two bottles randomly selected from each batch; one randomly allocated to immediate testing and the other to one month after storage testing.

**n < 40: Outliers or strong skewness?** Differences have no outliers or strong skewness; ok to perform matched pairs *t* procedure.

Compute test statistic

$$t = \frac{\bar{d} - \mu_d}{s_d/\sqrt{n}} = \frac{0.43 - 0}{0.909/\sqrt{10}} = 1.50$$

$\bar{d} = 0.43$
$s_d = .909$

31-21

Example: Matched Pairs Test

# Example: Matched Pairs t Test (Cola Sweetness)

Step 3 **SOLVE:** (cont.) Obtain *P*-value for $t = 1.50$ $df = 10 - 1 = 9$

Table C t distribution critical values

| | Confidence Level *C* | | | | | | | | | | | |
|---|---|---|---|---|---|---|---|---|---|---|---|---|
| df | 50% | 60% | 70% | 80% | 90% | 95% | 96% | 98% | 99% | 99.5% | 99.8% | 99.9% |
| 9 | 0.703 | 0.883 | 1.100 | 1.38 | 1.833 | 2.262 | 2.398 | 2.821 | 3.250 | 3.690 | 4.297 | 4.781 |
| One-sided *P* | .25 | .20 | .15 | .10 | .05 | .025 | .02 | .01 | .005 | .0025 | .001 | .0005 |

t = 1.50 $.10 > P > .05$

Step 4 **CONCLUDE:** Draw conclusions in context.

$0.10 > P > 0.05 = \alpha$ (level of significance)

Fail to reject the null hypothesis.

**Interpretion in context:**

Conclude that the evidence is not strong enough to say the cola lost sweetness after one month of storage at $\alpha = 0.05$.

31-22

Op Example: Matched Pairs Test

# Optional Example:

## Tensile strength for Sutures vs. Tape:

Step 1 **STATE** the problem and identify essential information.

Medical researchers wanted to determine whether the tensile strength for incisions treated by suture is different from those treated by tape. Ten rats received two identical incisions on their backs. One incision is randomly selected to be sutured and the other is taped. After 40 days they measure the tensile strength of the treated incisions.

*(Nonparametrics Statistical Methods Based on Ranks* by Lehmann.*)*

| | |
|---|---|
| Type of Alternative: | Two sided |
| Sample Size: | 10 |
| Null value ($\mu_0$): | 0 |

Step 2 **PLAN:** 2 measures on each rat--do matched pairs *t*-test.

Specify $H_0$ and $H_a$ in terms of $\mu_d$; choose $\alpha$.

$H_0: \mu_d = 0$ versus $H_a: \mu_d \neq 0$

$\alpha = 0.05$



31-23

Op Example: Matched Pairs Test

# Optional Example:

## Tensile strength for Sutures vs. Tape:

Step 3 **SOLVE:** Collect data (conduct experiment)

| Rat | Taped | Sutures | Difference |
|---|---|---|---|
| 1 | 659 | 452 | 207 |
| 2 | 984 | 587 | 397 |
| 3 | 397 | 460 | -63 |
| 4 | 574 | 787 | -213 |
| 5 | 447 | 351 | 96 |
| 6 | 479 | 277 | 202 |
| 7 | 676 | 234 | 442 |
| 8 | 761 | 516 | 245 |
| 9 | 647 | 577 | 70 |
| 10 | 577 | 513 | 64 |



31-24

Op Example: Matched Pairs Test

# Optional Example:

## Tensile strength for Sutures vs. Tape:

Step 3

**CrunchIt! Output**

Dotplot

-200 -100 0 100 200 300 400

tape-suture

**Checks: Treatment randomly assigned to incision. No outliers or strong skewness.**

Paired T statistics

Options

**Hypothesis test results:**

$\mu_1 - \mu_2$ : mean of the paired difference between tape and suture

$H_0 : \mu_1 - \mu_2 = 0$

$H_A : \mu_1 - \mu_2 \neq 0$

| Difference | Sample Diff. | Std. Err. | DF | T-Stat | P-value |
|---|---|---|---|---|---|
| tape - suture | 144.7 | 62.7889 | 9 | 2.3045475 | 0.0467 |

31-25

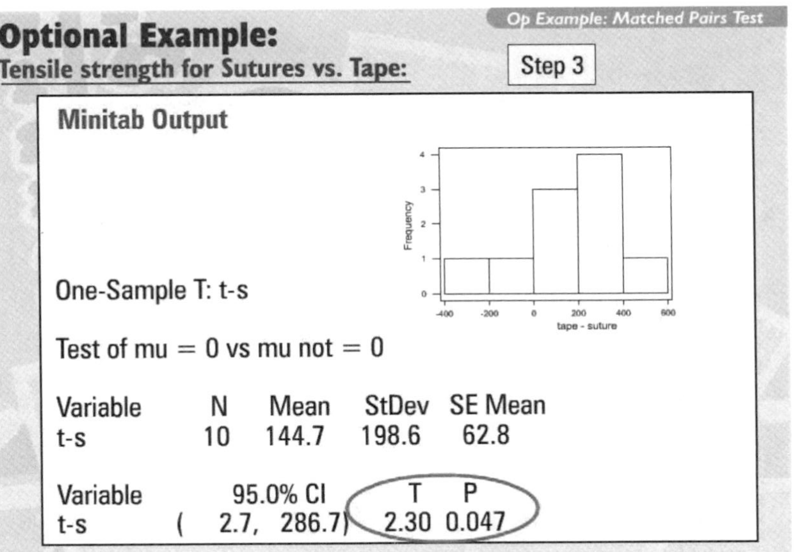


31-26

Op Example: Matched Pairs Test

## Optional Example:

**Tensile strength for Sutures vs. Tape:**

Step 3

**S-Plus Output**

One-sample t-Test

data: t.s in rats.txt
t = 2.3045, df = 9, p-value = 0.0467
alternative hypothesis: true mean is not equal to 0
95 percent confidence interval:
2.661647 286.738353
sample estimates:
mean of x
144.7

31-27

Op Example: Matched Pairs Test

## Optional Example:

**Tensile strength for Sutures vs. Tape:**

Step 4 **CONCLUDE:** Draw conclusions in context.

P-value = 0.0467 < $\alpha$ = 0.05

**Reject $H_0$**

**Interpretion in context:**

Conclude that the tensile strength for incisions treated by tape is significantly different from those treated by suture at $\alpha = 0.05$.

31-28

Matched Pairs C.I.

## Steps for Creating Confidence Interval for $\mu_d$

Step 1 **STATE** the problem.

Step 2 **PLAN:** Recognize need for a confidence interval for mean difference for matched pairs t; specify confidence level.

Step 3 **SOLVE:** Collect data--random allocation or SRS with pre/post.
Plot differences; compute $\bar{d}$ and $s_d$.
Check: data collection ok and no outliers in differences (n < 40)
Calculate confidence interval for $\mu_d$, the mean difference:

$$\bar{d} \pm t^*\left[\frac{s_d}{\sqrt{n}}\right]$$

where $\bar{d}$ = mean of differences
$s_d$ = standard deviation of differences
n = # of pairs
df = n − 1

Step 4 **CONCLUDE:** Interpret confidence interval in context.

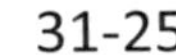

31-29

Example: Matched Pairs C.I.

## Example: Confidence Interval (Left vs. Right)

Step 1 **STATE** the problem.

- Two identical knobs--one with clockwise (right) screw action and one with counterclockwise (left) screw action.
- 25 right-handed students will turn each knob a specified distance with their right hand; order of knobs will be randomized.
- Time for each turn is response variable; differences of left minus right will be computed and analyzed.

**Research Question:**
What is the average difference in time required for right-handed students to turn a knob to the left versus to the right?

Step 2 **PLAN:**
Estimate the mean difference with a 95% confidence interval.

31-30

Example: Matched Pairs C.I.

## Example: Confidence Interval (Left vs. Right)

Level of confidence: 95%

| n | 25 |
|---|---|
| $\bar{d}$ | 13.32 |
| $s_d$ | 22.94 |
| Confidence Level | 95% |

Step 3 **SOLVE:** Collect data: 25 students turn both knobs--order is randomized.

Plot differences;

Differences
-40 -20 0 20 40 50 Diff

| Obs | Left | Right | Diff |
|---|---|---|---|
| 1 | 137 | 113 | 24 |
| 2 | 105 | 105 | 0 |
| 3 | 133 | 130 | 3 |
| 4 | 108 | 101 | 7 |
| 5 | 115 | 138 | -23 |
| 6 | 170 | 118 | 52 |
| 7 | 103 | 87 | 16 |
| 8 | 145 | 116 | 29 |
| 9 | 78 | 75 | 3 |
| 10 | 107 | 96 | 11 |
| 11 | 84 | 122 | -38 |
| 12 | 148 | 103 | 45 |
| 13 | 147 | 116 | 31 |
| 14 | 87 | 107 | -20 |
| 15 | 166 | 118 | 48 |
| 16 | 146 | 103 | 43 |
| 17 | 123 | 111 | 12 |
| 18 | 135 | 104 | 31 |
| 19 | 112 | 111 | 1 |
| 20 | 93 | 89 | 4 |
| 21 | 76 | 78 | -2 |
| 22 | 116 | 100 | 16 |
| 23 | 78 | 89 | -11 |
| 24 | 101 | 85 | 16 |
| 25 | 123 | 88 | 35 |

Compute $\bar{d}$ to estimate $\mu_d$: $\bar{d} = 13.32$
Compute $s_d$ to estimate $\sigma_d$: $s_d = 22.94$

Check conditions
Order of knobs was randomized; data has no strong skewness or outliers ➧ ok to proceed.

31-31

Example: Matched Pairs C.I.

## Example: Confidence Interval (Left vs. Right)

| n | 25 |
|---|---|
| $\bar{d}$ | 13.32 |
| $s_d$ | 22.94 |
| Confidence Level | 95% |

Step 3 **SOLVE:** (cont.) Compute interval

$df = n - 1 = 25 - 1 = 24$

$\bar{d} \pm t^* \left[\frac{s_d}{\sqrt{n}}\right]$ $13.32 \pm 9.45$ $[3.87 , 22.77]$

Step 4 **CONCLUDE:** Interpret interval in context.

**Conclusion:** We are 95% confident that the true mean difference between left and right times is between 3.87 and 22.77 seconds.

Note: Since zero is not in the confidence interval, we can conclude that it takes longer on average for a right-handed student to turn a knob counter-clockwise than clockwise.

31-32

## Vocabulary

**Conditions**
**Matched Pairs Design**
**Matched Pairs *t* Procedure**
**Robustness**

32-1

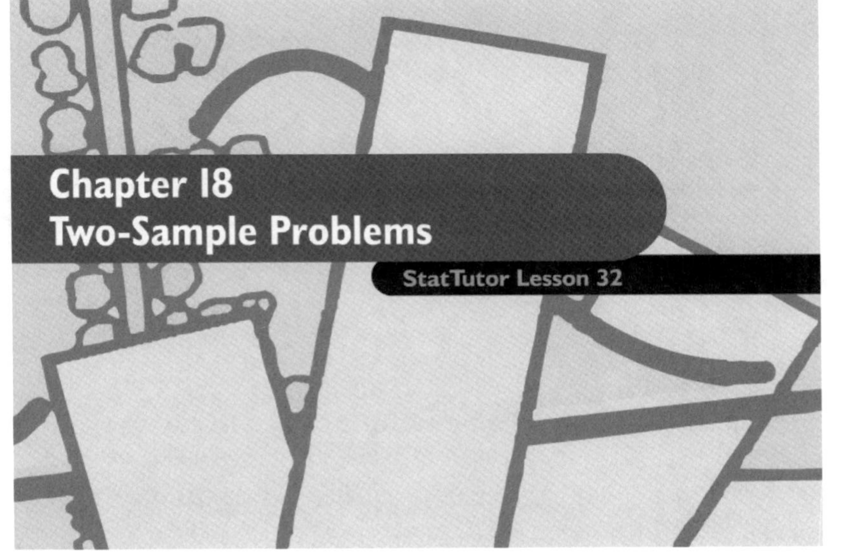


32-2

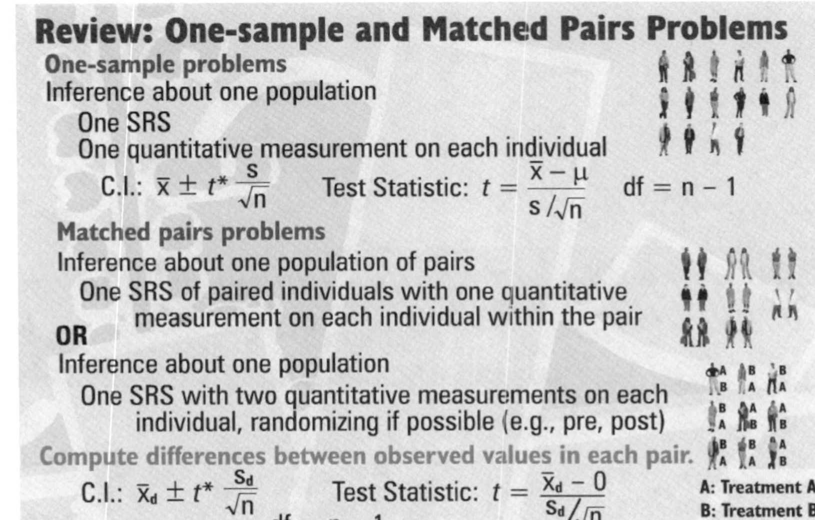

## Objectives

1. Identify when a problem requires comparing two means from two independent populations.
2. Distinguish between a single sample, a matched pairs, and a two-sample problem based on a problem description.
3. Explain the sampling distribution implications when comparing two population means.
4. Conduct a test of significance that compares two population means; estimate the difference between two population means.
5. List the guidelines for robustness and apply them to the two sample *t*-procedures.

32-3

## Two-Sample Problems

Basic Practice of Statistics Chapter 18

32-4

## Review: One-sample and Matched Pairs Problems

**One-sample problems**

Inference about one population

One SRS

One quantitative measurement on each individual

C.I.: $\bar{x} \pm t^* \frac{s}{\sqrt{n}}$ Test Statistic: $t = \frac{\bar{x} - \mu}{s/\sqrt{n}}$ df = n − 1

**Matched pairs problems**

Inference about one population of pairs

One SRS of paired individuals with one quantitative measurement on each individual within the pair

**OR**

Inference about one population

One SRS with two quantitative measurements on each individual, randomizing if possible (e.g., pre, post)

**Compute differences between observed values in each pair.**

C.I.: $\bar{x}_d \pm t^* \frac{s_d}{\sqrt{n}}$ Test Statistic: $t = \frac{\bar{x}_d - 0}{s_d/\sqrt{n}}$ df = n − 1

A: Treatment A
B: Treatment B

32-5

## Two-Sample Problems

Compare two populations or two treatments

**Two Populations (Survey)**

Take two separate SRS's. (Like stratified sample with 2 strata)
One quantitative measurement on each individual.

Sample 1 from Population 1 | Sample 2 from Population 2

**Two Treatments (Experiment)**

Randomly divide individuals into two treatment groups.
One quantitative measurement on each individual.

Random Allocation → Treatment 1
Random Allocation → Treatment 2

32-6

Two-Sample Problems

# Comparing Two Population Means

Basic Practice of Statistics Chapter 18

32-7

Two-Sample Problems

## Examples of Two-Sample Problems

Compare mean weight of filling of double stuffed with mean weight of filling of regular oreos.

$n_{\text{Regular Oreo}} = 49$

$n_{\text{Double stuffed}} = 52$

Fail to reject $H_0$

Compare mean stop time of fully actuated with mean stop time of pre-timed stop lights.

Is $\mu_{\text{Fully actuated}} < \mu_{\text{Pre-timed}}$?

32-8

Two-Sample Problems

# Two-Sample *t* Procedures

Basic Practice of Statistics Chapter 18

32-9



## Notation for Comparing Two Population Means

| | One population | | One Sample | |
|---|---|---|---|---|
| Mean | $\mu$ | | $\bar{x}$ | |
| Standard deviation | $\sigma$ | | $s$ | |
| | **Two populations** | | **Two Samples** | |
| Means | $\mu_1$ | $\mu_2$ | $\bar{x}_1$ | $\bar{x}_2$ |
| Standard deviations | $\sigma_1$ | $\sigma_2$ | $s_1$ | $s_2$ |

**How should we combine two parameters to get one for comparison?**

**Sum** $\mu_1 + \mu_2$? ☹ Not informative

**Difference** $\mu_1 - \mu_2$? ☺ Informative and mathematically nice

**Product** $\mu_1 \bullet \mu_2$? ☹ Not informative

**Ratio** $\mu_1 / \mu_2$? 😐 Informative but not mathematically nice

**What is the corresponding statistic?** $\bar{x}_1 - \bar{x}_2$

32-10

Two-Sample Problems

## Notation for Comparing Two Population Means

| | One population | | One Sample | |
|---|---|---|---|---|
| Mean | $\mu$ | | $\bar{x}$ | |
| Standard deviation | $\sigma$ | | $s$ | |
| | **Two populations** | | **Two Samples** | |
| Means | $\mu_1$ | $\mu_2$ | $\bar{x}_1$ | $\bar{x}_2$ |
| Standard deviations | $\sigma_1$ | $\sigma_2$ | $s_1$ | $s_2$ |

**How should we combine two parameters to get one for comparison?**

$\mu_1 - \mu_2$ In words: Difference between two population means

$\bar{x}_1 - \bar{x}_2$ In words: Difference between two sample means

**What is the corresponding statistic?** $\bar{x}_1 - \bar{x}_2$

32-11



## Sampling Distribution of $\bar{x}_1 - \bar{x}_2$

Both populations Normally distributed

**What are the sampling distributions of $\bar{x}_1$ and $\bar{x}_2$?**

$\bar{x}_1$: Normally distributed with mean, $\mu_1$, and standard deviation, $\frac{\sigma_1}{\sqrt{n_1}}$

$\bar{x}_2$: Normally distributed with mean, $\mu_2$, and standard deviation, $\frac{\sigma_2}{\sqrt{n_2}}$

**What is the sampling distribution of $\bar{x}_1 - \bar{x}_2$?**

$\bar{x}_1 - \bar{x}_2$: Normally distributed with mean, $\mu_1 - \mu_2$,

and standard deviation, $\sqrt{\left(\frac{\sigma_1}{\sqrt{n_1}}\right)^2 + \left(\frac{\sigma_2}{\sqrt{n_2}}\right)^2} = \sqrt{\frac{\sigma_1^2}{n_1} + \frac{\sigma_2^2}{n_2}}$

32-12



## Measuring Variability of $\bar{x}_1 - \bar{x}_2$

$$\sqrt{\frac{\sigma_1^2}{n_1} + \frac{\sigma_2^2}{n_2}} = \sqrt{\frac{\sigma^2}{n_1} + \frac{\sigma^2}{n_2}} \approx s_p\sqrt{\frac{1}{n_1} + \frac{1}{n_2}}$$

To maximize degrees of freedom, we assume $\sigma_1 = \sigma_2$.

**Question:** How does the formula appear if $\sigma_1 = \sigma_2 = \sigma$?

**Replace $\sigma_1$ and $\sigma_2$ with $\sigma$ in formula!**

**Question:** Can we simplify the formula?

**Yes, by bringing $\sigma$ outside the radical!!!**

**Question:** How do we estimate $\sigma$?

**With $s_p$, the square root of weighted average of $s_1^2$ and $s_2^2$, weighted by their degrees of freedom: $(n_1 - 1)$ and $(n_2 - 1)$.**

$s_p = \sqrt{\frac{(n_1 - 1)s_1^2 + (n_2 - 1)s_2^2}{n_1 + n_2 - 2}}$ **called the pooled estimate of $\sigma$.**

32-13

Two-Sample Problems

## Comparing Two-Sample Means

Compare two populations or two treatments

**Two Populations (Surveys)**

- Take two separate SRS's from each of two distinct populations.
- Measure same quantitative variable on individuals in both samples.
- Perform test of hypothesis on $H_0: \mu_1 - \mu_2 = 0$.
- If significant, compute a confidence interval to estimate $\mu_1 - \mu_2$.

**Two Treatments (Experiments)**

- Randomly divide individuals into two groups.
- Apply different treatment to each group.
- Measure same quantitative variable on individuals in both groups.
- Perform a test of hypothesis on $H_0: \mu_{T1} - \mu_{T2} = 0$.
- If significant, compute a confidence interval to estimate $\mu_{T1} - \mu_{T2}$.
  T1 = Treatment 1 and T2 = Treatment 2

Note: $H_0: \mu_1 - \mu_2 = 0$ is equivalent to $H_0: \mu_1 = \mu_2$

32-14

Conditions for Comparing Means

## Conditions

**Data collection:**

**Sampling:** Two independent SRS's are taken—one from each of two separate populations.

**Experimenting:** Individuals are randomly allocated to two treatment groups.

**No matching!**

**Distribution:**

**In theory:** Both populations are Normally distributed and $\sigma_1 = \sigma_2$.

**In practice:** Both distributions should have similar shapes with no outliers.

**AND** $\dfrac{\text{largest s}}{\text{smallest s}} < 2$

Means and standard deviations for both populations are unknown.

32-15

Components of Two Sample t

## Two-Sample Pooled *t* Procedure

Basic Practice of Statistics Chapter 18

32-16

Components of Two Sample t

## Hypotheses

| Null Hypothesis | Alternative Hypothesis |
|---|---|
| $H_0$: No difference in population means or treatment means | $H_a$: One mean is greater than the other **OR** $H_a$: Means are not equal |
| $H_0: \mu_1 - \mu_2 = 0$ or $H_0: \mu_1 = \mu_2$ | $H_a: \mu_1 - \mu_2 > 0$ or $H_a: \mu_1 > \mu_2$ (one sided) **OR** $H_a: \mu_1 - \mu_2 \neq 0$ or $H_a: \mu_1 \neq \mu_2$ (two sided) |

32-17

Components of Two Sample t

## Test Statistic

For testing $H_0$: $\mu_1 - \mu_2 = 0$ or equivalently $H_0$: $\mu_1 = \mu_2$

Since the parameter is $\mu_1 - \mu_2$, 0 is the hypothesized value for $\mu_1 - \mu_2$.

**Recall the general formula for a test statistic:**

$$\frac{\text{Estimate} - \text{Hypothesized value for } \mu_1 - \mu_2}{\text{Standard deviation of estimate}}$$

Since $\bar{x}_1 - \bar{x}_2$ is approximately Normal for sufficiently large $n_1$ and $n_2$ with mean: $\mu_1 - \mu_2$ and standard deviation: $\sigma\sqrt{\frac{1}{n_1} + \frac{1}{n_2}}$

$$\frac{\bar{x}_1 - \bar{x}_2 - 0}{\sigma\sqrt{\frac{1}{n_1} + \frac{1}{n_2}}}$$

**Estimating σ with $s_p$, we get:**

$$t = \frac{\bar{x}_1 - \bar{x}_2 - 0}{s_p\sqrt{\frac{1}{n_1} + \frac{1}{n_2}}} \quad \text{where} \quad s_p = \sqrt{\frac{(n_1 - 1)s_1^2 + (n_2 - 1)s_2^2}{n_1 + n_2 - 2}}$$

$$df = n_1 + n_2 - 2$$

32-18

Components of Two Sample t

## Confidence Interval for Difference between Means

$\mu_1 - \mu_2$ = difference between two population means (parameter)

$\bar{x}_1 - \bar{x}_2$ = difference between two sample means (statistic)

$\bar{x}_1 - \bar{x}_2$ is a point estimate of $\mu_1 - \mu_2$.

**Recall the general formula for a confidence interval:**

Point Estimate ± (Table value) (Standard deviation of estimate)

Since $\bar{x}_1 - \bar{x}_2$ is approximately Normal for sufficiently large $n_1$ and $n_2$ with mean: $\mu_1 - \mu_2$ and standard deviation: $\sigma\sqrt{\frac{1}{n_1} + \frac{1}{n_2}}$

$$\bar{x}_1 - \bar{x}_2 \pm (\text{Table value})\, \sigma\sqrt{\frac{1}{n_1} + \frac{1}{n_2}}$$

**Estimating σ with $s_p$, we get:**

$$\bar{x}_1 - \bar{x}_2 \pm t^* \, s_p\sqrt{\frac{1}{n_1} + \frac{1}{n_2}} \quad \text{where} \quad s_p = \sqrt{\frac{(n_1 - 1)s_1^2 + (n_2 - 1)s_2^2}{n_1 + n_2 - 2}}$$

$$df = n_1 + n_2 - 2$$

32-19

Components of Two Sample t

## Formulas for Statistical Inference

**Pooled *t* Procedure**

| Test Statistic Formula for $H_0$: $\mu_1 = \mu_2$ or $H_0$: $\mu_1 - \mu_2 = 0$ | Confidence Interval Formula for $\mu_1 - \mu_2$ (Gives approximate interval) |
|---|---|
| $t = \frac{(\bar{x}_1 - \bar{x}_2) - 0}{s_p\sqrt{\frac{1}{n_1} + \frac{1}{n_2}}}$ | $\bar{x}_1 - \bar{x}_2 \pm t^* \cdot s_p\sqrt{\frac{1}{n_1} + \frac{1}{n_2}}$ |
| *t* has a *t* distribution with df = $n_1 + n_2 - 2$ | *t** is a value from the *t* table with df = $n_1 + n_2 - 2$ |

Obtain *P*-value from *t* table.

Gives a margin of error for level of confidence, *C*.

32-20

Two-Sample t Steps

## Example of the Pooled Two-Sample *t* Procedures

Basic Practice of Statistics Chapter 18

32-21



## Steps for Two-Sample *t* Test of Significance

**Pooled Two-Sample *t* Method**

Step 1 **STATE**: Describe the problem.

Step 2 **PLAN**: Recognize need for comparing two means.
Specify $H_0$ and $H_a$ in terms of $\mu_1$ and $\mu_2$; choose $\alpha$.

Step 3 **SOLVE**: Collect data--random allocation or 2 independent SRS's.
Plot both data sets; compute $\bar{x}_1$, $\bar{x}_2$, $s_1$, and $s_2$.
Check: data collection, no outliers if $n_1 + n_2 < 40$, $\frac{\text{largest s}}{\text{smallest s}} < 2$
Calculate test statistic:

$$t = \frac{(\bar{x}_1 - \bar{x}_2) - 0}{s_p\sqrt{\frac{1}{n_1} + \frac{1}{n_2}}} \quad \text{where} \quad s_p = \sqrt{\frac{(n_1 - 1)s_1^2 + (n_2 - 1)s_2^2}{n_1 + n_2 - 2}} \quad \text{and} \quad df = n_1 + n_2 - 2$$

Obtain *P*-value from *t* table.

Step 4 **CONCLUDE**: Draw conclusions in context.

**Using software is recommended to get more accurate *P*-values.**

32-22



## Randomized Design Example (Two Treatments)

**Pooled Two-Sample *t* Method**

Step 1 **STATE** the problem and identify essential information.

A pharmaceutical company is conducting pre-clinical trials of an experimental anti-depressant drug. Since several subjects are complaining of dryness, a technician is assigned to investigate with 20 rats. She plans to randomly allocate 10 rats to receive the drug injection and 10 rats to receive a saline injection and measure their water intake during the next 24 hour period. Using $\alpha = 0.05$, the research question is:
***"Does the anti-depressant cause an increase in water consumption?"***

| | |
|---|---|
| Type of Alternative: | greater than |
| Null value ($\mu_D - \mu_S$): | 0 |
| $n_D$: | 10 |
| $n_S$: | 10 |
| $\alpha$: | 0.05 |

Step 2 **PLAN:** Need two-sample *t*-test for means.

Specify $H_0$ and $H_a$; choose $\alpha$.

$H_0$: $\mu_D - \mu_S = 0$ versus $H_a$: $\mu_D - \mu_S > 0$

32-23



## Randomized Design Example (Two Treatments)

**Pooled Two-Sample *t* Method**

Step 3 **SOLVE**: Collect data by conducting experiment.



32-24



## Randomized Design Example (Two Treatments)

**Pooled Two-Sample *t* Method**

Step 3 **SOLVE:** Plot each data set, compute $\bar{x}_D$, $\bar{x}_S$ and $s_D$ and $s_S$.

| Drug | Saline |
|---|---|
| 8.2 | 8.5 |
| 9.0 | 7.2 |
| 8.8 | 7.7 |
| 8.3 | 8.0 |
| 7.5 | 8.6 |
| 9.2 | 7.8 |
| 9.9 | 8.7 |
| 7.8 | 7.8 |
| 8.4 | 8.0 |
| 7.7 | 7.0 |

| | Drug | Placebo |
|---|---|---|
| $\bar{x}$ | 8.48 | 7.93 |
| s | 0.750 | 0.564 |
| n | 10 | 10 |

Side-By-Side Stemplot
Leaf unit = 0.1

| Drug | | Placebo |
|---|---|---|
| | 7 | 0 2 |
| 5 7 8 | 7 | 7 8 8 |
| 2 3 4 | 8 | 0 0 |
| 8 | 8 | 5 6 7 |
| 0 2 | 9 | |
| 9 | 9 | |

32-25

## Randomized Design Example (Two Treatments)

**Pooled Two-Sample *t* Method**

Step 3 **SOLVE:** (cont.) Check conditions

Check: data collection — random allocation of rats to treatments ✓

no outliers if $n_1 + n_2 < 40$ — $n_1 + n_2 = 20$ & no outliers ✓

$\frac{\text{largest s}}{\text{smallest s}} < 2$ — $\frac{\text{largest s}}{\text{smallest s}} = \frac{0.750}{0.564} = 1.33 < 2$ ✓

| Drug | Saline |
|---|---|
| 8.2 | 8.5 |
| 9.0 | 7.2 |
| 8.8 | 7.7 |
| 8.3 | 8.0 |
| 7.5 | 8.6 |
| 9.2 | 7.8 |
| 9.9 | 8.7 |
| 7.8 | 7.8 |
| 8.4 | 8.0 |
| 7.7 | 7.0 |

| | Drug | Saline |
|---|---|---|
| $\bar{x}$ | 8.48 | 7.93 |
| s | 0.750 | 0.564 |
| n | 10 | 10 |

Side-By-Side Stemplot
Leaf unit = 0.1

| Drug | | Saline |
|---|---|---|
| | 7 | 0 2 |
| 5 7 8 | 7 | 7 8 8 |
| 2 3 4 | 8 | 0 0 |
| 8 | 8 | 5 6 7 |
| 0 2 | 9 | |
| 9 | 9 | |

32-26



## Randomized Design Example (Two Treatments)

**Pooled Two-Sample *t* Method**

Step 3 **SOLVE:** (cont.) Check conditions

Rats randomly assigned to treatments; no outliers in either data set; standard deviations approximately equal ⇒ use of pooled *t* procedure is ok.

...ation of rats to treatments ✓

... + $n_2 = 20$ & no outliers ✓

$\frac{.750}{.564} = 1.33 < 2$ ✓

| Drug | Saline |
|---|---|
| 8.2 | 8.5 |
| 9.0 | 7.2 |
| 8.8 | 7.7 |
| 8.3 | 8.0 |
| 7.5 | 8.6 |
| 9.2 | 7.8 |
| 9.9 | 8.7 |
| 7.8 | 7.8 |
| 8.4 | 8.0 |
| 7.7 | 7.0 |

| | Drug | Saline |
|---|---|---|
| $\bar{x}$ | 8.48 | 7.93 |
| s | 0.750 | 0.564 |
| n | 10 | 10 |

Side-By-Side Stemplot
Leaf unit = 0.1

| Drug | | Saline |
|---|---|---|
| | 7 | 0 2 |
| 5 7 8 | 7 | 7 8 8 |
| 2 3 4 | 8 | 0 0 |
| 8 | 8 | 5 6 7 |
| 0 2 | 9 | |
| 9 | 9 | |

32-27



## Randomized Design Example (Two Treatments)

**Pooled Two-Sample *t* Method**

Step 3 **SOLVE:** (cont.) Calculate test statistic

$\bar{x}_D - \bar{x}_S = 8.48 - 7.93 = 0.55$

$$s_p = \sqrt{\frac{(n_D - 1)s_D^2 + (n_S - 1)s_S^2}{n_D + n_S - 2}} = \sqrt{\frac{(10-1)0.750^2 + (10-1)0.564^2}{10 + 10 - 2}} = 0.6635$$

$$t = \frac{(\bar{x}_D - \bar{x}_S) - 0}{s_p\sqrt{\frac{1}{n_D} + \frac{1}{n_S}}} = \frac{(8.48 - 7.93) - 0}{0.6635\sqrt{\frac{1}{10} + \frac{1}{10}}} = \frac{0.55}{0.297} = 1.853$$

| | Drug | Saline |
|---|---|---|
| $\bar{x}$ | 8.48 | 7.93 |
| s | 0.750 | 0.564 |
| n | 10 | 10 |

32-28



## Randomized Design Example (Two Treatments)

**Pooled Two-Sample *t* Method**

Step 3 **SOLVE:** (cont.) Find *P*-value for $t = 1.853$.

$df = n_D + n_S - 2 = 10 + 10 - 2 = 18$

$.05 > P > .025$

| 18 | 0.688 | 0.862 | 1.067 | 1.330 | 1.734 | 2.101 | 2.214 | 2.552 | 2.878 | 3.197 | 3.611 | 3.922 |
|---|---|---|---|---|---|---|---|---|---|---|---|---|
| One-sided *P* | .25 | .20 | .15 | .10 | .05 | .025 | .02 | .01 | .005 | .0025 | .001 | .0005 |

$1.734 < 1.853 < 2.101$

32-29



## Randomized Design Example (Two Treatments)

**Pooled Two-Sample *t* Method**

**Step 3** **SOLVE:** (cont.) Find *P*-value for $t = 1.853$.

$$df = n_D + n_S - 2 = 10 + 10 - 2 = 18$$

$$.05 > P > .025$$

**Step 4** **CONCLUDE:** Draw conclusions in context.

*P*-value: $.025 < P < .05 = \alpha$ (level of significance)

Sufficient evidence to reject the null hypothesis at $\alpha = 0.05$

Conclusion in context: At $\alpha = 0.05$, the average water intake for the rats in the drug group is significantly greater than the average water intake for the rats in the placebo group.
**Valid experiment: The anti-depressant drug *causes* an increase in thirst in rats.**

32-30



## 90% Confidence Interval for $\mu_1 - \mu_2$

**Pooled Two-Sample *t* Method**

$$s_p = \sqrt{\frac{(n_D - 1)s_D^2 + (n_S - 1)s_S^2}{n_D + n_S - 2}} = \sqrt{\frac{(10-1)0.750^2 + (10-1)0.564^2}{10 + 10 - 2}} = 0.6635$$

$$\bar{x}_1 - \bar{x}_2 \pm t^* \cdot s_p \sqrt{\frac{1}{n_1} + \frac{1}{n_2}} \rightarrow 8.48 - 7.93 \pm 1.734 \cdot 0.6635 \sqrt{\frac{1}{10} + \frac{1}{10}}$$

Confidence level = 90%

df = 10 + 10 − 2 = 18

$\rightarrow$ 0.55 ± 1.734 (0.297)

$\rightarrow$ (0.036, 1.064)

| | Drug | Saline |
|---|---|---|
| $\bar{x}$ | 8.48 | 7.93 |
| s | 0.750 | 0.564 |
| n | 10 | 10 |

32-31



## 90% Confidence Interval for $\mu_1 - \mu_2$

**Pooled Two-Sample *t* Method**

$$s_p = \sqrt{\frac{(n_D - 1)s_D^2 + (n_S - 1)s_S^2}{n_D + n_S - 2}} = \sqrt{\frac{(10-1)0.750^2 + (10-1)0.564^2}{10 + 10 - 2}} = 0.6635$$

$$\bar{x}_1 - \bar{x}_2 \pm t^* \cdot s_p \sqrt{\frac{1}{n_1} + \frac{1}{n_2}} \rightarrow 8.48 - 7.93 \pm 1.734 \cdot 0.6635 \sqrt{\frac{1}{10} + \frac{1}{10}}$$

Confidence level = 90%

df = 10 + 10 − 2 = 18

$\rightarrow$ 0.55 ± 1.734 (0.297)

$\rightarrow$ (0.036, 1.064)

Interpretation in context: The difference between the true mean water intake of rats given the drug and the true mean water intake of rats given the placebo is somewhere between 0.036 and 1.064 ml with 90% confidence.

**Note: The confidence interval does not include 0; hence $\mu_D \neq \mu_S$, confirming our conclusion from the test of significance.**

32-32



## Using Statistical Software Minitab

**Pooled Two-Sample *t* Method**

Two-sample T for drug vs saline

| | N | Mean | StDev | SE Mean |
|---|---|---|---|---|
| drug | 10 | 8.480 | 0.750 | 0.24 |
| placebo | 10 | 7.930 | 0.564 | 0.18 |

Difference = mu drug - mu saline
Estimate for difference: 0.550
95% lower bound for difference: 0.036
T-test of difference = 0(vs>): T-Value = 1.85 P-Value = .040 DF=18
Both use Pooled StDev = 0.663

**Note: For a one-sided test, Minitab gives a one-sided confidence interval; the lower endpoint of a 90% two-sided confidence interval compares with a 95% one-sided interval.**

32-33



## Using Statistical Software StatCrunch

### Pooled Two-Sample *t* Method

**Hypothesis test results:**

$\mu_1$ : mean of var1

$\mu_2$ : mean of var2

$\mu_1 - \mu_2$ : mean difference

$H_0 : \mu_1 - \mu_2 = 0$

$H_A : \mu_1 - \mu_2 > 0$

(with pooled variances)

| Difference | Sample Mean | Std. Err. | DF | T-Stat | P-value |
|---|---|---|---|---|---|
| $\mu_1 - \mu_2$ | 0.55 | 0.29659176 | 18 | 1.8544009 | 0.0401 |

**Difference between two sample means**

32-34



## Using Statistical Software StatCrunch

### Pooled Two-Sample *t* Method

**Hypothesis test results:**

$\mu_1$ : mean of var1

$\mu_2$ : mean of var2

$\mu_1 - \mu_2$ : mean difference

$H_0 : \mu_1 - \mu_2 = 0$

$H_A : \mu_1 - \mu_2 > 0$

(with pooled variances)

| Difference | Sample Mean | Std. Err. | DF | T-Stat | P-value |
|---|---|---|---|---|---|
| $\mu_1 - \mu_2$ | 0.55 | 0.29659176 | 18 | 1.8544009 | 0.0401 |

**Standard error of difference between two sample means**

32-35



## Conditions Revisited

Basic Practice of Statistics Chapter 18

32-36



## Conditions

**Data collection:**

**Sampling:** Two independent SRS's are taken—one from each of two separate populations.

**Experimenting:** Individuals are randomly allocated to two treatment groups.

**What do we do if ...?**

- samples are not independent?
  Do not use pooled two-sample *t*; consider matched pairs.
- samples are not SRS's or subjects are not randomized?
  Use good judgment – inferential results may be worthless.

32-37

Conditions for Two Sample *t*

## Conditions

**Distribution:**

**In theory:** Both populations are Normally distributed and $\sigma_1 = \sigma_2$.

**Normality in practice:**

- Choose equal sample sizes whenever possible for best results.
- If $n_1 + n_2 \geq 40$, apply CLT and use pooled t; results are approx.
- If $n_1 + n_2 < 40$, check for similar shapes and no outliers.

**What do we do if outliers?** Don't use pooled two-sample *t* procedure; check with expert for other procedures.

**Equal standard deviations in practice:**

- Check: $\frac{\text{largest s}}{\text{smallest s}} < 2$

**What do we do if largest s is more than twice smallest?**

Use of pooled *t* is ok if sample sizes are nearly equal or large; otherwise, a different *t* procedure should be used.

32-38

## Vocabulary

**Equal Standard Deviations**

**Difference between Two Means**

**Pooled Two Sample *t* Test**

**Robustness**

33-1

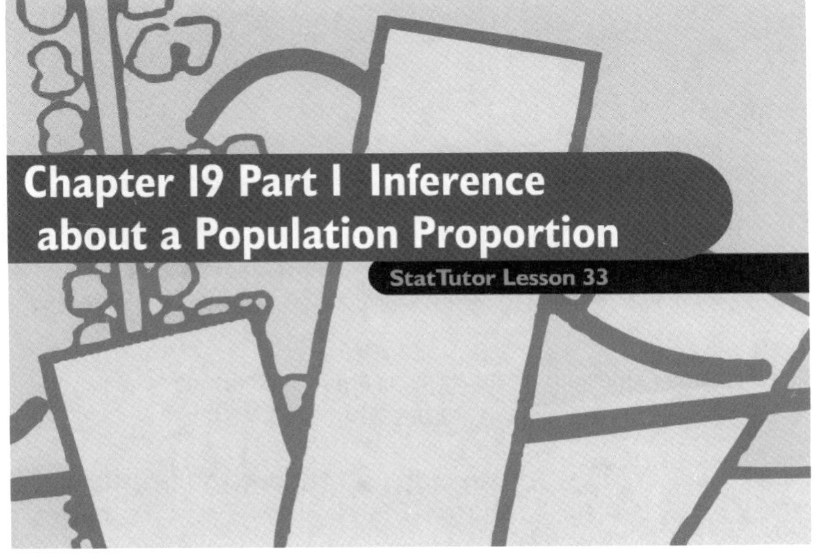


33-2

## Lesson Objectives

1. Give notation for sample and population proportions.
2. Create an approximate sampling distribution of $\hat{p}$.
3. Describe effect of increasing the sample size, n, and changing p on the center, spread, and shape of the sampling distribution of $\hat{p}$.
4. State characteristics of the sampling distribution of $\hat{p}$; connect shape to the Central Limit Theorem.
5. List and check rules for applying the Central Limit Theorem.
6. Apply the CLT to a real problem; show how to use the normal approximation to find probabilities on $\hat{p}$.
7. Explain why the CLT justifies taking one SRS of size n from a population and utilizing the normal approximation to make inferences about $\hat{p}$.

33-3

Notation & Terms

## The Sample Proportion $\hat{p}$

Basic Practice of Statistics Chapter 19

33-4

Notation & Terms

## Categorical Data and Proportions

**Population:** All male students at BYU.

**Question of interest:** What proportion are married?

**Success (category of interest):** Married

**Failure (all other categories):** Not married

**Parameter of interest:** p = proportion of all male BYU students who are married.

Married Male Single Male

**Formula:** $p = \dfrac{\text{Number of "successes" in population}}{\text{Total number in population}}$

$= \dfrac{\text{\# of married males at BYU}}{\text{Total \# of males at BYU}} = \dfrac{4{,}848}{15{,}707} = 0.308$

**30.8% of all male BYU students are married.**

33-5

Notation & Terms

## Categorical Data and Proportions

**Sample:** A random sample of 200 male students at BYU.

**Survey Question:** Are you married?

**Success (category of interest):** Married

**Failure (all other categories):** Not married

**Statistic of interest:** $\hat{p}$ = proportion of male students in the sample who are married.

Married Male | Single Male

**Formula:** $\hat{p} = \dfrac{\text{Number of "successes" in sample}}{\text{Sample size}}$

$= \dfrac{\text{\# of married males in sample}}{n} = \dfrac{59}{200} = 0.295$

**29.5% of the male BYU students in the sample are married.**

33-6

Notation & Terms

## Categorical Data and Proportions

**Summary**

| | | | |
|---|---|---|---|
| p | Population proportion | Parameter | $(0 < p < 1)$ |
| $\hat{p}$ | Sample proportion | Statistic | $(0 < \hat{p} < 1)$ |

33-7

Simulating Sampling Distribution of $\hat{p}$

## Definitions of Sampling Distribution of $\hat{p}$

**Theoretical Sampling Distribution of $\hat{p}$:** The distribution of all $\hat{p}$'s from all possible samples of the same size from the same population.

**Approximate Sampling Distribution of $\hat{p}$:** The distribution of $\hat{p}$'s obtained from taking repeated SRS's of the same size from the same population.

33-8

"Playing the Game"

## Creating Approximate Sampling Distribution of $\hat{p}$

**"Play the Game"**

1. Use a known population with known parameter, p.
2. Take an SRS of size, n.
3. Compute sample statistic, $\hat{p}$, to estimate population parameter, p.
4. Repeat steps 2 **&** 3 many times.
5. Use $\hat{p}$'s to create a histogram representing the **approximate sampling distribution of $\hat{p}$.**
6. Note **shape, center, and spread** of the sampling distribution of $\hat{p}$.

33-9

"Playing the Game"

## Example 1: p = Proportion for Stephen Douglas

**Population:** All voters in the 1860 election

**Individual:** A voter in the 1860 election

**Success:** A vote for Stephen Douglas

**Failure:** A vote for anyone other than Stephen Douglas

**Parameter of interest:** p = proportion of votes for Stephen Douglas

**Formula:** $p = \frac{\text{Number of "successes" in population}}{\text{Total number in population}}$

$= \frac{\text{\# of votes for Douglas}}{\text{Total \# of voters in 1860 election}} = 0.21$

33-10

"Playing the Game"

## Example 1: p = Proportion for Stephen Douglas

**Step I: Population of voters in I860 election with p = 0.2I for Doulas**

Population Distribution (Douglas)

1.0, 0.8, 0.6, 0.4, 0.2, 0.0

0 Failure, 1 Success

**1860 Election: Voter Preference**

| | Popular | % | Electoral | % |
|---|---|---|---|---|
| **Lincoln** | 1,864,735 | 40 | 180 | 59 |
| **Douglas** | 979,425 | 21 | 12 | 4 |
| **Breckinridge** | 669,472 | 14 | 72 | 24 |
| **Fusion** | 595,846 | 13 | 0 | 0 |
| **Bell** | 576,414 | 12 | 39 | 13 |

http://jefferson.village.virginia.edu/vshadow2/outlines/election.html

33-11

"Playing the Game"

## Example 1: p = Proportion for Stephen Douglas

**Steps 2-6: Creating the approximate sampling distribution of $\hat{p}$**

2. Take SRS of 20 voters.
3. Compute $\hat{p}$, the proportion of votes for Douglas.
4. Repeat the sampling process many times to obtain approximate sampling distribution of $\hat{p}$.
5. Use $\hat{p}$'s to create histogram representing approximate sampling distribution of $\hat{p}$.
6. Note center, spread and shape.

Population (1860 Election)

p = 0.21

p = population proportion (parameter) = 0.21

Douglas Supporters

Sample (n = 20)

Douglas 1860 (n = 20)

0.0 0.1 0.2 0.3 0.4 0.5 0.6

$\hat{p}$ = sample proportion (statistic)

$\hat{p}$ = 0.20
0.15
0.25 0.15 0.05 0.35 0.15
0.25 0.25 0.10 0.35 :
0.10 0.10 0.20 0.25 :

33-12

Effect of Sample Size

**Simulate sampling distributions of $\hat{p}$ when n = 40 and n = 400**

Douglas 1860 (n = 40)

0.0 0.1 0.2 0.3 0.4 0.5

$\hat{p}$ = 0.225 0.125 0.225 0.100 0.250
0.200 0.225 0.125 0.300 0.175
0.125 0.275 0.250 0.325 0.150
0.275 0.100 0.200 0.125 :
0.300 0.175 0.150 0.200 :

Douglas 1860 (n = 400)

0.1 0.2 0.3

$\hat{p}$ = 0.1750 0.1800 0.1700 0.2000 0.1975
0.1725 0.2375 0.2025 0.2100 0.1850
0.2025 0.2325 0.1650 0.2425 0.2075
0.2675 0.1825 0.1725 0.2050 :
0.2175 0.1900 0.2025 0.2400 :

33-13

Effect of Sample Size

## Effect of Increasing n on Center, Spread and Shape

**Sampling Distribution of $\hat{p}$**

1. Mean of sampling distribution = Population proportion, p ⇨ Increasing n has no effect. [$\hat{p}$ is unbiased estimate of p]
2. As *n* increases, the spread of the sampling distribution decreases.
3. As *n* increases, the shape of the sampling distribution becomes more normal.

Sampling Distribution: Proportion Voting for Douglas

Sampling Distribution (n=20) | Sampling Distribution (n=40) | Sampling Distribution (n=400)

33-14

Effect of Sample Size and p

## Example 2: p = Proportion of Voters for Lincoln

**Population:** All voters in the 1860 election

**Individual:** A voter in the 1860 election

**Success:** A vote for Abraham Lincoln

**Failure:** A vote for anyone other than Abraham Lincoln

**Parameter of interest:** p = proportion of votes for Abraham Lincoln = 0.4

33-15

Effect of Sample Size and p

## Example 2: p = Proportion of Voters for Lincoln

**Population:** All voters in the 1860 election **Parameter:** p = 0.4

Simulate sampling distributions for $\hat{p}$ with n = 20, 40 and 400.

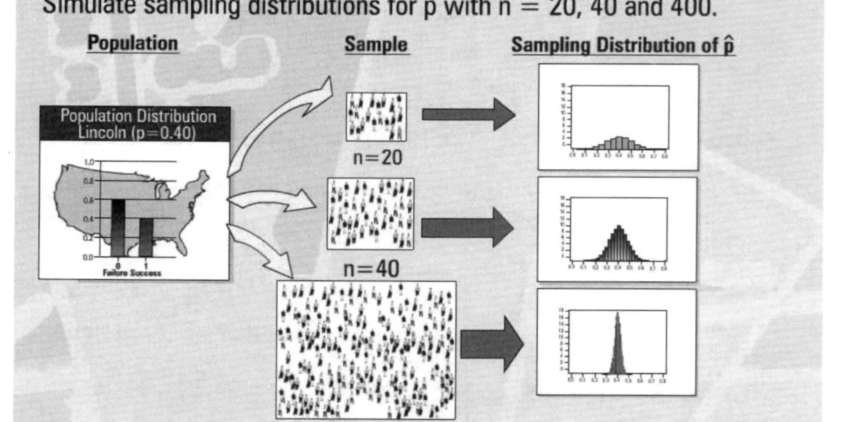


33-16

Sampling Distribution of $\hat{p}$, n = 40

## Comparing Sampling Distributions for n = 40

Empirical Sampling Distributions of $\hat{p}$

Douglas p = 0.21 | Lincoln p = 0.40

**Centers:** Both are centered at their respective p.

**Spreads:** Sampling distribution of $\hat{p}$ for Lincoln has slightly larger spread.

**Shapes:** Sampling distribution of $\hat{p}$ for Lincoln is more normal.

**Why? Stay tuned!**

33-17

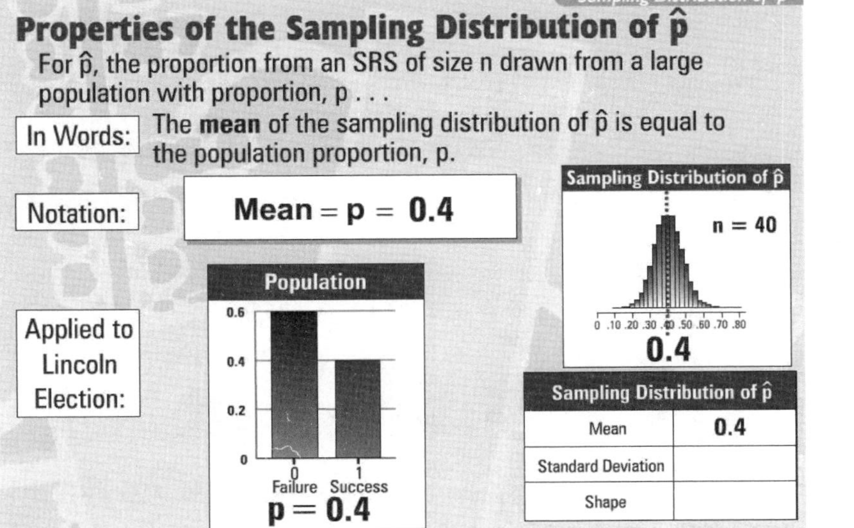


33-18

*Sampling Distribution of $\hat{p}$*

## Properties of the Sampling Distribution of $\hat{p}$

For $\hat{p}$, the proportion from an SRS of size n drawn from a large population with proportion, p . . .

**In Words:** The **standard deviation** of the sampling distribution is inversely proportional to the square root of *n*.

**Notation:** $\sqrt{\frac{p(1-p)}{n}} = \sqrt{\frac{0.4(1-0.4)}{40}} = 0.0775$

**Applied to Lincoln Election:**

Population: Failure, Success; p = 0.4

Sampling Distribution of $\hat{p}$: n = 40; 0.4

| Sampling Distribution of $\hat{p}$ | |
|---|---|
| Mean | 0.4 |
| Standard Deviation | 0.0775 |
| Shape | |

33-19

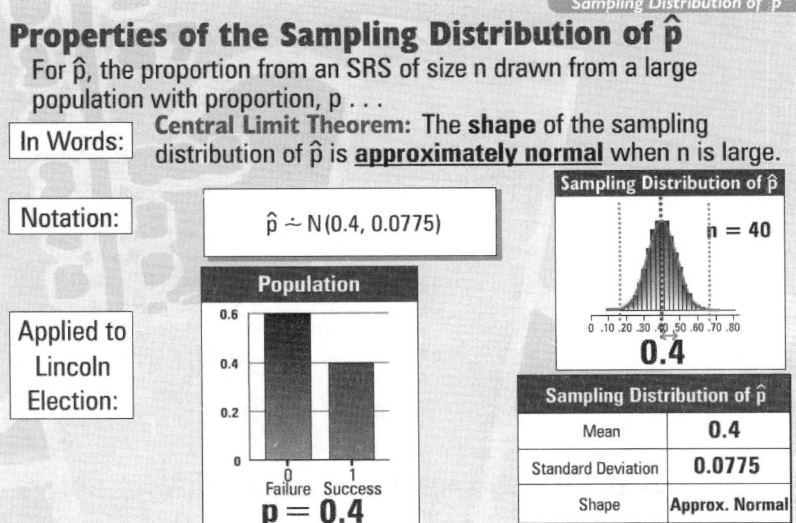


33-20

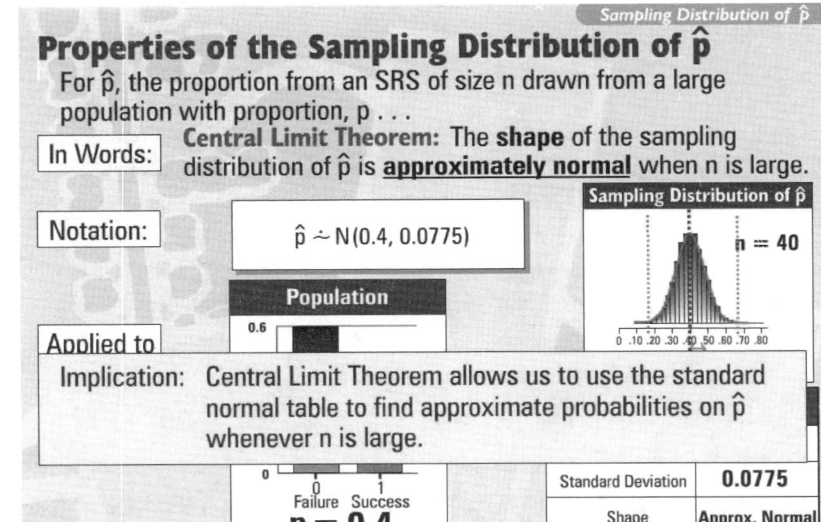

33-21

*Sampling Distribution of $\hat{p}$ & CLT*

## Comparing Sampling Distributions for n = 40

Empirical Sampling Distributions of $\hat{p}$

0.0 0.1 0.2 0.3 0.4 0.5
Douglas p = 0.21

0.0 0.1 0.2 0.3 0.4 0.5 0.6 0.7 0.8
Lincoln p = 0.40

**Standard deviation of $\hat{p}$**

**For Douglas**

$$\sqrt{\frac{p(1-p)}{n}} = \sqrt{\frac{.21(1-.21)}{40}} = \sqrt{\frac{0.166}{40}} = 0.064$$

**For Lincoln**

$$\sqrt{\frac{p(1-p)}{n}} = \sqrt{\frac{.40(1-.40)}{40}} = \sqrt{\frac{0.240}{40}} = 0.077$$

33-22

*Sampling Distribution of $\hat{p}$ & CLT*

## Comparing Sampling Distributions for n = 40

Empirical Sampling Distributions of $\hat{p}$

0.0 0.1 0.2 0.3 0.4 0.5
Douglas p = 0.21

0.0 0.1 0.2 0.3 0.4 0.5 0.6 0.7 0.8
Lincoln p = 0.40

The sampling distribution of $\hat{p}$ for Lincoln is more normal than the sampling distribution of $\hat{p}$ for Douglas. Why?

- Values of p are bounded between 0 and 1.
- Values of p close to these boundaries require larger sample sizes for the sampling distribution to be approximately normal.
- For Douglas p = 0.21 is closer to these boundaries than p = 0.40 for Lincoln.

**The CLT requirement for *"n large"* depends on p and 1 – p; we check both n·p and n·(1 – p).**

33-23

*Rules for Applying CLT*

## Rules for Applying CLT

**The Normal approximation to the sampling distribution of $\hat{p}$ is appropriate when:**

1. The data are from an SRS
2. n is large enough so that:
   a) $np \geq 10$
   and
   b) $n(1-p) \geq 10$
3. Population is at least 10 times larger than sample ($N \geq 10n$)
   --Only check if population size is given.
   --(Generally, this requirement is met so we seldom need to check it.)

33-24

*Rules for Applying CLT*

## Example: Douglas Voters (n=40, p = 0.21)

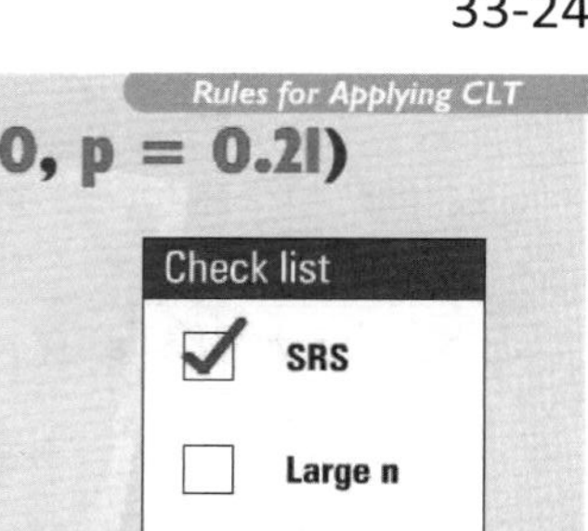


1. Are data from a SRS? Yes
2. Is n large enough so that:
   a) $np \geq 10$? NO!
   $(40)(0.21) = 8.4 < 10$
   and
   b) $n(1-p) \geq 10$? Yes
   $(40)(0.79) = 31.6 \geq 10$

**Normal approximation to this sampling distribution of $\hat{p}$ is not advised.**

33-25



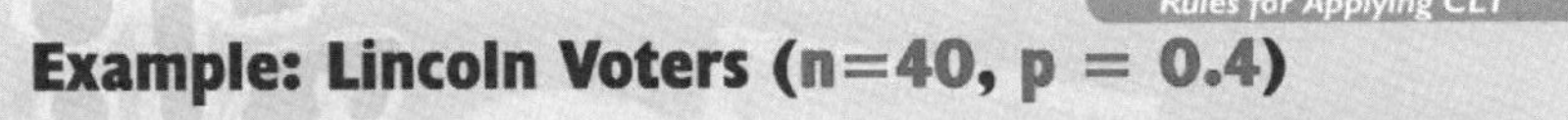

## Example: Lincoln Voters (n=40, p = 0.4)

1. Are data from a SRS? Yes

2. Is n large enough so that:
   a) $np \geq 10$? Yes
      $(40)(0.4) = 16.0 \geq 10$

and

   b) $n(1 - p) \geq 10$? Yes
      $(40)(0.6) = 24.0 \geq 10$

**Normal approximation to this sampling distribution of $\hat{p}$ is appropriate.**



33-26



## Test Your Knowledge: Sampling Distribution of $\hat{p}$

**Suppose $p = 0.05$. What happens to the shape of the sampling distribution as n increases?** It gets closer to normal as n increases.



33-27



## How Likely?

Let p = proportion of births that are boys.
Assume $p = 0.5$ in usual birthing conditions.

Officials in India are concerned about selective abortions.

One large hospital reported 100 births in 24 hours: 80 boys and 20 girls.

**Is the event of getting 80 or more boys in 100 births unlikely if $p = 0.5$?**

**Does this provide evidence of selective abortions?**

Let's compute the probability and find out.



33-28



## How Likely?

Assuming $p = 0.5$ is true, what is the probability of getting 80 or more boys in 100 births? (i.e., what is the probability that $\hat{p} \geq 0.8$)?

**Needed: the sampling distribution of $\hat{p}$ assuming $p = 0.5$ is true.**

Mean $= p = 0.5$

The standard deviation of $\hat{p}$:

$$\sqrt{\frac{p(1-p)}{n}} = \sqrt{\frac{0.5\,(1-0.5)}{100}} = 0.05$$

**Is the shape approximately Normal?**

Checking Assumptions:
SRS? Assume ok
Is $np > 10$? Yes $100(0.5) = 50 > 10$
Is $n(1 - p) > 10$? Yes $100(0.5) = 50 > 10$
Implications? **Shape is approximately Normal.**

33-29



## How Likely?

Assuming $p = 0.5$ is true, what is the probability of getting 80 or more boys in 100 births? (i.e., what is the probability that $\hat{p} \geq 0.8$)?

**Needed: the sampling distribution of $\hat{p}$ assuming $p = 0.5$ is true.**

Mean $= p = 0.5$

The standard deviation of $\hat{p}$:

$$\sqrt{\frac{p(1-p)}{n}} = \sqrt{\frac{0.5\,(1-0.5)}{100}} = 0.05$$

Shape is approximately Normal.

Approx. Sampling Distribution of $\hat{p}$

Probability

Standard Normal Distribution

Area = 0.0000 (from Table A)

$$z = \frac{\hat{p} - p}{\sqrt{\frac{p(1-p)}{n}}} = \frac{0.8 - 0.5}{0.05} = 6.00$$

$z = 6.00$ is off the chart!!

**The probability of 80 or more boys in 100 births is essentially zero if $p = 0.5$. This is very unlikely to occur by chance.**

33-30



## Why CLT Justifies Taking One SRS

**In Statistical Practice:**

- Take one sample of size n.
- Use $\hat{p}$ to make inferences about the population parameter, p, with confidence intervals and tests of significance.
- Need the sampling distribution of $\hat{p}$ to make inferences about p using $\hat{p}$.
- Imagine taking all possible samples to create the sampling distribution of $\hat{p}$ for every inference.
- Instead we approximate the sampling distribution of $\hat{p}$ using facts about center, spread and shape. (CLT gives shape.)

0.0 0.1 0.2 0.3 0.4 0.5

Sampling Distribution of $\hat{p}$

33-31

## Summary

**Three Different Distributions**

| | Population<br>Categorical Data | Sample<br>Categorical Data | Sampling Distribution of $\hat{p}$ |
|---|---|---|---|
| Proportion<br>of success | p | $\hat{p}$ | Doesn't apply |
| Center | Categorical data don't have center | Categorical data don't have center | p |
| Spread | Categorical data don't have spread | Categorical data don't have spread | $\sqrt{p(1-p)/n}$ |
| Shape | Bar graphs don't have shape | Bar graphs don't have shape | Approx. Normal if n is large<br>$np \geq 10$, $n(1-p) \geq 10$ |
| Probability using Normal Table | Never | Never | Only if sampling distribution is approx. Normal |

33-32



## Test Statistic for Proportion

We want to test $H_0$: $p = p_0$ where $p_0$ is the hypothesized value for p.

**Recall the general formula for a test statistic:**

$$\frac{\text{Estimate} - \text{Hypothesized value for p}}{\text{Standard deviation expected under } H_0}$$

$\hat{p} \sim N\left(p, \sqrt{\frac{p\,(1-p)}{n}}\right)$ when $np \geq 10$ and $n(1-p) \geq 10$,

$$Z = \frac{\hat{p} - p_0}{\sqrt{\frac{p\,(1-p)}{n}}}$$

33-33

Formulate Test Statistic

## Test Statistic for Proportion

$$z = \frac{\hat{p} - p_0}{\sqrt{\frac{p_0(1-p_0)}{n}}}$$

**Question:** What is the problem with this formula in practice?

**p is unknown!**

**Question:** What should we do?

**Use $p_0$ to compute the standard deviation since we assume $H_0$ to be true!**

**Question:** When can the standard Normal table be used to find the *P*-value corresponding to this test statistic?

**Whenever data are collected with an SRS and $np_0 \geq 10$ and $n(1 - p_0) \geq 10$.**

33-34

Formulate Confidence Interval

## Confidence Interval for Proportion

$\hat{p}$ is a point estimate of p.

**Problem: $\hat{p}$ as a point estimate has no measure of error.**
**Solution: use a confidence interval to estimate p.**

**Recall the general formula for a confidence interval:**

Point Estimate ± Margin of Error

Point Estimate ± (Table value) • (Standard deviation of estimate)

$\hat{p} \doteq N\left(p, \sqrt{\frac{p(1-p)}{n}}\right)$ for sufficiently large n

$$\hat{p} \pm z^* \sqrt{\frac{p(1-p)}{n}}$$

33-35

Formulate Confidence Interval

## Confidence Interval for Proportion

$$\hat{p} \pm z^* \sqrt{\frac{\hat{p}(1-\hat{p})}{n}}$$

**Question:** What is the problem with this formula in practice?

**p is unknown!**

**Question:** What should we do?

**Use $\hat{p}$ to estimate p in standard deviation!**

$\sqrt{\frac{\hat{p}(1-\hat{p})}{n}}$ is called standard error of $\hat{p}$.

**Question:** Should we use t* instead of z*?

**No, because we don't need to estimate σ.**

**Question:** When can the standard normal table be used to find z*?

**Whenever data are from an SRS and $n\hat{p} \geq 15$ and $n(1 - \hat{p}) \geq 15$ (i.e., counts of successes and failures are both at least 15).**

33-36

Conditions for Proportion

## Conditions for Inference about a Proportion

- Data can be regarded as an SRS.
  --Most important condition.
- Population is at least 10 times larger than the sample.
  --Ensures that the standard deviation of $\hat{p}$ is close to $\sqrt{\frac{p(1-p)}{n}}$.
- Sample size is large enough to ensure that the distribution of *z* is close to standard Normal.
  --"How large is large enough?" depends on inferential procedure.

**REMINDER: All checks of "Is n large enough?" involve some form of:**
**$n \cdot p$ and $n \cdot (1 - p)$.**

## Vocabulary

Central Limit Theorem for Proportion
Margin of Error
Mean of the Sampling Distribution of $\hat{p}$
Population proportion (p)
p
$\hat{p}$
Sample proportion ($\hat{p}$)
Sampling Distribution of $\hat{p}$
Standard Deviation (of the Sampling Distribution) of $\hat{p}$
Standard error of $\hat{p}$
$z^*$

34-1

# Chapter 19 Part 2 Inference about a Population Proportion

StatTutor Lesson 34

34-2

## Objectives

1. Explain confidence interval for p formula by identifying the standard error and margin of error.
2. Apply the confidence interval formula when appropriate and interpret results in context.
3. Give and interpret a plus four confidence interval for p for small n.
4. Estimate the sample size needed to meet specifications about margin of error, level of confidence and assumed value of p.
5. Conduct a test of significance on the population proportion, p, and check assumptions.
6. Compare inferential procedures for proportions with means.

34-3

Standard Error & Margin of Error

## Large-Sample Confidence Intervals for Proportion

Basic Practice of Statistics Chapter 19

34-4

Standard Error & Margin of Error

## Large Sample Confidence Interval Estimate for p

**Confidence Interval Formula:** $\hat{p} \pm z^* \sqrt{\dfrac{\hat{p}(1-\hat{p})}{n}}$

$\hat{p}$ is a **point estimate** of p, the population proportion.

**Standard error** of $\hat{p}$ is an estimate, using sample data, of the standard deviation of sampling distribution of $\hat{p}$.

**Margin of error** is table value (multiplier) times standard error; it measures the maximum difference that could exist between $\hat{p}$ and p at a specified level of confidence.

34-5

Confidence Interval Steps

## Steps for Constructing a Confidence Interval for p

1. **STATE** the research question.
2. **PLAN:** Recognize need for a confidence interval for p.
   Identify parameter (p) being estimated in words.
   Select large sample z procedure; set level of confidence.
3. **SOLVE:**
   Collect data and compute $\hat{p}$ as an estimate of p.
   Check: SRS and counts of successes and failures at least 15.
   (i.e., both $n\hat{p} \geq 15$ and $n(1-\hat{p}) \geq 15$.)

   Compute interval: $\hat{p} \pm z^* \sqrt{\frac{\hat{p}(1-\hat{p})}{n}}$
4. **CONCLUDE:** Interpret confidence interval in context.

34-6

Applying C. I. Formula

## Example 1: Presidential Approval Rating

Step 1 **STATE** the research question.

**Source**

The Gallup Poll, May 2006
President Bush's approval rating: 33%
($\hat{p} = 0.33$, n = 1002)

Step 2 **PLAN:** p is the proportion of all Americans who approve of President Bush's job as president.

Construct a 95% large-sample z confidence interval for p.

| | |
|---|---|
| **Sample proportion, $\hat{p}$** | 0.33 |
| **Sample size, n** | 1002 |
| **Level of Confidence** | 95% |

**Politics**

Poll: Bush's Approval Rating at All Time Low

| How Is Bush Handling His Job as President? | |
|---|---|
| Approve | 33% |
| Disapprove | 63% |
| **How is Bush Handling the Economy** | |
| Approve | 34% |
| Disapprove | 64% |
| **How is Bush Handling Terrorists?** | |
| Approve | 70% |
| Disapprove | 29% |

34-7

Applying C. I. Formula

## Example 1: Presidential Approval Rating

Step 3 **SOLVE:**
Gallop contacts **1002** individuals.
Compute $\hat{p}$ as an estimate of p. $\hat{p} = 0.33$

| | |
|---|---|
| **Sample proportion, $\hat{p}$** | **0.33** |
| **Sample size, n** | **1002** |
| **Level of Confidence** | **95%** |

Percent
Disapprove / No Opinion
Approve
Bush Approval Rating

Check $n\hat{p} \geq 15$ and $n(1-\hat{p}) \geq 15$:
$(n)(\hat{p}) = 1002 \cdot 0.33 = 331 > 15$ ✔
$(n)(1-\hat{p}) = 1002 \cdot 0.67 = 671 > 15$ ✔

Yes! **Data collected appropriately; counts of successes and failures both exceed 15; ok to proceed.**

34-8

Applying C. I. Formula

## Example 1: Presidential Approval Rating

Step 3 **SOLVE**: (Cont.) Compute interval.

| | |
|---|---|
| **Sample proportion, $\hat{p}$** | **0.33** |
| **Sample size, n** | **1002** |
| **Level of Confidence** | **95%** |

- Input $\hat{p}$
- Input n
- Find and input z*

$0.33 \pm 1.96 \sqrt{\frac{0.33(1-0.33)}{1002}}$

$0.33 \pm 0.03 \rightarrow (0.30, 0.36)$ or 30% to 36%

Step 4 **CONCLUDE**: Interpret interval in context.

We are 95% confident that the true proportion of all Americans who approved Bush's job as President was somewhere between 30% and 36% in May, 2006.

34-9

*Applying C. I. Formula*

## Comparison: Media Report & Our Results

**How Bush Is Handling His Job as President**

| | |
|---|---|
| Approve | 33% |
| Disapprove | 64% |

| | |
|---|---|
| YES | 33% |
| No | 61% |

Sampling error: +/- 3%

**The survey of 1,002 adult Americans was conducted May 5 - 11, 2006 and has a margin of error +/- 3 percentage points.**

His approval on the economy is only slightly higher at 34%.

**Media Report:**
33% with margin of error of 3%

**Ours:**
$0.33 \pm 0.03 \Rightarrow (0.30, 0.36)$ with 95% confidence
or $33\% \pm 3\%$ $\Rightarrow$ 30% to 36% with 95% confidence

**Conclusion:** Same interval, but media reported no level of confidence.
**Media often fails to report level of confidence. Though unreported, it is usually 95%.**

34-10

*Applying C. I. Formula*

## Example 2: Alcohol and Family Problems

Step 1 **STATE** problem:

**GALLUP NEWS SERVICE**

**Thirty-Six Percent Say Drinking Has Caused Family Problems**

"An increasing number of Americans are telling Gallup that drinking has been a problem in their family, particularly in recent years. As recently as 1994, the rate of self-reported problems was just 27%. However, this rose to 30% in 1997 and reached 36% – the all time high– in this most recent survey. The results below are based on telephone interviews with a randomly selected national sample of 1,039 adults, 18 years and older, conducted September 23-26, 1999. For results based on samples of this size, one can say with 95 percent confidence that the error attributable to sampling and other random effects could be plus or minus 3 percentage points."

| | |
|---|---|
| **Sample proportion, $\hat{p}$** | 0.36 |
| **Sample size, n** | 1039 |
| **Level of Confidence** | 95% |

34-11

*Applying C. I. Formula*

## Example 2: Alcohol and Family Problems

| | |
|---|---|
| **Sample proportion, $\hat{p}$** | 0.36 |
| **Sample size, n** | 1039 |
| **Level of Confidence** | 95% |

Step 2 **PLAN:** p is the proportion who feel drinking is a problem in their family. Give **95%** confidence interval for p.

Step 3 **SOLVE**
Collect data; select SRS of size n **1039**
Plot data; compute $\hat{p}$ as an estimate of p: **0.36**
Check conditions:

1. Simple random sample? No, but definitely a probability sample
2. Is n large enough? Don't know counts; use n and $\hat{p}$.
   a) $n\hat{p} \geq 15$? and $(n)(\hat{p}) = 1039 \cdot 0.36 = 374.0 > 15$ ✔
   b) $n(1-\hat{p}) \geq 15$? $(n)(1-\hat{p}) = 1039 \cdot 0.64 = 665.0 > 15$ ✔

Yes! **Data collected as probability sample; counts of successes and failures exceed 15; ok to proceed.**

34-12

*Applying C. I. Formula*

## Example 2: Alcohol and Family Problems

| | |
|---|---|
| **Sample proportion, $\hat{p}$** | 0.36 |
| **Sample size, n** | 1039 |
| **Level of Confidence** | 95% |

Step 3 **SOLVE** (cont.) Compute interval

- Input $\hat{p}$
- Input n
- Find and input z*

$0.36 \pm 1.96\sqrt{\frac{0.36(1-0.36)}{1039}}$ $\rightarrow 0.36 \pm 0.03$
$\rightarrow (0.33, 0.39)$

Step 4 **CONCLUDE** Interpret interval in context:

The true percentage of those who feel drinking is a problem in their family is somewhere in the interval 33% to 39% with 95% confidence.

34-13

Plus Four Confidence Interval

# Accurate Confidence Intervals for a Proportion

Basic Practice of Statistics Chapter 19

34-14

Plus Four Confidence Interval

## Plus Four Confidence Intervals

CAUTION

**For large sample confidence intervals:** $\hat{p} \pm z^* \sqrt{\frac{\hat{p}(1-\hat{p})}{n}}$

The actual confidence level is usually *less* than the confidence level specified unless the sample size is very large.

**What if sample size is not "very large"?**
Use a plus four confidence interval!

**Plus four estimate of p:** $\tilde{p} = \frac{\text{Count of successes in sample} + 2}{n + 4}$

**Plus four confidence interval for p:** $\tilde{p} \pm z^* \sqrt{\frac{\tilde{p}(1-\tilde{p})}{n+4}}$

**Plus four intervals are valid when:**

- SRS
- confidence level is at least 90%.
- sample size is at least 10.

34-15

Confidence Interval Steps

**Steps for Creating Plus Four Confidence Interval for p**

1. **STATE** the research question.
2. **PLAN:** Recognize need for a confidence interval for p.
   Identify parameter (p) being estimated in words.
   Select plus four C. I. procedure; set level of confidence.
3. **SOLVE:**
   Collect data; compute $\tilde{p} = \frac{x+2}{n+4}$ as an estimate of p.
   Check: SRS, $n \geq 10$ and level of confidence $\geq 90\%$.
   Compute interval: $\tilde{p} \pm z^* \sqrt{\frac{\tilde{p}(1-\tilde{p})}{n+4}}$
4. **CONCLUDE:** Interpret confidence interval in context.

34-16

Applying Confidence Interval Formu

## Example: Using Duct Tape to Remove Warts

Step 1 **STATE** problem:

**Eighty-five percent treated with duct tape got rid of their warts.**

Researchers studied the use of duct tape in removing warts. They instructed subjects to wear duct tape over their warts for six days. Then, they were to remove the tape and soak the area in water. After soaking, they were told to scrub the area with an emery board or pumice stone and then reapply duct tape. This treatment lasted for a maximum of two months. Of the 26 patients treated with duct tape, 22 got rid of their warts. The researchers want to estimate the proportion who got rid of their warts with a 95% confidence interval.

$$\tilde{p} = \frac{x+2}{n+4} = \frac{22+2}{26+4} = \frac{24}{30} = 0.80$$

| | |
|---|---|
| **Sample proportion, $\tilde{p}$** | 0.80 |
| **Sample size, n** | 26 |
| **Level of Confidence** | 95% |

34-17

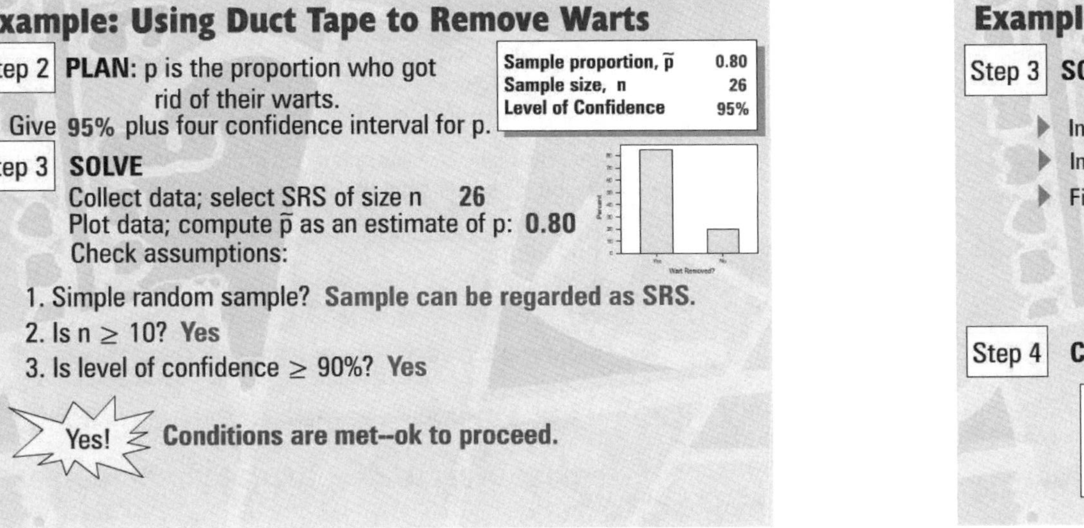


34-18

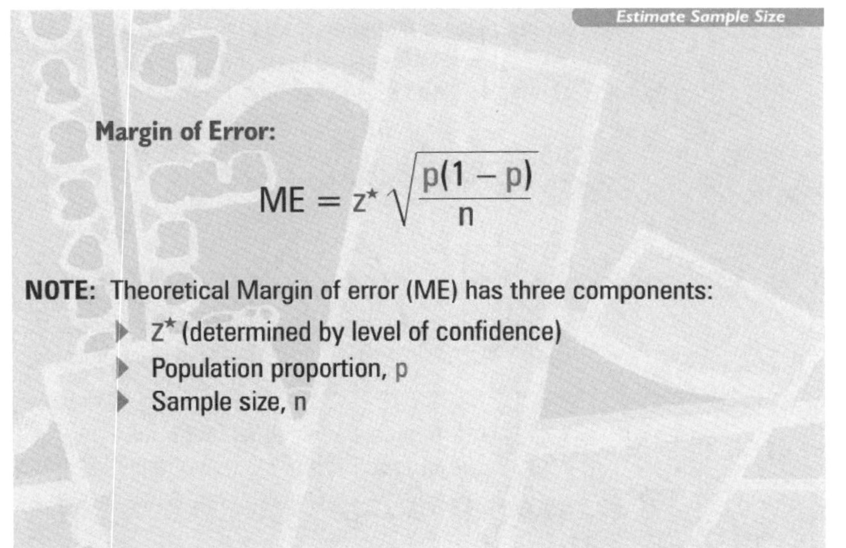


34-19

Estimate Sample Size

## Choosing the Sample Size

Basic Practice of Statistics Chapter 19

34-20

Estimate Sample Size

**Margin of Error:**

$$ME = z^* \sqrt{\frac{p(1-p)}{n}}$$

**NOTE:** Theoretical Margin of error (ME) has three components:

- $z^*$ (determined by level of confidence)
- Population proportion, p
- Sample size, n

## To calculate sample size,

$$ME = z^* \sqrt{\frac{p^*(1-p^*)}{n}}$$

1. Choose desired value for margin of error (ME)
2. Input appropriate $z^*$ for desired level of confidence
3. Use $p^*$ as a best guess for p
4. Solve for n $$n = \left(\frac{z^*}{ME}\right)^2 p^*(1-p^*)$$





## What to Use for $p^*$, Our Best Guess for p

$$n = \left(\frac{z^*}{ME}\right)^2 p^*(1-p^*)$$

- If possible, use a value from prior information.
- If no prior information is available, use $p^* = 0.5$.

**Why $p^* = 0.5$?**

Formula has $p^*(1-p^*)$ so consider possible values for $p^*(1-p^*)$:

What value of $p^*$ gives the maximum for $p^*(1-p^*)$?

$p^* = .5$

**Conclusion:**

- Using $p^* = 0.5$ always produces an adequate sample size. (May be larger than necessary.)
- Any other value for $p^*$ yields a smaller sample size.





## Common Sample Sizes Reported in Media

Assumes $p^* = 0.5$ and level of confidence = 95%

| Reported Margin of Error | Reported Sample Size |
|---|---|
| 2.5% | approx. 1600 |
| 3.0% | 1000 - 1100 |
| 5.0% | 400 - 500 |

**Important Note:** *The size of the population, N, does not appear in the sample size formula. Size of the population has little effect on the required sample size under our assumptions.*

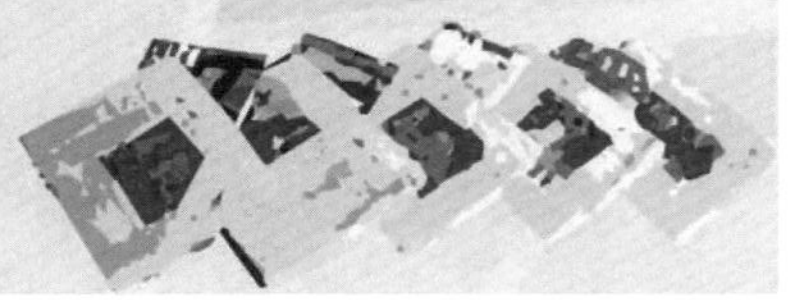





## Example: Determining Required Sample Size

You are planning a sample survey to estimate the percentage of voters who plan to vote for the incumbent mayor in an election. You want to estimate p with 95% confidence and a margin of error no greater than 3%. How large a sample do you need?

**No prior information available for the value of p!**

| $p^*$ | 0.50 |
|---|---|
| Confidence Level | 95% |
| ME | 0.03 |

34-25

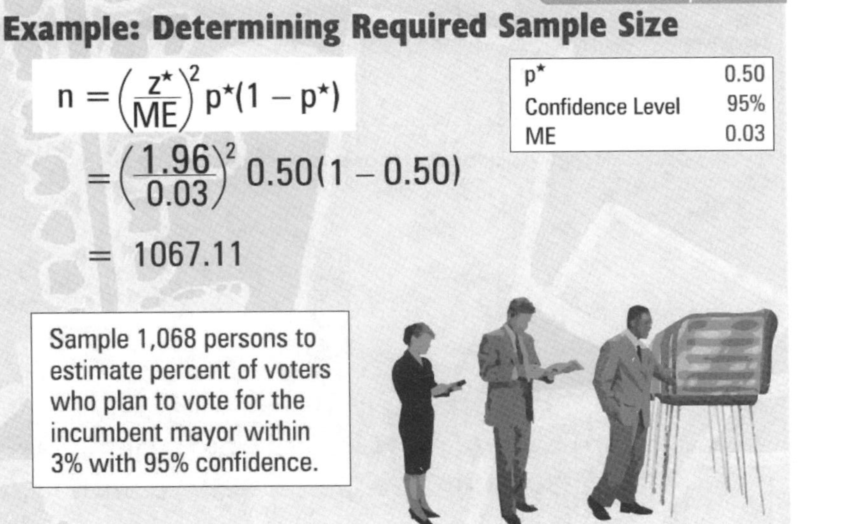


34-26

Estimate Sample Size

## Sample Size Calculator

Change ME, p* and level of confidence to see their effect on n.

Compute

$n = \left(\frac{z^*}{ME}\right)^2 p^* (1-p^*)$

Clear All

$n = \left(\frac{0.000}{0}\right)^2 0.00\,(1 - 0.00) = 0000000$

C Level of Confidence: 80% | 90% | 95% | 96% | 98% | 99% | 99.9%

C Proportion Guess: 0.10 | 0.20 | 0.30 | 0.40 | 0.50 | 0.60 | 0.70 | 0.80 | 0.90

C ME: 0.005 | 0.01 | 0.02 | 0.03 | 0.05 | 0.10 | 0.15

34-27

Testing $H_0$: $p = p_0$

## Significance Tests for a Proportion

Basic Practice of Statistics Chapter 19

34-28

Testing $H_0$: $p = p_0$

## Hypotheses and Conditions

| Null Hypothesis: | | Test Statistic: | |
|---|---|---|---|
| $H_0$: $p = p_0$ | $0 < p_0 < 1$ | | $z = \dfrac{\hat{p} - p_0}{\sqrt{\dfrac{p_0(1 - p_0)}{n}}}$ |

| Alternative Hypothesis: | *P*-value: | *P*-value Region: |
|---|---|---|
| $H_a$: $p > p_0$ | $P(Z \geq z)$ | One-sided, right |
| $H_a$: $p < p_0$ | $P(Z \geq z)$ | One-sided, left |
| $H_a$: $p \neq p_0$ | $2 \cdot P(Z \geq \lvert z \rvert)$ | Two-sided |

**Conditions needing to be checked:**

- SRS
- $np_0 \geq 10$ and $n(1 - p_0) \geq 10$

**Note:** **Since we assume $H_0$ to be true, use $p_0$ in checks and when computing standard deviation of $\hat{p}$ in the test statistic.**

34-29



## Four Steps in Test of Significance on Proportion

Step 1. **STATE** the research question.

Step 2. **PLAN**: Recognize need to test proportion.
Select one sample z procedure for proportion.
Determine $H_0$ and $H_a$ and set $\alpha$.

Step 3. **SOLVE:** Collect data and compute $\hat{p}$ as an estimate of p.
Check: SRS and both $np_0 \geq 10$ and $n(1 - p_0) \geq 10$

Calculate test statistic $z = \dfrac{\hat{p} - p_0}{\sqrt{\dfrac{p_0(1-p_0)}{n}}}$

Obtain *P*-value

Step 4. **CONCLUDE:** Interpret test results in context.

34-30



## Example 1: Being Well-Off Financially

Step 1 **STATE** the problem and identify the essential information.

73% of first-year college students recently surveyed identified "being very well-off financially" as an important personal goal. A state university interviewed 200 first-year students, wanting to know if the proportion of first-year students at this university who think being very well-off is important differs significantly from the national value of 73%. Test at $\alpha = 0.05$.

| | |
|---|---|
| Null Value ($p_0$): | 0.73 |
| Type of Alternative: | Two-sided |
| Sample Size: | 200 |
| $\alpha$: | 0.05 |

Step 2 **PLAN:** Select *z* test on p; give $H_0$, $H_a$ and $\alpha$

$H_0$: $p = 0.73$  $H_a$: $p \neq 0.73$  $\alpha = 0.05$

34-31



## Example 1: Being Well-Off Financially

Step 3 **SOLVE:** Collect data using SRS of 200 first year students.
Plot data and compute $\hat{p}$ as an estimate of p.

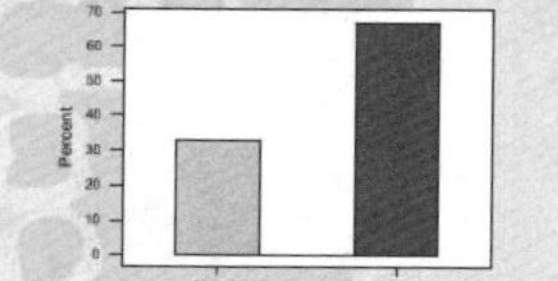


" 66% of 200 first-year students in survey say that this goal is important."
$\hat{p} = 0.66$, $n = 200$

| | |
|---|---|
| Null Value ($p_0$): | 0.73 |
| Type of Alternative: | Two-sided |
| Sample Size: | 200 |
| $\alpha$: | 0.05 |

34-32



## Example 1: Being Well-Off Financially

Step 3 **SOLVE:** (cont.) Check conditions.

1. Are data from a SRS? Yes, presumably
2. Is n large enough for $p_0 = 0.73$?
   a) $np_0 \geq 10$? Yes $(200)(0.73) = 146 > 10$
   b) $n(1 - p_0) \geq 10$? Yes $(200)(0.27) = 54 > 10$

Check list
- ✓ **SRS**
- ✓ **Large n**

Yes! **Assumptions are met; ok to proceed.**
**(Sampling distribution of $\hat{p}$ is approximately normal.)**

| | |
|---|---|
| Null Value ($p_0$): | 0.73 |
| Type of Alternative: | Two-sided |
| Sample Size: | 200 |
| $\alpha$: | 0.05 |

34-33



## Example 1: Being Well-Off Financially

Step 3 **SOLVE** (cont.) Computing test statistic and obtaining *P*-value

" 66% of 200 first-year students in survey say that this goal is important."
$\hat{p} = 0.66, \ n = 200$

### Visualizing the Test of Significance

| | |
|---|---|
| Shape | Approximately normal |
| Center | Mean under $H_0$: $p = 0.73$ |
| Spread | Standard Deviation of $\hat{p}$ under $H_0$: |

$$\sqrt{\frac{p_0(1-p_0)}{n}} = \sqrt{\frac{0.73(1-0.73)}{200}} = 0.0314$$

Test Statistic:

$$z = \frac{\hat{p} - p_0}{\sqrt{\frac{p_0(1-p_0)}{n}}} = \frac{0.66 - 0.73}{0.0314} = -2.23$$

Approximate Sampling Distribution of $\hat{p}$ under $H_0$

*P*-value = Area in the left tail

0.00 0.50 0.66 0.73 1.00

| | |
|---|---|
| Null Value ($p_0$): | 0.73 |
| Type of Alternative: | Two-sided |
| Sample Size: | 200 |
| $\alpha$: | 0.05 |

34-34



## Example 1: Being Well-Off Financially

Step 3 **SOLVE** (cont.) Computing test statistic and obtaining *P*-value

" 66% of 200 first-year students in survey say that this goal is important."
$\hat{p} = 0.66, \ n = 200$

Find the *P*-value for $z = -2.23$ (Two-sided alternative)

$$\begin{aligned} P\text{-value} &= P(z \le -2.23) + P(z \ge 2.23) \\ &= 2 \cdot P(z \le -2.23) \\ &= 2\,(0.0129) \\ &= 0.0258 \end{aligned}$$

Table A Standard Normal Probabilities

| z | .00 | .01 | .02 | .03 | .04 | .05 | .06 | .07 | .08 | .09 |
|---|---|---|---|---|---|---|---|---|---|---|
| -3.4 | .0003 | .0003 | .0003 | .0003 | .0003 | .0003 | .0003 | .0003 | .0003 | .0002 |
| -3.3 | .0005 | .0005 | .0005 | .0004 | .0004 | .0004 | .0004 | .0004 | .0004 | .0003 |
| -3.2 | .0007 | .0007 | .0006 | .0006 | .0006 | .0006 | .0006 | .0005 | .0005 | .0005 |
| -3.1 | .0010 | .0009 | .0009 | .0009 | .0008 | .0008 | .0008 | .0008 | .0007 | .0007 |
| -3.0 | .0013 | .0013 | .0013 | .0012 | .0012 | .0011 | .0011 | .0011 | .0010 | .0010 |
| -2.9 | .0019 | .0018 | .0018 | .0017 | .0016 | .0016 | .0015 | .0015 | .0014 | .0014 |
| -2.8 | .0026 | .0025 | .0024 | .0023 | .0023 | .0022 | .0021 | .0021 | .0020 | .0019 |
| -2.7 | .0035 | .0034 | .0033 | .0032 | .0031 | .0030 | .0029 | .0028 | .0027 | .0026 |
| -2.6 | .0047 | .0045 | .0044 | .0043 | .0041 | .0040 | .0039 | .0038 | .0037 | .0036 |
| -2.5 | .0062 | .0060 | .0059 | .0057 | .0055 | .0054 | .0052 | .0051 | .0049 | .0048 |
| -2.4 | .0082 | .0080 | .0078 | .0075 | .0073 | .0071 | .0069 | .0068 | .0066 | .0064 |
| -2.3 | .0107 | .0104 | [illegible] | [illegible] | [illegible] | .0094 | .0091 | .0089 | .0087 | .0084 |
| -2.2 | .0139 | .0136 | [illegible] | .0129 | [illegible] | .0122 | .0119 | .0116 | .0113 | .0110 |
| -2.1 | .0179 | .0174 | [illegible] | [illegible] | [illegible] | .0158 | .0154 | .0150 | .0146 | .0143 |

Standard Normal Distribution

0.0129
+0.0129
0.0258

-3 -2.23 0 2.23 3

| | |
|---|---|
| Null Value ($p_0$): | 0.73 |
| Type of Alternative: | Two-sided |
| Sample Size: | 200 |
| $\alpha$: | 0.05 |

34-35



## Example 1: Being Well-Off Financially

Step 3 **SOLVE** (cont.) Computing test statistic and obtaining *P*-value

" 66% of 200 first-year students in survey say that this goal is important."
$\hat{p} = 0.66, \ n = 200$

Find the *P*-value for $z = -2.23$ (Two-sided alternative)

$$\begin{aligned} P\text{-value} &= P(z \le -2.23) + P(z \ge 2.23) \\ &= 2 \cdot P(z \le -2.23) \\ &= 2\,(0.0129) \\ &= 0.0258 \end{aligned}$$

Step 4 **CONCLUDE:** Draw conclusions in context.

$\alpha = 0.05 > P\text{-value} = 0.0258$

Reject $H_0$ at $\alpha = 0.05$.

At $\alpha = 0.05$, we can conclude that the percentage of students at this state university who feel "being very well-off financially is important" differs significantly from the national value of 73%.

34-36



## Example 2: Autism

Step 1: **STATE** the problem and identify essential information.

But soon coincidence became suspicion, because although genes are a factor, as many as 40 children among Brick Township's 6,000 3-to 10-year-olds have the developmental disorder. It is more than three times the national average of 1 in 500.

$$p_0 = \frac{1}{500} = 0.002$$

| | |
|---|---|
| Null Value ($p_0$): | 0.002 |
| Type of Alternative: | greater than |
| Sample Size: | 6,000 |
| $\alpha$: | ? |

Step 2 **PLAN:** Select *z* test on p; give $H_0$, $H_a$ and $\alpha$

$H_0$: $p = 0.002$ $H_a$: $p > 0.002$

**Note: No level of significance is given. Choose your own!**

34-37

*Test of Hypothesis on p*

## Example 2: Autism

Step 3 **SOLVE:** (cont.) Plot data; compute $\hat{p}$ as an estimate of p

| | |
|---|---|
| Null Value ($p_0$): | 0.002 |
| Type of Alternative: | greater than |
| Sample Size: | 6,000 |
| α: | ? |

...40 children among Brick Township's 6,000 3-to 10-year-olds have the developmental disorder...

Brick Township　Natinal Average

Developmental Disorder

$$\hat{p} = \frac{40}{6{,}000} = 0.0067$$

34-38

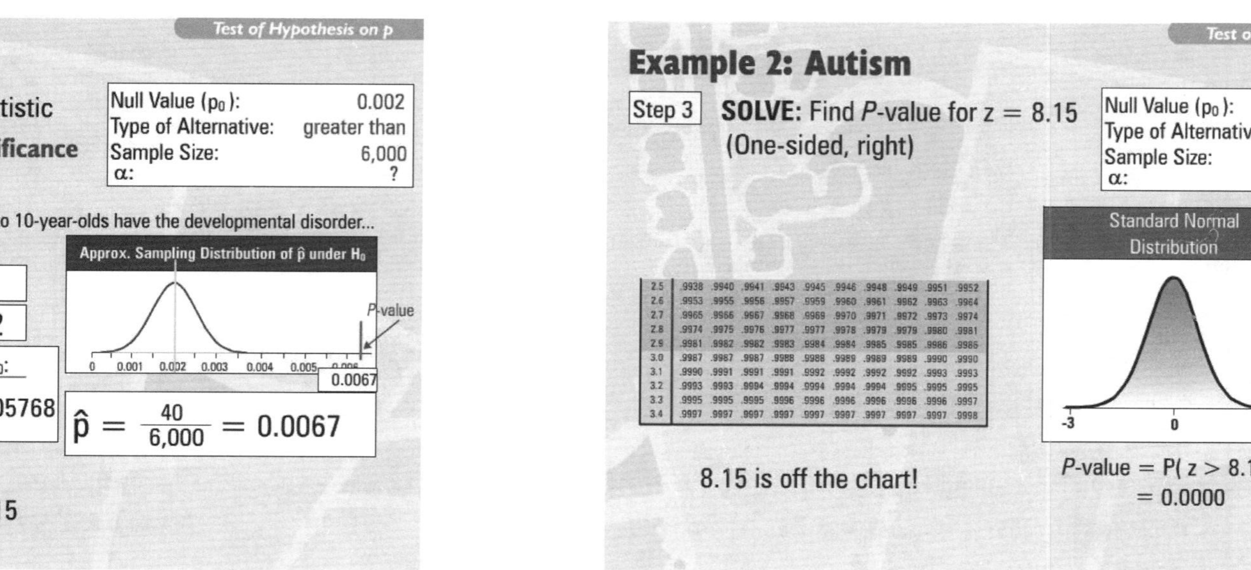

*Test of Hypothesis on p*

## Example 2: Autism

Step 3 **SOLVE** (cont.): Check conditions

| | |
|---|---|
| Null Value ($p_0$): | 0.002 |
| Type of Alternative: | greater than |
| Sample Size: | 6,000 |
| α: | ? |

...40 children among Brick Township's 6,000 3-to 10-year-olds have the developmental disorder...



1. Are data from a SRS? No
2. Is n large enough for $p_0 = 0.002$?
   a) $np_0 \geq 10$? Yes　$(6000)(0.002) = 12 > 10$
   b) $n(1 - p_0) \geq 10$? Yes　$(6000)(0.998) = 5988 > 10$

**Sample is large enough for shape of sampling distribution of $\hat{p}$ to be approximately normal, but randomness is suspect; proceed with caution.**

34-39

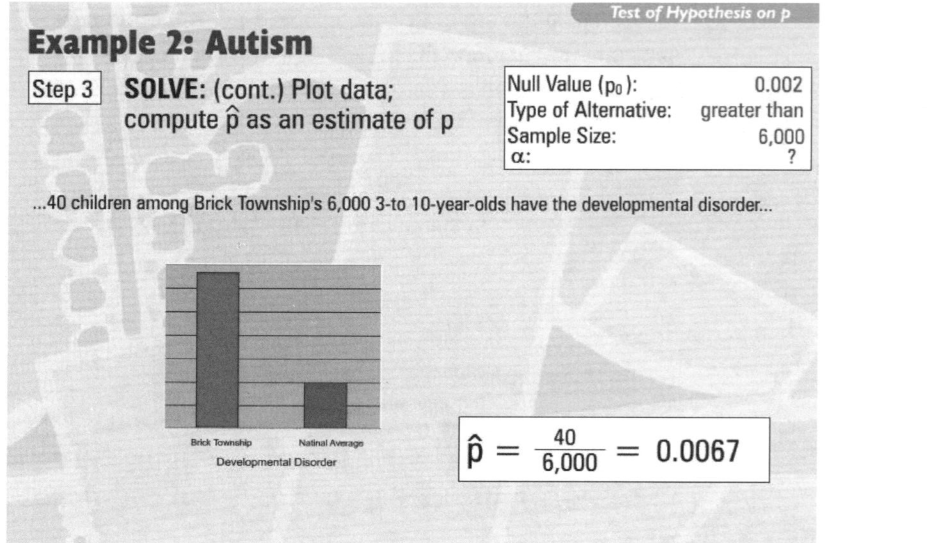

*Test of Hypothesis on p*

## Example 2: Autism

Step 3 **SOLVE:** Compute test statistic

**Visualizing the Test of Significance**

| | |
|---|---|
| Null Value ($p_0$): | 0.002 |
| Type of Alternative: | greater than |
| Sample Size: | 6,000 |
| α: | ? |

...40 children among Brick Township's 6,000 3-to 10-year-olds have the developmental disorder...

| | |
|---|---|
| Shape | Approximately normal |
| Center | Mean under $H_0$: $p = 0.002$ |
| Spread | Standard Deviation of $\hat{p}$ under $H_0$: |

$$\sqrt{\frac{p_0(1-p_0)}{n}} = \sqrt{\frac{0.002(1-0.002)}{6{,}000}} = 0.0005768$$



$$\hat{p} = \frac{40}{6{,}000} = 0.0067$$

**Test Statistic:**

$$z = \frac{\hat{p} - p_0}{\sqrt{\frac{p_0(1-p_0)}{n}}} = \frac{0.0067 - 0.002}{0.0005768} = 8.15$$

34-40

*Test of Hypothesis on p*

## Example 2: Autism

Step 3 **SOLVE:** Find *P*-value for z = 8.15 (One-sided, right)

| | |
|---|---|
| Null Value ($p_0$): | 0.002 |
| Type of Alternative: | greater than |
| Sample Size: | 6,000 |
| α: | ? |

| | | | | | | | | | | |
|---|---|---|---|---|---|---|---|---|---|---|
| 2.5 | .9938 | .9940 | .9941 | .9943 | .9945 | .9946 | .9948 | .9949 | .9951 | .9952 |
| 2.6 | .9953 | .9955 | .9956 | .9957 | .9959 | .9960 | .9961 | .9962 | .9963 | .9964 |
| 2.7 | .9965 | .9966 | .9967 | .9968 | .9969 | .9970 | .9971 | .9972 | .9973 | .9974 |
| 2.8 | .9974 | .9975 | .9976 | .9977 | .9977 | .9978 | .9979 | .9979 | .9980 | .9981 |
| 2.9 | .9981 | .9982 | .9982 | .9983 | .9984 | .9984 | .9985 | .9985 | .9986 | .9986 |
| 3.0 | .9987 | .9987 | .9987 | .9988 | .9988 | .9989 | .9989 | .9989 | .9990 | .9990 |
| 3.1 | .9990 | .9991 | .9991 | .9991 | .9992 | .9992 | .9992 | .9992 | .9993 | .9993 |
| 3.2 | .9993 | .9993 | .9994 | .9994 | .9994 | .9994 | .9994 | .9995 | .9995 | .9995 |
| 3.3 | .9995 | .9995 | .9995 | .9996 | .9996 | .9996 | .9996 | .9996 | .9996 | .9997 |
| 3.4 | .9997 | .9997 | .9997 | .9997 | .9997 | .9997 | .9997 | .9997 | .9997 | .9998 |

8.15 is off the chart!

Standard Normal Distribution

-3　0　3　8.15

*P*-value = P( z > 8.15)
= 0.0000

34-41



## Example 2: Autism

Step 4 **CONCLUDE:** Draw conclusions in context.

*P*-value = 0.0000 $< \alpha$

| | |
|---|---|
| Null Value ($p_0$): | 0.002 |
| Type of Alternative: | greater than |
| Sample Size: | 6,000 |
| $\alpha$: | ? |

Conclusion in context: Brick Township has a significantly higher percentage of autistic children than the national value of 0.2%.

**Lurking Variables?**

The United States has no t "clusters" of autism. But the center for Disease Control be higher in given areas because parents and doctors ar

"There's been a lot of change in are diagnosed," said the CDC's Coleen Boyle.

Township Administrator Scott McFadden said the numbers may be higher because some families with autistic children moved to the area for the school district's highly regarded autism program, one of the first in the state.

Observational Study
Not an SRS
Limitations apply

34-42



## Statistical Inference: A Comparison

**One population; one sample**

| | Confidence Interval Formula | Null Hypothesis | Test Statistic |
|---|---|---|---|
| Proportion<br>p unknown<br>(n large) | $\hat{p} \pm z^* \sqrt{\frac{\hat{p}(1-\hat{p})}{n}}$<br>SRS; counts of successes and failures at least 15 | $H_0$: $p = p_0$ | $z = \frac{\hat{p} - p_0}{\sqrt{\frac{p_0(1-p_0)}{n}}}$<br>SRS; $np_0 \geq 10$ and $n(1 - p_0) \geq 10$ |
| Mean<br>$\mu$ unknown<br>$\sigma$ unknown | $\bar{x} \pm t^* \frac{s}{\sqrt{n}}$<br>SRS; no outliers or strong skewness if $n < 40$. | $H_0$: $\mu = \mu_0$ | $t = \frac{\bar{x} - \mu_0}{s/\sqrt{n}}$<br>SRS; no outliers or strong skewness if $n < 40$. |

34-43

## Vocabulary

- One-Sample Proportion *z* Test
- Large One-Sample Proportion *z* Confidence Interval
- Accurate One-Sample Proportion *z* Confidence Interval
- Population proportion (p)
- Sample proportion ($\hat{p}$)
- Margin of error
- Standard error of $\hat{p}$
- $z^*$
- $p^*$

35-1

35-2

## Objectives

1. Specify notation for two sample proportion procedures.
2. Specify when to use two sample proportion inferential procedures.
3. Determine the distribution of $\hat{p}_1 - \hat{p}_2$.
4. Specify the confidence interval formula for estimating $p_1 - p_2$ and the test statistic formula for testing $H_0$: $p_1 = p_2$; outline a test of significance.
5. Conduct a test of significance on $H_0$: $p_1 - p_2 = 0$ when assumptions are met; estimate $p_1 - p_2$ with a confidence interval.
6. Estimate $p_1 - p_2$ with a confidence interval with a plus four confidence for small sample sizes.

35-3

Notation for Two Proportions

# Two-Sample Problems: Proportions

Basic Practice of Statistics Chapter 20

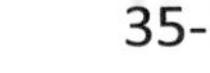

35-4

Notation for Two Proportions

## Notation for Comparing Two Proportions from Two Independent Populations/Treatments

| Population | Size | Population Proportion |
|---|---|---|
| 1 | $N_1$ | $p_1$ |
| 2 | $N_2$ | $p_2$ |

| Sample | Sample Size | Sample Proportion |
|---|---|---|
| 1 | $n_1$ | $\hat{p}_1$ |
| 2 | $n_2$ | $\hat{p}_2$ |

**Parameter:** $p_1 - p_2$ = difference between two population proportions

**Statistic:** $\hat{p}_1 - \hat{p}_2$ = difference between two sample proportions

$\hat{p}_1 - \hat{p}_2$ estimates $p_1 - p_2$

35-5



## View Movie Clip.

**Video Example Characteristics:**

Explanatory Variable: Aspirin treatment vs. Placebo treatment
Response Variable: Whether subject had a heart attack
Objective: Compare heart attack rates for the two treatments

**Two Proportion Problem Characteristics:**
**Explanatory variable and response variable are both categorical.**

Objective: Compare proportions of success from two populations or two treatments.

35-6



## Computing Proportions from a Two-Way Table

Of 22,071 doctors participating in the study, 11,037 were randomly assigned to take aspirin and 11,034 were assigned to the placebo group. Only 104 doctors who took aspirin had a heart attack whereas 189 who received the placebo had a heart attack.

$\hat{p}_1 - \hat{p}_2 = 0.009 - 0.017 = -0.008$
= the difference between the proportion of doctors taking aspirin who had heart attacks and the proportion of doctors receiving placebo who had heart attacks.

$\hat{p}_1 =$ fraction of doctors who had heart attacks in the aspirin (treatment) group $= \frac{104}{11{,}037} = 0.009$

$\hat{p}_2 =$ fraction of doctors who had heart attacks in the placebo group $= \frac{189}{11{,}034} = 0.017$

(Conditionals)

$\hat{p} =$ fraction of doctors (regardless of group) who had heart attacks–pooled sample proportion $= \frac{293}{22{,}071} = 0.013$ (Marginal)

35-7

## The Sampling Distribution of a Difference between Proportions

Basic Practice of Statistics Chapter 20

35-8

## Review: Properties of Sampling Distribution of $\hat{p}$

**For $\hat{p}$ from an SRS of size n from a large population with proportion, p:**

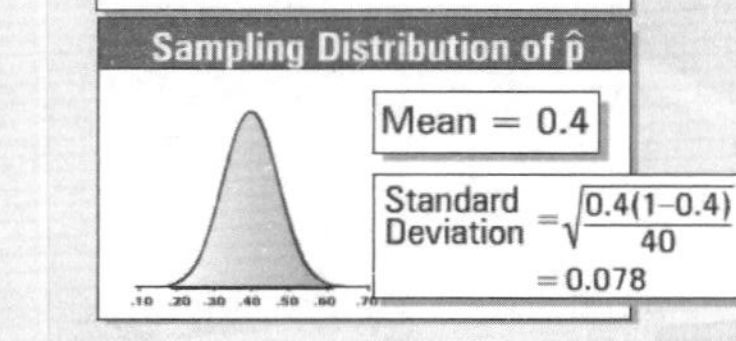


1) Mean of sampling distribution of $\hat{p}$:

**Mean = p**

2) Standard deviation of sampling distribution of $\hat{p}$:

$\text{Standard Deviation} = \sqrt{\frac{p(1-p)}{n}}$

3) **Central Limit Theorem**
Shape of sampling distribution of $\hat{p}$:
Approximately normal when $np \geq 10$ and $n(1 - p) \geq 10$

35-9



## What is the Sampling distribution of $\hat{p}_1 - \hat{p}_2$?

**Fact:**

$\hat{p}_1 \doteq N\left(p_1, \sqrt{\frac{p_1(1-p_1)}{n_1}}\right)$ for SRS and $n_1p_1 \geq 10$ and $n_1(1-p_1) \geq 10$,

and $\hat{p}_2 \doteq N\left(p_2, \sqrt{\frac{p_2(1-p_2)}{n_2}}\right)$ for SRS and $n_2p_2 \geq 10$ and $n_2(1-p_2) \geq 10$,

**Sampling distribution of $\hat{p}_1 - \hat{p}_2$:**

$$\hat{p}_1 - \hat{p}_2 \doteq N\left(p_1 - p_2, \sqrt{\frac{p_1(1-p_1)}{n_1} + \frac{p_2(1-p_2)}{n_2}}\right)$$

**Conditions:**

Two independent SRS's or random allocation

$n_1p_1 \geq 5$ <u>and</u> $n_1(1-p_1) \geq 5$ <u>and</u> $n_2p_2 \geq 5$ <u>and</u> $n_2(1-p_2) \geq 5$.

Note: Because we have two data sets, we use 5 instead of 10.

35-10

Sampling Distribution of $\hat{p}_1 - \hat{p}_2$

## What is the Sampling distribution of $\hat{p}_1 - \hat{p}_2$?

**Fact:**

$\hat{p}_1 \doteq N\left(p_1, \sqrt{\frac{p_1(1-p_1)}{n_1}}\right)$ for SRS and $n_1p_1 \geq 10$ and $n_1(1-p_1) \geq 10$,

and $\hat{p}_2 \doteq N\left(p_2, \sqrt{\frac{p_2(1-p_2)}{n_2}}\right)$ for SRS and $n_2p_2 \geq 10$ and $n_2(1-p_2) \geq 10$,

**Sampling distribution of $\hat{p}_1 - \hat{p}_2$:**

$$\hat{p}_1 - \hat{p}_2 \doteq N\left(p_1 - p_2, \sqrt{\frac{p_1(1-p_1)}{n_1} + \frac{p_2(1-p_2)}{n_2}}\right)$$

**Conditions:**

Two independent SRS's or random allocation

$n_1p_1 \geq 5$ <u>and</u> $n_1(1-p_1) \geq 5$ <u>and</u> $n_2p_2 \geq 5$ <u>and</u> $n_2(1-p_2) \geq 5$.

Note: Because we have two data sets, we use 5 instead of 10.

35-11



## Confidence Interval for Difference between Proportions

$p_1 - p_2$ = difference between two population proportions (parameter)

$\hat{p}_1 - \hat{p}_2$ = difference between two sample proportions (statistic)

$\hat{p}_1 - \hat{p}_2$ is a point estimate of $p_1 - p_2$.

**Problem: $\hat{p}_1 - \hat{p}_2$ as a point estimate has no measure of error.**

**Solution: use a confidence interval to estimate $p_1 - p_2$.**

35-12



## Confidence Interval for Difference between Proportions

**Recall the general formula for a confidence interval:**

Point Estimate ± (Table value) • (Standard deviation of estimate)

Since $\hat{p}_1 - \hat{p}_2 \doteq N\left(p_1 - p_2, \sqrt{\frac{p_1(1-p_1)}{n_1} + \frac{p_2(1-p_2)}{n_2}}\right)$

$$\hat{p}_1 - \hat{p}_2 \pm z^* \sqrt{\frac{p_1(1-p_1)}{n_1} + \frac{p_2(1-p_2)}{n_2}}$$

is the confidence interval estimate for $p_1 - p_2$

35-13

*Confidence Interval Formula*

## Confidence Interval for Difference between Proportions

$$\hat{p}_1 - \hat{p}_2 \pm z^* \sqrt{\frac{\hat{p}_1(1-\hat{p}_1)}{n_1} + \frac{\hat{p}_2(1-\hat{p}_2)}{n_2}}$$

**Question:** What is the problem with this formula in practice?

**$p_1$ and $p_2$ are unknown!**

**Question:** What should we do?

**Use $\hat{p}_1$ and $\hat{p}_2$ to estimate $p_1$ and $p_2$!**

**Question:** When is use of this formula appropriate?

**Whenever SRS's are taken (or individuals are randomized) and number of successes and failures in both samples are 10 or more.**

**If given percentages, check:**
**$n_1\hat{p}_1 \geq 10$, $n_1(1 - \hat{p}_1) \geq 10$, $n_2\hat{p}_2 \geq 10$ and $n_2(1 - \hat{p}_2) \geq 10$.**

35-14

*Confidence Interval Steps*

## Steps of Confidence Interval for $p_1$ - $p_2$

Step 1. **STATE** the research question.

Step 2. **PLAN:** Recognize need to estimate difference between two proportions with confidence interval.

Step 3. **SOLVE:** Collect data and compute $\hat{p}_1$, and $\hat{p}_2$.
Check: two independent SRS's or individuals randomly allocated and counts of successes and failures $\geq$ 10 for both samples.
[i.e., $n_1\hat{p}_1 \geq 10$, $n_1(1 - \hat{p}_1) \geq 10$, $n_2\hat{p}_2 \geq 10$ and $n_2(1 - \hat{p}_2) \geq 10$]
Calculate confidence interval:

$$(\hat{p}_1 - \hat{p}_2) \pm z^* \sqrt{\frac{\hat{p}_1(1-\hat{p}_1)}{n_1} + \frac{\hat{p}_2(1-\hat{p}_2)}{n_2}}$$

Called standard error

Step 4. **CONCLUDE:** Interpret confidence interval in context.

35-15

*Confidence Interval Steps*

## Steps of Confidence Interval for $p_1$ - $p_2$

Step 1. **STATE** the research question.

Step 2. **PLAN:** Recognize need to estimate difference between two proportions with confidence interval.

Step 3. **SOLVE:** Collect data and compute $\hat{p}_1$, and $\hat{p}_2$.
Check: two independent SRS's or individuals randomly allocated and counts of successes and failures $\geq$ 10 for both samples.
[i.e., $n_1\hat{p}_1 \geq 10$, $n_1(1 - \hat{p}_1) \geq 10$, $n_2\hat{p}_2 \geq 10$ and $n_2(1 - \hat{p}_2) \geq 10$]
Calculate confidence interval:

$$(\hat{p}_1 - \hat{p}_2) \pm z^* \sqrt{\frac{\hat{p}_1(1-\hat{p}_1)}{n_1} + \frac{\hat{p}_2(1-\hat{p}_2)}{n_2}}$$

Called margin of error

Step 4. **CONCLUDE:** Interpret confidence interval in context.

35-16

*Confidence Interval for $p_1$ - $p_2$*

**State:**
**What is the size of the difference between the proportion of doctors having heart attacks taking aspirin and the proportion of doctors having heart attacks taking the placebo?**

**Plan:** Construct 95% confidence interval for the size of the difference:

| | Heart Attack | No Heart Attack | Totals |
|---|---|---|---|
| Aspirin | 104 | 10,933 | 11,037 |
| Placebo | 189 | 10,845 | 11,034 |
| Totals | 293 | 21,778 | 22,071 |

| | |
|---|---|
| $\hat{p}_1$ | 0.009 |
| $\hat{p}_2$ | 0.017 |
| $\hat{p}$ | 0.013 |

**Solve:** Check conditions; if ok, proceed.

1. Two SRS's or randomized? Yes, doctors randomized into two groups
2. Is $n_1$ large enough? Yes
   a) # of successes $\geq$ 10?
   104 > 10
   b) # of failures $\geq$ 10?
   10,933 > 10
3. Is $n_2$ large enough? Yes
   a) # of successes $\geq$ 10?
   189 > 10
   b) # of failures $\geq$ 10?
   10,845 > 10

Yes!

Assumptions are met; ok to proceed.

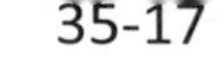

35-17

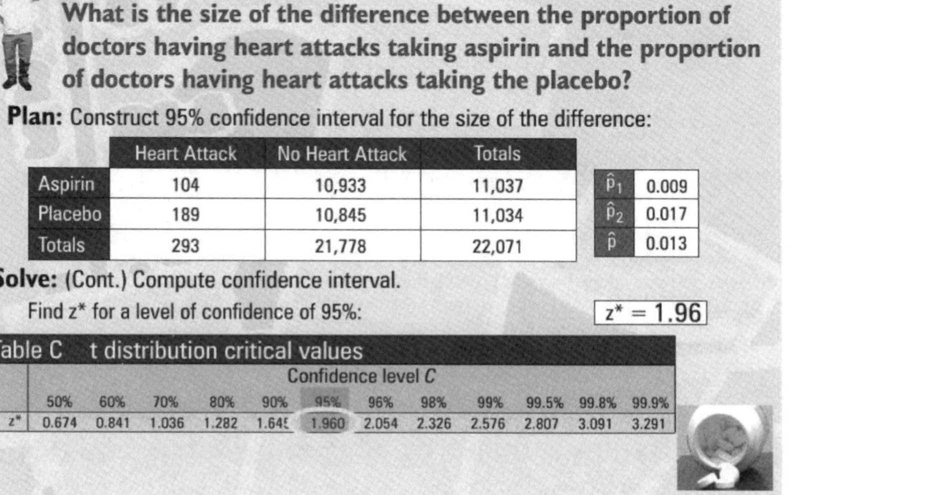

*Confidence Interval for $p_1 - p_2$*

**State:**
**What is the size of the difference between the proportion of doctors having heart attacks taking aspirin and the proportion of doctors having heart attacks taking the placebo?**

**Plan:** Construct 95% confidence interval for the size of the difference:

| | Heart Attack | No Heart Attack | Totals |
|---|---|---|---|
| Aspirin | 104 | 10,933 | 11,037 |
| Placebo | 189 | 10,845 | 11,034 |
| Totals | 293 | 21,778 | 22,071 |

| | |
|---|---|
| $\hat{p}_1$ | 0.009 |
| $\hat{p}_2$ | 0.017 |
| $\hat{p}$ | 0.013 |

**Solve:** (Cont.) Compute confidence interval.

Find z* for a level of confidence of 95%:

$z^* = 1.96$

Table C t distribution critical values

| | Confidence level *C* | | | | | | | | | | | |
|---|---|---|---|---|---|---|---|---|---|---|---|---|
| | 50% | 60% | 70% | 80% | 90% | 95% | 96% | 98% | 99% | 99.5% | 99.8% | 99.9% |
| z* | 0.674 | 0.841 | 1.036 | 1.282 | 1.645 | 1.960 | 2.054 | 2.326 | 2.576 | 2.807 | 3.091 | 3.291 |

35-18

*Confidence Interval for $p_1 - p_2$*

**State:**
**What is the size of the difference between the proportion of doctors having heart attacks taking aspirin and the proportion of doctors having heart attacks taking the placebo?**

**Plan:** Construct 95% confidence interval for the size of the difference:

| | Heart Attack | No Heart Attack | Totals |
|---|---|---|---|
| Aspirin | 104 | 10,933 | 11,037 |
| Placebo | 189 | 10,845 | 11,034 |
| Totals | 293 | 21,778 | 22,071 |

| | |
|---|---|
| $\hat{p}_1$ | 0.009 |
| $\hat{p}_2$ | 0.017 |
| $\hat{p}$ | 0.013 |

**Solve:** (Cont.) Compute confidence interval.

$z^* = 1.96$

$$(\hat{p}_1 - \hat{p}_2) \pm z^* \sqrt{\frac{\hat{p}_1(1-\hat{p}_1)}{n_1} + \frac{\hat{p}_2(1-\hat{p}_2)}{n_2}}$$

$$(0.009 - 0.017) \pm 1.96 \sqrt{\frac{0.009(1-0.009)}{11{,}037} + \frac{0.017\,(1-0.017)}{11{,}034}}$$

$$-0.008 \pm 0.003 \longrightarrow (-0.011, -0.005)$$

35-19

*Confidence Interval for $p_1 - p_2$*

**State:**
**What is the size of the difference between the proportion of doctors having heart attacks taking aspirin and the proportion of doctors having heart attacks taking the placebo?**

**Plan:** Construct 95% confidence interval for the size of the difference:

**Conclude:**

We are 95% confident that aspirin lowers the risk of a heart attack by 0.5% to 1.1% for doctors.

Note 1: These results only apply to doctors because the life style for others is different from doctors.

Note 2: Entire interval is negative $\longrightarrow p_1 - p_2 < 0$ or $p_1 < p_2$.

35-20

*Plus Four Confidence Interval Formu*

# Accurate Confidence Intervals for Comparing Proportions

**Basic Practice of Statistics Chapter 20**

35-21

*Plus Four Confidence Interval Formula*

## Plus Four Confidence Intervals

CAUTION

**For large sample confidence intervals:**

$$(\hat{p}_1 - \hat{p}_2) \pm z^* \sqrt{\frac{\hat{p}_1(1-\hat{p}_1)}{n_1} + \frac{\hat{p}_2(1-\hat{p}_2)}{n_2}}$$

- The actual confidence level is usually *less* than the confidence level specified unless the sample sizes are very large.
- Inaccuracy is not as serious as for the large sample confidence interval for a single proportion, p.

**Adding four imaginary observations, one to each success and failure count for both samples, greatly improves the accuracy.**

**Plus four estimate of $p_1$:** $\tilde{p}_1 = \frac{\text{Count of successes in sample \#1} + 1}{n_1 + 2}$

**Plus four estimate of $p_2$:** $\tilde{p}_2 = \frac{\text{Count of successes in sample \#2} + 1}{n_2 + 2}$

Use $\tilde{p}_1$ and $\tilde{p}_2$ in place of $\hat{p}_1$ and $\hat{p}_2$ in the confidence interval formula.

**Checks:** Independent SRS's and both sample sizes are at least 5.

35-22

*Confidence Interval Steps*

**Steps for Creating Plus Four Confidence Interval for $p_1 - p_2$**

1. **STATE** the research question.
2. **PLAN:** Recognize need for confidence interval for $p_1 - p_2$.
   Identify parameter ($p_1 - p_2$) being estimated in words.
   Select plus four C. I. procedure; set level of confidence.
3. **SOLVE:**
   Collect data; compute $\tilde{p}_1$ and $\tilde{p}_2$

   Check: Independent SRS's, and both sample sizes are $\geq 5$.

   Compute interval: $(\tilde{p}_1 - \tilde{p}_2) \pm z^* \sqrt{\frac{\tilde{p}_1(1-\tilde{p}_1)}{n_1+2} + \frac{\tilde{p}_2(1-\tilde{p}_2)}{n_2+2}}$
4. **CONCLUDE:** Interpret confidence interval in context.

35-23

*Applying Confidence Interval Formula*

## Example: Using Duct Tape to Remove Warts

Step 1 **STATE** problem: **Is duct tape as effective as freezing?**

Researchers studied the use of duct tape in removing warts. Sixty-one patients between the ages of 3 and 22 were randomly allocated to two treatment groups--one group had duct tape applied to their warts and the other had liquid nitrogen applied to their warts. Only 51 patients completed the study. Of the 26 patients whose warts were treated with duct tape, 22 got rid of their warts. In the freezing group, 15 of the 25 patients got rid of their warts. The researchers want to estimate the difference in the proportions of patients in the two treatment groups who got rid of their warts with a 95% confidence interval.

Step 2 **PLAN**: Need plus four confidence interval for $p_1 - p_2$.

$p_1$ = proportion in duct tape group who got rid of their warts.

$p_2$ = proportion in freezing group who got rid of their warts.

| | |
|---|---|
| **Successes in sample #1** | 22 |
| **Sample size, $n_1$** | 26 |
| **Successes in sample #2** | 15 |
| **Sample size, $n_2$** | 25 |
| **Level of confidence** | 95% |

35-24

*Applying Confidence Interval Formula*

## Example: Using Duct Tape to Remove Warts

Step 3 **SOLVE**: Data already collected.
Compute $\tilde{p}_1$ and $\tilde{p}_2$.

| | |
|---|---|
| **Successes in sample #1** | 22 |
| **Sample size, $n_1$** | 26 |
| **Successes in sample #2** | 15 |
| **Sample size, $n_2$** | 25 |
| **Level of confidence** | 95% |

$$\tilde{p}_1 = \frac{\text{Count of successes in sample \#1} + 1}{n_1 + 2} = \frac{22 + 1}{26 + 2} = \frac{23}{28} = 0.821$$

$$\tilde{p}_2 = \frac{\text{Count of successes in sample \#2} + 1}{n_2 + 2} = \frac{15 + 1}{25 + 2} = \frac{16}{27} = 0.593$$

$\tilde{p}_1 = 0.821$

$\tilde{p}_2 = 0.593$

35-25

Applying Confidence Interval Formula

## Example: Using Duct Tape to Remove Warts

**Step 3** **SOLVE**: Data already collected.
Compute $\tilde{p}_1$ and $\tilde{p}_2$.

| | |
|---|---|
| **Successes in sample #1** | 22 |
| **Sample size, $n_1$** | 26 |
| **Successes in sample #2** | 15 |
| **Sample size, $n_2$** | 25 |
| **Level of confidence** | 95% |

Check conditions:

1. SRS's or random allocation?
   **Patients randomly allocated.**
2. Is $n_1 \geq 5$? **Yes**
3. Is $n_2 \geq 5$? **Yes**

$\tilde{p}_1 = 0.821$

$\tilde{p}_2 = 0.593$

Yes! **Conditions are met--ok to proceed.**

35-26

Applying Confidence Interval Formula

## Example: Using Duct Tape to Remove Warts

**Step 3** **SOLVE** (cont.) Compute interval.

| | |
|---|---|
| **Successes in sample #1** | 22 |
| **Sample size, $n_1$** | 26 |
| **Successes in sample #2** | 15 |
| **Sample size, $n_2$** | 25 |
| **Level of confidence** | 95% |

Find $z^*$ for a level of confidence of 95%: $z^* = 1.96$

$$(\tilde{p}_1-\tilde{p}_2) \pm z^* \sqrt{\frac{\tilde{p}_1(1-\tilde{p}_1)}{n_1+2} + \frac{\tilde{p}_2(1-\tilde{p}_2)}{n_2+2}}$$

$$(0.821-0.593) \pm 1.96 \sqrt{\frac{0.821(1-0.821)}{26+2} + \frac{0.593(1-0.593)}{25+2}}$$

$\tilde{p}_1 = 0.821$

$\tilde{p}_2 = 0.593$

$$0.228 \pm 0.233 \longrightarrow (-0.005, 0.461)$$

**Step 4** **CONCLUDE** Interpret interval in context:

The true difference between the percentage of those with warts who get rid of them using duct tape and the percentage of those with warts who get rid of them with freezing is somewhere between −0.5% and 46.1% with 95% confidence.

35-27

Test Statistic Formula

# Significance Tests for Comparing Proportions

Basic Practice of Statistics Chapter 20

35-28

Test Statistic Formula

## Test Statistic Formula

For testing $H_0$: $p_1 = p_2$ or equivalently $H_0$: $p_1 - p_2 = 0$:

Since the parameter is $p_1 - p_2$, 0 is the hypothesized value for $p_1 - p_2$.

**Recall the general formula for a test statistic:**

$$\frac{\text{Estimate} - \text{Hypothesized value for } p_1 - p_2}{\text{Standard deviation expected under } H_0}$$

Since $\hat{p}_1 - \hat{p}_2 \mathrel{\dot\sim} N\left(p_1 - p_2, \sqrt{\frac{p_1(1-p_1)}{n_1} + \frac{p_2(1-p_2)}{n_2}}\right)$

$$z = \frac{\hat{p}_1 - \hat{p}_2 - 0}{\sqrt{\frac{p_1(1-p_1)}{n_1} + \frac{p_2(1-p_2)}{n_2}}} = \frac{\hat{p}_1 - \hat{p}_2}{\sqrt{\frac{p_1(1-p_1)}{n_1} + \frac{p_2(1-p_2)}{n_2}}}$$

35-29



## Test Statistic Formula

$$z = \frac{\hat{p}_1 - \hat{p}_2}{\sqrt{\frac{\hat{p}(1-\hat{p})}{n_1} + \frac{\hat{p}(1-\hat{p})}{n_2}}} = \frac{\hat{p}_1 - \hat{p}_2}{\sqrt{\hat{p}(1-\hat{p})\left(\frac{1}{n_1} + \frac{1}{n_2}\right)}}$$

**Question:** What is the problem with this formula in practice?

**$p_1$ and $p_2$ are unknown!**

**Question:** What should we do?

**Use $\hat{p}$, the marginal proportion, to estimate $p_1$ and $p_2$ in standard deviation since we assume $H_0$: $p_1 = p_2$ to be true!**

**Question:** Can we simplify the formula?

**Yes, by factoring out $\hat{p}(1 - \hat{p})$.**

**Question:** When can we use this z to obtain *P*-value from the standard normal table?

**Whenever SRS's are taken (or individuals are randomized) and $n_1\hat{p} \geq 5$, $n_1(1 - \hat{p}) \geq 5$, $n_2\hat{p} \geq 5$ and $n_2(1 - \hat{p}) \geq 5$.**

35-30



## Test Statistic Formula

**For testing $H_0$: $p_1 = p_2$**

$$z = \frac{\hat{p}_1 - \hat{p}_2}{\sqrt{\hat{p}(1-\hat{p})\left(\frac{1}{n_1} + \frac{1}{n_2}\right)}}$$

where $\hat{p}$ = marginal proportion of success

Note: $\hat{p}$ is called the pooled sample proportion.

35-31



## Steps of Significance Test on $H_0$: $p_1 = p_2$

Step 1. **STATE** the research question.

Step 2. **PLAN:** Recognize need to compare two proportions.
Select two sample z procedure for proportions.
Determine $H_0$ and $H_a$ and set $\alpha$.

Step 3. **SOLVE:** Collect data and compute $\hat{p}_1$, $\hat{p}_2$ and $\hat{p}$.

Check: two independent SRS's or individuals randomly allocated and $n_1\hat{p} \geq 5$, $n_1(1 - \hat{p}) \geq 5$, $n_2\hat{p} \geq 5$ and $n_2(1 - \hat{p}) \geq 5$

Calculate test statistic: $z = \frac{(\hat{p}_1 - \hat{p}_2) - 0}{\sqrt{\hat{p}(1-\hat{p})\left(\frac{1}{n_1} + \frac{1}{n_2}\right)}}$

Obtain *P*-value.

Step 4. **CONCLUDE:** Interpret test results in context.

35-32



## Completely Randomized Design: Aspirin and Heart Attacks

Can we conclude from this study that taking aspirin reduces the chance of having a heart attack at $\alpha$ =.05?

| | Heart Attack | No Heart Attack | Totals |
|---|---|---|---|
| Aspirin | 104 | 10,933 | 11,037 |
| Placebo | 189 | 10,845 | 11,034 |
| Totals | 293 | 21,778 | 22,071 |

Step 1 **STATE** the problem and identify the essential information.

| Type of Alternative: | less than |
|---|---|
| $n_1$ (sample size, aspirin): | 11,037 |
| $n_2$ (sample size, placebo): | 11,034 |
| $\alpha$: | 0.05 |

Step 2 **PLAN**: Do two-sample z test.

$p_1$ = heart attack rate in aspirin group

$p_2$ = heart attack rate in placebo group

State hypotheses; choose significance level ($\alpha$):

$H_0$: $p_1 = p_2$ (or $H_0$: $p_1 - p_2 = 0$)

$H_a$: $p_1 < p_2$ ($H_a$: $p_1 - p_2 < 0$)

$\alpha = 0.05$

35-33

Test of Hypothesis

## Completely Randomized Design: Aspirin and Heart Attacks

Step 3 **SOLVE:** Compute $\hat{p}_1$, $\hat{p}_2$ and $\hat{p}$, the pooled sample proportion.

| | Heart Attack | No Heart Attack | Totals |
|---|---|---|---|
| Aspirin | 104 | 10,933 | 11,037 |
| Placebo | 189 | 10,845 | 11,034 |
| Totals | 293 | 21,778 | 22,071 |

**$\hat{p}_1$ = fraction of doctors who had heart attacks in the aspirin (treatment) group** $= \frac{104}{11{,}037} = 0.009$

**$\hat{p}_2$ = fraction of doctors who had heart attacks in the placebo group** $= \frac{189}{11{,}034} = 0.017$

**$\hat{p}$ = fraction of doctors (regardless of group) who had heart attacks–pooled sample proportion** $= \frac{293}{22{,}071} = 0.013$

| | |
|---|---|
| $\hat{p}_1$ | **0.009** |
| $\hat{p}_2$ | **0.017** |
| $\hat{p}$ | **0.013** |

35-34

Test of Hypothesis

## Completely Randomized Design: Aspirin and Heart Attacks

Step 3 **SOLVE:** (cont) Check conditions:

| | |
|---|---|
| Type of Alternative: | less than |
| $n_1$ (sample size, aspirin): | 11,037 |
| $n_2$ (sample size, placebo): | 11,034 |
| $\alpha$: | 0.05 |

1. Two SRS's or units randomized?
   Yes, doctors randomized into two groups
2. Is $n_1$ large enough? Yes
   a) $n_1\hat{p} \geq 5$?
   $(11037)(0.013) = 143.5 > 5$
   b) $n_1(1-\hat{p}) \geq 5$?
   $(11037)(1 - 0.013) = 10893.5 > 5$
3. Is $n_2$ large enough? Yes
   a) $n_2\hat{p} \geq 5$?
   $(11034)(0.013) = 143.4 > 5$
   b) $n_2(1-\hat{p}) \geq 5$?
   $(11034)(1 - 0.013) = 10893.6 > 5$

Yes!

Conditions are met; ok to proceed.

Check list
- ✓ **SRS's**
- ✓ **Large n's**

| | |
|---|---|
| $\hat{p}_1$ | **0.009** |
| $\hat{p}_2$ | **0.017** |
| $\hat{p}$ | **0.013** |

35-35

Test of Hypothesis

## Completely Randomized Design: Aspirin and Heart Attacks

Step 3 **SOLVE** (cont.) Compute test statistic and obtain *P*-value.

| | |
|---|---|
| Type of Alternative: | less than |
| $n_1$ (sample size, aspirin): | 11,037 |
| $n_2$ (sample size, placebo): | 11,034 |
| $\alpha$: | 0.05 |

$$z = \frac{(\hat{p}_1 - \hat{p}_2) - 0}{\sqrt{\hat{p}(1-\hat{p})\left(\frac{1}{n_1} + \frac{1}{n_2}\right)}}$$

$$= \frac{(\mathbf{0.009} - \mathbf{0.017}) - 0}{\sqrt{\mathbf{0.013}(1 - \mathbf{0.013})\left(\frac{1}{\mathbf{11037}} + \frac{1}{\mathbf{11034}}\right)}}$$

$z = -\mathbf{5.14}$

| | |
|---|---|
| $\hat{p}_1$ | **0.009** |
| $\hat{p}_2$ | **0.017** |
| $\hat{p}$ | **0.013** |

35-36

Test of Hypothesis

## Completely Randomized Design: Aspirin and Heart Attacks

Step 3 **SOLVE** (cont.) Compute test statistic and obtain *P*-value.

$z = -\mathbf{5.14}$  *P*-value = $P(z < -5.14) = 0.000$

| | |
|---|---|
| Type of Alternative: | less than |
| $n_1$ (sample size, aspirin): | 11,037 |
| $n_2$ (sample size, placebo): | 11,034 |
| $\alpha$: | 0.05 |

Off the chart!

Table A Standard Normal Probabilities

| z | .00 | .01 | .02 | .03 | .04 | .05 | .06 | .07 | .08 | .09 |
|---|---|---|---|---|---|---|---|---|---|---|
| -3.4 | .0003 | .0003 | .0003 | .0003 | .0003 | .0003 | .0003 | .0003 | .0003 | .0002 |
| -3.3 | .0005 | .0005 | .0005 | .0004 | .0004 | .0004 | .0004 | .0004 | .0004 | .0003 |
| -3.2 | .0007 | .0007 | .0006 | .0006 | .0006 | .0006 | .0006 | .0005 | .0005 | .0005 |
| -3.1 | .0010 | .0009 | .0009 | .0009 | .0008 | .0008 | .0008 | .0008 | .0007 | .0007 |
| -3.0 | .0013 | .0013 | .0013 | .0012 | .0012 | .0011 | .0011 | .0011 | .0010 | .0010 |
| -2.9 | .0019 | .0018 | .0018 | .0017 | .0016 | .0016 | .0015 | .0015 | .0014 | .0014 |
| -2.8 | .0026 | .0025 | .0024 | .0023 | .0023 | .0022 | .0021 | .0021 | .0020 | .0019 |
| -2.7 | .0035 | .0034 | .0033 | .0032 | .0031 | .0030 | .0029 | .0028 | .0027 | .0026 |
| -2.6 | .0047 | .0045 | .0044 | .0043 | .0041 | .0040 | .0039 | .0038 | .0037 | .0036 |
| -2.5 | .0062 | .0060 | .0059 | .0057 | .0055 | .0054 | .0052 | .0051 | .0049 | .0048 |
| -2.4 | .0082 | .0080 | .0078 | .0075 | .0073 | .0071 | .0069 | .0068 | .0066 | .0064 |
| -2.3 | .0107 | .0104 | .0102 | .0099 | .0096 | .0094 | .0091 | .0089 | .0087 | .0084 |
| -2.2 | .0139 | .0136 | .0132 | .0129 | .0125 | .0122 | .0119 | .0116 | .0113 | .0110 |
| -2.1 | .0179 | .0174 | .0170 | .0166 | .0162 | .0158 | .0154 | .0150 | .0146 | .0143 |

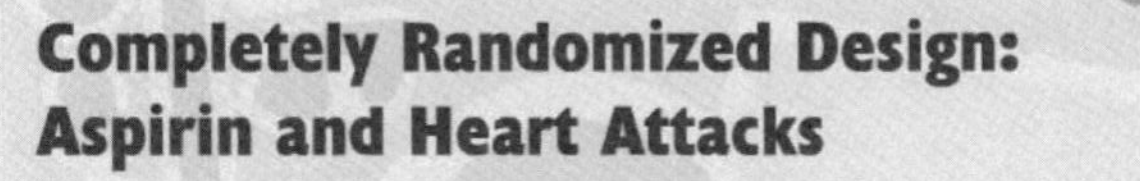

35-37

Test of Hypothesis

## Completely Randomized Design: Aspirin and Heart Attacks

Step 3 **SOLVE** (cont.) Compute test statistic and obtain *P*-value.

$z = -$ **5.14** | *P*-value $= P(z < -5.14) = 0.000$

| Type of Alternative: | less than |
|---|---|
| $n_1$ (sample size, aspirin): | 11,037 |
| $n_2$ (sample size, placebo): | 11,034 |
| $\alpha$: | 0.05 |

Step 4 **CONCLUDE:** Draw conclusions in context

*P*-value = 0.000 so reject $H_0$ at $\alpha = 0.05$

At $\alpha = 0.05$, we conclude that the heart attack rate for doctors taking aspirin is significantly less than the heart attack rate for doctors taking the placebo and hence, taking aspirin reduces the risk of a heart attack.

Confidence interval for $p_1 - p_2$: (−0.011, −0.005)

⟶ $p_1 - p_2 < 0$ or $p_1 < p_2$.

35-38

## Vocabulary

**Population proportion (p)**
**Sample proportion ($\hat{p}$)**
**Margin of error**
**Standard error**
**Two-Sample Problem**
**Pooled Sample Proportion**
**$z^*$**

$p_1 - p_2$
$\hat{p}_1 - \hat{p}_2$

36-1

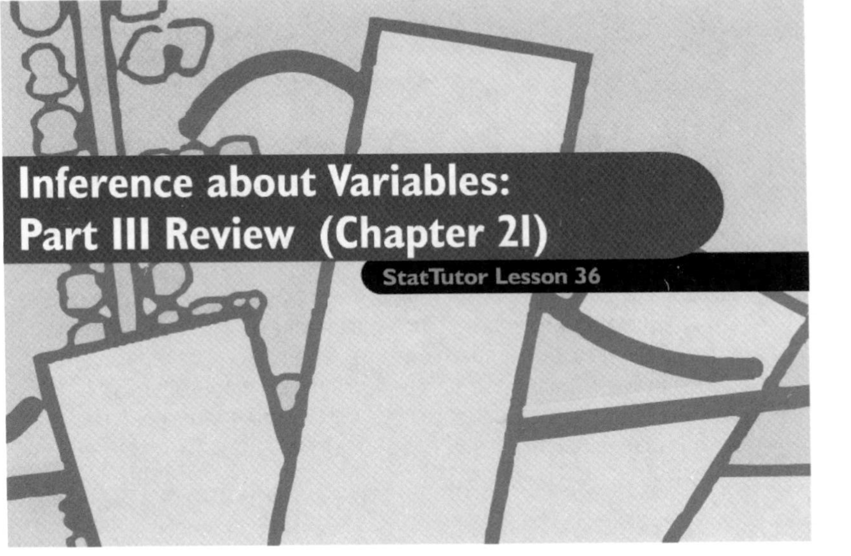


36-2

## Objectives

1. Contrast formulas for means and proportions for both one and two sample inferential procedures.
2. Select appropriate procedure for inferential analysis on means and proportions for both one and two sample inferential procedures.

36-3

*Comparing Formulas*

## Interesting Connections: Confidence Intervals

All require SRS's or randomization

**ONE-SAMPLE PROBLEMS:**

**Mean**

$$\bar{x} \pm \underbrace{t^* \frac{s}{\sqrt{n}}}_{\text{Margin of Error}}$$

Check: (1) No outliers or strong skewness or (2) $n \geq 40$

**Proportion**

$$\hat{p} \pm \underbrace{z^* \sqrt{\frac{\hat{p}(1-\hat{p})}{n}}}_{\text{Margin of Error}}$$

Check: Counts of successes and failures are both at least 15

**TWO INDEPENDENT SAMPLE PROBLEMS:**

**Difference between Two Means**

$$(\bar{x}_1 - \bar{x}_2) \pm \underbrace{t^* \sqrt{\frac{s_1^2}{n_1} + \frac{s_2^2}{n_2}}}_{\text{Margin of error}}$$

Check: (1) Similar-shaped populations with $n_1 = n_2 \geq 5$ or (2) no outliers or strong skewness or (3) $n_1 + n_2 \geq 40$

**Difference between Two Proportions**

$$(\hat{p}_1 - \hat{p}_2) \pm \underbrace{z^* \sqrt{\frac{\hat{p}_1(1-\hat{p}_1)}{n_1} + \frac{\hat{p}_2(1-\hat{p}_2)}{n_2}}}_{\text{Margin of error}}$$

Check: Counts of successes and failures are each at least 10 in both samples

36-4

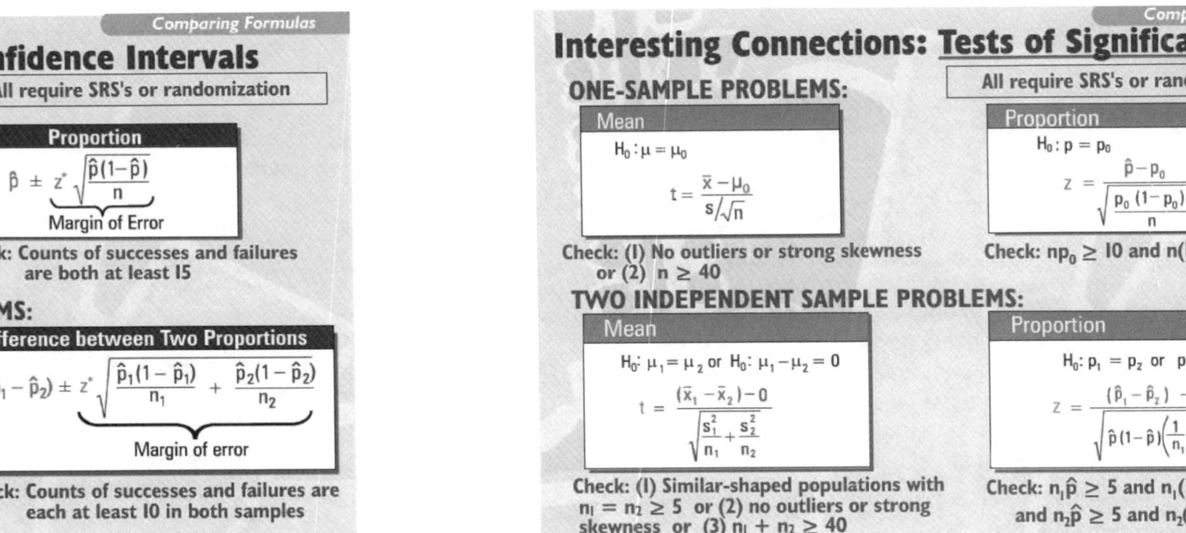

*Comparing Formulas*

## Interesting Connections: Tests of Significance

All require SRS's or randomization

**ONE-SAMPLE PROBLEMS:**

**Mean**

$H_0: \mu = \mu_0$

$$t = \frac{\bar{x} - \mu_0}{s/\sqrt{n}}$$

Check: (1) No outliers or strong skewness or (2) $n \geq 40$

**Proportion**

$H_0: p = p_0$

$$z = \frac{\hat{p} - p_0}{\sqrt{\frac{p_0(1-p_0)}{n}}}$$

Check: $np_0 \geq 10$ and $n(1 - p_0) \geq 10$

**TWO INDEPENDENT SAMPLE PROBLEMS:**

**Mean**

$H_0: \mu_1 = \mu_2$ or $H_0: \mu_1 - \mu_2 = 0$

$$t = \frac{(\bar{x}_1 - \bar{x}_2) - 0}{\sqrt{\frac{s_1^2}{n_1} + \frac{s_2^2}{n_2}}}$$

Check: (1) Similar-shaped populations with $n_1 = n_2 \geq 5$ or (2) no outliers or strong skewness or (3) $n_1 + n_2 \geq 40$

**Proportion**

$H_0: p_1 = p_2$ or $p_1 - p_2 = 0$

$$z = \frac{(\hat{p}_1 - \hat{p}_2) - 0}{\sqrt{\hat{p}(1-\hat{p})\left(\frac{1}{n_1} + \frac{1}{n_2}\right)}}$$

Check: $n_1\hat{p} \geq 5$ and $n_1(1 - \hat{p}) \geq 5$ and $n_2\hat{p} \geq 5$ and $n_2(1 - \hat{p}) \geq 5$

36-5



## Identifying Procedures

| | Type of Response Variable | |
|---|---|---|
| | Quantitative (Means) | Categorical (Proportions) |
| ONE SAMPLE | **One response:** One sample t<br>**Two paired responses:** Matched pairs t<br>X and Y: Regression (Chapter 24) | **One response:** One sample z<br>Two responses: (Chapter 23) |
| TWO INDEPENDENT SAMPLES | **One response:** Two sample t | **One response**<br>**2 categories:** Two sample z<br>>2 categories: (Chapter 23) |
| THREE OR MORE INDEPENDENT SAMPLES | One response: (Chapter 25) | One response: (Chapter 23) |

36-6



## You Make the Call #1

A chemist and molecular biologist jointly designed a new drug that they believe will cure the common cold. To test the drug, subjects experiencing the onset of a cold are randomly assigned to two groups; one group is given the new drug, and the other a placebo. Duration of the cold is measured on each subject. The subjects do not know whether they are receiving the drug or the placebo. Which procedure should be used to determine whether the new drug is effective?

| Mean(s) |
|---|
| One Sample t-test for Mean |
| Matched Pairs t-test for Mean |
| Two Sample t-test for Means |

| Proportion(s) |
|---|
| One Sample z-test for Proportion |
| Two Sample z-test for Proportions |

36-7



## You Make the Call #2

A medical researcher believes that a particular medical procedure is causing patient vitamin B6 levels to increase. To test this claim, she takes a random sample of patients and draws a blood sample on each patient before and after the medical procedure to measure vitamin B6 levels. Which test should be used to determine if the medical procedure is causing patient vitamin B6 levels to increase?

| Mean(s) |
|---|
| One Sample t-test for Mean |
| Matched Pairs t-test for Mean |
| Two Sample t-test for Means |

| Proportion(s) |
|---|
| One Sample z-test for Proportion |
| Two Sample z-test for Proportions |

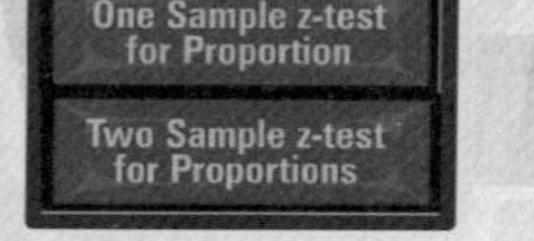

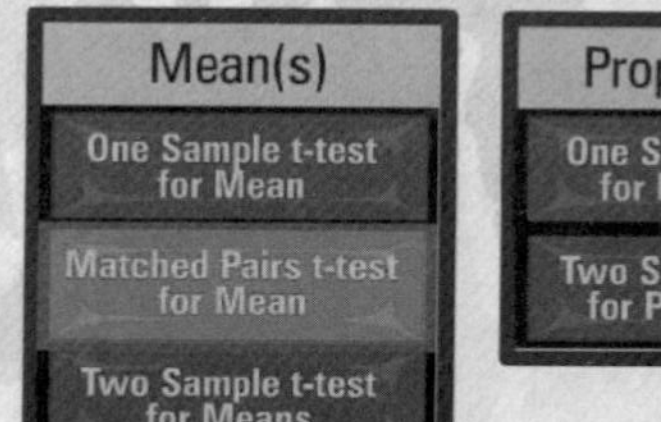

36-8



## You Make the Call #3

An information technology test is given to network engineers and has a worldwide pass rate of 73.8%. Concerns about cheating have prompted investigations in several countries. In one country, a sample of sixty-seven engineers has a pass rate of 88.1%. Is the pass rate for the sample of engineers from this country significantly greater than the worldwide pass rate?

| Mean(s) |
|---|
| One Sample t-test for Mean |
| Matched Pairs t-test for Mean |
| Two Sample t-test for Means |

| Proportion(s) |
|---|
| One Sample z-test for Proportion |
| Two Sample z-test for Proportions |

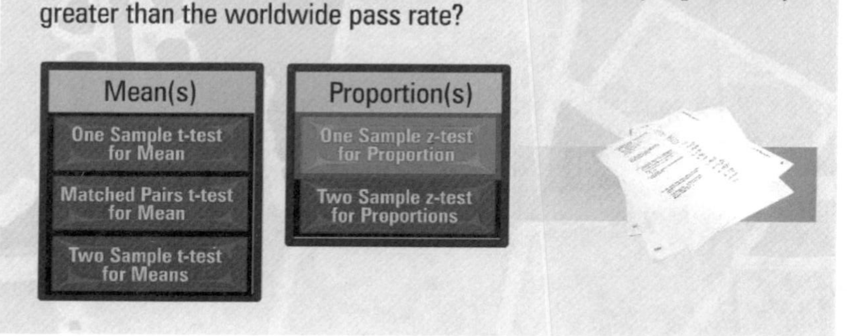

36-9

*Identifying procedures*

## You Make the Call #4

Researchers conducted a study on 832 people who had undergone surgery for colorectal adenomas or benign tumors. About half were given calcium supplements and the other half got placebos. During the four year study, 127 of the 409 people taking calcium developed at least one adenoma, compared with 159 of the 423 taking placebos. The research question was, "Does taking a calcium supplement reduce the tumor rate more than taking a placebo?"

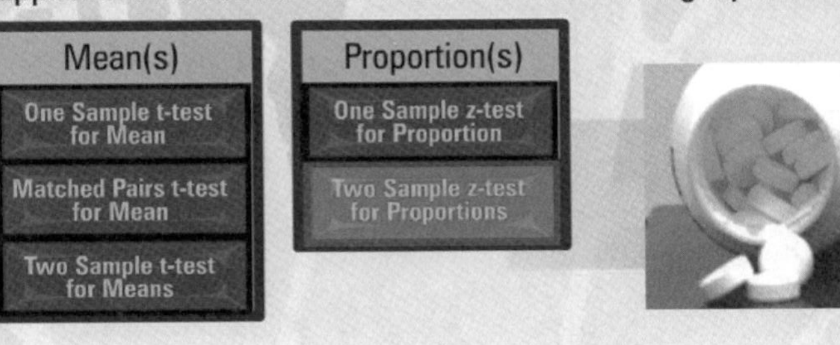


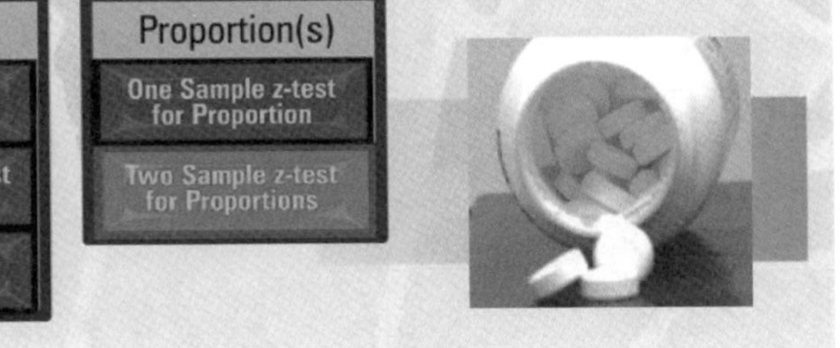

36-10

*Identifying procedures*

## You Make the Call #5

An optical laboratory advertises that it only charges an average of $55.00 for a pair of prescription glasses. In response to many consumer complaints about excessive charges, the state consumer affairs department sampled 23 prescriptions filled by the laboratory. For the sample, the mean price charged was $65.25 with a standard deviation of $18.88. Which test should be used to determine if there is sufficient evidence to accuse the laboratory of false advertising?

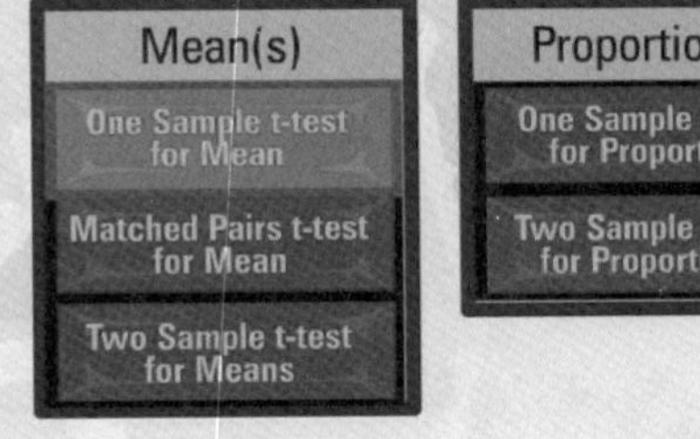

36-11

## Vocabulary

- One Sample t for Mean
- Two Independent Sample t for Means
- Matched Pairs t for Mean
- One-Sample z for Proportion
- Two-Sample z for Proportions

37-1

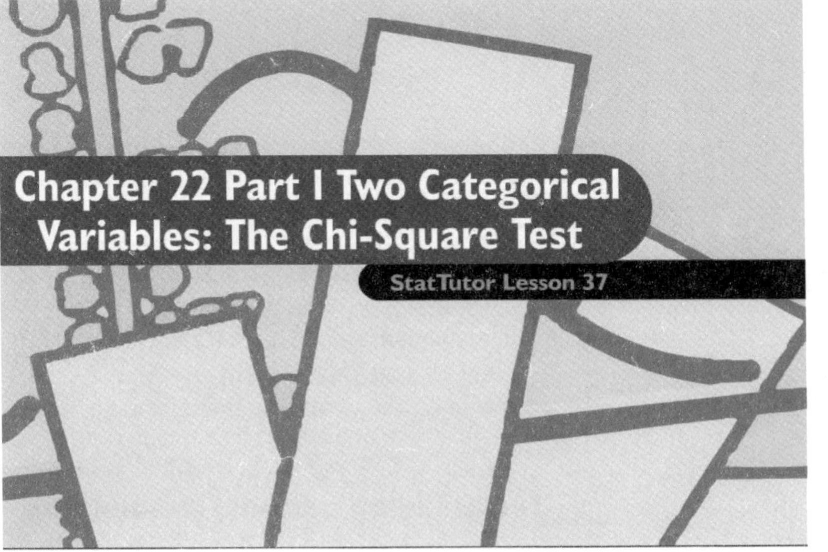


37-2

## Objectives

1. Recognize when a problem requires comparing three or more proportions; connect use of all possible z tests on a set of data to the problem of multiple analyses.
2. Summarize data collected from a comparison of three or more populations using a two-way table.
3. Write appropriate null and alternative hypotheses for a test of significance.
4. Compute expected counts for a two-way table and evaluate them in relationship to the observed counts.
5. Describe the Chi-square statistic and when it would support or contradict the null hypothesis.
6. Conduct a test of hypothesis for data from a two-way table when assumptions are met.
7. Explain components of the Chi-square distribution table; use it to find probabilities.

37-3

*Two-Way Table*

## Two-way Tables

Basic Practice of Statistics Chapter 22

37-4

*Two-Way Table*

## Example: A Smoking Survey in Arizona

**Explanatory Variable**

Smoking habit of student's parents
(both smoke / one smokes / neither smokes)

**Response Variable**

Smoking habit of student
(smokes / does not smoke)

**Recall:**
No association ⇒ conditionals same
Association ⇒ conditionals different

**Conditional Distributions:**

Students' Smoking Habits vs. Parents' Smoking Habits

| | Student smokes | Student does not smoke | Bar Graphs |
|---|---|---|---|
| Both parents smoke % | 400 / 1780 ⇒ 22.5% | 1380 / 1780 ⇒ 77.5% | |
| One parent smokes % | 416 / 2239 ⇒ 18.6% | 1823 / 2239 ⇒ 81.4% | |
| Neither parent smokes% | 188 / 1356 ⇒ 13.9% | 1168 / 1356 ⇒ 86.1% | |
| Total | 1004 | 4371 | 5375 |

37-5



# The Problem of Multiple Comparisons

Basic Practice of Statistics Chapter 22

37-6



## Problems of Multiple Comparisons

**Explanatory variable:** parents smoking status: both / one / neither

**Response variable:** whether student smokes: yes / no

**Is student smoking related to parent's smoking?**

$p_1$ = proportion of students who smoke when both parents smoke
$p_2$ = proportion of students who smoke when one parent smokes
$p_3$ = proportion of students who smoke when neither parent smokes

| Comparisons | Hypotheses | *P*-value |
|---|---|---|
| both parents vs. one parent | $H_0$: $p_1 = p_2$ ⟶ | *P*-value$_1$ |
| both parents vs. neither parent | $H_0$: $p_1 = p_3$ ⟶ | *P*-value$_2$ |
| one parent vs. neither parent | $H_0$: $p_2 = p_3$ ⟶ | *P*-value$_3$ |

37-7



## Problems of Multiple Comparisons

- Three hypotheses, three *P*-values
  - Don't know which *P*-value to use.
  - Cannot interpret the three *P*-values as a group
  - Don't have an hypothesis that compares all 3 proportions together.
- The more tests performed, the greater the probability of rejecting at least one null hypothesis due to chance.

  --The greater the risk of making a type I error on at least one test
  → the overall $\alpha$ for all tests combined is inflated.

**Needed: One overall test (one null hypothesis, one test statistic, one P-value) to test equality of three or more proportions.**

37-8



## Problems of Multiple Comparisons

- Three hypotheses, three *P*-values

**Overall test procedure: The Chi-Square Test**

Test Statistic: $\chi^2$ (read kī-square as in kite)

**If significant, do a follow-up analysis:**

- Compare percents
- Look at components of test statistic

**Needed: One overall test (one null hypothesis, one test statistic, one P-value) to test equality of three or more proportions.**

37-9



# Expected Counts in Two-Way Tables

Basic Practice of Statistics Chapter 22

37-10



## Testing for Relationship

**Explanatory (Row) Variable:** Smoking habit of student's parents

**Response (Column) Variable:** Smoking habit of student

**Is student smoking related to parent's smoking?**

**Students' Smoking Habits vs. Parents' Smoking Habits**

| | Student smokes | Student does not smoke |
|---|---|---|
| Both parents smoke | 400 | 1380 |
| One parent smokes | 416 | 1823 |
| Neither parent smokes | 188 | 1168 |

37-11



## Null & Alternative Hypotheses for Chi-Square Test

**Recall:** Conditional distributions same ⟶ No association

$p_1$ = proportion of students who smoke when both parents smoke

$p_2$ = proportion of students who smoke when one parent smokes

$p_3$ = proportion of students who smoke when neither parent smokes

If $p_1 = p_2 = p_3$, then there is no relationship between student smoking and whether both, one or neither parent smokes.

**Null Hypothesis:**

**$H_0$: No relationship between student smoking and parents smoking.**

**Alternative Hypothesis:**

**$H_a$: Relationship between student smoking and parents smoking.**

**Alternative hypothesis is not one-sided or two-sided, but "many" sided.**

37-12



**We obtain "Observed" counts from the data.**

**We compute "Expected" counts from row and column totals.**

- **"Expected"** counts are counts we "expect" to see if $H_0$: No relationship (no difference in proportions) is true.

| Student: | Smokes | Doesn't smoke | Row Totals |
|---|---|---|---|
| Both parents smoke | 332.5 | | 1780 |
| One parent smokes | | | 2239 |
| Neither parent smokes | | | 1356 |
| **Column Totals** | 1004 | 4371 | 5375 |

| Legend |
|---|
| Observed Counts |
| Expected Counts |
| Marginal Totals |

**General Formula:**

$$\text{Expected count} = \frac{\text{row total x column total}}{\text{table total}}$$

Estimate proportion who smoke under $H_0$: No relationship.

Estimate the number (count) we "expect" to smoke when both parents smoke under $H_0$.

$$(4371)\left(\frac{1004}{5375}\right) = \frac{1780 \cdot 1004}{5375} = 332.5$$

37-13

Observed and Expected Counts

**We obtain "Observed" counts from the data.**
**We compute "Expected" counts from row and column totals.**

- **"Expected"** counts are counts we "expect" to see if $H_0$: No relationship (no difference in proportions) is true.

| Student: | Smokes | Doesn't smoke | Row Totals |
|---|---|---|---|
| Both parents smoke | 332.5 | 1447.5 | 1780 |
| One parent smokes | 418.2 | 1820.8 | 2239 |
| Neither parent smokes | 253.3 | 1102.7 | 1356 |
| Column Totals | 1004 | 4371 | 5375 |

| Legend |
|---|
| Observed Counts |
| Expected Counts |
| Marginal Totals |

**General Formula:**

$$\text{Expected count} = \frac{\text{row total} \times \text{column total}}{\text{table total}}$$

Find expected counts for remaining cells. Note the Z pattern of the computational process.

Note: Expected counts typically have decimals.

37-14

Observed and Expected Counts

## Two-Way Table with "Observed" and "Expected"

| Student: | Smokes | | Doesn't smoke | | Row Totals |
|---|---|---|---|---|---|
| Both parents smoke | 400 | 332.5 | 1380 | 1447.5 | 1780 |
| One parent smokes | 416 | 418.2 | 1823 | 1820.8 | 2239 |
| Neither parent smokes | 188 | 253.3 | 1168 | 1102.7 | 1356 |
| Column Totals | 1004 | | 4371 | | 5375 |

| Legend |
|---|
| Observed Counts |
| Expected Counts |
| Marginal Totals |

Both **"Observed Counts"** and **"Expected Counts"** have the same **"Marginal Totals."**

Remember that **"Expected Counts"** are computed assuming the null hypothesis is true.

37-15

Chi-Square Test Statistic

## The Chi-Square Test Statistic

Basic Practice of Statistics Chapter 22

37-16

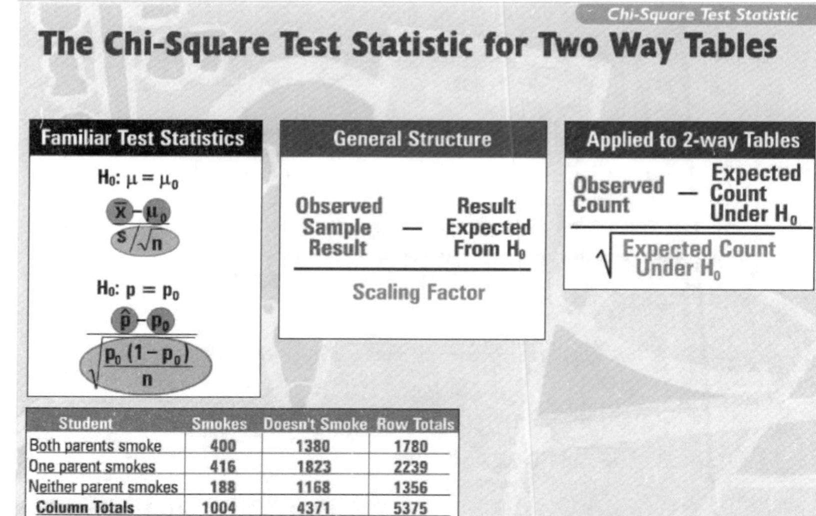


| Student | Smokes | Doesn't Smoke | Row Totals |
|---|---|---|---|
| Both parents smoke | 400 | 1380 | 1780 |
| One parent smokes | 416 | 1823 | 2239 |
| Neither parent smokes | 188 | 1168 | 1356 |
| Column Totals | 1004 | 4371 | 5375 |

37-17

Chi-Square Test Statistic

## The Chi-Square Test Statistic for Two Way Tables

$$\frac{\text{Observed Count} - \text{Expected Count Under } H_0}{\sqrt{\text{Expected Count Under } H_0}}$$

| Student | Smokes | Doesn't Smoke | Row Totals |
|---|---|---|---|
| Both parents smoke | 400 | 1380 | 1780 |
| One parent smokes | 416 | 1823 | 2239 |
| Neither parent smokes | 188 | 1168 | 1356 |
| Column Totals | 1004 | 4371 | 5375 |

Needs to be computed one cell at a time.

37-18

Chi-Square Test Statistic

## The Chi-Square Test Statistic for Two Way Tables

Problem: sum could equal zero due to arithmetic properties rather than statistical properties.
Solution: square terms

$$\sum\left(\frac{\text{Observed Count} - \text{Expected Count Under } H_0}{\sqrt{\text{Expected Count Under } H_0}}\right)^2$$

| Student | Smokes | Doesn't Smoke | Row Totals |
|---|---|---|---|
| Both parents smoke | 400 | 1380 | 1780 |
| One parent smokes | 416 | 1823 | 2239 |
| Neither parent smokes | 188 | 1168 | 1356 |
| Column Totals | 1004 | 4371 | 5375 |

Sum over all cells to get one test statistic.

37-19

Chi-Square Test Statistic

## The Chi-Square Test Statistic for Two Way Tables

$\chi^2$ denotes the chi-square test statistic (pronounced "ki" as in kite.)

$$\chi^2 = \sum \frac{(\text{Observed} - \text{Expected})^2}{\text{Expected}}$$

| Student | Smokes | Doesn't Smoke | Row Totals |
|---|---|---|---|
| Both parents smoke | 400 | 1380 | 1780 |
| One parent smokes | 416 | 1823 | 2239 |
| Neither parent smokes | 188 | 1168 | 1356 |
| Column Totals | 1004 | 4371 | 5375 |

37-20

Chi-Square Test Statistic

## The Chi-Square Test Statistic for Two Way Tables

$$\chi^2 = \sum \frac{(\text{Observed} - \text{Expected})^2}{\text{Expected}}$$

The numerator is squared, so it is always positive.

The denominator is an expected count and is always positive.

Hence, $\chi^2$ is always positive.

37-21

Chi-Square Test Statistic

## The Chi-Square Test Statistic for Two Way Tables

Remember: **"Expected Counts"** are computed assuming the null hypothesis is true.

$$\chi^2 = \sum \frac{(\text{Small Difference})^2}{\text{Expected}} \text{ is "Small"}$$

If **"Observed"** counts are approximately equal to **"Expected"** counts, chi-square is close to 0.

**A small chi-square test statistic supports the null hypothesis.**

37-22

Chi-Square Test Statistic

## The Chi-Square Test Statistic for Two Way Tables

Remember: **"Expected Counts"** are computed assuming the null hypothesis is true.

$$\chi^2 = \sum \frac{(\text{Large Difference})^2}{\text{Expected}} \text{ is "Large"}$$

If **"Observed"** counts differ markedly in size from **"Expected"** counts, chi-square test statistic is significantly greater than 0.

**A large chi-square test statistic supports the alternative hypothesis.**

37-23

Chi-Square Test Statistic

## The Chi-Square Test Statistic for Two Way Tables

**Question:** How do we decide if

$$\chi^2 = \sum \frac{(\text{Observed} - \text{Expected})^2}{\text{Expected}}$$

is "small"? (i.e., evidence does not disagree with $H_0$ so don't reject $H_0$?)
is "large"? (i.e., evidence disagrees with $H_0$ so reject $H_0$?)

**Answer:** We need a sampling distribution of chi-square test statistics from all possible samples under $H_0$.

**What distribution approximates this sampling distribution?**

Approximated by a chi-square distribution.

0 5 10 15 20 25 $\chi^2$

37-24

Steps of Chi-Square Test

**Four Step Chi-Square Test of Significance for a r x 2 (Two-Way) Table**

Step 1 **STATE** the problem.

Step 2 **PLAN:** Recognize need to perform Chi-Square test.
Specify $H_0$ and $H_a$; choose significance level ($\alpha$).

**$H_0$: No relationship between variables** **$H_a$: Relationship between variables**

Step 3 **SOLVE:** Collect data--independent SRS's or random allocation.
Summarize r x 2 table; compute expected counts.

$$\text{Expected} = \frac{(\text{Row Total}) \times (\text{Column Total})}{\text{Table Total}}$$

Check conditions: SRS's or random allocation and expected counts $\geq 5$; proceed if met.

Compute test statistic: $\chi^2 = \sum \frac{(\text{Observed} - \text{Expected})^2}{\text{Expected}}$

Obtain *P*-value. $df = (r-1) \cdot (c-1)$

Step 4 **CONCLUDE:** Draw conclusions in context.

37-25

Chi-Square Test Example

## Example: Chi-Square Test of Significance

**Step 1** **STATE** the problem.

In Arizona a survey was conducted of students smoking habits. Each student was asked whether he or she smokes. Each was also asked to categorize their parents as to whether both smoke, one smokes or neither smokes.

**Step 2** **PLAN**: Compare three proportions with Chi-Square test. Specify $H_0$ and $H_a$; choose significance level ($\alpha$).

$H_0$: No relationship between student smoking and parents smoking habits.

$H_a$: Relationship between student smoking and parents smoking habits.

**Choose $\alpha = 0.02$**

37-26

Chi-Square Test Example

## Example: Chi-Square Test of Significance

**Step 3** **SOLVE**: Collect data using SRS.

Summarize data in r x c table; compute expected counts.

| Student: | Smokes | | Doesn't smoke | | Row Totals |
|---|---|---|---|---|---|
| Both parents smoke | 400 | 332.5 | 1380 | 1447.5 | 1780 |
| One parent smokes | 416 | 418.2 | 1823 | 1820.8 | 2239 |
| Neither parent smokes | 188 | 253.3 | 1168 | 1102.7 | 1356 |
| **Column Totals** | 1004 | | 4371 | | 5375 |

| Legend |
|---|
| Observed Counts |
| Expected Counts |
| Marginal Totals |

Check conditions; proceed if met.

Check: Was an SRS taken? **YES**

Check: Are all "expected counts" > 5? **YES**

37-27

Chi-Square Test Example

## Example: Chi-Square Test of Significance

**Step 3** **SOLVE** (cont.): Compute test statistic and obtain *P*-value.

| Student: | Smokes | | Doesn't smoke | | Row Totals |
|---|---|---|---|---|---|
| Both parents smoke | 400 | 332.5 | 1380 | 1447.5 | 1780 |
| One parent smokes | 416 | 418.2 | 1823 | 1820.8 | 2239 |
| Neither parent smokes | 188 | 253.3 | 1168 | 1102.7 | 1356 |
| **Column Totals** | 1004 | | 4371 | | 5375 |

| Legend |
|---|
| Observed Counts |
| Expected Counts |
| Marginal Totals |

$$\chi^2 = \sum \frac{(\text{Observed} - \text{Expected})^2}{\text{Expected}}$$

$$\chi^2 = \frac{(400 - 332.5)^2}{332.5} + \frac{(1380 - 1447.5)^2}{1447.5} + \frac{(416 - 418.2)^2}{418.2} + \frac{(1823 - 1820.8)^2}{1820.8} + \frac{(188 - 253.3)^2}{253.3} + \frac{(1168 - 1102.7)^2}{1102.7}$$

$$\chi^2 = 13.71 + 3.15 + 0.01 + 0.00 + 16.83 + 3.87 = 37.57$$

37-28

Chi-Square Test Example

## Example: Chi-Square Test of Significance

**Step 4** **CONCLUDE:** Draw conclusions in context.

Recall: $H_0$: No relationship $H_a$: Relationship

| Student: | Smokes | | Doesn't smoke | | Row Totals |
|---|---|---|---|---|---|
| Both parents smoke | 400 | 332.5 | 1380 | 1447.5 | 1780 |
| One parent smokes | 416 | 418.2 | 1823 | 1820.8 | 2239 |
| Neither parent smokes | 188 | 253.3 | 1168 | 1102.7 | 1356 |
| **Column Totals** | 1004 | | 4371 | | 5375 |

| Legend |
|---|
| Observed Counts |
| Expected Counts |
| Marginal Totals |

P-value: 0.000 $< \alpha = 0.02$ Reject $H_0$.

Conclusion in context: There is a relationship between student smoking and parents smoking ⟶ student smoking rates differ.

- Which proportion(s) are different from which?
- Which cell(s) contributed most to the Chi-square test statistic?

37-29



## Example: Chi-Square Test of Significance

Step 4 **CONCLUDE:** Draw conclusions in context.

Recall: $H_0$: No relationship  $H_a$: Relationship

| Student: | Smokes | | Doesn't smoke | | Row Totals |
|---|---|---|---|---|---|
| Both parents smoke | 400 | 332.5 | 1380 | 1447.5 | 1780 |
| One parent smokes | 416 | 418.2 | 1823 | 1820.8 | 2239 |
| Neither parent smokes | 188 | 253.3 | 1168 | 1102.7 | 1356 |
| **Column Totals** | 1004 | | 4371 | | 5375 |

| Legend |
|---|
| Observed Counts |
| Expected Counts |
| Marginal Totals |

P-value: 0.000 $< \alpha = 0.02$   Reject $H_0$.

Conclusion in context: There is a relationship between student smoking and parents smoking ⟶ student smoking rates differ.

- Which proportion(s) are different from which?
- Which cell(s) contributed most to the Chi-square test statistic?

37-30



## Example: Chi-Square Test of Significance

### Identifying Major Contributors to $\chi^2$

**Guideline:** If an individual Chi-square component $\geq 4$, the corresponding cell is a major contributor to the test statistic.

| Student: | Smokes | | Doesn't smoke | | Row Totals |
|---|---|---|---|---|---|
| Both parents smoke | 400 | 22.5% | 1380 | 77.5% | 100% |
| One parent smokes | 416 | 18.6% | 1823 | 81.4% | 100% |
| Neither parent smokes | 188 | 13.9% | 1168 | 86.1% | 100% |
| **Column Totals** | 1004 | | 4371 | | 5375 |

| Legend |
|---|
| Observed Counts |
| Expected Counts |
| Marginal Totals |

1. Apply Guideline

2. Convert to percentages

3. Interpret
   - Probable significant difference between observed and expected in Student smokes/Both parents smoke and Student smokes/Neither parent smokes cells.
   - Effect of both parents smoke is different from neither parent smokes.
   - Whether parents smoke appears to affect whether student smokes.

37-31



## Cell Counts Required for Chi-Square Tests

Basic Practice of Statistics Chapter 22

37-32



## Conditions for Using the Chi-square Test

**Sampling Conditions:**

- Independent SRS's from each of several populations or individuals randomly allocated to treatments.
  ---Each individual classified according to one categorical variable.

**OR**

- A single SRS
  ---Each individual classified according to two categorical variables.

**Expected Count Conditions:**

- All **expected** counts must be one or greater.
- No more than 20% of **expected** counts can be less than 5.
  ---For a 2 x 2 table, all **expected** counts must be 5 or greater.

**If conditions are met,** then the sampling distribution of

$$\sum \frac{(\text{Observed} - \text{Expected})^2}{\text{Expected}}$$

is approximately chi-square.

37-33



## Conditions for Using the Chi-square Test

**Sampling Conditions:**

- Independent SRS's from each of several populations or individuals randomly allocated to treatments.
  ---Each individual classified according to one categorical variable.

**OR**

- A single SRS
  ---Each individual classified according to two categorical variables.

**Expected Count Conditions:**

**WARNING:**

**If any expected count is < 1,**
**or if more than 20% of the expected counts are < 5,**
**then unnaturally large chi-square test statistics can result from arithmetic properties rather than true significance.**

Expected

37-34



## Cautions

**Beware of:**

- Chi-square test results without SRS, stratified sampling or random allocation.
- Cause and effect conclusions based solely on a test of significance unless an experiment was performed.

37-35



## The Chi-Square Distributions

Basic Practice of Statistics Chapter 22

37-36



### Density curves for different chi-square distributions



**Properties of Chi-square distributions**

- All values are positive.
- df characterize curves.
- Shapes are right skewed.
- Skewness diminishes with increasing df.

37-37

*Chi-Square Distribution & Table*

## Chi-Square Test Statistic: Degrees of Freedom

df: A function of the number of rows and columns in two-way table

For a table with r rows and c columns: df = (r – 1)•(c – 1)

**Example:**

| Treatment | Relapse | No relapse | Row Totals |
|---|---|---|---|
| Desipramine | 10 | 14 | 24 |
| Lithium | 18 | 6 | 24 |
| Placebo | 20 | 4 | 24 |
| **Column Totals** | 48 | 24 | 72 |

**df = 2 • 1 = 2**

$$\chi^2 = \sum \frac{(\text{Observed} - \text{Expected})^2}{\text{Expected}} = 10.5$$

$\chi^2$ Distribution

df = 2

37-38

*Chi-Square Distribution & Table*

## How to Use Chi-Square Table to Find *P*-value

TABLE E Chi-Square distribution critical values

Upper tail probability .01 > P > .005

| df | .25 | .20 | .15 | .10 | .05 | .025 | .02 | .01 | .005 | .0025 | .001 | .0005 |
|---|---|---|---|---|---|---|---|---|---|---|---|---|
| 1 | 1.32 | 1.64 | 2.07 | 2.71 | 3.84 | 5.02 | 5.41 | 6.63 | 7.88 | 9.14 | 10.83 | 12.12 |
| 2 | 2.77 | 3.22 | 3.79 | 4.61 | 5.99 | 7.38 | 7.82 | 9.21 | 10.60 | 11.98 | 13.82 | 15.20 |
| 3 | 4.11 | 4.64 | 5.32 | 6.25 | 7.81 | 9.35 | 9. | [illegible] | [illegible] | 32 | 16.27 | 17.73 |
| 4 | 5.39 | 5.99 | 6.74 | 7.78 | 9.49 | 11.14 | 11.67 | 13.28 | 14.86 | 16.42 | 18.47 | 20.00 |
| 5 | 6.63 | 7.29 | 8.12 | 9.24 | 11.07 | 12.83 | 13.39 | 15.09 | 16.75 | 18.39 | 20.51 | 22.11 |
| 6 | 7.84 | 8.56 | 9.45 | 10.64 | 12.59 | 14.45 | 15.03 | 16.81 | 18.55 | 20.25 | 22.46 | 24.10 |

9.21 < 10.5 < 10.60

***P*-value:** .005 < P < .01

**CrunchIt! output:**

Test for independence of Drug and Column

| Statistic | DF | Value | P-value |
|---|---|---|---|
| Chi-square | 2 | 10.5 | 0.0052 |

$$\chi^2 = \sum \frac{(\text{Observed} - \text{Expected})^2}{\text{Expected}} = 10.5$$

$\chi^2$ Distribution

df = 2

*P*-value

37-39

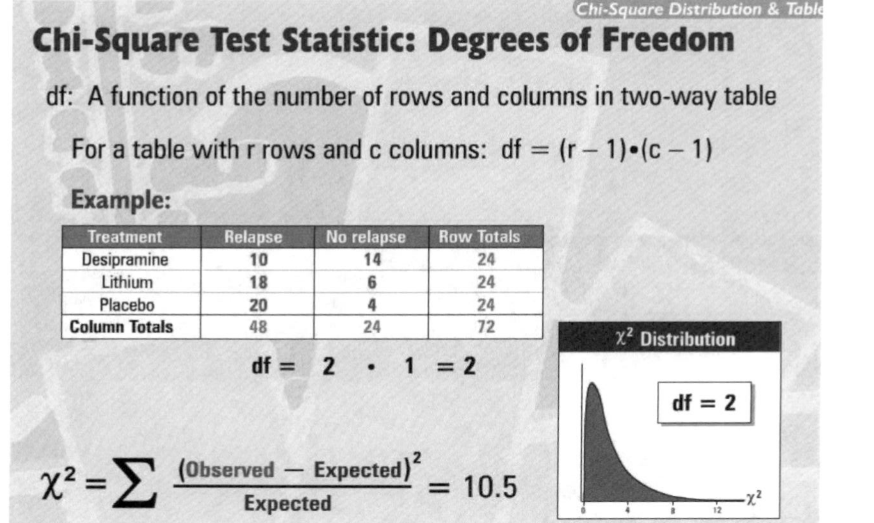

38-1

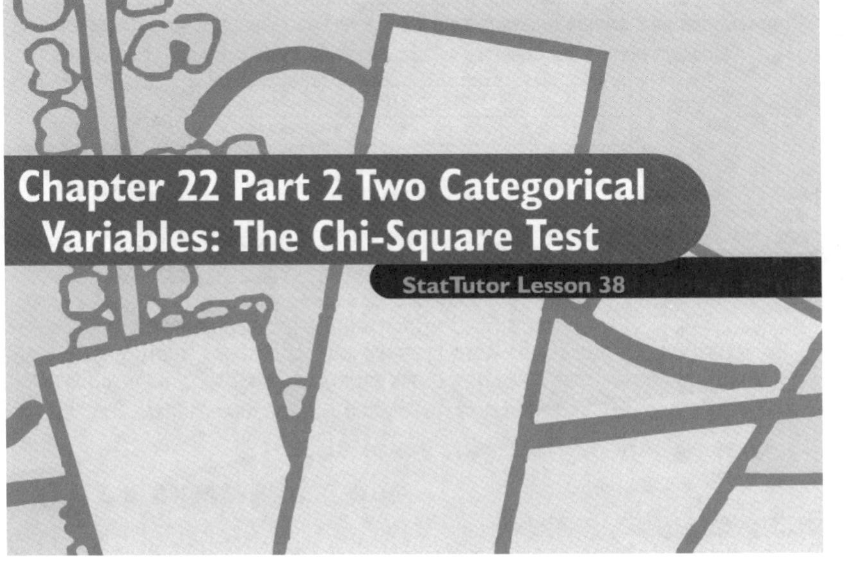


38-2

## Objectives

1. Differentiate between three methods of obtaining data for two-way tables: completely random experiments, stratified sampling, or SRS sampling.
2. Contrast the null and alternative hypotheses for the three methods of collecting data.
3. Evaluate expected cell counts for valid use of the chi-square test.

38-3

*Possible Chi-square Test Hypotheses*

## Uses of the Chi-Square Test

Basic Practice of Statistics Chapter 22

38-4

*Possible Chi-square Test Hypotheses*

## Three Ways to Collect Data for a Chi-Square Test

1. **Single simple random sample**
   --respondent asked two questions with categorical responses

   $H_0$: No relationship between row variable and column variable.
   $H_a$: Row variable and column variable are related.

2. **Multiple populations with simple random sample from each**
   --respondent asked one question with categorical responses

   $H_0$: No relationship: population distributions are the same.
   $H_a$: Relationship: population distributions are NOT the same (at least one differs).

3. **Completely randomized experiment**
   --categorical response variable

   $H_0$: No relationship: treatment distributions are the same.
   $H_a$: Relationship: treatment distributions are NOT the same (at least one differs).

**Different data collection--different hypotheses--same chi-square test.**

38-5

*Ways to Produce Two-Way Tables*

## The r x c Two-Way Table

### Data from a Simple Random Sample--two questions

**r categories and c categories for two response variables, respectively**

Example: An SRS of 8,235 male managers and professionals employed by a large manufacturing firm were classified in two ways, by marital status and by job grade.

Response variable: marital status c = 4

4 x 4 Table

Response variable: job grade r = 4

| Job Grade | Marital Status: Single | Married | Divorced | Widowed | Total |
|---|---|---|---|---|---|
| 1 | 58 39.08 | 874 896.44 | 15 14.61 | 8 4.87 | 955 |
| 2 | 222 173.47 | 3927 3979.05 | 70 64.86 | 20 21.62 | 4239 |
| 3 | 50 101.90 | 2396 2337.30 | 34 38.10 | 10 12.70 | 2490 |
| 4 | 7 22.55 | 533 517.21 | 7 8.43 | 4 2.81 | 551 |
| Total | 337 | 7730 | 126 | 42 | 8235 |

Legend: Observed Counts; Expected Counts; Marginal Totals

$H_0$: Job Grade is not associated with (is independent of) Marital Status.
$H_a$: Job Grade is associated with Marital Status.

38-6

*Ways to Produce Two-Way Tables*

## The r x c Two-Way Table

### Data from a Simple Random Sample--two questions

**r categories and c categories for two response variables, respectively**

Example: An SRS of 8,235 male managers and professionals employed by a large manufacturing firm were classified in two ways, by marital status and by job grade.

Response variable: marital status c = 4

4 x 4 Table

Response variable: job grade r = 4

| Job Grade | Marital Status: Single | Married | Divorced | Widowed | Total |
|---|---|---|---|---|---|
| 1 | 58 39.08 | 874 896.44 | 15 14.61 | 8 4.87 | 955 |
| 2 | 222 173.47 | 3927 3979.05 | 70 64.86 | 20 21.62 | 4239 |
| 3 | 50 101.90 | 2396 2337.30 | 34 38.10 | 10 12.70 | 2490 |
| 4 | 7 22.55 | 533 517.21 | 7 8.43 | 4 2.81 | 551 |
| Total | 337 | 7730 | 126 | 42 | 8235 |

Legend: Observed Counts; Expected Counts; Marginal Totals

Row totals should reflect relative size of category in population

Only table total is fixed.

Column totals should reflect relative size of category in population

$H_0$: Job Grade is not associated with (is independent of) Marital Status.
$H_a$: Job Grade is associated with Marital Status.

38-7

*Ways to Produce Two-Way Tables*

## The r x c Two-Way Table

### Data from Several Samples--One Question

**r strata (r populations) and c categories (response variable)**

Example: One thousand students were sampled from each class at a major university and asked if they supported a plan to cut several intercollegiate sports programs.

Response variable: opinion c = 5

4 x 5 Table

Explanatory variable: Class Populations: r = 4

| Group | Disagree | Somewhat Disagree | Somewhat Agree | Agree | No Opinion | Total |
|---|---|---|---|---|---|---|
| Freshman | 153 172.0 | 387 328.3 | 223 243.0 | 56 136.5 | 181 120.3 | 1,000 |
| Sophomore | 75 172.0 | 304 328.3 | 296 243.0 | 187 136.5 | 138 120.3 | 1,000 |
| Junior | 84 172.0 | 345 328.3 | 349 243.0 | 119 136.5 | 103 120.3 | 1,000 |
| Senior | 376 172.0 | 277 328.3 | 104 243.0 | 184 136.5 | 59 120.3 | 1,000 |
| Total | 688 | 1313 | 972 | 546 | 481 | 4,000 |

Legend: Observed Counts; Expected Counts; Marginal Totals

$H_0$: No relationship: distribution of opinion is the same for all four classes.
$H_a$: Relationship: at least one class has a distribution of opinion that is different.

38-8

*Ways to Produce Two-Way Tables*

## The r x c Two-Way Table

### Data from Several Samples--One Question

**r strata (r populations) and c categories (response variable)**

Example: One thousand students were sampled from each class at a major university and asked if they supported a plan to cut several intercollegiate sports programs.

Response variable: opinion c = 5

4 x 5 Table

Explanatory variable: Class Populations: r = 4

| Group | Disagree | Somewhat Disagree | Somewhat Agree | Agree | No Opinion | Total |
|---|---|---|---|---|---|---|
| Freshman | 153 172.0 | 387 328.3 | 223 243.0 | 56 136.5 | 181 120.3 | 1,000 |
| Sophomore | 75 172.0 | 304 328.3 | 296 243.0 | 187 136.5 | 138 120.3 | 1,000 |
| Junior | 84 172.0 | 345 328.3 | 349 243.0 | 119 136.5 | 103 120.3 | 1,000 |
| Senior | 376 172.0 | 277 328.3 | 104 243.0 | 184 136.5 | 59 120.3 | 1,000 |
| Total | 688 | 1313 | 972 | 546 | 481 | 4,000 |

Legend: Observed Counts; Expected Counts; Marginal Totals

Row totals were pre-determined by the survey designer.

$H_0$: No relationship: distribution of opinion is the same for all four classes.
$H_a$: Relationship: at least one class has a distribution of opinion that is different.

## The r x c Two-Way Table

### Data from a Completely Random Experiment

**r treatments (explanatory variable); c categories (response variable)**

Example: Three treatments (desipramine, lithium and placebo) were given to cocaine users trying to break the habit to determine which best helped prevent relapse. Response variable: whether user relapsed c = 2

3 x 2 Table

Explanatory variable: treatments r = 3

| Treatment | Relapse | | No Relapse | | Row Totals |
|---|---|---|---|---|---|
| Desipramine | 10 | 16 | 14 | 8 | 24 |
| Lithium | 18 | 16 | 6 | 8 | 24 |
| Placebo | 20 | 16 | 4 | 8 | 24 |
| Column Totals | 48 | | 24 | | 72 |

| Legend |
|---|
| Observed Counts |
| Expected Counts |
| Marginal Totals |

Row totals were pre-determined by the researcher.

$H_0$: No relationship: proportion of relapse is the same for all treatments.

$H_a$: Relationship: At least one proportion of relapse is different.





## Practice 1: Kissing Example

Which method of data collection?

- Simple Random Sample--two questions
- Several Samples--one question
- Completely Random Experiment

Example: At a large church sponsored university 329 students were surveyed using an SRS and asked the following questions:

1) What is your class standing? (Fresh / Soph / Jr / Sr / Graduate)
2) In your opinion, is kissing on the first date appropriate? Never ___ Seldom___ Sometimes ___ or Usually___?

| Class | Never | Seldom | Sometimes | Usually | Row Totals |
|---|---|---|---|---|---|
| Freshman | 29 | 15 | 7 | 0 | 51 |
| Sophomore | 15 | 32 | 24 | 3 | 74 |
| Junior | 20 | 25 | 27 | 2 | 74 |
| Senior | 24 | 30 | 28 | 11 | 93 |
| Graduate | 12 | 11 | 14 | 0 | 37 |
| Column Totals | 100 | 113 | 100 | 16 | 329 |

Clue: Each student was asked two questions; only table total is fixed.





## Practice 2: Hatching Python Eggs

Which method of data collection?

- Simple Random Sample--two questions
- Several Samples--one question
- Completely Random Experiment

Example: Researchers randomly assigned newly laid Python eggs to one of three temperatures: hot, neutral or cold to determine whether temperature influences hatching rates.

| | Hatched | Didn't hatch | Total |
|---|---|---|---|
| Cold | 16 | 11 | 27 |
| Neutral | 38 | 18 | 56 |
| Hot | 75 | 29 | 104 |
| Total | 129 | 58 | 187 |

Clue: Researcher determined which eggs were assigned to which temperature.





## Practice 3: Country Comparisons

Which method of data collection?

- Simple Random Sample--two questions
- Several Samples--one question
- Completely Random Experiment

A probability sample of adults was selected from each of three countries – the United States, India, and France. Each adult was asked the question, "Do you think it is, or is not, morally wrong for a couple to have a baby if they are not married?"

Source: http://www.gallup.com/Special_Reports/family.html

| Country | Wrong | Not wrong | No opinion | Row Totals |
|---|---|---|---|---|
| United States | 470 | 500 | 30 | 1000 |
| India | 840 | 140 | 20 | 1000 |
| France | 80 | 910 | 10 | 1000 |
| Column Totals | 1390 | 1550 | 60 | 3000 |

| Legend |
|---|
| Observed Counts |
| Expected Counts |
| Marginal Totals |

**Note: The exact sample sizes for each country were not given in the report, but were approximately 1000. This table assumes each sample size was 1000 persons.**

Clue: Separate samples were obtained from each country.

38-13



## Steps of Chi-square Test

Step 1 **STATE** the problem.

Step 2 **PLAN**: Recognize need for Chi-Square test.
Specify $H_0$ and $H_a$; choose $\alpha$.

| One SRS--two questions | Multiple samples--one question or CRD |
|---|---|
| $H_0$: No relationship between row and column variables. | $H_0$: No relationship: population (treatment) distributions are the same. |
| $H_a$: Relationship between row and column variables. | $H_a$: Relationship: population (treatment) distributions are not the same (at least one differs). |

Step 3 **SOLVE**: Collect data--SRS, multiple SRS's or random allocation.
Summarize data in r x c table; compute expected counts.

$$\text{Expected} = \frac{(\text{Row Total}) \times (\text{Column Total})}{\text{Table Total}}$$

Check conditions: SRS(s) or random allocation and E's $\geq 5$.
Compute test statistic:

$$\chi^2 = \sum \frac{(\text{Observed} - \text{Expected})^2}{\text{Expected}}$$

Obtain *P*-value.

$$df = (r - 1) \cdot (c - 1)$$

Step 4 **CONCLUDE**: Draw conclusions in context.

38-14



## Example: Chi-Square Test of Significance

Step 1 **STATE** the problem.

Three treatments, a placebo and two medications (desipramine, an anti-depressant, and lithium, a standard treatment) were compared to determine which best helped cocaine users break the habit. Seventy-two chronic users of cocaine who wanted to break the habit were randomly divided into three treatment groups with 24 assigned to each treatment. The response variable was whether the subject relapsed into cocaine use after three years.

Step 2 **PLAN**: Test relationship with Chi-Square test.
Specify $H_0$ and $H_a$; choose significance level ($\alpha$).

$H_0$: The proportions of subjects who relapse are equal for all three treatments or $p_1 = p_2 = p_3$.

$H_a$: The proportion of subjects who relapse is different for at least one treatment.

**Choose $\alpha = 0.02$**

38-15



## Example: Chi-Square Test of Significance

Step 3 **SOLVE**: Collect data using random allocation.



38-16



## Example: Chi-Square Test of Significance

Step 3 **SOLVE**: Collect data using random allocation.
Summarize data in r x c table; compute expected counts.

| Treatment | Relapse | | No Relapse | | Row Totals |
|---|---|---|---|---|---|
| Desipramine | 10 | 16 | 14 | 8 | 24 |
| Lithium | 18 | 16 | 6 | 8 | 24 |
| Placebo | 20 | 16 | 4 | 8 | 24 |
| Column Totals | 48 | | 24 | | 72 |

| Legend |
|---|
| Observed Counts |
| Expected Counts |
| Marginal Totals |

**General Formula:**

$$\text{Expected count} = \frac{\text{row total} \times \text{column total}}{\text{table total}}$$

Note: Expected counts typically have decimals.

38-17



## Example: Chi-Square Test of Significance

Step 3 **SOLVE**: Collect data using random allocation.
Summarize data in r x c table; compute expected counts.

| Treatment | Relapse | | No Relapse | | Row Totals |
|---|---|---|---|---|---|
| Desipramine | 10 | 16 | 14 | 8 | 24 |
| Lithium | 18 | 16 | 6 | 8 | 24 |
| Placebo | 20 | 16 | 4 | 8 | 24 |
| **Column Totals** | 48 | | 24 | | 72 |

| Legend |
|---|
| Observed Counts |
| Expected Counts |
| Marginal Totals |

Check conditions; proceed if met.

Check: Were independent SRS's taken?
OR Were subjects randomly allocated to treatments? **YES**

Check: Are all "expected counts" > 5? **YES**
If not, are all "expected counts" > 1?
and do 80% or more cells have "expected counts" > 5?

38-18



## Example: Chi-Square Test of Significance

Step 3 **SOLVE** (cont.): Compute test statistic and obtain *P*-value.

| Treatment | Relapse | | No Relapse | | Row Totals |
|---|---|---|---|---|---|
| Desipramine | 10 | 16 | 14 | 8 | 24 |
| Lithium | 18 | 16 | 6 | 8 | 24 |
| Placebo | 20 | 16 | 4 | 8 | 24 |
| **Column Totals** | 48 | | 24 | | 72 |

| Legend |
|---|
| Observed Counts |
| Expected Counts |
| Marginal Totals |

$$\chi^2 = \sum \frac{(\text{Observed} - \text{Expected})^2}{\text{Expected}}$$

$$\chi^2 = \frac{(10-16)^2}{16} + \frac{(14-8)^2}{8} + \frac{(18-16)^2}{16} + \frac{(6-8)^2}{8} + \frac{(20-16)^2}{16} + \frac{(4-8)^2}{8}$$

$$\chi^2 = 2.25 + 4.50 + 0.25 + 0.50 + 1.00 + 2.00 = 10.5$$

38-19



## Example: Chi-Square Test of Significance

Step 3 **SOLVE** (cont.): Compute test statistic and obtain P-value.

| Treatment | Relapse | | No Relapse | | Row Totals |
|---|---|---|---|---|---|
| Desipramine | 10 | 16 | 14 | 8 | 24 |
| Lithium | 18 | 16 | 6 | 8 | 24 |
| Placebo | 20 | 16 | 4 | 8 | 24 |
| **Column Totals** | 48 | | 24 | | 72 |

| Legend |
|---|
| Observed Counts |
| Expected Counts |
| Marginal Totals |

$$\chi^2 = \sum \frac{(\text{Observed} - \text{Expected})^2}{\text{Expected}} = \mathbf{10.5}$$

df = 2

**Software output:**

Test for independence of Drug and Column

| Statistic | DF | Value | P-value |
|---|---|---|---|
| Chi-square | 2 | 10.5 | 0.0052 |

38-20



## Example: Chi-Square Test of Significance

Step 4 **CONCLUDE:** Draw conclusions in context.

$H_0$: Proportions of relapse are equal. $H_a$: At least one $p_i$ is different.

| Treatment | Relapse | | No Relapse | | Row Totals |
|---|---|---|---|---|---|
| Desipramine | 10 | 16 | 14 | 8 | 24 |
| Lithium | 18 | 16 | 6 | 8 | 24 |
| Placebo | 20 | 16 | 4 | 8 | 24 |
| **Column Totals** | 48 | | 24 | | 72 |

| Legend |
|---|
| Observed Counts |
| Expected Counts |
| Marginal Totals |

P-value: .0052 $< \alpha = 0.02$ Reject $H_0$.

Conclusion in context: The proportion of relapses for at least one treatment group is different from the others.

- Which proportion(s) are different from which?
- Which cell(s) contributed most to the Chi-square test statistic?

38-21



## Example: Chi-Square Test of Significance

### Identifying Major Contributors to $\chi^2$

**Guideline:** If an individual Chi-square component $\geq 4$, the corresponding cell is a major contributor to the test statistic.

| Treatment | Relapse | No Relapse | Row Totals |
|---|---|---|---|
| Desipramine | 42% | 58% | 100% |
| Lithium | 75% | 25% | 100% |
| Placebo | 83% | 17% | 100% |
| **Column Totals** | 48 | 24 | 72 |

| Legend |
|---|
| Observed Counts |
| Expected Counts |
| Marginal Totals |

1. Apply Guideline
2. Convert to percentages
3. Interpret
   - Probable significant difference between observed and expected in Desipramine/No Relapse cell.
   - Effect of desipramine is different from lithium and placebo.
   - Lithium and placebo don't appear to differ.

38-22

## Vocabulary

Chi-square Test Statistic
Degrees of Freedom
Expected Count ("Expected")
Marginal Totals
Observed Count ("Observed")
r x c Table

39-1

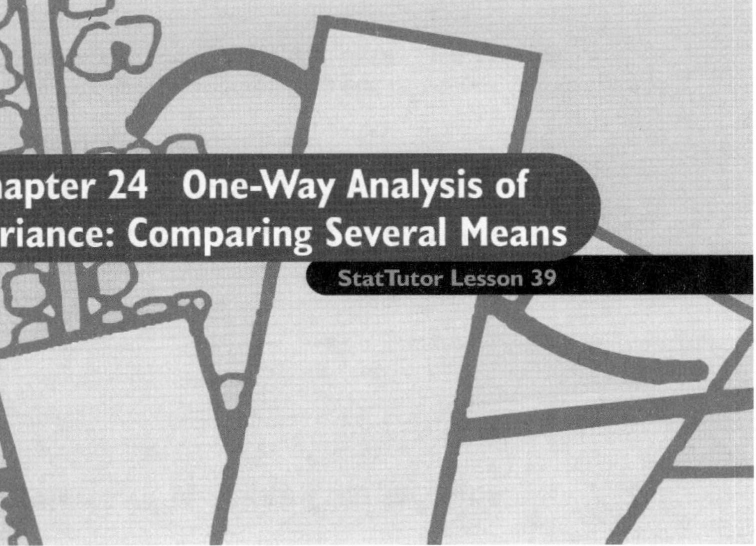


39-2

## Lesson Objectives

1. Recognize when a problem requires comparing three or more means.
2. Connect the use of all possible t tests on a set of data to the problem of multiple comparisons.
3. Write the appropriate null and alternative hypotheses for comparing three or more means.
4. Justify using variances to test hypotheses on means.
5. Use side-by-side boxplots and variance estimates to assess probable differences among sample means.
6. List and check assumptions that validate the use of analysis of variance.
7. Perform an analysis of variance testing equality of means using computer output.

39-3

Comparing More Than Two Means

## Introduction to Chapter 24 ANOVA: Comparing Several Means

Basic Practice of Statistics

39-4

Comparing More Than Two Means

## How Do We Compare Three or More Means?

A study comparing three different teaching styles.

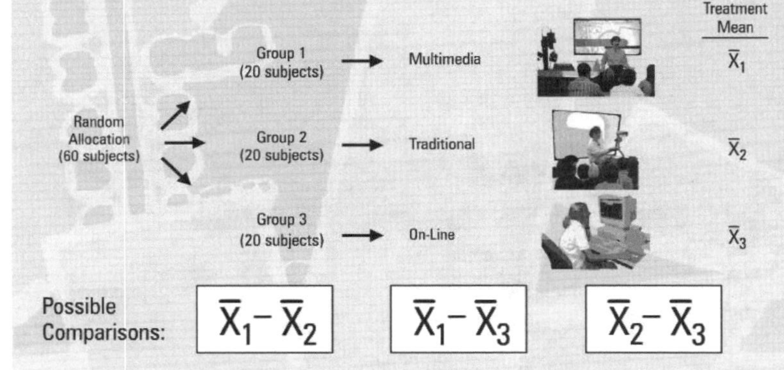


Possible Comparisons: $\bar{X}_1 - \bar{X}_2$ $\bar{X}_1 - \bar{X}_3$ $\bar{X}_2 - \bar{X}_3$

**Analysis of Variance (ANOVA): a procedure for comparing 3 or more means.**

39-5

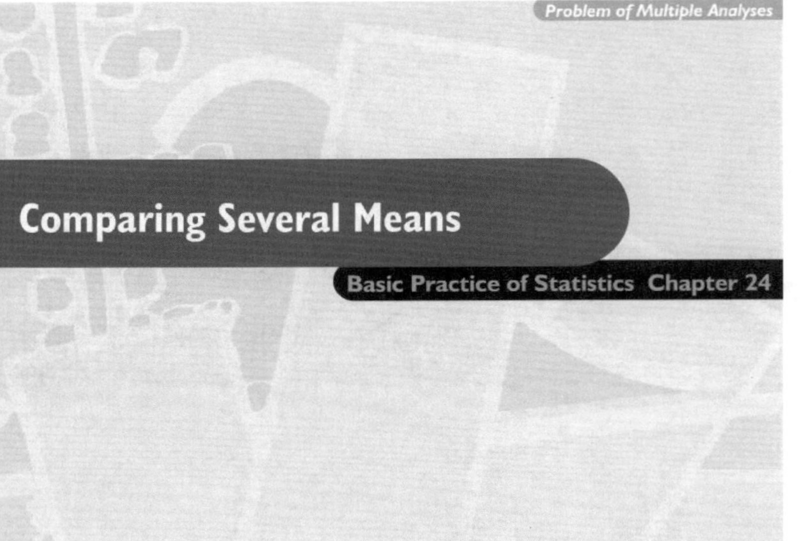


39-6

Problem of Multiple Analyses

## Three Two Sample *t* Tests of Significance

Treatment 1: Multimedia — Treatment 2: Traditional — Treatment 3: On-Line

| Hypotheses | Test Statistics | *P*-values |
|---|---|---|
| $H_0$: $\mu_1 = \mu_2$ → | $t_1 = \frac{(\bar{x}_1 - \bar{x}_2) - 0}{\sqrt{\frac{s_1^2}{n_1} + \frac{s_2^2}{n_2}}}$ | *P*-value$_1$ |
| $H_0$: $\mu_1 = \mu_3$ → | $t_2 = \frac{(\bar{x}_1 - \bar{x}_3) - 0}{\sqrt{\frac{s_1^2}{n_1} + \frac{s_3^2}{n_3}}}$ | *P*-value$_2$ |
| $H_0$: $\mu_2 = \mu_3$ → | $t_3 = \frac{(\bar{x}_2 - \bar{x}_3) - 0}{\sqrt{\frac{s_2^2}{n_2} + \frac{s_3^2}{n_3}}}$ | *P*-value$_3$ |

39-7

Problem of Multiple Analyses

## Problems of Multiple Comparisons

- Three null hypotheses, three *P*-values.
  - -Don't know which *P*-value to use.
  - -Cannot interpret them as a group.
  - -Don't have a hypothesis that compares all 3 means together.
- Multiple tests: The more tests performed
  - - the greater the probability of observing an extreme statistic due to chance.
  - -the greater the probability of declaring significance for at least one test when all differences are really due to chance alone. (The overall type I error rate for all tests combined is inflated.)

**Needed: One overall test (one null hypothesis, one test statistic, one P-value) to test equality of three or more means.**

39-8

Problem of Multiple Analyses

## Problems of Multiple Comparisons

- Three null hypotheses, three *P*-values.
  - -Don't know which *P*-value to use.

**1. Overall Test**
**Test Procedure: One-way Analysis of Variance (ANOVA)**
Test Statistic: F Ratio of Variances

**2. Follow-up Analysis** if overall test is significant.
Comparison of confidence intervals for individual means.

(The overall type I error rate for all tests combined is inflated.)

**Needed: One overall test (one null hypothesis, one test statistic, one P-value) to test equality of three or more means.**

39-9



# The Analysis of Variance *F* test

Basic Practice of Statistics Chapter 24

39-10



## Stating Hypotheses for ANOVA

**Purpose of ANOVA (Analysis of Variance)**
Compare k population (or treatment) means.

**Both hypotheses need to include all k means.**

$H_0$: $\mu_1 = \mu_2 = \mu_3 = \ldots = \mu_k$

$H_a$: At least one mean is different from the others (i.e., not all means are equal)

39-11



## Insect Experiment Example: Analysis of Variance

Step 1 **STATE** problem; identify essential information.

To detect harmful insects in farm fields, researchers put up sticky boards and examine the insects trapped on the boards. Which colors attract insects best? They randomly placed six boards of each of four colors in a field of oats and measured the number of cereal leaf beetles trapped. Does the mean number of insects differ for the colors: blue, green, white, and yellow?

| | |
|---|---|
| Type of Alternative: | means differ |
| Sample Size: | 6 boards *4 colors = 24 |
| Treatments: | four colors |
| Responses: | # of beetles/board |

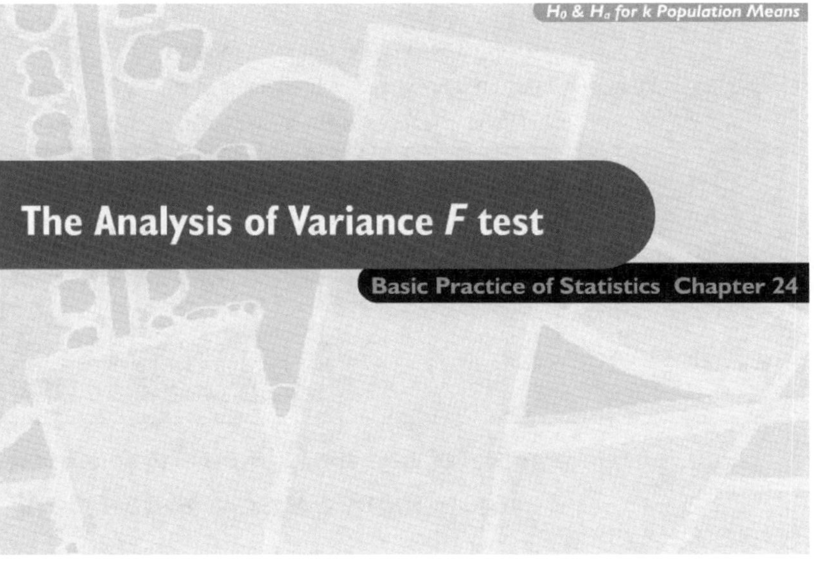

Step 2 **PLAN**: Compare four means with ANOVA; state $H_0$, $H_a$, and $\alpha$.

$H_0$: $\mu_{blue} = \mu_{green} = \mu_{white} = \mu_{yellow}$
$H_a$: At least one mean is different

Let $\alpha = 0.05$

39-12



## Insect Experiment Example: Analysis of Variance

Step 3 **SOLVE:** Collect data by randomly placing boards in field.

| Board color | Insects trapped | | | | | |
|---|---|---|---|---|---|---|
| Blue | 16 | 11 | 20 | 21 | 14 | 7 |
| Green | 37 | 32 | 20 | 29 | 37 | 32 |
| White | 21 | 12 | 14 | 17 | 13 | 20 |
| Yellow | 45 | 59 | 48 | 46 | 38 | 47 |

Boxplots (axis 0–60; blue, green, white, yellow)

Plot data; compute sample means and standard deviations.

| Level | N | Mean | StDev |
|---|---|---|---|
| Blue | 6 | 14.833 | 5.345 |
| Green | 6 | 31.167 | 6.306 |
| White | 6 | 16.167 | 3.764 |
| Yellow | 6 | 47.167 | 6.795 |

$$\frac{\text{Largest s}}{\text{Smallest s}} = \frac{6.795}{3.764} = 1.81$$

**Check** conditions of equal variance, normality and independent SRS's.
Equal variance ✓ No outliers or skewness ✓ Random allocation ✓

**Ok to proceed.**

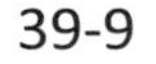

39-13

Example of ANOVA

## Insect Experiment  Example: Analysis of Variance

Step 3 **SOLVE** (cont.): Find F test statistic and $P$-value using software.

```
Analysis of Variance
Source      DF        SS         MS          F         P
Factor       3    4134.0     1378.0      42.84     0.000
Error       20     643.3       32.2
Total       23    4777.3
                               Individual 95% CIs For Mean
                               Based on Pooled StDev
Level   N    Mean    StDev    --+---------+---------+---------+----
Blue    6  14.833    5.345    (---*---)
Green   6  31.167    6.306                (---*---)
White   6  16.167    3.764     (---*---)
Yellow  6  47.167    6.795                            (---*---)
                              --+---------+---------+---------+----
Pooled StDev = 5.672           12        24        36        48
```

Step 4 **CONCLUDE:** Draw conclusions in context.

$P = 0.000 < 0.05 = \alpha$ ⇨ Reject the null hypothesis

Conclusion in Context: The mean number of insects attracted is significantly different for at least one color.

39-14

Example of ANOVA

## Follow-up Analysis

**What color (or colors) attracts the most insects?**

Look at boxplots and confidence intervals.

Boxplots

60, 50, 40, 30, 20, 10, 0

blue green white yellow

```
   MS          F         P
1378.0      42.84     0.000
  32.2

Individual 95% CIs For Mean
Based on Pooled StDev
--+---------+---------+---------+----
(---*---)
                (---*---)
 (---*---)
                            (---*---)
--+---------+---------+---------+----
 12        24        36        48
```

- Blue and white intervals overlap–means don't differ significantly.
- Yellow and green intervals don't overlap–means differ significantly and are both significantly greater than means for blue or white.

**Recommendation: Use yellow as attractant color; green is next best.**

39-15

Op Example of ANOVA

## Follow-up Analysis: a Final Note

**Suppose we have $H_0$: $\mu_1 = \mu_2 = \mu_3 = \mu_4$ and all conditions are met.**

```
Analysis of Variance for Percent
Source     DF       SS       MS       F        P
List        3    920.5    306.8    4.92    0.003
Error      92   5738.2     62.4
Total      95   6658.6
                                Individual 95% CIs For Mean
                                Based on Pooled StDev
Level       N     Mean    StDev  -+---------+---------+---------+-----
1          24   32.750    7.409                  (-------*------)
2          24   29.667    8.058           (-------*------)
3          24   25.250    8.316 (------*-------)
4          24   25.583    7.779   (------*------)
                                 -+---------+---------+---------+-----
Pooled StDev =   7.898           24        28        32        36
```

$P = 0.003$ ⇨ reject $H_0$ ⇨ need follow-up analysis.

**Conclusion:** $\mu_1$ is significantly greater than $\mu_3$ and $\mu_4$, which don't differ.
$\mu_2$ does not differ significantly from $\mu_1$, $\mu_3$ and $\mu_4$.

39-16

ANOVA F Test Statistic

## The Idea of Analysis of Variance

Basic Practice of Statistics Chapter 24

39-17

ANOVA F Test Statistic

## Test Statistic for Analysis of Variance

$$F = \frac{\text{Observed Variation in the sample means}}{\text{Expected Variation in the sample means if population means are equal}}$$

**Observed variation** = Variation among sample means.

**Expected variation** = Variation among individuals within samples.

39-18

ANOVA F Test Statistic

## Case I: $H_0$ is True (All Means Equal)

**Situation:**

- 4 identical normally distributed populations (k=4)
- $H_0$ is true: $\mu_1 = \mu_2 = \mu_3 = \mu_4 = 50$

Equal variances: $\sigma_1^2 = \sigma_2^2 = \sigma_3^2 = \sigma_4^2 = 4$

- SRS of size $n_i = 20$ from each population; compute $\overline{x}_i$

$$F = \frac{\text{Observed Variation in the sample means}}{\text{Expected Variation in the sample means if population means are equal}}$$



39-19

ANOVA F Test Statistic

## Case I: $H_0$ is True (All Means Equal)

**Situation:**

- 4 identical normally distributed populations (k=4)

If $H_0$ is true, **Observed Variation** is approximately equal to **Expected Variation**

$$F = \frac{\text{Observed Variation in the sample means}}{\text{Expected Variation in the sample means if population means are equal}}$$



39-20

ANOVA F Test Statistic

## Case 2: $H_a$ is True (Population Means Unequal)

**Situation:**

- 4 different normally distributed populations
- $H_a$ is true: $\mu_1 = 56$ $\mu_2 = 48$ $\mu_3 = 44$ $\mu_4 = 52$

Equal variances: $\sigma_1^2 = \sigma_2^2 = \sigma_3^2 = \sigma_4^2 = 4$

- SRS of size $n_i = 20$ from population; compute $\overline{x}_i$

$$F = \frac{\text{Observed Variation in the sample means}}{\text{Expected Variation in the sample means if population means are equal}}$$

39-21

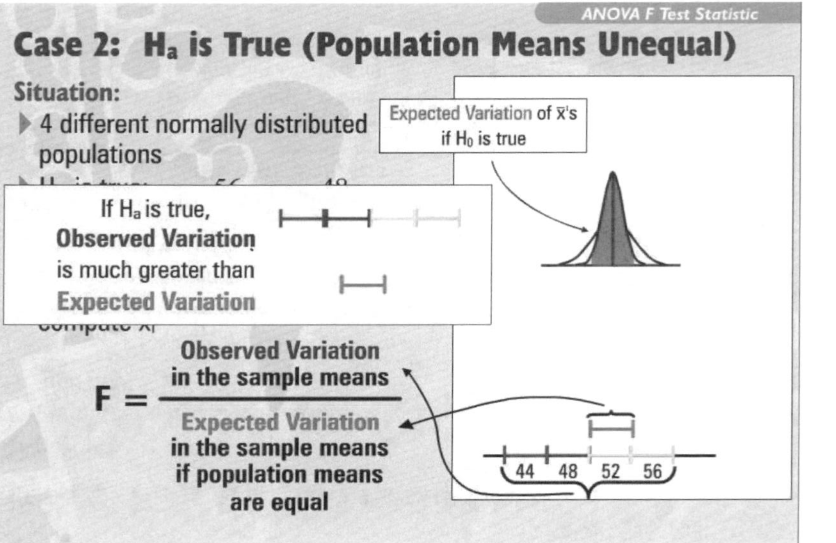


39-22

ANOVA F Test Statistic

## Side-by-Side Boxplots and Variance Computations

**Case I with $H_0$ true:**

Four identical normal populations

$\mu_1 = \mu_2 = \mu_3 = \mu_4 = 50$

$\sigma_1^2 = \sigma_2^2 = \sigma_3^2 = \sigma_4^2 = 4$

$n_1 = n_2 = n_3 = n_4 = 20$

| Sample: | 1 | 2 | 3 | 4 |
|---|---|---|---|---|
| | 52 | 49 | 50 | 51 |
| | 48 | 50 | 47 | 51 |
| | 47 | 50 | 51 | 51 |
| | 50 | 49 | 49 | 50 |
| | ⋮ | ⋮ | ⋮ | ⋮ |
| $\bar{x}_i =$ | 49.37 | 49.64 | 49.43 | 50.39 |
| $s_i^2 =$ | 5.24 | 3.24 | 5.02 | 4.93 |

Boxplots

Compute Variance

$$F = \frac{\text{Observed variation in the sample means}}{\text{Expected variation in the sample means if population means are equal}} = \frac{4.41}{4.61} = 0.96$$

39-23

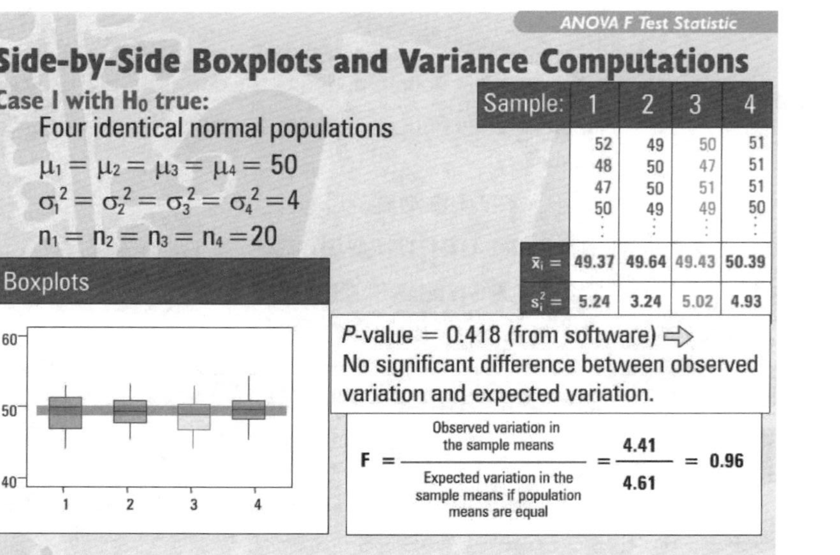


39-24

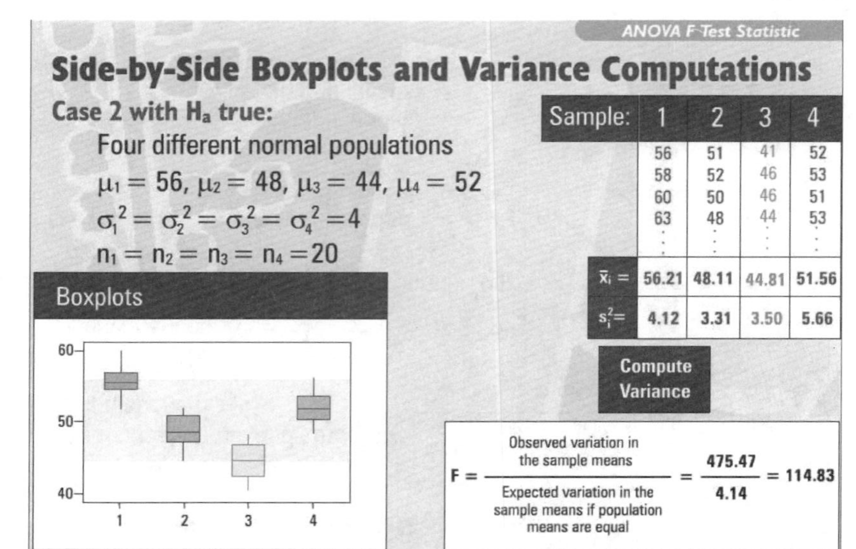

39-25

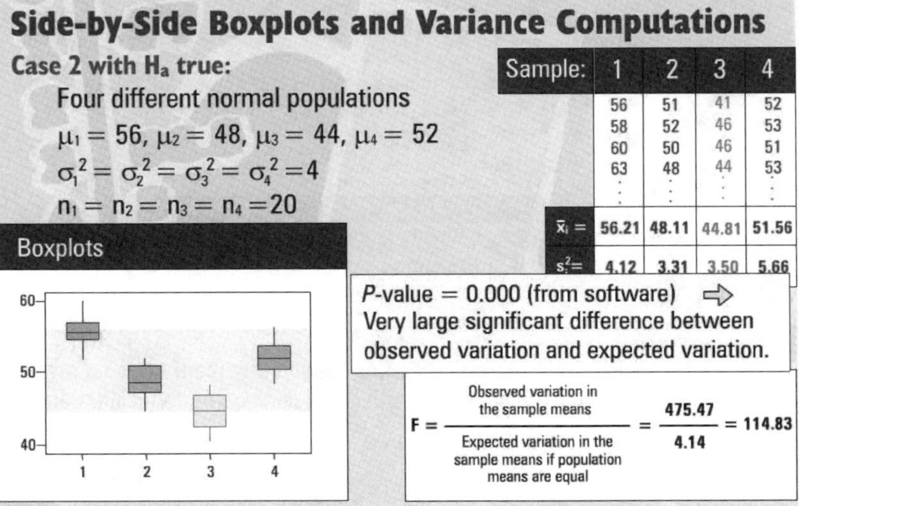


39-26

*ANOVA F Test Statistic*

## ANOVA and the F Test Statistic

Analysis of Variance provides both observed (or numerator) variance and expected (or denominator) variance using one dataset.

If $H_0$ is true, $F \approx 1$ If $H_0$ is false, $F > 1$

F test statistic and *P*-value obtained using software.

**Case 1** $\mu_1 = \mu_2 = \mu_3 = \mu_4 = 50$

| Sample: | 1 | 2 | 3 | 4 |
|---|---|---|---|---|
| | 52 | 49 | 50 | 51 |
| | 48 | 50 | 47 | 51 |
| | 47 | 50 | 51 | 51 |
| | 50 | 49 | 49 | 50 |
| | ⋮ | ⋮ | ⋮ | ⋮ |
| $\bar{x}_i =$ | 49.37 | 49.64 | 49.43 | 50.39 |
| $s_i^2 =$ | 5.24 | 3.24 | 5.02 | 4.93 |

F = 0.96 P = .418 **Do not reject $H_0$**

**Case 2** $\mu_1 = 56$ $\mu_2 = 48$ $\mu_3 = 44$ $\mu_4 = 52$

| Sample: | 1 | 2 | 3 | 4 |
|---|---|---|---|---|
| | 56 | 51 | 41 | 52 |
| | 58 | 52 | 46 | 53 |
| | 60 | 50 | 46 | 51 |
| | 63 | 48 | 44 | 53 |
| | ⋮ | ⋮ | ⋮ | ⋮ |
| $\bar{x}_i =$ | 56.21 | 48.11 | 44.81 | 51.56 |
| $s_i^2 =$ | 4.12 | 3.31 | 3.50 | 5.66 |

F = 114.83 P = .000 **Reject $H_0$**

39-27

*ANOVA F Test Statistic*

## ANOVA and the F Test Statistic

$$F = \frac{\text{Observed Variation in the sample means}}{\text{Expected Variation in the sample means if population means are equal}}$$

F test statistic and *P*-value computations usually done by a computer.

39-28

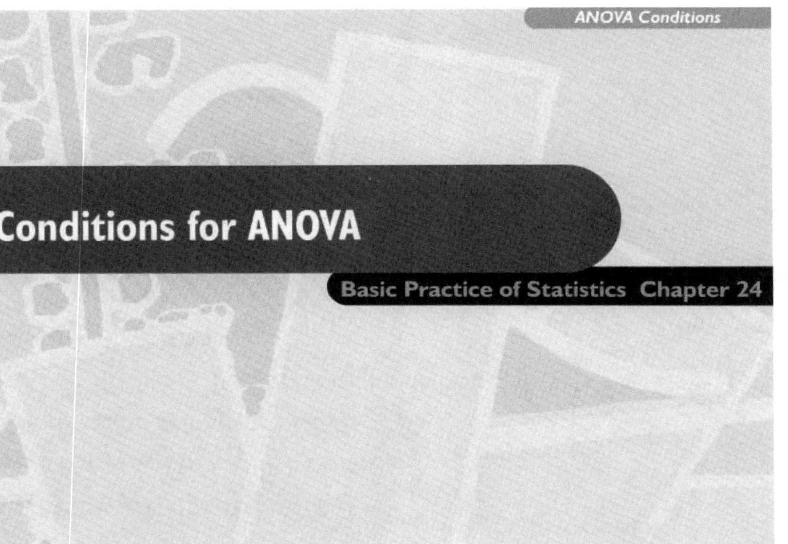

39-29

ANOVA Conditions

## What Are Conditions for ANOVA?

| Population 1 | Population 2 | • • • | Population k |
|---|---|---|---|
| $\mu_1$ | $\mu_2$ | | $\mu_k$ |
| $N(\mu_1, \sigma)$ | $N(\mu_2, \sigma)$ | | $N(\mu_k, \sigma)$ |

**Normality**
Each population has a normal distribution.
**Check:** Plot data: look out for outliers and strong skewness.

**Equal Variances**
All populations have equal variances (and standard deviations.)
**Check:** Compare sample standard deviations. $\frac{\text{largest s}}{\text{smallest s}} < 2$

**Independence**
The k data sets are independent of each other.
**Check:** Examine data collection for random allocation of subjects to k treatments or k separate SRS's (stratified sampling).

39-30

ANOVA Conditions

## Violation of Conditions

**What happens when ANOVA conditions are violated?**

Departures from normality?

ANOVA is robust! Check for outliers and skewness.

Unequal Variances?

ANOVA is robust! Especially if sample sizes are equal and no sample is very small.

Check: $\frac{\text{largest s}}{\text{smallest s}} < 2$

Lack of random allocation or independent SRS's?

ANOVA is not robust!

39-31

Example of ANOVA

## Hot Dog Example

Step 1 **STATE** problem.

Is there evidence to conclude that the mean sodium content of hotdogs differs for beef, meat and poultry hotdogs?

Step 2 **PLAN:** Perform ANOVA on three means; state $H_0$, $H_a$, and $\alpha$.

$H_0$: $\mu_{beef} = \mu_{meat} = \mu_{poultry}$
$H_a$: At least one mean is different

Set $\alpha = 0.10$.

Step 3 **SOLVE:** Collect data taking independent SRS's of three types of hotdogs.

| Hotdog Type | Sodium Content |
|---|---|
| Beef | 495 477 425 322 482 587 370 322 479 375<br>330 300 386 401 645 440 317 319 298 |
| Meat | 253 458 506 473 545 496 360 387 386<br>507 393 405 372 144 511 405 428 339 |
| Poultry | 430 375 396 383 387 542 359 357 528<br>513 426 513 358 581 588 522 545 |

39-32

Example of ANOVA

## Hot Dog Example

Step 3 **SOLVE** (cont.): **Plot** data; compute means, standard deviations.

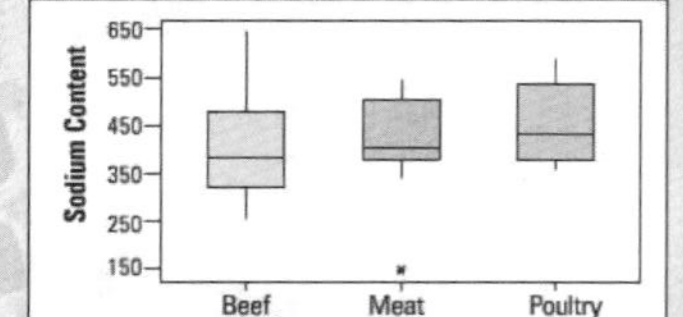


| Level | N | Mean | StDev |
|---|---|---|---|
| Beef | 20 | 401.2 | 102.4 |
| Meat | 17 | 418.5 | 93.9 |
| Poultry | 17 | 459.0 | 84.7 |

**Check** conditions of equal variance, normality & independent SRS's.

$\frac{\text{Largest s}}{\text{Smallest s}} = \frac{102.4}{84.7} = 1.21 < 2$ **Equal variance ok**

Although beef boxplot is slightly skewed and there is one outlier for meat hotdogs, total sample size is 54. **Normality ok**

Hot dog samples were taken independently. **Independent SRS's ok**

**Ok to proceed.**

39-33

Example of ANOVA

## Hot Dog Example

Step 3 **SOLVE** (cont.): Find F test statistic and $P$-value using software.

ANOVA table:

| Source | df | SS | MS | F-Stat | P-value |
|---|---|---|---|---|---|
| Treatments | 2 | 31738.715 | 15869.357 | 1.777791 | 0.1793 |
| Error | 51 | 455248.78 | 8926.446 | | |
| Total | 53 | 486987.5 | | | |

Step 4 **CONCLUDE:** Draw conclusions in context.

$P = 0.179 > 0.10 = \alpha$ ⇨ Fail to reject the null hypothesis

Conclusion in Context: Insufficient evidence to conclude that the mean sodium contents differ significantly for the hotdog types.

**Confidence intervals for the means**

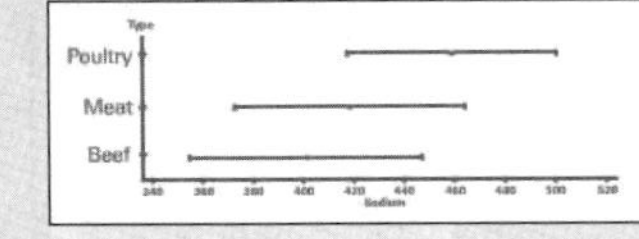


39-34

## Vocabulary:

**ANOVA or Analysis of Variance**
**Equal Variance**
**Follow-up Analyses**
**F Test Statistic**
**Independence**
**Multiple Comparisons**
**Normality**
**Overall Type I Error Rate**

40-1

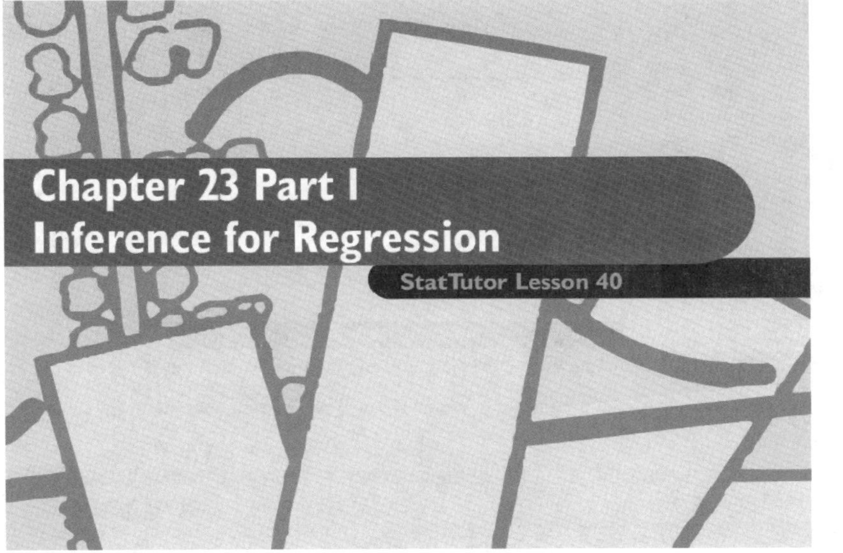


40-2

## Objectives

1. Outline and apply the four steps of statistical problem solving in regression analysis.
2. Associate the statistics of the least-squares regression line with the parameters of the theoretical (true) regression model.
3. List the assumptions and describe how to check them using a scatterplot, a residual plot and a histogram of residuals.
4. Estimate $\sigma$, the standard deviation of y about the true regression model.
5. Justify testing $H_0$: $\beta = 0$ as a test for determining whether X is useful for predicting Y. Outline and apply the steps for testing $H_0$: $\beta = 0$.
6. Describe how to estimate $\beta$ with a confidence interval; compute and interpret a confidence interval for $\beta$.

40-3

Regression Analysis

# Introduction to Chapter 23 Inference for Regression

Basic Practice of Statistics Chapter 23

40-4

Regression Analysis

## Outline of Regression Analysis

**I. STATE Question:** Investigate possible explanatory variables that might explain variation in the response variable of interest, determine which X would best predict Y and ask: "Is there a linear relationship between X and Y?"

**II. PLAN Solution:** Plan to examine scatterplot for linear relationship, to obtain a linear regression equation and to perform a *t*-test on whether a linear relationship exists between X and Y.

**III. SOLVE:**

**Data Production:** Collect bivariate data for the X and Y variables.

**Data Summarization:** Construct a scatterplot of the data collected on X and Y; if the relationship is linear, obtain a linear least-squares regression equation.

**Data analysis:** Check conditions, obtain test statistic and *P*-value.

**IV. CONCLUDE:** Decide whether X can be used to predict Y. If so, use the linear regression equation for prediction.

40-5

*Regression Analysis*

**I. STATE Question:**

A forest service official needs to predict the total volume of lumber on a piece of forest service land. She hopes predicting volume of wood from tree diameter for individual trees will help predict total volume for the piece of forest land. She investigates, "Can volume of wood for a tree be predicted by its diameter?"

**II. PLAN Solution:**

She plans to examine the data with a scatterplot, obtain a least-squares regression equation, and then to test whether a tree's diameter can be used to predict its volume of wood.

40-6

*Regression Analysis*

**III. SOLVE**

**Collect data:** For a sample of 31 trees, measure the diameter of each tree and then its volume of wood.

**Construct** a scatterplot of data collected on X and Y and check for linear pattern. Is the relationship linear? **Yes**

**Scatterplot of Tree Data**

n=31

Volume (100*board*ft) vs. Diameter (in)

| Tree | X<br>Diameter (in) | Y<br>Volume (100board•ft) |
|---|---|---|
| 1 | 8.3 | 10.3 |
| 2 | 8.6 | 10.3 |
| 3 | 8.8 | 10.2 |
| 4 | 10.5 | 16.4 |
| 5 | 10.7 | 18.8 |
| 6 | 10.8 | 19.7 |
| 7 | 11.0 | 15.6 |
| 8 | 11.0 | 18.2 |
| 9 | 11.1 | 22.6 |
| 10 | 11.2 | 19.9 |
| 11 | 11.3 | 24.2 |
| 12 | 11.4 | 21.0 |
| 13 | 11.4 | 21.4 |
| 14 | 11.7 | 21.3 |
| 15 | 12.0 | 19.1 |
| 16 | 12.9 | 22.2 |
| 17 | 12.9 | 33.8 |
| 18 | 13.3 | 27.4 |
| 19 | 13.7 | 25.7 |
| 20 | 13.8 | 24.9 |
| 21 | 14.0 | 34.5 |
| 22 | 14.2 | 31.7 |
| 23 | 14.5 | 36.3 |
| 24 | 16.0 | 38.3 |
| 25 | 16.3 | 42.6 |
| 26 | 17.3 | 55.4 |
| 27 | 17.5 | 55.7 |
| 28 | 17.9 | 58.3 |
| 29 | 18.0 | 51.5 |
| 30 | 18.0 | 51.0 |
| 31 | 20.6 | 77.0 |

40-7

*Regression Analysis*

**III. SOLVE (cont.)**

**Data Summarization:** Obtain the least-squares regression line.

$\hat{y} = a + b\,x = -36.944 + 5.066\,x$

$b = r\frac{s_y}{s_x} = 0.967\,\frac{16.44}{3.138} = 5.066$

$a = \bar{y} - b\,\bar{x} = 30.17 - (5.066)13.248 = -36.944$

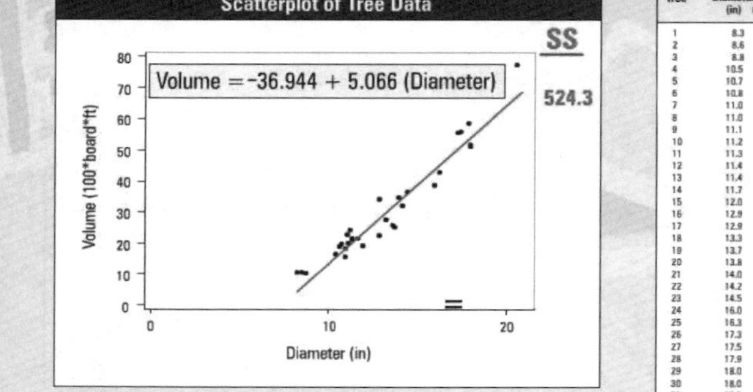


| Tree | X<br>Diameter (in) | Y<br>Volume (100board•ft) |
|---|---|---|
| 1 | 8.3 | 10.3 |
| 2 | 8.6 | 10.3 |
| 3 | 8.8 | 10.2 |
| 4 | 10.5 | 16.4 |
| 5 | 10.7 | 18.8 |
| 6 | 10.8 | 19.7 |
| 7 | 11.0 | 15.6 |
| 8 | 11.0 | 18.2 |
| 9 | 11.1 | 22.6 |
| 10 | 11.2 | 19.9 |
| 11 | 11.3 | 24.2 |
| 12 | 11.4 | 21.0 |
| 13 | 11.4 | 21.4 |
| 14 | 11.7 | 21.3 |
| 15 | 12.0 | 19.1 |
| 16 | 12.9 | 22.2 |
| 17 | 12.9 | 33.8 |
| 18 | 13.3 | 27.4 |
| 19 | 13.7 | 25.7 |
| 20 | 13.8 | 24.9 |
| 21 | 14.0 | 34.5 |
| 22 | 14.2 | 31.7 |
| 23 | 14.5 | 36.3 |
| 24 | 16.0 | 38.3 |
| 25 | 16.3 | 42.6 |
| 26 | 17.3 | 55.4 |
| 27 | 17.5 | 55.7 |
| 28 | 17.9 | 58.3 |
| 29 | 18.0 | 51.5 |
| 30 | 18.0 | 51.0 |
| 31 | 20.6 | 77.0 |

40-8

*Regression Analysis*

**III. SOLVE (cont.)**

**Check** conditions and **test** whether the linear regression model is useful for prediction. **Estimate** slope with a confidence interval.

**IV. CONCLUDE:** Decide whether a tree's diameter can be used to predict its volume.

X Y

In this chapter we will discuss

- Conditions necessary for statistical inference.
- How to check these conditions.
- Parameters of the theoretical linear regression model.
- Statistics used to estimate those model parameters.
- How to test slope to determine if model is useful for prediction.
- How to obtain a confidence interval for estimating slope.
- How to use the linear regression model for prediction and how to construct interval estimates of those predictions.

40-9



# Conditions for Regression Inference

Basic Practice of Statistics Chapter 23

40-10



## Conditions of the Theoretical Regression Model

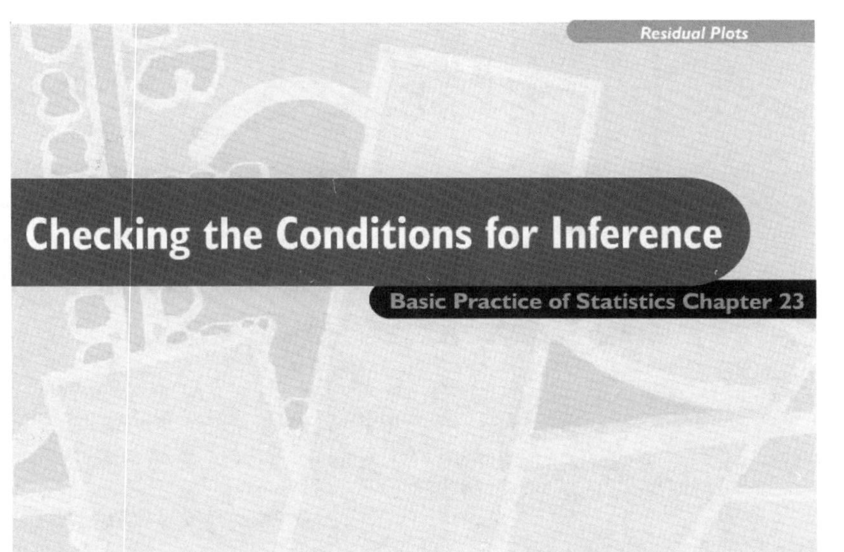


**Linearity** $\mu_Y$ has a straight-line relationship with X ($\mu_Y = \alpha + \beta X$).

**Equal Standard Deviation** The standard deviation of Y ($\sigma$) about $\mu_Y$ is the same for all values of X.

**Normality** At each value of X, Y is Normally distributed around $\mu_Y$.

**Independence** The y's at one X value are independent of y's at another X value.

40-11



## Checking Conditions for Regression Inference

**Patterns indicating inference is appropriate / is not appropriate.**

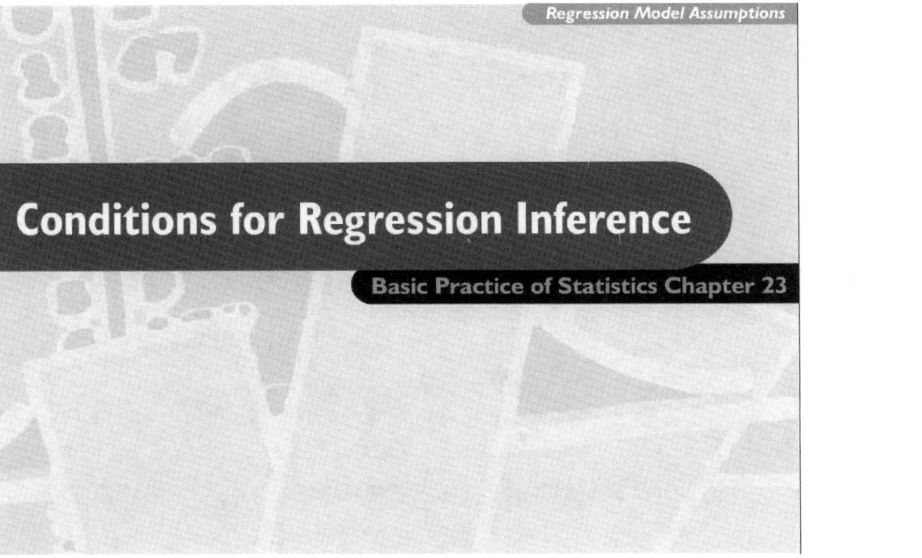


40-12



# Checking the Conditions for Inference

Basic Practice of Statistics Chapter 23

40-13

Residual Plots

## Review: Residual Plots

**Residual:** The difference between observed y value and $\hat{y}$, the value predicted by the regression line; i.e., residual = $y - \hat{y}$

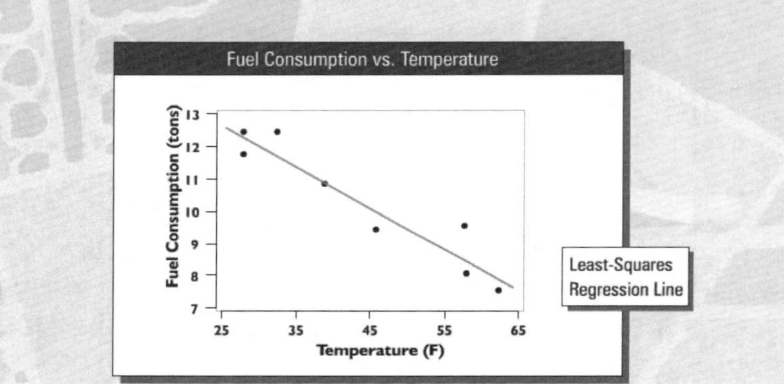


40-14

Residual Plots

## Review: Residual Plots

**Residual:** The difference between observed y value and $\hat{y}$, the value predicted by the regression line; i.e., residual = $y - \hat{y}$

**Residual Plot:** A scatterplot of the residuals versus the observed x values (or the $\hat{y}$'s).

40-15

Regression Model Conditions

## Conditions of the Theoretical Regression Model

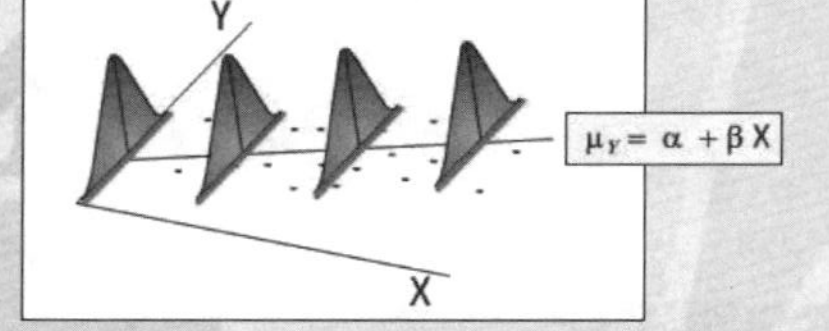


**Linearity** $\mu_Y$ has a straight-line relationship with X ($\mu_Y = \alpha + \beta X$).

**Equal Standard Deviation** The standard deviation of Y ($\sigma$) about $\mu_Y$ is the same for all values of X.

**Normality** At each value of X, Y is Normally distributed around $\mu_Y$.

**Independence** The y's at one X value are independent of y's at another X value.

40-16

Regression Model Conditions

## Condition Checks for Inference in Regression

**Linearity**

- Check scatterplot for a linear pattern.
- Check residual plot (plot of residuals versus x's) for a smile or a frown pattern that indicates lack of linearity.

40-17

Regression Model Conditions

## Condition Checks for Inference in Regression

**Equal Standard Deviation**

- Check scatterplot to see whether the scatter of data points about the regression line is roughly the same over the entire range of the data.
- Check residual plot for a megaphone pattern that indicates non-constant standard deviation.

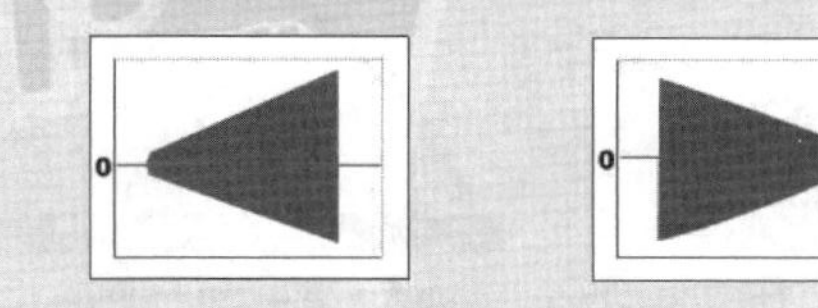


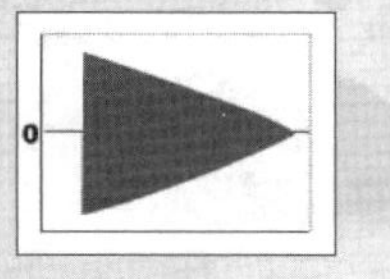


40-18

Regression Model Conditions

## Condition Checks for Inference in Regression

**Normality**

- Check histogram or stemplot of residuals for skewness or other major departures from Normality--like outliers.
  ---*t* procedures are robust with respect to Normality especially for large samples.
- Prediction intervals have a stricter requirement for Normality. (to be covered later)

HISTOGRAM of RESIDUALS

```
Stem-and-leaf of RESIDUALS
N  = 24
Leaf Unit = 1.0

 -4|42
 -3|3
 -2|
 -1|883
 -0|8443322
  0|058
  1|0255
  2|14
  3|6
  4|
  5|0
```

**Plots of residuals having no outliers or strong skewness.**

40-19

Regression Model Conditions

## Condition Checks for Inference in Regression

**Normality**

- Check histogram or stemplot of residuals for skewness or other major departures from Normality--like outliers.
  ---*t* procedures are robust with respect to Normality especially for large samples.
- Prediction intervals have a stricter requirement for Normality. (to be covered later)

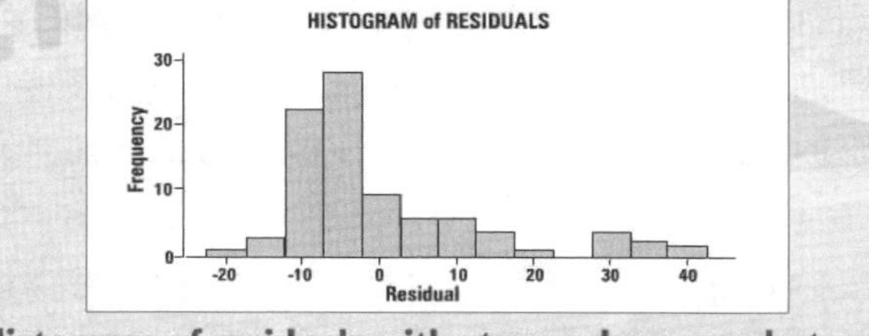


**Histogram of residuals with strong skewness, but n = 92.**

40-20

Regression Model Conditions

## Condition Checks for Inference in Regression

**Normality**

- Check histogram or stemplot of residuals for skewness or other major departures from Normality--like outliers.
  ---*t* procedures are robust with respect to Normality especially for large samples.
- Prediction intervals have a stricter requirement for Normality. (to be covered later)

**Residual plots indicating outliers.**

40-21

*Regression Model Conditions*

## Condition Checks for Inference in Regression

**Independence**

- Repeated measures on the same individual are not allowed.
- Data collected over time often lacks independence.
- Checks for independence require methods beyond the scope of this course.

40-22

*Regression Model Conditions*

## Condition Checks for Inference in Regression

**Do these plots indicate problems?**

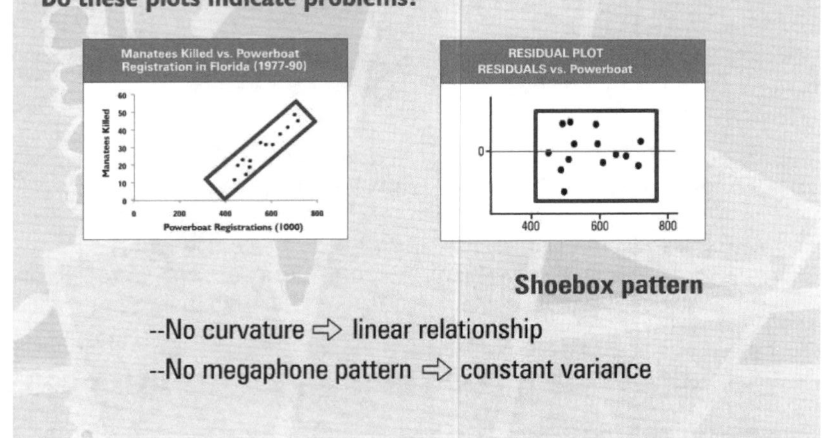


**Shoebox pattern**

--No curvature ⇨ linear relationship

--No megaphone pattern ⇨ constant variance

40-23

*Regression Model Conditions*

## Condition Checks for Inference in Regression

**Do these plots indicate problems?**

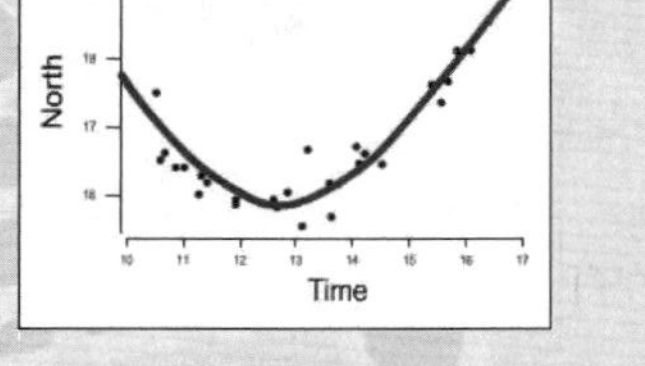


RESIDUAL PLOT (Residual vs. Time)

**Curvature** **Smile**

--Curvature ⇨ No linear relationship

40-24

*Regression Model Conditions*

## Condition Checks for Inference in Regression

**Do these plots indicate problems?**

Runners' Lung Capacity vs. Run Time

Runners' Lung Capacity vs. RESIDUALS

--No curvature ⇨ linear relationship

--No megaphone pattern ⇨ constant variance

40-25

Regression Model Conditions

## Condition Checks for Inference in Regression

**Do these plots indicate problems?**



--Megaphone pattern ⇨ non-constant variance

40-26

Regression Model Conditions

## Condition Checks for Inference in Regression

**Does this histogram of residuals indicate a problem?**



**n = 9**

For n = 9, this outlier indicates lack of normality.

40-27

Theoretical Regression Model

## Estimating the Parameters

Basic Practice of Statistics Chapter 23

40-28

Theoretical Regression Model

## Linear Regression Models: Parameters & Statistics

**Theoretical Linear Regression Model (the True Regression Line)**

$$\mu_y = \alpha + \beta x$$

where $\mu_y$ is the mean of the y's at that x
$\alpha$ is the theoretical y-intercept
and $\beta$ is the theoretical slope
($\mu_y$, $\alpha$ and $\beta$ are parameters.)

**Least-Squares Regression Line**

$$\hat{y} = a + b x$$

where $\hat{y}$ is the predicted y at that x
a is the unbiased estimate of the true y-intercept, $\alpha$
and b is the unbiased estimate of the true slope, $\beta$
($\hat{y}$, a and b are all statistics.)

**We perform tests on $\beta$ and construct confidence intervals for $\beta$.**

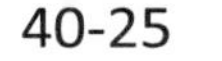

40-29

Estimating $\sigma$

## Estimating $\sigma$, the Standard Deviation of Y about $\mu_Y$

**Why estimate $\sigma$?** To get a value of s to use in the inferential formulas.

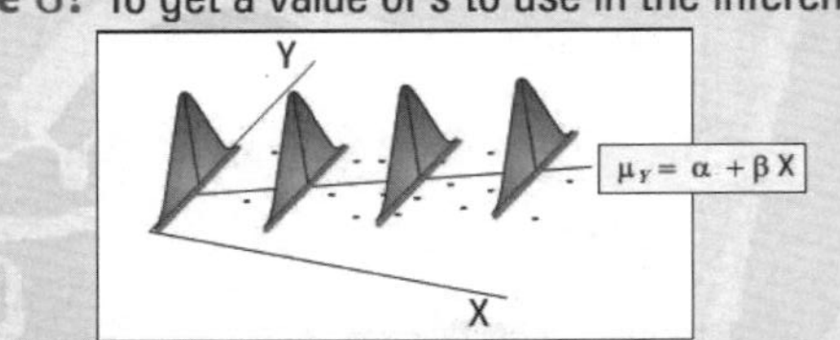


$\sigma$ = standard deviation of Y about the theoretical line

Recall: **Residual = observed y – predicted y = $y - \hat{y}$**

Residuals help estimate $\sigma$.

$\sigma$ is estimated by:

$$s = \sqrt{\frac{1}{n-2}\sum \text{residual}^2} = \sqrt{\frac{1}{n-2}\sum (y-\hat{y})^2}$$

**s is called "regression standard error"; it measures the variability of the y's about the regression line.**

40-30

Estimating $\sigma$

## Estimating $\sigma$, the Standard Deviation of Y about $\mu_Y$

**Visualizing s, a measure of the variation of Y about the regression line and an estimate of $\sigma$.**

$$s = \sqrt{\frac{\sum (\text{Residual})^2}{n-2}} = \sqrt{\frac{\sum (y-\hat{y})^2}{n-2}}$$

Sum of Squared Residuals

n – 2

Scatterplot of Tree Data

Residual

Squared Residuals

Diameter (in)

40-31

Estimating $\sigma$

## Using CrunchIt! to Find s

In CrunchIt!'s regression output, s is called "Estimate of error standard deviation."

**Regression Output**

**Simple linear regression results:**
**Dependent Variable:** volume
**Independent Variable:** diameter

Sample size: 31
Estimate of error standard deviation: 4.2519875

| Parameter | Estimate | Std. Err. | DF | T-Stat | P-Value |
|---|---|---|---|---|---|
| Intercept | -36.94346 | 3.365145 | 29 | -10.978267 | <0.0001 |
| x | 5.0658565 | 0.24737695 | 29 | 20.478289 | <0.0001 |

40-32

Testing $H_0$: $\beta = 0$

## Testing the Hypothesis of No Linear Relationship

Basic Practice of Statistics Chapter 23

40-33



## Hypotheses for Testing If Linear Relationship Exists

**Thought question:** Which parameter, $\alpha$ or $\beta$, should we test to determine whether X is useful for predicting Y?

Recall: For a chi-square test of independence, we tested
$H_0$: There is NO relationship between two categorical variables.
$H_a$: There is a relationship between two categorical variables.

Similarly, in regression analysis, we want to test
$H_0$: There is NO linear relationship between two numerical variables.
$H_a$: There is a linear relationship between two numerical variables.

These hypotheses can also be stated
$H_0$: X is NOT useful for predicting Y.
$H_a$: X is useful for predicting Y.

40-34



## Hypotheses for Testing If Linear Relationship Exists

$H_0$: X is NOT useful for predicting Y

Every value of X predicts the same value of Y.

This implies $\beta = 0$.

X does not help predict Y

$H_a$: X is useful for predicting Y

Every value of X predicts a different value of Y.

This implies $\beta \neq 0$.

X helps to predict Y

So, the hypotheses can also be stated $H_0: \beta = 0$ versus $H_a: \beta \neq 0$.

40-35



## Steps for Testing $H_0: \beta = 0$

Step 1 **STATE QUESTION:** After identifying a possible explanatory variable that might predict the response variable of interest, ask: "Is there a linear relationship between X and Y?"

Step 2 **PLAN SOLUTION:** Recognize need to collect data, to examine a scatterplot for linearity, to obtain the least-squares regression equation and to test slope to determine whether X can be used to predict Y; state $H_0$ and $H_a$ and select $\alpha$.

$$H_0: \beta = 0 \text{ vs. } H_a: \beta \neq 0$$

40-36



## Steps for Testing $H_0: \beta = 0$

Step 3 **SOLVE:** **Collect** bivariate data for the X and Y variables.

**Construct** a scatterplot of data collected on X and Y; if relationship is linear, obtain a linear least-squares regression equation.

**Check** conditions of linearity, equal variance and Normality by

1. checking residual plot for a pattern. A smile or a frown indicates violation of linearity and a megaphone indicates violation of equal variance.
2. checking histogram of residuals for strong skewness or outliers which indicate lack of normality.

**Compute** test statistic and obtain *P*-value.

| $t = \frac{b - 0}{SE_b}$ | $SE_b = \frac{s}{\sqrt{\sum(x - \bar{x})^2}}$ | Degrees of freedom = n − 2 |
|---|---|---|

Step 4 **CONCLUDE:** Draw conclusions about whether the linear regression equation of Y on X can be used for predicting Y.

40-37



## Tree Data Example of Testing $H_0$: $\beta = 0$

**Step 1** **STATE Question:** A forest service official needs to predict the total volume of lumber in a piece of forest service land. She hopes the prediction of volume of wood from tree diameter for individual trees will predict total volume for the piece of forest service land. She investigates:

**Can diameter of a tree predict its volume of wood?**

**Step 2** **PLAN Solution:** Recognize need to test slope; state $H_0$ and $H_a$ in terms of $\beta$; choose significance level ($\alpha$).

$H_0$: $\beta = 0$ $\quad$ $H_a$: $\beta > 0$ $\quad$ $\alpha = 0.05$

Note: $H_a$ is only upper-tailed because the lower tail doesn't make sense; i.e., we don't expect tree volume to decrease as diameter increases.

40-38



## Tree Data Example of Testing $H_0$: $\beta = 0$

**Step 1** **STATE Question:**
**Can diameter of a tree predict its volume of wood?**

**Step 2** **PLAN Solution:** $H_0$: $\beta = 0$ $\quad$ $H_a$: $\beta > 0$ $\quad$ $\alpha = 0.05$

**Step 3** **SOLVE: Collect** data--measure diameter and volume of wood for 31 trees.
**Construct** a scatterplot of the data collected on diameter and volume; **obtain** regression equation.

Scatterplot

**Regression Output**

**Simple linear regression results:**
**Dependent Variable:** volume
**Independent Variable:** diameter

$\hat{y} = -36.9 + 5.07\,x$

Sample size: 31
Correlation coefficient: 0.9671
Estimate of error standard deviation: 4.2519875

| Parameter | Estimate | Std. Err. | DF | T-Stat | P-Value |
|---|---|---|---|---|---|
| Intercept | -36.94346 | 3.365145 | 29 | -10.978267 | <0.0001 |
| x | 5.0658565 | 0.24737695 | 29 | 20.478289 | <0.0001 |

40-39



## Tree Data Example of Testing $H_0$: $\beta = 0$

**Step 3** **SOLVE (cont.):**
**Check** residual plot for patterns and histogram of residuals for skewness and outliers; proceed if both plots show no violations.

Residual Plot

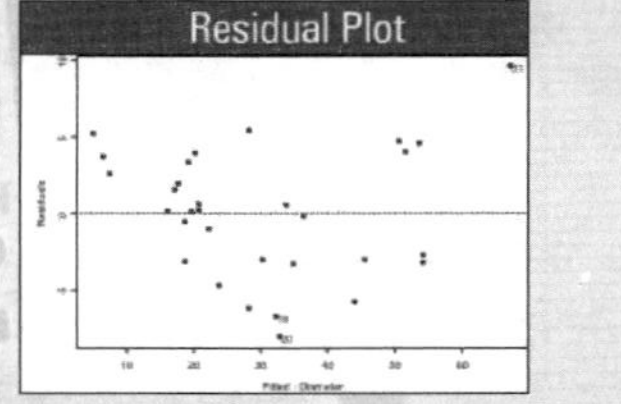

Histogram of Residuals

**Residual plot has no pattern; histogram of residuals has no outliers and is not stongly skewed so ok to proceed.**

40-40



## Tree Data Example of Testing $H_0$: $\beta = 0$

**Step 3** **SOLVE (cont.):**
**Check** residual plot for patterns and histogram of residuals for skewness and outliers; proceed if both plots show no violations.
**Compute** test statistic and obtain *P*-value.

| $t = \frac{b-0}{SE_b}$ | $SE_b = \frac{s}{\sqrt{\sum (x-\bar{x})^2}}$ | Degrees of freedom = n – 2 |
|---|---|---|

$$t = \frac{b-0}{SE_b} = \frac{5.0659-0}{0.2474} = 20.4783$$

**Regression Output**

**Simple linear regression results:**
**Dependent Variable:** volume
**Independent Variable:** diameter

Sample size: 31
Correlation coefficient: 0.9671
Estimate of error standard deviation: 4.2519875

| Parameter | Estimate | Std. Err. | DF | T-Stat | P-Value |
|---|---|---|---|---|---|
| Intercept | -36.94346 | 3.365145 | 29 | -10.978267 | <0.0001 |
| x | 5.0658565 | 0.24737695 | 29 | 20.478289 | <0.0001 |

40-41



## Tree Data Example of Testing $H_0$: $\beta = 0$

**Step 3** **SOLVE (cont.):**

**Check** residual plot for patterns and histogram of residuals for skewness and outliers; proceed if both plots show no violations.

**Compute** test statistic and obtain *P*-value.

$t = 20.4783$ $df = n - 2 = 31 - 2 = 29$

One sided *P*-value from *t*-table: **P** < 0.0005

Two sided *P*-value from CrunchIt! output: **P** <0.0001

**Step 4** **CONCLUDE:** Draw conclusions.

P-value < 0.0001 < $\alpha$ = 0.05

Reject $H_0$; conclude there is a significant linear relationship between diameter of a tree and its volume of wood; diameter can be used to predict volume.

| | | | | | |
|---|---|---|---|---|---|
| Intercept | -36.94346 | 3.365145 | 29 | -10.978267 | <0.0001 |
| x | 5.0658565 | 0.24737695 | 29 | 20.478289 | <0.0001 |

40-42



# Confidence Intervals for the Regression Slope

Basic Practice of Statistics Chapter 23

40-43



## Steps for Estimating $\beta$ with a Confidence Interval

**Step 1** **STATE QUESTION:** Ask a question about estimating slope.

**Step 2** **PLAN SOLUTION:** Recognize need for a confidence interval estimate of slope; specify confidence level.

**Step 3** **SOLVE:** **Collect** bivariate data for X and Y on n individuals. **Construct** scatterplot and check for linearity; if linear, obtain values for b and $SE_b$ using statistical software.

**Check** residual plot for patterns or outliers; check histogram of residuals for strong skewness or outliers; proceed if no patterns, outliers or strong skewness.

**Compute** confidence interval for $\beta$.

| $b \pm t^* SE_b$ | $SE_b = \frac{s}{\sqrt{\sum(x-\bar{x})^2}}$ | Degrees of freedom = n – 2 |
|---|---|---|

**Step 4** **CONCLUDE:** Interpret confidence interval for $\beta$ in context.

40-44



## Tree Data Example of Estimating $\beta$ with CI

**Step 1** **STATE:** What is the estimated slope for predicting volume?

**Step 2** **PLAN:** Recognize need for confidence interval estimate of $\beta$; choose level of confidence-- 95% .

**Step 3** **SOLVE:** Data previously collected on 31 trees. Scatterplot constructed and checked for linearity. Obtain b and $SE_b$ using statistical software.

$b = 5.0659$ $SE_b = 0.2474$

Previous check of residuals indicated no problems.

Compute confidence interval for $\beta$: $df = n - 2 = 29$

$b \pm t^*(SE_b)$ ➧ $5.0659 \pm 0.5059$ ➧ $(4.56, 5.57)$

| | X | Y |
|---|---|---|
| Tree | Diameter (in) | Volume (100board-ft) |
| 1 | 8.3 | 10.3 |
| 2 | 8.6 | 10.3 |
| 3 | 8.8 | 10.2 |
| 4 | 10.5 | 16.4 |
| 5 | 10.7 | 18.8 |
| 6 | 10.8 | 19.7 |
| 7 | 11.0 | 15.6 |
| 8 | 11.0 | 18.2 |
| 9 | 11.1 | 22.6 |
| 10 | 11.2 | 19.9 |
| 11 | 11.3 | 24.2 |
| 12 | 11.4 | 21.0 |
| 13 | 11.4 | 21.4 |
| 14 | 11.7 | 21.3 |
| 15 | 12.0 | 19.1 |
| 16 | 12.9 | 22.2 |
| 31 | 20.6 | 77.0 |

**Step 4** **CONCLUDE:** Interpretation in context:

For every 1 inch increase in tree diameter, the average increase in tree volume is between 456 to 557 board feet with 95% confidence.

40-45

## Vocabulary

**Equal Standard Deviation**
**Independence**
**Normality of Y at each X**
**Scatterplot**
**Residual Plot**
**Theoretical (True) Regression Model**
**Estimated Regression Model (Least-Squares Line)**
**$\sigma$, the Standard Deviation of Y about the True Regression Line**
$\mu_Y$
**a**
**b**
$\alpha$
$\beta$
**y**

41-1

# Chapter 23 Part 2
# Inference for Regression

StatTutor Lesson 41

41-2

## Objectives

1. Perform a test on lack of correlation.
2. Use a least-squares regression line to predict y at $X = x^*$.
3. Distinguish between a confidence interval for $\mu_y$ at $X = x^*$ and a prediction interval for y at the same $X = x^*$.
4. Recognize the interval form of a confidence interval for $\mu_y$ at $X = x^*$ and interpret in the interval context.
5. Recognize the interval form of a prediction interval for y at $X = x^*$ and interpret in the interval context.
6. Compare width of a confidence interval for $\mu_y$ at $X = x^*$ with width of a prediction interval for y at the same $X = x^*$.

41-3

*Testing Relationship Example*

## Testing Lack of Correlation

Basic Practice of Statistics Chapter 23

41-4

*Testing Relationship Example*

## Example: Testing Relationship U.S. Draft Lottery

**Step I: STATE Question** In the first draft lottery of the Vietnam war in 1970, 366 capsules, each containing a number for a day of the year (e.g. February 12 = #43), were placed in a large black box. In a public drawing of the capsules, men born on the date in the first capsule drawn were the first to be drafted; those born on the date in the second capsule drawn were next and so on. After the drawing was complete, news reporters observed that those born later in the year had lower draft numbers. Further inquiry revealed that the capsules had been filled and mixed in the box a month at a time with January birthdates first and December birthdates last. The capsules were then poured from the box into the two-foot deep bowl from which they were drawn.

**Is draft number related to birth date?**

**Step 2: PLAN Solution** Perform a test on whether there is a relationship between draft number and birth date.

*Population correlation symbol*

Since $\beta = \rho \frac{\sigma_y}{\sigma_x}$, a test of $\beta = 0$ is equivalent to a test of $\rho = 0$.

$H_0$: $\beta = 0$ *There is no relationship.* $H_a$: $\beta \neq 0$ *Relationship exists.* $\alpha = ?$

41-5

*Testing Relationship Example*

## Example: Testing Relationship U.S. Draft Lottery

**Step 3 SOLVE (cont.): Construct** a scatterplot of birth date and draft number; check scatterplot for linearity and unusual observations.

Faint negative trend visible; no unusual observations.

Obtaining a linear least-squares regression equation is not necessary as we are not interested in prediction. We simply want to test for relationship.

**Test** whether a relationship exists between birth date and draft number.

1970 US Draft Lottery
Day of Year vs. Draft Number

r = -0.226

| BD# | Draft# |
|---|---|
| 1 | 305 |
| 2 | 159 |
| 3 | 251 |
| 4 | 215 |
| 5 | 101 |
| 6 | 224 |
| 7 | 306 |
| 8 | 199 |
| 9 | 194 |
| . | . |

41-6

*Testing Relationship Example*

## Example: Testing Relationship U.S. Draft Lottery

**Test** relationship

**Check** conditions of linearity, equal variance and normality.

Check residual plot for lack of linearity and unequal variance; check histogram of residuals for skewness and outliers.

No pattern in residual plot; histogram of residuals has no outliers and is not stongly skewed so ok to proceed.

1970 US Draft Lottery
Day of Year vs. Draft Number

r = -0.226

Residual Plot

Residual Histogram

| BD# | Draft# |
|---|---|
| 1 | 305 |
| 2 | 159 |
| 3 | 251 |
| 4 | 215 |
| 5 | 101 |
| 6 | 224 |
| 7 | 306 |
| 8 | 199 |
| 9 | 194 |
| . | . |

41-7

*Testing Relationship Example*

## Example: Testing Relationship U.S. Draft Lottery

**Test** relationship

**Compute** test statistic and obtain *P*-value.

$$t = \frac{b}{SE_b} = \frac{-0.2261}{0.05106} = -4.43$$

From CrunchIt! printout: *P*-value = <0.0001 < $\alpha$

**Step 4 CONCLUDE** Draw conclusions in context.

Reject $H_0$; conclude that there is a significant relationship between draft number and # of day of birth.

1970 US Draft Lottery

*Editorial note: The real issue here is not about slope but about whether the process of drawing was random. Because there is a significant relationship between draft number and # of day of birth, we conclude that the method of selection was not random.*

| Parameter | Estimate | Std. Err. | DF | T-Stat | P-Value |
|---|---|---|---|---|---|
| Intercept | 225.00922 | 10.811966 | 364 | 20.81113 | <0.0001 |
| size | -0.2260594 | 0.0510617 | 364 | -4.4271812 | <0.0001 |

41-8

# Inference about Prediction

Basic Practice of Statistics Chapter 23

41-9

## Review

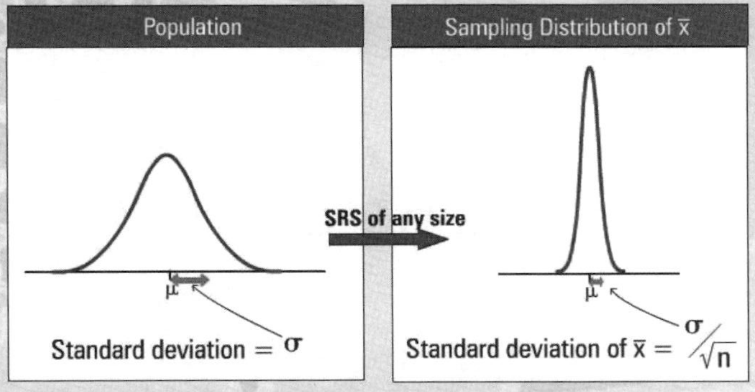

**Population**

SRS of any size

**Sampling Distribution of $\bar{x}$**

Standard deviation $= \sigma$

Standard deviation of $\bar{x} = \sigma/\sqrt{n}$

Standard deviation, $\sigma$, measures variability of individuals.

Standard deviation of $\bar{x}$, $\sigma/\sqrt{n}$, measures variability of sample means.

41-10

## Review

**I. State Question:** Can diameter of a tree be used to predict volume of wood for that tree?

**II. Plan Solution:** Recognize need to test slope; specify hypotheses:

$$H_0: \beta = 0 \text{ vs } H_a: \beta \neq 0; \text{ set } \alpha.$$

**III. Solve:**

**Data Production** Collect bivariate data for the X and Y variables.

**Data Summarization** Construct a scatterplot; obtain a linear least-squares regression equation.

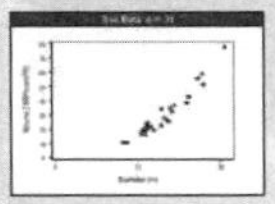

$$\hat{y} = -78.88 + 5944.8\,x$$

**Data Analysis** Check conditions of linearity, equal variance and normality. Obtain test statistic value and *P*-value.

**IV. Conclude:** Tree diameter can be used to predict volume of wood.

In this lesson we will use the least-squares regression line to make predictions and discuss two interpretations of these predictions with their associated errors.

41-11

*Predicting Y Using Equation*

## Using Regression Equation to Predict Y for X = x*

**Example:** Using $\hat{y} = -36.944 + 5.066\,x$, predict volume for a tree with diameter = 16 inches.

Predicted tree volume = 44.11 x 100 * board ft = 4,411 board feet

| Obs | Diameter (in) | Volume (100board•ft) |
|---|---|---|
| 1 | 8.3 | 10.3 |
| 2 | 8.6 | 10.3 |
| 3 | 8.8 | 10.2 |
| 4 | 10.5 | 16.4 |
| 5 | 10.7 | 18.8 |
| 6 | 10.8 | 19.7 |
| . | . | . |
| . | . | . |
| . | . | . |
| 28 | 17.9 | 58.3 |
| 29 | 18.0 | 51.5 |
| 30 | 18.0 | 51.0 |
| 31 | 20.6 | 77.0 |

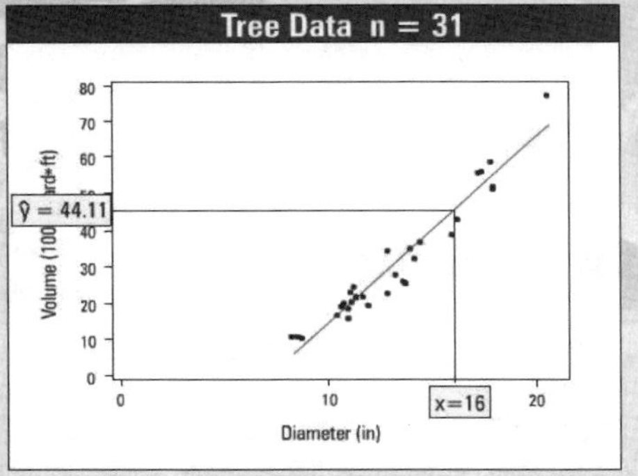

**Tree Data n = 31**

$\hat{y} = 44.11$

x=16

Diameter (in)

**Regression Equation**

$\hat{y} = -36.946 + 5.066(x)$

$= 44.11$

41-12

*Two Intervals for Prediction*

## Two Interpretations of Predicted Y

For tree diameter, x = 16 inches, predicted tree volume is $\hat{y} = 4{,}411$ board ft.

**Interpretation 1:**
4,411 estimates the **mean board feet of all trees** ($\mu_y$) having diameter (x) of 16 inches.

**Interpretation 2:**
4,411 estimates the total board feet (y) for **one particular tree** whose diameter (x) is 16 inches.

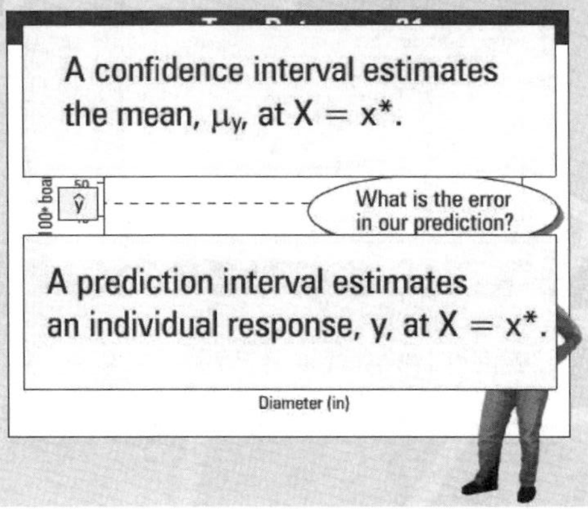

A confidence interval estimates the mean, $\mu_y$, at X = x*.

What is the error in our prediction?

A prediction interval estimates an individual response, y, at X = x*.

Diameter (in)

41-13

Confidence Interval for predicted $\mu_y$

## Interpretation 1: Confidence Interval for Mean, $\mu_y$, when X = x*

**Generic form of C.I.:** estimate ± (table value)•(S.E. of estimate)

When X takes the value x*, a level C **confidence interval for the mean,** $\mu_y$, is

$$\hat{y} \pm t^* SE_{\hat{\mu}}$$

t* is from the t-table with degrees of freedom: n – 2

Standard error ($SE_{\hat{\mu}}$) is

$$SE_{\hat{\mu}} = s\sqrt{\frac{1}{n} + \frac{(x^* - \bar{x})^2}{\sum(x-\bar{x})^2}}$$

$$\text{where } s = \sqrt{\frac{\sum(y-\hat{y})^2}{n-2}}$$

Tree Data n = 31

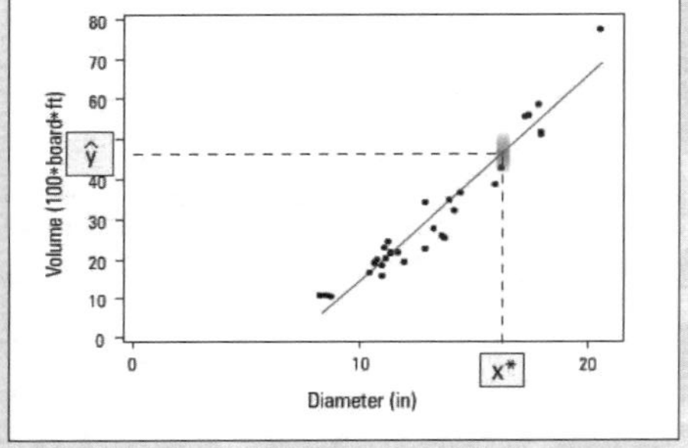

Volume (100•board•ft)
ŷ
x*
Diameter (in)


41-14

Confidence Interval for predicted $\mu_y$

## Example of Interpretation 1: A confidence Interval for $\mu_y$ when tree diameter x* = 16 inches

We are estimating the mean volume of wood for all trees with 16 inch diameters.

**95% Confidence Interval**

$$\hat{y} \pm t^* SE_{\hat{\mu}}$$

$x^* = 16$ $\bar{x} = 13.248$
$\hat{y} = 44.11$ $s = 4.252$
$t^* = 2.045$ $n = 31$

$$SE_{\hat{\mu}} = s\sqrt{\frac{1}{n} + \frac{(x^* - \bar{x})^2}{\sum(x-\bar{x})^2}}$$

$$= 4.252\sqrt{\frac{1}{31} + \frac{(16-13.248)^2}{295.44}}$$

$= 1.02306$

44.11 ± 2.045 (1.02306)

44.11 ± 2.09217

[ 42.02, 46.20 ]

Tree Data n = 31

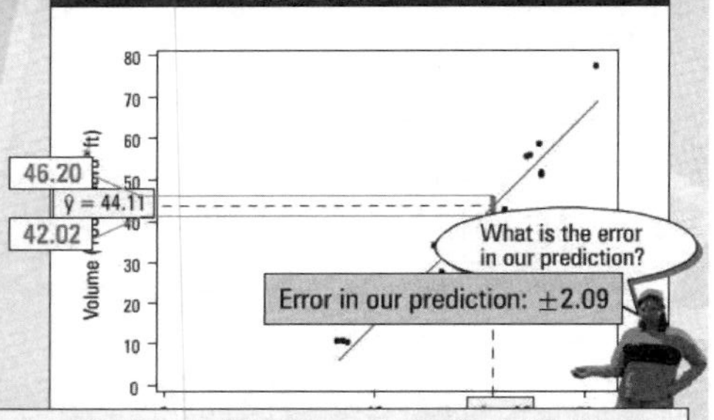

46.20
ŷ = 44.11
42.02
Volume
What is the error in our prediction?
Error in our prediction: ±2.09


We are 95% confident that the mean volume for all trees with 16 inch diameters is between 4,202 and 4,620 board-feet.

41-15

Confidence Interval for predicted $\mu_y$

## Example of Interpretation 1: A confidence Interval for $\mu_y$ when tree diameter x* = 11 inches

We are estimating the mean volume of wood for all trees with 11 inch diameters.

The error in our prediction is 2.09 for x* = 16, but it is 1.93 for x* = 11. Why?
Because x* = 16 is farther from $\bar{x}$ than x* = 11 so the prediction is less precise.

$$SE_{\hat{\mu}} = s\sqrt{\frac{1}{n} + \frac{(x^* - \bar{x})^2}{\sum(x-\bar{x})^2}}$$

$$= 4.252\sqrt{\frac{1}{31} + \frac{(11-13.248)^2}{295.44}}$$

$= 0.94416$

18.78 ± 2.045 (0.94416)

18.78 ± 1.9308

[ 16.85, 20.71 ]

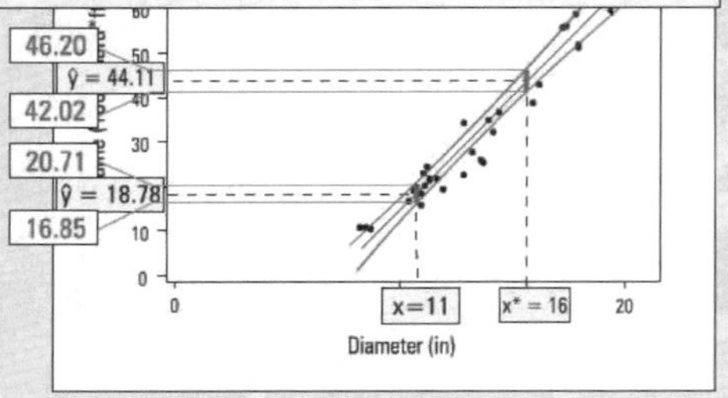

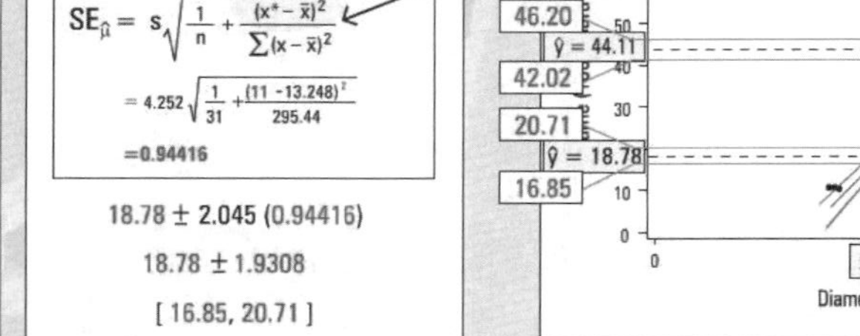

46.20
ŷ = 44.11
42.02
20.71
ŷ = 18.78
16.85
x=11
x* = 16
Diameter (in)


41-16

Prediction Interval for y

## Two Interpretations of Predicted Y

For tree diameter, x = 16 inches, predicted tree volume is $\hat{y}$ = 4,411 board ft.

**Interpretation 1:**
4,411 estimates the **mean board feet of all trees** ($\mu$) having diameter (x) of 16 inches.

Tree Data n = 31

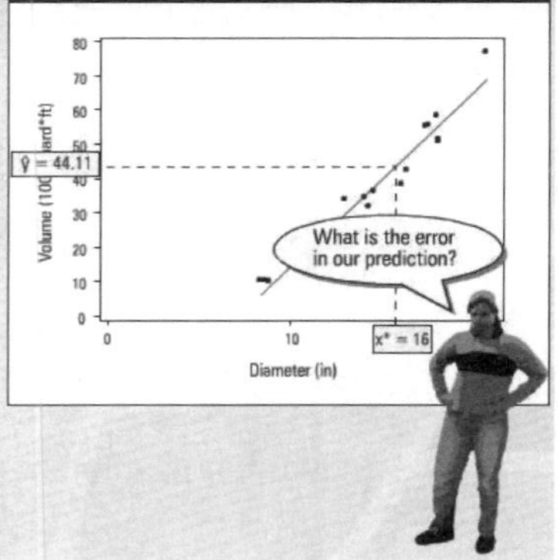

ŷ = 44.11
What is the error in our prediction?
x* = 16
Diameter (in)


**Interpretation 2:**
4,411 estimates the total board feet (y) for **one particular tree** whose diameter (x) is 16 inches.

41-17

Prediction Interval for y

## Interpretation 2: Prediction Interval on y for X = x*

**Generic form of C.I.:** estimate ± (table value)•(S.E. of estimate)

When X takes the value x*, a level C prediction interval on y for **one particular observation** is

$$\hat{y} \pm t^* SE_{\hat{y}}$$

t* is from the t-table with degrees of freedom: n – 2

The standard error ($SE_{\hat{y}}$) is

$$SE_{\hat{y}} = s\sqrt{1+\frac{1}{n}+\frac{(x^*-\bar{x})^2}{\Sigma(x-\bar{x})^2}}$$

$$\text{where } s = \sqrt{\frac{\Sigma(y-\hat{y})^2}{n-2}}$$

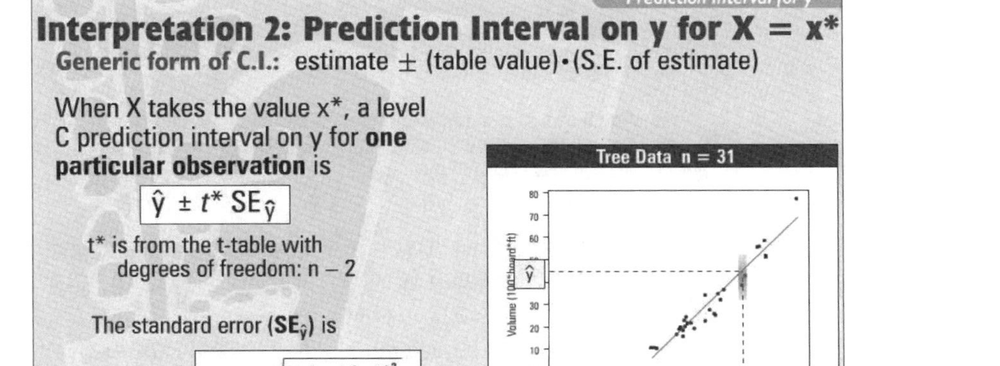


$$SE_{\hat{y}} = \sqrt{s^2 + (SE_{\hat{\mu}})^2}$$

41-18

Prediction Interval for y

## Example of Interpretation 2: A Prediction Interval on Y when tree diameter x* = 16 inches

**95% Prediction Interval**

$$\hat{y} \pm t^* SE_{\hat{y}}$$

$x^* = 16$ $\quad \bar{x} = 13.248$

$\hat{y} = 44.11$ $\quad s = 4.252$

$t^* = 2.045$ $\quad n = 31$

$$SE_{\hat{y}} = s\sqrt{1+\frac{1}{n}+\frac{(x^*-\bar{x})^2}{\Sigma(x-\bar{x})^2}}$$

$$= 4.252\sqrt{1+\frac{1}{31}+\frac{(16-13.248)^2}{295.44}}$$

$= 4.37334$

44.11 ± 2.045 (4.37334)

44.11 ± 8.943480

[35.17 , 53.05]

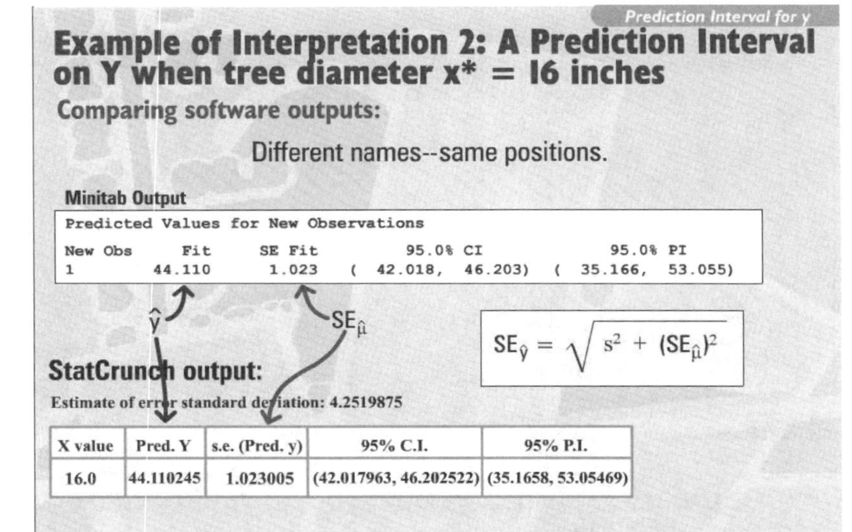


We are 95% confident that the volume of wood for a tree with 16 inch diameter is between 3,517 and 5,305 board-feet.

41-19

Prediction Interval for y

## Example of Interpretation 2: A Prediction Interval on Y when tree diameter x*=11 inches

**95% Prediction Interval**

$$\hat{y} \pm t^* SE_{\hat{y}}$$

$x^* = 11$ $\quad \bar{x} = 13.248$

$\hat{y} = 18.78$ $\quad s = 4.252$

$t^* = 2.045$ $\quad n = 31$

$$SE_{\hat{y}} = s\sqrt{1+\frac{1}{n}+\frac{(x^*-\bar{x})^2}{\Sigma(x-\bar{x})^2}}$$

$$= 4.252\sqrt{1+\frac{1}{31}+\frac{(11-13.248)^2}{295.44}}$$

$= 4.35568$

18.78 ± 2.045 (4.35568)

18.78 ± 8.9073692

[9.87 , 27.69]

Tree Data n = 31

Prediction Interval Bands across all x* values

53.05; ŷ = 44.11; 35.17; 27.69; ŷ = 18.78; 9.87

x* = 11; x* = 16; Diameter (in)

41-20

Prediction Interval for y

## Example of Interpretation 2: A Prediction Interval on Y when tree diameter x* = 16 inches

**Comparing software outputs:**

Different names--same positions.

**Minitab Output**

```
Predicted Values for New Observations

New Obs     Fit     SE Fit       95.0% CI              95.0% PI
1         44.110     1.023   ( 42.018,  46.203)  ( 35.166,  53.055)
```

$\hat{y}$ $\quad SE_{\hat{\mu}}$

$$SE_{\hat{y}} = \sqrt{s^2 + (SE_{\hat{\mu}})^2}$$

**StatCrunch output:**

Estimate of error standard deviation: 4.2519875

| X value | Pred. Y | s.e. (Pred. y) | 95% C.I. | 95% P.I. |
|---|---|---|---|---|
| 16.0 | 44.110245 | 1.023005 | (42.017963, 46.202522) | (35.1658, 53.05469) |

Prediction Interval for y

## Example of Interpretation 2: A Prediction Interval on Y when tree diameter x* = 16 inches

**What if you want 90% intervals and software only gives 95% intervals?**

**Confidence interval for the mean of all y's at X = x***

$\hat{y} \pm t^* SE_{\hat{\mu}}$ ➡ Pred. Y ± $t^*$ [s.e. (Pred. Y)]  df = n − 2

➡ 44.110245 ± 1.699 [1.023005]  df = 29

**Prediction interval for an individual y at X = x***

$\hat{y} \pm t^* SE_{\hat{y}}$ ➡ Pred. Y ± $t^* \sqrt{s^2 + [\text{s.e. (Pred. Y)}]^2}$  df = n − 2

➡ $44.110245 \pm 1.699 \sqrt{4.2519875^2 + [1.023005]^2}$  df = 29

**StatCrunch output:**

Estimate of error standard deviation: 4.2519875

| X value | Pred. Y | s.e. (Pred. y) | 95% C.I. | 95% P.I. |
|---|---|---|---|---|
| 16.0 | 44.110245 | 1.023005 | (42.017963, 46.202522) | (35.1658, 53.05469) |



Compare C.I. & P.I. Widths

## Comparing Width of Confidence Interval with Width of Prediction Interval at X = x*

**Confidence Interval for $\mu_y$ at X = x***

$\hat{y} \pm t^* SE_{\hat{\mu}}$

where $SE_{\hat{\mu}} = s\sqrt{\frac{1}{n} + \frac{(x^* - \bar{x})^2}{\sum(x - \bar{x})^2}}$

For $x^* = 16$, $SE_{\hat{\mu}} = 1.023$

**Prediction Interval for y at X = x***

$\hat{y} \pm t^* SE_{\hat{y}}$

where $SE_{\hat{y}} = s\sqrt{1 + \frac{1}{n} + \frac{(x^* - \bar{x})^2}{\sum(x - \bar{x})^2}}$

For $x^* = 16$, $SE_{\hat{y}} = 4.373$

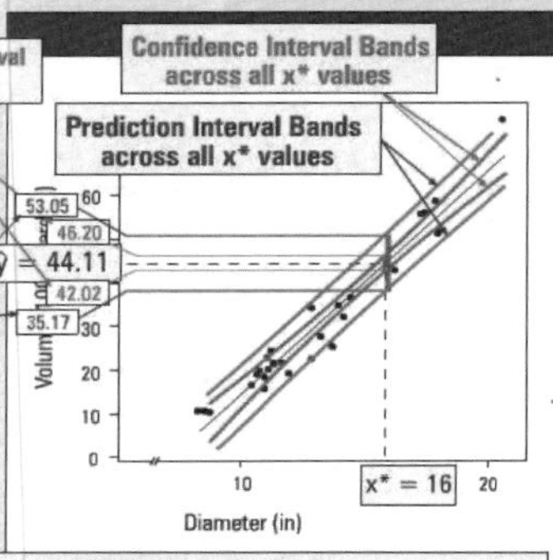

Confidence Interval for x* = 16"
Confidence Interval Bands across all x* values
Prediction Interval Bands across all x* values
Prediction Interval for x* = 16"
53.05
46.20
$\hat{y}$ = 44.11
42.02
35.17
Volume
Diameter (in)
x* = 16

Confidence intervals are narrower than prediction intervals. Why?

Because confidence intervals estimate the mean of the y's at X = x* whereas prediction intervals estimate the individual values of y at X = x*.



Regression Example with Prediction

## Diamond Example

**Step I: STATE Question** Diamonds vary a lot in price. Diamond buyers know that size, cut, clarity, color and number and type of flaws play a role in setting price. If diamonds with minimal flaws are selected with approximately the same cut, clarity and color, can size be used to predict price?

**Step II: PLAN Solution** Decide to obtain the least-squares regression equation and to test slope. State $H_0$, $H_a$ and select $\alpha$.

$H_0: \beta = 0$  $H_a: \beta > 0$  $\alpha = 0.05$

Note: $H_a$ is only upper-tailed because the lower tail doesn't make sense; i.e., we don't expect price to decrease as size increases.



Regression Example with Prediction

## Diamond Example $H_0: \beta = 0$

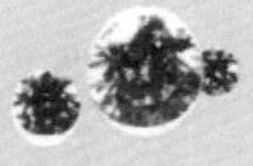

**Step III: Data Production** A sample of 17 nearly flawless diamonds of approximately the same cut, clarity and color was obtained and size and price recorded.

**Data Summarization** Examine a scatterplot of the data collected on size and price; relationship appears linear so obtain a linear least-squares regression equation.

$\hat{Y} = -78.88 + 5944.8\ X$

| Diamond | X: Size (Carat) | Y: Price (Dollars) |
|---|---|---|
| 1 | .27 | 1500 |
| 2 | .17 | 980 |
| 3 | .32 | 1800 |
| 4 | .23 | 1220 |
| 5 | .30 | 1800 |
| 6 | .28 | 1530 |
| 7 | .27 | 1475 |
| 8 | .25 | 1380 |
| 9 | .18 | 900 |
| 10 | .22 | 1200 |

Scatterplot

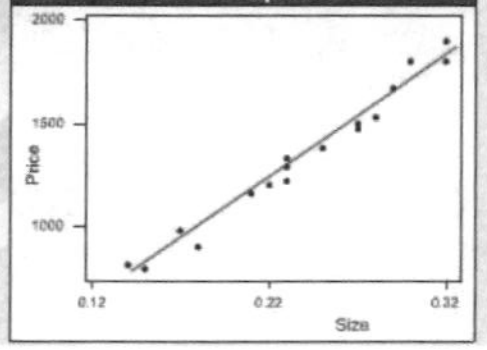

Price
Size

**Regression Output**

**Simple linear regression results:**
**Dependent Variable:** price
**Independent Variable:** size

Sample size: 17
Correlation coefficient: 0.9849
Estimate of sigma: 60.7722

| Parameter | Estimate | Std. Err. | DF | T-Stat | P-Value |
|---|---|---|---|---|---|
| Intercept | -78.87881 | 66.198616 | 15 | -1.1915478 | 0.252 |
| size | 5944.813 | 270.2282 | 15 | 21.99923 | <0.0001 |

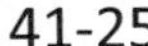

41-25

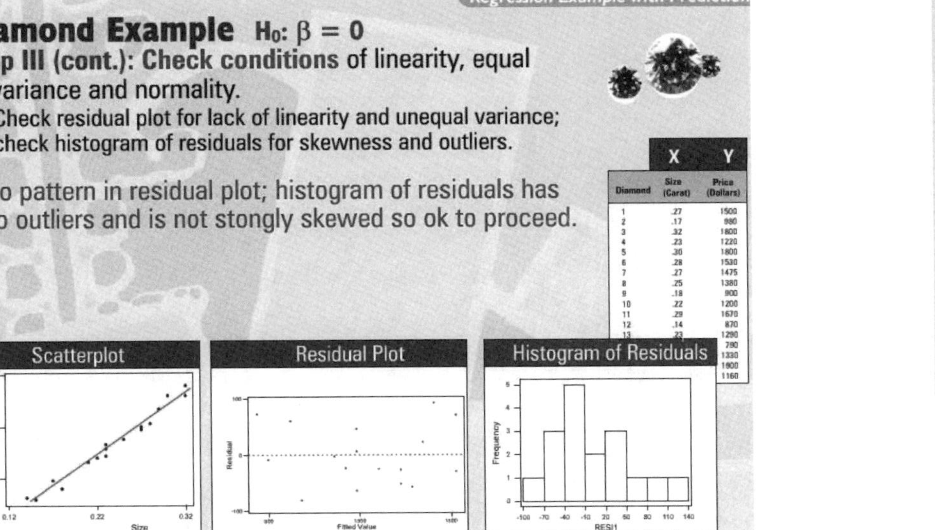


41-26

Regression Example with Prediction

## Diamond Example $H_0$: $\beta = 0$

**Step III (cont.): Obtain** test statistic and *P*-value.

$t = 21.999$

Two sided *P*-value from computer output: $<0.0001$

One sided *P*-value: $<0.0001$

**Step IV CONCLUDE** Draw conclusions in context.

*P*-value $< 0.0001 < \alpha = 0.05$

Reject $H_0$; conclude there is a significant linear relationship between size of a diamond and its price; size can be used to predict price.

**Independent Variable:** size

Sample size: 17
Correlation coefficient: 0.9849
Estimate of sigma: 60.7722

| Parameter | Estimate | Std. Err. | DF | T-Stat | P-Value |
|---|---|---|---|---|---|
| Intercept | -78.87881 | 66.198616 | 15 | -1.1915478 | 0.252 |
| size | 5944.813 | 270.2282 | 15 | 21.99923 | <0.0001 |

41-27

Regression Example with Prediction

## Diamond Example 90% CI for $\beta$

**Step 1** **STATE** What is the value of the true slope?

**Step 2** **PLAN** Obtain a 90% confidence interval for slope.

**Step 3** **SOLVE** 17 diamonds selected and size and price measured.
Scatterplot already examined for linearity and outliers.

$b = 5944.8$ and $SE_b = 270.23$

Conditions previously checked with residual plot and histogram of residuals and found to be ok.

Compute confidence interval for $\beta$: $df = n - 2 = 15$

$b \pm t^*(SE_b)$ ➧ $5944.8 \pm 473.71$ ➧ $(5471.1, 6418.5)$

**Step 4** **CONCLUDE** Interpret interval in context:

Usual Interpretation: For every 1 carat increase in diamond size, the average increase in price is between \$5471.10 and \$6418.50 with 90% confidence.

*Editorial note: The data vary from 0.14 carats to 0.32 carats in size with a range = .18 which is much less than 1 carat; therefore, the interpretation should be:* "For every .1 carat increase in diamond size, the average increase in price is between \$547.11 and \$641.85 with 90% confidence."

41-28

Regression Example with Prediction

## Diamond Example Prediction-95%

**Example:** Using $\hat{y} = -78.88 + 5944.8\,x$, predict price of a diamond with size = .25 carats.

Predicted Price = \$1407.32 **Use Software to Find 95% Intervals**

Scatterplot

Regression Equation
$\hat{y} = -78.88 + 5944.8(x)$
$= 1407.32$

$\hat{y} = 1407.32$ x=.25

Prediction of the price of a diamond larger than .32 carats is risky! Relationship is curved for larger sizes.

41-29

Regression Example with Prediction

## Diamond Example Prediction-95%

**Example:** Using $\hat{y} = -78.88 + 5944.8x$, predict price of a diamond with size = .25 carats.

Predicted Price = $1407.32 **Use Software to Find 95% Intervals**

**StatCrunch output:**

| X value | Pred. Y | s.e. (Pred. y) | 95% C.I. | 95% P.I. |
|---|---|---|---|---|
| 0.25 | 1407.32 | 15.046 | 1375.26, 1439.39 | 1273.88, 1540.77 |

95% Confidence Interval for $\mu_y$: **($1,375.26, $1,439.39)**

The mean price of 0.25 carat diamonds is between $1375.26 and $1439.39 with 95% confidence.

95% Prediction Interval for y: **($1,273.88, $1,540.77)**

The price of a 0.25 carat diamond will be between $1273.88 and $1540.77 with 95% confidence.

41-30

Regression Example with Prediction

## Diamond Example Prediction-95%

**Example:** Using $\hat{y} = -78.88 + 5944.8x$, predict price of a diamond with size = .25 carats.

Predicted Price = $1407.32 **Use Software to Find 95% Intervals**

**Minitab output:**

```
Predicted Values for New Observations
New Obs     Fit    SE Fit       95.0% CI              95.0% PI
1        1407.3      15.0   (1375.3,  1439.4)   (1273.9,  1540.8)
```

95% Confidence Interval for $\mu_y$: **($1,375.26, $1,439.39)**

The mean price of 0.25 carat diamonds is between $1375.26 and $1439.39 with 95% confidence.

95% Prediction Interval for y: **($1,273.88, $1,540.77)**

The price of a 0.25 carat diamond will be between $1273.88 and $1540.77 with 95% confidence.

41-31

## Vocabulary

**Confidence Interval**
**Prediction Interval**
**Specified x***

42-1

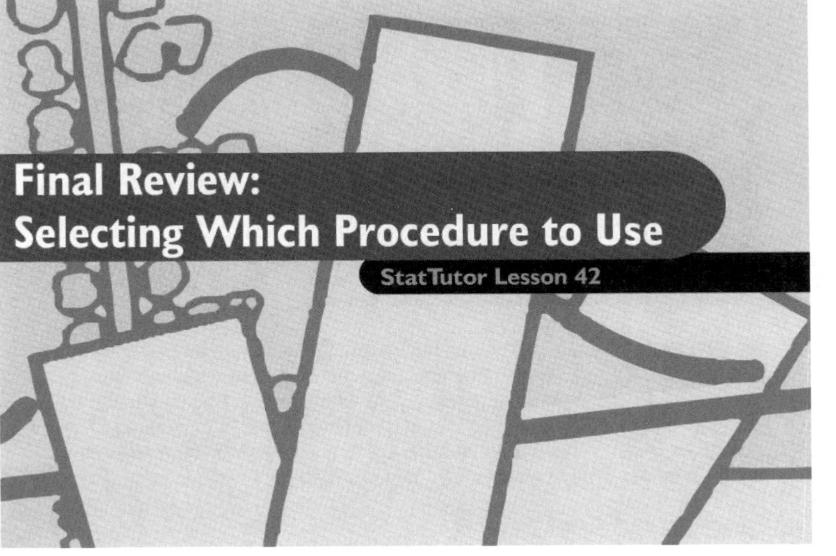


42-2

## Objectives

1. Categorize all inferential procedures discussed in this course as to whether the response variable is quantitative or categorical and as to whether the procedure is for data from one sample, two samples, or three or more samples.

2. Determine whether a problem needs an inferential procedure for means or proportions and whether it is a one sample, two sample or three or more sample problem.

42-3

*Classifying Procedures*

## Classifying Procedures

| | Type of Response Variable | |
|---|---|---|
| | Quantitative (Means) | Categorical (Proportions) |
| ONE SAMPLE | **One response:** One sample t<br>**Two paired responses:** Matched pairs t<br>**Regression of X on Y:** t test on slope | **One response:**<br>**2 categories:** One sample z<br>**>2:** $\chi^2$ Goodness of fit<br>**Two responses:** $\chi^2$ Test of independence |
| TWO INDEPENDENT SAMPLES | **One response:** Two sample t | **One response**<br>**2 categories:** Two sample z<br>**>2:** $\chi^2$ Test of homogeneity |
| THREE OR MORE INDEPENDENT SAMPLES | **One response:** ANOVA | **One response:** $\chi^2$ Test of homogeneity |

42-4

*Identifying Procedures*

## Scenario #1

A national hardware chain has decided to stock one of two low flush toilets to appeal to ecologically conservative customers. A study is commissioned to compare the average water usage of the two toilet models. Twenty toilets of each model are connected to a toilet flush test system and the number of liters of water used per flush is recorded. What procedure should be used for this test?

Mean(s) or proportion(s)?

One sample?
Two samples or treatments?
Three or more samples or treatments?

One response?
Two responses?

| Mean(s) | Proportion(s) |
|---|---|
| One Sample t-test for Mean | One Sample z-test for Proportion |
| Two Sample t-test for Means | Two Sample z-test for Proportions |
| Matched Pairs t-test for Mean | Chi-Square Test of Homogeneity |
| Analysis of Variance | Chi-Square Test of Independence |
| Regression: t-test on Slope | |

42-5

*Identifying Procedures*

## Scenario #2

Political analysts want to know if there is an association between candidate preference and religious affiliation (Catholic, Protestant, Jewish, Other) for the upcoming presidential race. Voters will be polled as they exit different voting locations. What procedure should be used for this test?

Mean(s) or proportion(s)?

One sample?
Two samples or treatments?
Three or more samples or treatments?

One response?
Two responses?

| Mean(s) | Proportion(s) |
|---|---|
| One Sample t-test for Mean | One Sample z-test for Proportion |
| Two Sample t-test for Means | Two Sample z-test for Proportions |
| Matched Pairs t-test for Mean | Chi-Square Test of Homogeneity |
| Analysis of Variance | Chi-Square Test of Independence |
| Regression: t-test on Slope | |

42-6

*Identifying Procedures*

## Scenario #3

An agricultural researcher is investigating the moisture retention capability of a new soil conditioner. Plots of several different soils at the research station are selected. The plots are divided in half and the soil conditioner is applied to one of the halves chosen randomly. The other half receives no soil conditioning. The moisture content in each half of all the plots is measured one week after the soil conditioner is applied. Which procedure should be used to test the moisture retention capability of the new soil conditioner?

Mean(s) or proportion(s)?

One sample?
Two samples or treatments?
Three or more samples or treatments?

One response?
Two responses?

| Mean(s) | Proportion(s) |
|---|---|
| One Sample t-test for Mean | One Sample z-test for Proportion |
| Two Sample t-test for Means | Two Sample z-test for Proportions |
| Matched Pairs t-test for Mean | Chi-Square Test of Homogeneity |
| Analysis of Variance | Chi-Square Test of Independence |
| Regression: t-test on Slope | |

42-7

*Identifying Procedures*

## Scenario #4

Due to tenant changes, the heating and cooling system in an office building controlled by zones does not match the current partitioning. To compare three different options for adjusting the temperature, the landlord randomly uses each of the options on one of three days. At the end of the day he surveys a random sample of occupants to determine whether they are satisfied or dissatisfied with the building's temperature for that day. Which is the correct procedure for this study?

Mean(s) or proportion(s)?

One sample?
Two samples or treatments?
Three or more samples or treatments?

One response?
Two responses?

| Mean(s) | Proportion(s) |
|---|---|
| One Sample t-test for Mean | One Sample z-test for Proportion |
| Two Sample t-test for Means | Two Sample z-test for Proportions |
| Matched Pairs t-test for Mean | Chi-Square Test of Homogeneity |
| Analysis of Variance | Chi-Square Test of Independence |
| Regression: t-test on Slope | |

42-8

*Identifying Procedures*

## Scenario #5

An office manager is considering an automated telephone attendant with voice dialing to free up the office staff from answering all incoming calls. The salesman claims that the automated attendant will correctly route 95% of the incoming calls without human intervention. Unless her test of one hundred randomly selected incoming calls shows that less than 95% are correctly routed, she will install the attendant. Which procedure should the office manager use for her test?

Mean(s) or proportion(s)?

One sample?
Two samples or treatments?
Three or more samples or treatments?

One response?
Two responses?

| Mean(s) | Proportion(s) |
|---|---|
| One Sample t-test for Mean | One Sample z-test for Proportion |
| Two Sample t-test for Means | Two Sample z-test for Proportions |
| Matched Pairs t-test for Mean | Chi-Square Test of Homogeneity |
| Analysis of Variance | Chi-Square Test of Independence |
| Regression: t-test on Slope | |

42-9

Identifying Procedures

## Scenario #6

A model-kit manufacturer needs to decide which of four brands of glue to include with a newly developed model. Due to likely exposure to sun, the most heat-tolerant glue needs to be selected. Forty kits are randomly divided into four groups of size ten and each group assembled with one brand of glue. The temperature at which the glue fails to adhere the parts when exposed to increasing heat is measured. What is the correct procedure for determining which glue is most suitable for assembling these models?

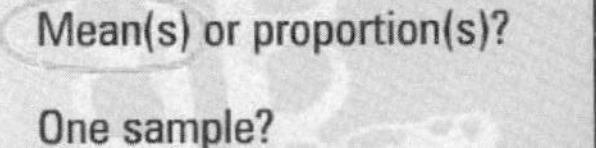

Mean(s) or proportion(s)?

One sample?
Two samples or treatments?
Three or more samples or treatments?

One response?
Two responses?

| Mean(s) | Proportion(s) |
|---|---|
| One Sample t-test for Mean | One Sample z-test for Proportion |
| Two Sample t-test for Means | Two Sample z-test for Proportions |
| Matched Pairs t-test for Mean | Chi-Square Test of Homogeneity |
| Analysis of Variance | Chi-Square Test of Independence |
| Regression: t-test on Slope | |

42-10

Identifying Procedures

## Scenario #7

The traffic department is very concerned that the average speed of motorists through a speed-reduced construction zone greatly exceeds the posted speed of 55 mph. Traffic speed sensors are placed in the construction zone and set to randomly select 45 approaching vehicles and capture their speeds. Which procedure should be used to test whether the fears of the traffic officials are justified?

Mean(s) or proportion(s)?

One sample?
Two samples or treatments?
Three or more samples or treatments?

One response?
Two responses?

| Mean(s) | Proportion(s) |
|---|---|
| One Sample t-test for Mean | One Sample z-test for Proportion |
| Two Sample t-test for Means | Two Sample z-test for Proportions |
| Matched Pairs t-test for Mean | Chi-Square Test of Homogeneity |
| Analysis of Variance | Chi-Square Test of Independence |
| Regression: t-test on Slope | |

42-11

Identifying Procedures

## Scenario #8

Researchers are testing a new vaccine to immunize against human papilloma-virus (HPV). HPV is the leading risk factor for cervical cancer. Three doses of either the vaccine or the placebo were given to women aged 16 to 23. At the end of the study women will be examined for HPV. What procedure should be used for this test?

Mean(s) or proportion(s)?

One sample?
Two samples or treatments?
Three or more samples or treatments?

One response?
Two responses?

| Mean(s) | Proportion(s) |
|---|---|
| One Sample t-test for Mean | One Sample z-test for Proportion |
| Two Sample t-test for Means | Two Sample z-test for Proportions |
| Matched Pairs t-test for Mean | Chi-Square Test of Homogeneity |
| Analysis of Variance | Chi-Square Test of Independence |
| Regression: t-test on Slope | |

42-12

Identifying Procedures

## Scenario #9

The manager of a local ice cream shop wants to predict daily sales based on forecasted high temperature for the day. Using data from sales for the previous year, what procedure should she use to model for prediction and then test whether the model is useful?

Mean(s) or proportion(s)?

One sample?
Two samples or treatments?
Three or more samples or treatments?

One response?
Two responses?

| Mean(s) | Proportion(s) |
|---|---|
| One Sample t-test for Mean | One Sample z-test for Proportion |
| Two Sample t-test for Means | Two Sample z-test for Proportions |
| Matched Pairs t-test for Mean | Chi-Square Test of Hpmogeneity |
| Analysis of Variance | Chi-Square Test of Independence |
| Regression: t-test on Slope | |

42-13

## Vocabulary

- One-Sample t for Mean
- Two-Sample t for Means
- One-Sample z for Proportion
- Two-Sample z for Proportions
- Matched Pairs t for Mean
- Chi-Square Test (Independence or Homogeneity)
- t Test on Slope
- ANOVA

## Lecture Review for exam 2

1. Hallux abducto valgus (called HAV) is a deformation of the big toe that is not common in youth and often requires surgery. Metatarsus adductus (called MA) is a turning in of the front part of the foot that is common in adolescents and usually corrects itself. Doctors used X-rays to measure the HAV angle (in degrees) of deformity as well as the MA angle (in degrees) in 37 patients under the age of 21 who came to a medical center for surgery to correct HAV. Doctors speculate that the severity of MA can help predict the severity of HAV.

Scatterplot

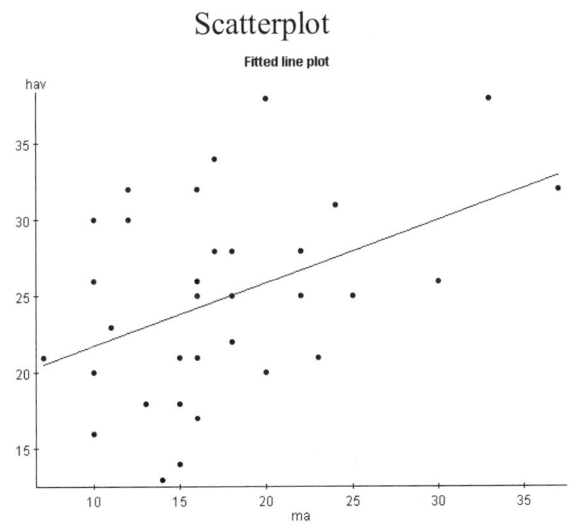


Residual plot

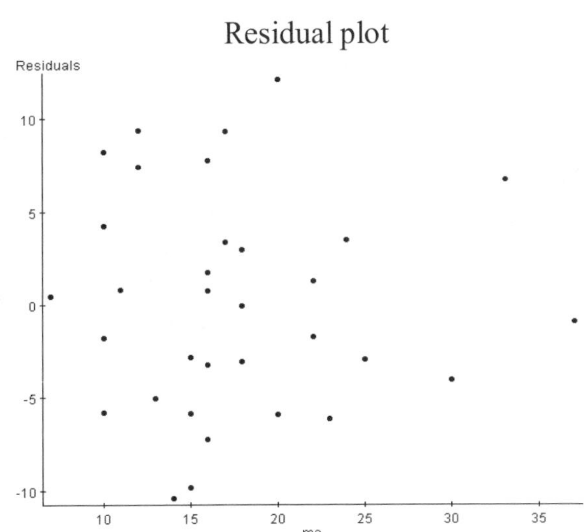


**Simple linear regression results:**
Dependent Variable: hav
Independent Variable: ma
hav = 17.6337 + 0.41313618 ma
Sample size: 36
R (correlation coefficient) = 0.4409
R-sq = 0.19438466

a. Describe form, direction and strength of the relationship between MA angle and HAV angle.

b. Does the residual plot reveal any potential problems?

c. Interpret slope in context.

d. Interpret $r^2$ in context.

e. A new patient has MA angle 25 degrees. What do you predict this patient's HAV angle to be?

f. Why would predicting HAV angle for an imaginary patient with MA angle of 45 be wrong?

g. Using your answers to parts a-d, does knowing MA angle allow doctors to predict HAV angle accurately?

h. Why is the line drawn on the scatter plot called *the least squares line*?

2. Wabash Tech has two professional schools, business and law. Here are the two-way tables to both schools categorized by gender and admissions decision. The percentages in parentheses are the conditional distributions in percent for the rows.

| **Business** | Admit | Deny | TOTAL |
|---|---|---|---|
| Male | 480 (80%) | 120 (20%) | 600 (100%) |
| Female | 180 (90%) | 20 (10%) | 200 (100%) |
| TOTAL | 660 (82.5%) | 140 (17.5%) | 800 (100%) |

| **Law** | Admit | Deny | TOTAL |
|---|---|---|---|
| Male | 10 (10%) | 90 (90%) | 100 (100%) |
| Female | 100 (33.3%) | 200 (66.7%) | 300 (100%) |
| TOTAL | 110 (27.5%) | 290 (72.5%) | 400 (100%) |

| **Overall** | Admit | Deny | TOTAL |
|---|---|---|---|
| Male | 490 (70%) | 210 (30%) | 700 (100%) |
| Female | 280 (56%) | 220 (44%) | 500 (100%) |
| TOTAL | 770 (64.2%) | 430 (35.8%) | 1200 (100%) |

a. For the combined table, what is the marginal distribution for admission decision?
b. For the combined table, what percent of the students are admitted?
c. For the combined table, what percent of the males are admitted?
d. For the combined table, what is the conditional distribution for gender given that they were admitted?
e. For the combined table, what is the conditional distribution for admission decision for males?

3. The following population distribution has a mean, $\mu = 5.0$, and standard deviation, $\sigma = 2.89$.

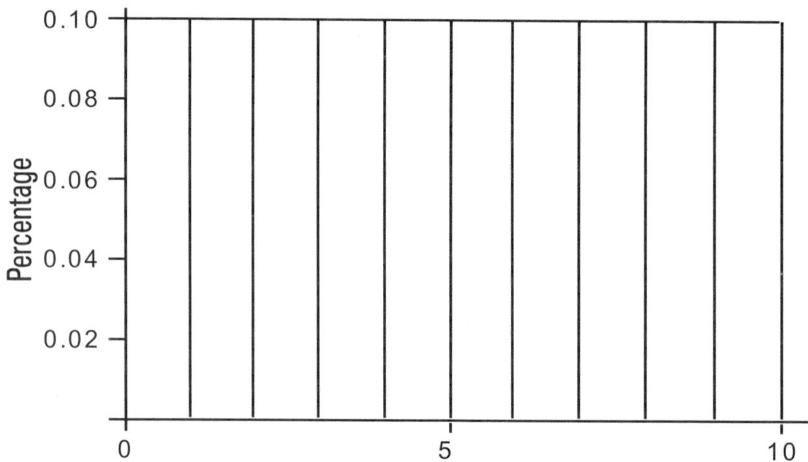


Suppose you plan to take a sample of size n = 100.
a. What does the sampling distribution of $\bar{x}$ from samples of size 100 tell us?
b. What is the mean of the sampling distribution of $\bar{x}$?
c. What is the standard deviation of the sampling distribution of $\bar{x}$?
d. What is the shape of the sampling distribution of $\bar{x}$?
e. Did we apply the Central Limit Theorem to determine shape in part d? (What does the Central Limit Theorem tell us?)
f. Between what two values are approximately 95% of all possible sample means?
g. What is the probability of obtaining a random sample that has a mean exceeding 5.1?
h. Why could we use the standard normal table to compute the probability in part g? (This illustrates the purpose of the Central Limit Theorem.)
i. Could we compute the probability of obtaining a sample mean exceeding 5.1 from a random sample of size 10 using the standard normal table? Why or why not?

4. **General true / false questions**

a. The shape of the histogram of sample data gets closer to the shape of the population as the sample size increases.

b. The shape of the sampling distribution of $\bar{x}$ is always normal or approximately normal.

c. The mean of the sampling distribution of $\bar{x}$ gets closer and closer to $\mu$ as sample size increases.

d. The standard deviation of the sampling distribution of $\bar{x}$ $(n > 1)$ is always smaller than the standard deviation of the original population.

e. The Central Limit Theorem allows us to compute probabilities on data in a sample from a non-normal population whenever the sample is large and SRS.

f. Probabilities on individuals in a population can only be computed if the population distribution is Normal.

g. The standard deviation of $\bar{x}$ is a short cut way of saying, "the standard deviation of the sampling distribution of $\bar{x}$."

h. The mean of data in a sample gets closer and closer to $\mu$ as sample size increases.

i. Approximately 95% of all possible $\bar{x}$'s will be within $2\sigma$ of $\mu$.

## Lecture Review for Exam 3

**1. Using16 measurements (in millimeters) of a critical dimension on a random sample of auto engine crankshafts from a Normally distributed population, we obtained the following 95% confidence interval estimate for μ: (223.97, 224.03)**

a. What are the simple conditions for this confidence interval for μ?

b. What is the population about which we want to make an inference?

c. What is the parameter we estimated with this confidence interval?

d. Using the information in parts b and c, interpret the confidence interval for μ in context.

e. The following are true/false statements about this interval:

i. This interval tells us that reasonable values for μ are all numbers between 223.97 and 224.03.

ii. We are 95% confident that the value of the sample mean of the 16 measurements will be in the interval, (223.97, 224.03).

iii. 95% of the time, when sampling crankshafts from this process, we will get the confidence interval, (223.97, 224.03).

iv. 95% of all possible crankshaft measurements will be in the interval, (223.97, 224.03).

v. The probability that the value for μ is in this 95% confidence interval, (223.97, 224.03), is 0.95

vi. *95% confidence* means that 95% of the time, we will get the value of μ in this confidence interval, (223.97, 224.03).

vii. *95% confidence* means that 95% of all possible random samples of 16 crankshafts will yield 95% confidence intervals for μ that actually contain the value of μ.

viii. *95% confidence* means that using this 95% confidence interval procedure for μ, we will obtain confidence intervals that actually contain the value of μ 95% of the time.

ix. We are 95% confident that the value of $\bar{x}$ is in the interval, (223.97, 224.03).

**2. Referring to the 16 crankshaft measurements described in question 1, the process mean is supposed to be μ = 224. The standard deviation is known to be σ = 0.060 mm.**

a. What are the simple conditions for testing the value of μ?

b. What hypotheses should be used to test whether the process is in control?

c. The sample mean for the 16 crankshafts is $\bar{x} = 224.002$. What is the value of the *z* test statistic?

d. What is the appropriate *P*-value?

e. On the basis of the *P*-value found in part d, what should we conclude at $\alpha = 0.05$?

**True or False:**

a. Researchers usually want to "prove" that the null hypothesis is correct.

b. We always assume $H_0$ is true when computing the test statistic and $P$-value.

c. Large $P$-values ($> \alpha$) provide evidence that $H_0$ is true.

d. Small $P$-values ($< \alpha$) provide evidence that $H_0$ is NOT true.

e. We always reject $H_0$ when $P$-value $< \alpha$.

f. The symbol $\bar{x}$ should never be used in $H_0$ or $H_a$.

g. We always believe $H_0$ when $P$-value $> \alpha$.

h. We always believe $H_a$ when $P$-value $< \alpha$.

*i.* $P$-value tells us the probability that $H_0$ is true.

j. "=" is always found in $H_0$, never in $H_a$.

k. Results of a test of significance are only declared statistically significant if $P$-value $< \alpha$.

**For the following problems:**

A. Decide whether the study is an experiment or observational.

B. State the parameter of interest in the context of the problem.

C. Decide whether a test of significance or a confidence interval estimate is required to answer the question.

D. List the conditions that need to be checked.

E. Perform the required analysis and answer the question.

4. A certain brand of fishing line claims to have an average breaking strength of 30 pounds. A group of fishermen become angry because this brand of line seems to break so easily and test 25 randomly selected lines of this brand. The mean breaking strength is 27.994 with a standard deviation of 0.846. A plot of the data follows. Do these data provide sufficient evidence for the fishermen to conclude that the average breaking strength is less than claimed? Use the four step process.

```
+-------+-------+-------+-------+-------+-----
25.90   26.60   27.30   28.00   28.70   29.40
```

**STATE**: Do these data provide sufficient evidence for the fishermen to conclude that the average breaking strength is less than claimed?

FORMULATE:

SOLVE:

CONCLUDE:

5. **STATE:**
Calculate a 95% confidence interval to estimate the true mean breaking strength of this brand of fishing line. Use the four-step process.

FORMULATE:

SOLVE:

CONCLUDE:

6. Gas mileage for 10 cars with dirty air filters and clean air filters was studied. Each car was tested once with a clean air filter and once with a dirty air filter (with the order of the testing randomized.) The research question is: "Do cars get better miles per gallon on average with clean air filters?" Use the four-step process to answer this question. Here are the results:

| **Car** | 1 | 2 | 3 | 4 | 5 | 6 | 7 | 8 | 9 | 10 |
|---|---|---|---|---|---|---|---|---|---|---|
| **Clean mpg** | 19 | 22 | 24 | 24.5 | 25 | 25 | 25.5 | 26 | 28 | 31 |
| **Dirty mpg** | 16 | 20 | 21 | 21.5 | 23 | 21 | 22.5 | 25 | 25 | 27 |

Stem and leaf of clean mpg

N = 10
Leaf Unit = 1.0
1 9
2
2 2
2 44555
2 6
2 8
3 1

Stem and leaf of dirty mpg

N = 10
Leaf Unit = 1.0
1 6
1
2 0111
2 23
2 55
2 7

Stem and leaf of differences

N = 10
Leaf Unit = 0.10
1 0
2 00
3 00000
4 00

| Variable | N | Mean | Median | Tr Mean | StDev | SE Mean |
|---|---|---|---|---|---|---|
| clean | 10 | 25.00 | 25.00 | 25.00 | 3.21 | 1.01 |
| dirty | 10 | 22.200 | 22.000 | 2.375 | 3.093 | 0.978 |
| diff | 10 | 2.800 | 3.000 | 2.875 | 0.919 | 0.291 |

**STATE:** "Do cars get better miles per gallon on average with clean air filters?"

FORMULATE:

SOLVE:

CONCLUDE:

7. It has been suggested that the arc of a bird's claw depends in part on their ecological niche. Two species of birds, a white-breasted nuthatch which is a trunk climber and a blue-crowned motmot which is a percher, were compared. Fifteen birds of each type were randomly selected and measured with the following results:

| Variable | N | Mean | Median | TrMean | StDev | SEMean |
|---|---|---|---|---|---|---|
| nuthatch | 15 | 129.45 | 128.80 | 129.70 | 8.81 | 2.27 |
| motmot | 15 | 116.71 | 119.81 | 117.10 | 9.73 | 2.51 |
| diff | 15 | 12.74 | 12.67 | 12.80 | 12.25 | 3.16 |

Stemplots of data show no outliers or strong skewness.

**STATE:** On the basis of these data, can you conclude that there is a significant difference in average claw arc?

FORMULATE:

SOLVE:

CONCLUDE:

**STATE:** Calculate a 95% confidence interval estimate for the difference between the mean claw arc lengths of the two species.

FORMULATE:

SOLVE:

CONCLUDE:

# In class Review for the Final

**#1** 24.36 Sparrowhawk colonies. **One of nature's patterns connects the percent of adult birds in a colony that return from the previous year and the number of new adults that join the colony. Can the percent of returning adult birds be use to predict the number of new adults that join the colony?**

a. Is this an experiment or an observational study? Can we conclude causation?

b. What are the explanatory and response variables? What type of variable are they?

c. What type of analysis should be performed to answer the research question?

d. State the hypotheses in words and in symbols for testing whether a linear relationship exists between the two variables "Percent return" and "new birds".

e. Is the condition of equal variance met? Why or why not?
Is the condition of linear relationship met? Why or why not?
Is the condition of Normality of residuals met? Why or why not?
Is it reasonable to assume that the 13 colonies are independent of each other? Why?

f. Using the regression printout, what are the values of the t test statistic and *P*-value for testing $H_0$: $\beta = 0$ (slope)?

g. Interpret slope in context.

h. What is a 95% confidence interval for $\beta$ (slope)?

i. Interpret $r^2$ in context.

j. What is the predicted number of new adult birds in a colony when 60% of the birds return?

k. What is a 95% confidence interval for the mean number of new adult birds when the return rate is 60%?

l. How does the 95% confidence interval for the mean number of new adult birds compare with the 95% prediction interval for the number of new adult birds when the return rate is 60%?

Plots for Exercise 24.36

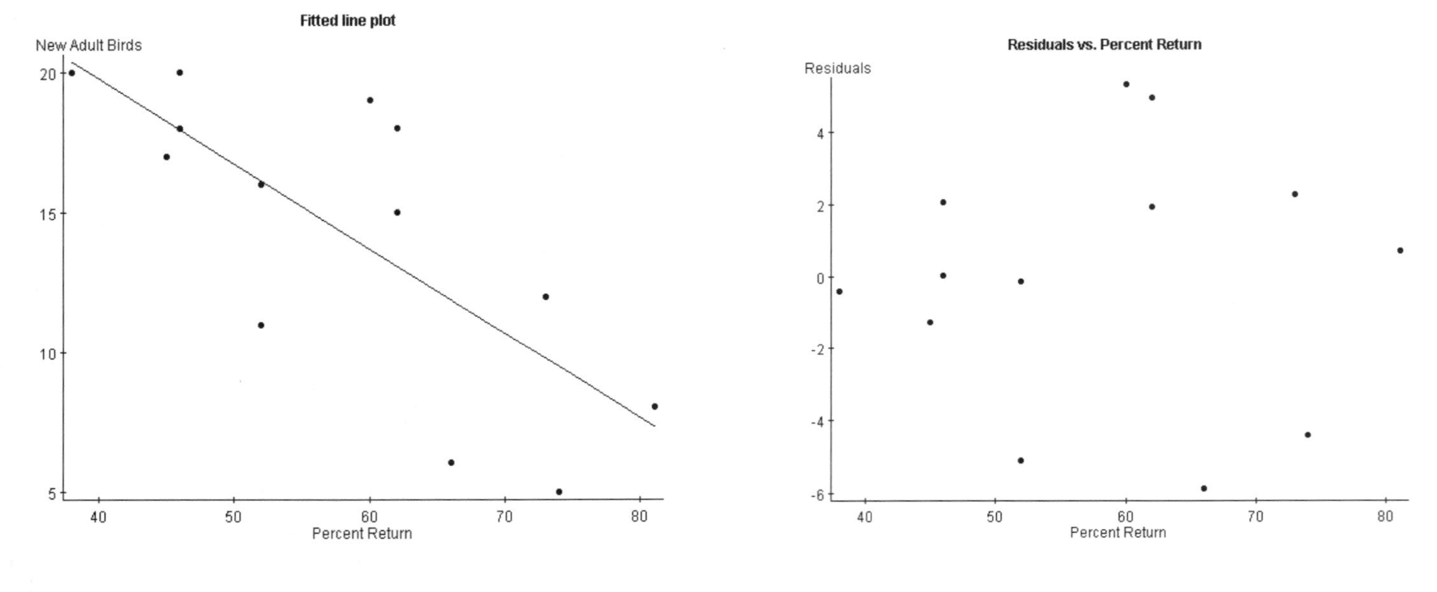


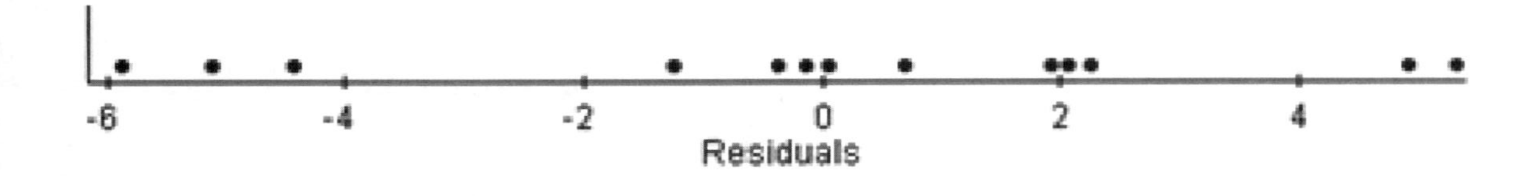


CrunchIt! output for Exercise 24.36:

**Simple linear regression results:**
Dependent Variable: New Adult Birds
Independent Variable: Percent Return
New Adult Birds = 31.93426 - 0.30402294 Percent Return
Sample size: 13
R (correlation coefficient) = -0.7485
R-sq = 0.5602033
Estimate of error standard deviation: 3.6668913

**Parameter estimates:**

| Parameter | Estimate | Std. Err. | DF | T-Stat | P-Value |
|---|---|---|---|---|---|
| Intercept | 31.93426 | 4.8376164 | 11 | 6.6012383 | <0.0001 |
| Slope | -0.30402294 | 0.08122003 | 11 | -3.7432015 | 0.0032 |

**Predicted values:**

| X value | Pred. Y | s.e.(Pred. y) | 95% C.I. | 95% P.I. |
|---|---|---|---|---|
| 60 | 13.692883 | 1.0271142 | (11.4322, 15.9535) | (5.31148, 22.074) |

**#2** 25.31 Nematodes and tomato plants. **How do nematodes (microscopic worms) affect plant growth? A botanist prepares 16 identical planting pots and then introduces different numbers of nematodes into the pots. He transplants a tomato seedling into each pot. For each plant he records the increase in height of the seedlings (in centimeters) 16 days after planting.**

a. Is this an experiment or an observational study? Are all three principles followed?

b. What are the explanatory and response variables? What type of variable are they?

c. What is the population of interest?

d. What analysis should be performed to answer the research question?

e. State the hypotheses for testing equality of means.

f. Are the conditions of equal variance, randomization, and Normality met? Why or why not?

g. Using the ANOVA printout, what are the values of the F test statistic and *P*-value for testing the hypotheses in part d?

h. On the basis of the *P*-value and confidence intervals, what can you conclude?

growth in cm in 16 days

0 nematods

4 6 8 10 12

1 nematod

4 6 8 10 12

5 nematods

4 6 8 10 12

10 nematods

4 6 8 10 12

**Analysis of Variance results:**

| Source | df | SS | MS | F-Stat | P-value |
|---|---|---|---|---|---|
| Treatments | 3 | 100.647 | 33.549 | 12.079739 | 0.0006 |
| Error | 12 | 33.328 | 2.777 | | |
| Total | 15 | 133.974 | | | |

**Factor means**

| nem | n | Mean | Std. Error | Confidence Interval |
|---|---|---|---|---|
| 0 | 4 | 10.65 | 1.0267 | (8.00, 13.30) |
| 1 | 4 | 10.425 | 0.7432 | (7.77, 13.20) |
| 5 | 4 | 5.6 | 0.6218 | (2.95, 8.25) |
| 10 | 4 | 5.45 | 0.8855 | (2.80, 8.10) |

**#3** 23.29 Who's online? **A sample survey by the Pew Internet and American Life Project asked a random sample of adults about use of the Internet and about the type of community they lived in. Is there are relationship between type of community and use of the Internet? Here are the data in this two-way table:**

| | Community Type | | |
|---|---|---|---|
| | Rural | Suburban | Urban |
| Internet users | 433 | 1072 | 536 |
| Nonusers | 463 | 627 | 388 |

a. Is this an experiment or an observational study? What sampling design was used?

b. What are the explanatory and response variables? What type of variable are they?

c. What type of analysis should be performed to answer the research question?

d. State the hypotheses for testing independence.

e. How many Rural adults do we expect to be Internet users?

e. Is the condition on expected counts met? Why or why not?

f. Using the chi-square printout, what are the degrees of freedom? the values of the □$^2$ test statistic and *P*-value for testing the hypotheses in part d?

g. On the basis of the *P*-value and confidence intervals, what can you conclude?

**Contingency table results for exercise 23.29:**

| **Cell format** |
|---|

| **Statistic** | **DF** | **Value** | **P-value** |
|---|---|---|---|
| Chi-square | ?? | 52.535 | <0.0001 |

| | Rural | Suburban | Urban | Total |
|---|---|---|---|---|
| Internet | 433<br>(21.22%)<br>519.7 | 1072<br>(52.52%)<br>985.4 | 536<br>(26.26%)<br>535.9 | 2041<br>(100.00%) |
| No internet | 463<br>(31.33%)<br>376.3 | 627<br>(42.42%)<br>713.6 | 388<br>(26.25%)<br>388.1 | 1478<br>(100.00%) |
| Total | 896<br>(25.46%) | 1699<br>(48.28%) | 924<br>(26.26%) | 3519<br>(100.00%) |

**#4. Suppose a standard spray will be used in an orchard unless the supervisor can show that the proportion of infected trees is less than 10%, in which case a cheaper, less effective spray will be used. 120 trees will be randomly sampled. Should the cheaper spray be used?**

a. What hypotheses should be tested?

b. Describe the sampling distribution of $\hat{p}$ assuming $H_0$ is true.

c. Are the necessary conditions met so that the standard normal curve can be used to obtain the *P*-value?

d. Suppose 10 trees in the sample are infected. What is the *P*-value?

e. Interpret the *P*-value in context.

f. What conclusions can be drawn at □ = 0.05?

g. What is the type I error for this test? Could we have made that error?

**#5. Suppose we are testing the hypothesis that there is no relationship between math skills and reading skills. The *P*-value for data collected on 20 randomly selected middle school students is less than .001 ( r = .89). We conclude that these results are statistically significant. Which of the following is a correct interpretation?**

a. The probability that there is no relationship between skills is less than .001.

b. The probability that ρ is significantly greater than zero is less than .001.

c. If there is no relationship between math and reading skills, the probability of getting an r of .89 or higher is less than .001.

d. Less than 0.1% of all middle school students have no relationship between their math and reading skills.

**#6 Bottling cola. A bottling company uses a filling machine to fill plastic bottles with cola. The bottles are supposed to contain 300 milliliters (ml). In fact, the contents vary according to a Normal distribution with mean $\mu = 298$ ml and standard deviation $\sigma = 3$ ml.**

a. What is the probability that an individual bottle contains less than 295 ml?

b. What is the probability that the mean contents of the bottles in a six-pack is less than 295 ml?

c. Did you apply the Central Limit Theorem in either part a or part b? Why or why not?

#7. Suppose speeds on a particular section of freeway in Ohio are normally distributed with a mean of 68 miles per hour and a standard deviation of 5 miles per hour.

a. Above what speed are the fastest 20% of the vehicles traveling?

b. Between what two values are 95% of the possible speeds?

**#8 The gypsy moth is a serious threat to oak and aspen trees. A stat agriculturalist places traps throughout the state to detect moths. The number of moths trapped has a strongly skewed distribution with mean of 0.5 standard deviation of 0.7.**

a. Describe the sampling distribution of $\overline{X}$ when 49 traps are randomly selected.

Mean:

Standard deviation:

Shape:

b. What is the approximate probability that the mean number of moths trapped in 49 traps exceeds 0.6 moths?

c. Did you apply the Central Limit Theorem in either part a) or part b)? If so, how?

**#9 What type of study (experimental design or sampling design) is each of the following:**

a. A new treatment for arthritis is being studied to see whether it alleviates pain. Patients are randomly assigned to either a group receiving the new treatment, a group receiving a standard treatment, celecoxib, or a placebo group.

b. Households in California are called through random digit dialing; each respondent is asked, "Did you have a live Christmas tree last year?"

c. Rats are randomly allocated to two groups. One group is placed on a tread wheel and the number of revolutions made in one minute is recorded. Twenty four hours later, those rats are given a drug and 30 minutes later placed on the tread wheel and measured. The rats in the other group are given a drug and after 30 minutes, they are placed on the tread wheel. Twenty-four hours later they are also again placed on the tread wheel only without receiving the drug.

d. Citizens in many countries are contacted and asked their opinion on the definition of marriage. Sampling is done within each country.

**#10 True / False:**

a. *P*-value is the probability that the null hypothesis is true.

b. Small *P*-values provide evidence against the null hypothesis.

c. Suppose a 95% confidence interval for $p$ is computed to be (0.24, 0.27). Then we can define *level of confidence* as the probability that the value of $p$ is between 0.24 and 0.27.

d. A sampling distribution of $\overline{x}$ gives all possible values for $\overline{x}$ together with their probabilities.

e. The *least squares line* is the line for which the sum of square deviations about the mean of the y's is minimized.

f. *P*-value is always computed assuming the null hypothesis is true.

g. Increasing level of confidence decreases margin of error.

h. A type I error is made whenever a true null hypothesis is rejected.

i. Blocking eliminates bias that occurs in completely randomized designs.

j. A boxplot can be used to display both categorical and quantitative data.

# INFERENCE FOR QUANTITATIVE DATA

| Name of procedure | Hypotheses | Conditions and how they can be satisfied | Test statistic for test of significance | Confidence Interval | Table |
|---|---|---|---|---|---|
| 1 sample z for means | $H_o$: $\mu = \mu_0$<br>$H_a$: $\mu\ (>, <, \neq)\ \mu_0$ | Randomization:<br>SRS (obs. study)<br>Normality of Samp. Dist. of $\bar{x}$ :<br>-Stated in problem, or<br>-Sample data appear Normal, or<br>-CLT ($n \geq 30$)<br>Sigma $\sigma$ known | $z = \frac{\bar{x} - \mu_0}{\sigma / \sqrt{n}}$ | $\bar{x} \pm z^* \frac{\sigma}{\sqrt{n}}$ | P-value:<br>A<br><br>z*:<br>C |
| 1 sample t for means | $H_o$: $\mu = \mu_0$<br>$H_a$: $\mu\ (>, <, \neq)\ \mu_0$ | Randomization:<br>SRS (obs. study)<br>Normality of Population:<br>-Stated in problem, or<br>-No outliers or extreme skewness in plot of data | $t = \frac{\bar{x} - \mu_0}{s / \sqrt{n}}$<br><br>df = n - 1 | $\bar{x} \pm t^* \frac{s}{\sqrt{n}}$<br><br>df = n - 1 | C |
| Matched pairs t for mean of differences | $H_o$: $\mu_d = 0$<br>$H_a$: $\mu_d\ (>, <, \neq)\ 0$ | See above – applied to differences | See above – applied to differences | See above – applied to differences | C |
| 2 sample t for difference of means (pooled variance) | $H_o$: $\mu_1 - \mu_2 = 0$ or $\mu_1 = \mu_2$<br>$H_a$: $\mu_1 - \mu_2\ (>, <, \neq)\ 0$ or $\mu_1\ (>, <, \neq)\ \mu_2$ | Randomization:<br>Two SRS's or RAT<br>Equal Population Stan. Deviation<br>Normality of Populations:<br>-Stated in problem, or<br>-No outliers or extreme skewness | $t = \frac{\bar{x}_1 - \bar{x}_2}{s_p \sqrt{\frac{1}{n_1} + \frac{1}{n_2}}}$<br><br>df = $n_1 + n_2$ - 2 | $\bar{x}_1 - \bar{x}_2 \pm t^* s_p \sqrt{\frac{1}{n_1} + \frac{1}{n_2}}$<br><br>df = df = $n_1 + n_2$ - 2 | C |
| ANOVA (Analysis of Variance) | $H_o$: $\mu_1 = \mu_2 = \ldots = \mu_k$<br>$H_a$: at least one $\mu$ is different (not all $\mu$'s are the same) | Randomization:<br>Multiple SRS's or RAT<br>Normality of Populations:<br>-Stated in problem, or<br>-No outliers or extreme skewness in plots of data<br>Equal Population Standard Deviation:<br>-Stated in problem, or<br>-(largest s) ÷ (smallest s) $\leq 2$ | F<br>(given in computer output) | Given in computer output | computer output |
| Linear Regression | $H_o$: $\beta = 0$ (there is no linear relationship between the 2 variables)<br>$H_a$: $\beta\ (>, <, \neq)\ 0$ (there is a linear relationship between the 2 variables) | Linearity:<br>residual plot (no curved pattern)<br>Independence:<br>SRS (obs. study) or RAT (exp.)<br>Normality:<br>histogram or stemplot of residuals appears Normal<br>Equal Pop. Standard Deviation:<br>residual plot (no megaphones) | $t = \frac{b}{SE_b}$<br><br>df = n - 2 | $b \pm t^* SE_b$<br><br>df = n - 2 | computer output |

# INFERENCE FOR CATEGORICAL DATA

| Name of procedure | Hypotheses | Conditions and how they can be satisfied | Test statistic for test of significance | Confidence Interval | Table |
|---|---|---|---|---|---|
| 1 sample z for proportions | $H_o$: $p = p_0$<br>$H_a$: $p\ (>, <, \neq)\ p_0$ | Randomization:<br>SRS (obs. study) or RAT (exp.)<br>Normality of Samp. Dist. of $\hat{p}$:<br>"np checks" → | $z = \dfrac{\hat{p} - p_0}{\sqrt{\dfrac{p_0(1-p_0)}{n}}}$<br>$np_0 \geq 10$<br>$n(1-p_0) \geq 10$ | $\hat{p} \pm z^* \sqrt{\dfrac{\hat{p}(1-\hat{p})}{n}}$<br>$n\hat{p} \geq 10$<br>$n(1-\hat{p}) \geq 10$ | P-value: A<br>z*: C |
| 2 sample z for proportions | $H_o$: $p_1 - p_2 = 0$ or $p_1 = p_2$<br>$H_a$: $p_1 - p_2\ (>, <, \neq)\ 0$ or $p_1\ (>, <, \neq)\ p_2$ | Randomization:<br>SRS (obs. study) or RAT (exp.)<br>Normality of Samp. Dist. of $\hat{p}$:<br>"np checks" → | $z = \dfrac{\hat{p}_1 - \hat{p}_2}{\sqrt{\hat{p}(1-\hat{p})\left(\dfrac{1}{n_1} + \dfrac{1}{n_2}\right)}}$<br>$n_1\hat{p} \geq 10$; $n_1(1-\hat{p}) \geq 10$;<br>$n_2\hat{p} \geq 10$; $n_2(1-\hat{p}) \geq 10$;<br>($\hat{p}$ = pooled proportion) | $\hat{p}_1 - \hat{p}_2 \pm z^* \sqrt{\left(\dfrac{\hat{p}_1(1-\hat{p}_1)}{n_1} + \dfrac{\hat{p}_2(1-\hat{p}_2)}{n_2}\right)}$<br>$n_1\hat{p}_1 \geq 10$; $n_1(1-\hat{p}_1) \geq 10$;<br>$n_2\hat{p}_2 \geq 10$; $n_2(1-\hat{p}_2) \geq 10$; | P-value: A<br>z*: C |
| Chi-Square | $H_o$: there is no association between the 2 variables<br>$H_a$: there is an association between the 2 variables | Randomization:<br>SRS (obs. study) or RAT (exp.)<br>All expected counts $\geq 5$ | $\chi^2 = \sum \dfrac{(observed - expected)^2}{expected}$<br>df = (r - 1)(c - 1)<br>(r = number of rows; c = number of columns) | | E |